9781483124728
AF819335

INTERNATIONAL SERIES OF MONOGRAPHS IN

PURE AND APPLIED MATHEMATICS

GENERAL EDITORS: I. N. SNEDDON AND M. STARK

EXECUTIVE EDITORS: J. P. KAHANE, A. P. ROBERTSON AND S. ULAM

VOLUME 102

RESIDUATION THEORY

RESIDUATION THEORY

T. S. Blyth

University of St. Andrews

M. F. Janowitz

University of Massachusetts

PERGAMON PRESS

OXFORD · NEW YORK · TORONTO

SYDNEY · BRAUNSCHWEIG

Pergamon Press Ltd., Headington Hill Hall, Oxford
Pergamon Press Inc., Maxwell House, Fairview Park, Elmsford, New York 10523
Pergamon of Canada Ltd., 207 Queen's Quay West, Toronto 1
Pergamon Press (Aust.) Pty. Ltd., 19a Boundary Street, Rushcutters Bay, N.S.W. 2011, Australia
Vieweg & Sohn GmbH, Burgplatz 1, Braunschweig

Copyright © 1972 T. S. Blyth; M. F. Janowitz

All Rights Reserved. No part of this publication may be reproduced, stored in a retrieval system, or transmitted, in any form or by any means, electronic, mechanical, photocopying, recording or otherwise, without the prior permission of Pergamon Press Ltd.

First edition 1972
Library of Congress Catalog Card No. 77-142177

848, 989

UNIVERSITY LIBRARY BIRMINGHAM

Printed in Germany

08 016408 0

CONTENTS

PREFACE

THE aim of the present volume is to add a substantial contribution to the textbook literature in the field of ordered algebraic structures. The fundamental notion which permeates the entire work is that of a residuated mapping and this is indeed the first unified account of this topic. The origin of this concept has been traced by J. Schmidt [26] to M. Benado [3] and G. Nöbeling [22, 23]. It also appears in the work of P. Dubreil [11] and R. Croisot [8]. The general theory of residuated mappings seems to have lain dormant for approximately 20 years until the appearance of papers by J. C. Derderian [9] and M. F. Janowitz [16, 17]; however, during this time particular types of residuated mappings were employed in studying residuated semigroups, principally by M. L. Dubreil-Jacotin [12], I. Molinaro [20], J. Querré [24] and T. S. Blyth [5].

This text has grown out of courses given by T.S.B. at the Universities of St. Andrews, Western Australia and Western Ontario and by M.F.J. at the Universities of Massachusetts, New Mexico and Western Michigan. In this (hopefully happy) marriage of our efforts, the choice of text material has, quite frankly, been selfish and more or less motivated by our own research interests. It was never our intention to write an encyclopaedia on the subject (we leave that happy task to someone else!) but rather to produce a self-contained and unified introduction to the subject which may be used either as a textbook or as a reference book in this area. In this connection we mention that many research papers are listed in the bibliography without explicit reference to their contents being made in the text. Many of these have had to be excluded because of space limitations and we hope that we have offended no one by so doing. The reader will undoubtedly find the present text useful in supplying the unified background material necessary to read those papers. Little attempt has been made to credit results to their originators and we have tried to present the material in a well-marshalled and readable manner without the clutter of numerous references.

The advantage of the combined efforts of a British and an American author is that the book is designed to satisfy a variety of courses on both sides of the Atlantic. For example, Chapter 1 may be used as an advanced under-graduate course on ordered sets and lattice theory; Chapters 1 and 2 as a one-semester post-graduate course on lattice theory; and the whole text as an M.Sc. course on lattices and residuated semigroups. We have included a large number of illustrative examples and exercises. The exercises are of varying degrees of difficulty, some serving to provide examples and counter-examples to supplement the text, some being designed to help the student gain intuition and some to extend the text material.

We assume that the reader has most of his under-graduate training behind him, so that he has a good grounding in abstract algebra; for example, we shall feel free to assume that the reader knows what is meant by a ring, an ideal of a ring, etc. We shall also assume that he is familiar with Zorn's axiom. Some knowledge of general topology will be helpful for some of the examples, but not essential for understanding the book. Though no prior knowledge of lattice theory is expected, the reader might find it helpful on occasion to consult a standard elementary text on the subject, for there will be times when we simply will not be able to delve as deeply as we would like into a given branch of the subject.

We have organized the text by dividing it into three chapters, the first of which contains an introduction to residuated mappings and lattice theory. This chapter has been specifically written with an advanced undergraduate course in mind and contains all of the elementary material which is required later. In Chapter 2 we deal with the concept of a Baer semigroup and employ residuated mappings to show how these semigroups may be used to study lattices. In so doing, we incorporate some of the important work of D. J. Foulis [13] and S. S. Holland, Jr. [15] on orthomodular lattices. Finally, in Chapter 3, we use the notion of a residuated mapping as a basis for a discussion of residuated semigroups. In particular, we show how a certain residuated semigroup plays a fundamental rôle in the study of homomorphic images of ordered semigroups, a starting point of which is a result of A. Bigard [4]. Whenever possible, we have phrased our results in terms of residuated mappings; for this reason, even one well versed in lattice theory would find here a fresh approach to the subject.

By far the majority of the results given here appear for the first time in book form and indeed some of them are only just seeing the lightf of day. Most of the material in Chapters 2 and 3 has been developed in the last decade; we hope that it may serve to inspire further research.

Our grateful thanks are due to Professors E. A. Schreiner and G. D. Crown for their valuable criticisms of the manuscript and to Dr T. P. Speed for his assistance in the proof-reading. Finally we would express our admiration at the ease with which the printers undertook a difficult task.

T. S. B.; M. F. J.

CHAPTER 1

FOUNDATIONS

1. Ordered sets

Let E be a set and let R be a binary relation between elements of E. Of the properties which R may enjoy, the most commonly encountered in mathematics are the following: R is said to be

(a) *reflexive* if $(\forall x \in E)\ xRx$;
(b) *transitive* if $(xRy$ and $yRz) \Rightarrow xRz$;
(c) *anti-symmetric* if $(xRy$ and $yRx) \Rightarrow x = y$;
(d) *symmetric* if $xRy \Rightarrow yRx$.

A relation R which satisfies (a), (b) and (d) on E is called an *equivalence relation* on E, as the reader will undoubtedly be aware. Although we shall meet with many equivalence relations in the pages which follow, we shall be concerned primarily with relations which satisfy the properties (a), (b), (c). A relation which satisfies these three properties on E will be called an *order relation* on E or simply an *ordering* on E. By an *ordered set* we shall mean a set E together with an ordering on it. We shall usually denote an ordering by the symbol $\leq$ so that the properties (a), (b), (c) become

(a) $(\forall x \in E)\ x \leq x$;
(b) $(x \leq y$ and $y \leq z) \Rightarrow x \leq z$;
(c) $(x \leq y$ and $y \leq x) \Rightarrow x = y$.

Upon occasions, however, we shall find it convenient to use a variation of this symbol.

EXAMPLE 1.1. The only binary relation on a set E which is both an equivalence relation and an ordering on E is the relation of equality.

EXAMPLE 1.2. The set $\mathbf{R}$ of real numbers is an ordered set, $\leq$ having its usual meaning. For each subset A of $\mathbf{R}$ we shall use the notation $A_+ = \{x \in A; x > 0\}$.

EXAMPLE 1.3. The set $\mathbf{P}(E)$ of all subsets of a set E is an ordered set under the relation $\subseteq$ of set inclusion.

EXAMPLE 1.4. The set $\mathbf{Z}_+$ of positive integers is an ordered set under the definition $m \preccurlyeq n \Leftrightarrow m$ is a factor of n.

EXAMPLE 1.5. Let E, F be sets with F ordered. The set Map (E, F) of all mappings of E into F is ordered under the definition

$$f \preccurlyeq g \Leftrightarrow (\forall x \in E) \quad f(x) \leq g(x).$$

EXAMPLE 1.6. If $E_1, \ldots, E_n$ are ordered sets, then so also is their Cartesian product $\bigtimes_{i=1}^{n} E_i$ under the definition

$$(x_1, \ldots, x_n) \preccurlyeq (y_1, \ldots, y_n) \Leftrightarrow (i = 1, \ldots, n) \;\; x_i \leq y_i.$$

More generally, if $(E_\alpha)_{\alpha \in A}$ is a family of ordered sets then $\bigtimes_{\alpha \in A} E_\alpha$ is an ordered set with respect to the ordering specified in Example 1.5:

$$(x_\alpha)_{\alpha \in A} \preccurlyeq (y_\alpha)_{\alpha \in A} \Leftrightarrow (\forall \alpha \in A) \; x_\alpha \leq y_\alpha.$$

We shall say that a set E is *totally ordered* (or forms a *chain*) if it is ordered in such a way that for any given elements $x, y \in E$ we have $x \leq y$ or $y \leq x$. The ordered set of Example 1.2 is totally ordered. If we define

$$x < y \Leftrightarrow (x \leq y \quad \text{and} \quad x \neq y),$$

then a totally ordered set may be described as an ordered set in which any two distinct elements x, y satisfy either $x < y$ or $y < x$. It should be noted, however, that the relation $<$ as defined above is not an ordering for it does not satisfy (a). Also, the relations $x \nleq y$ and $y < x$ are equivalent only in the case of a totally ordered set and not in the general case of an ordered set.

We say that two elements x, y of an ordered set E are *comparable* if $x \leq y$ or $y \leq x$ and denote this symbolically by writing $x \not\parallel y$. If, on the other hand, neither $x \leq y$ nor $y \leq x$ holds, then we say that x, y are *incomparable* and write $x \parallel y$. If E is an ordered set and F is a non-empty subset of E, then we shall say that F is *totally unordered* if the elements of

F are pairwise incomparable. This is equivalent to saying that in F we have $x \leq y \Leftrightarrow x = y$; in other words, the restriction to F of $\leq$ is equality.

EXAMPLE 1.7. Consider the set $E = \{a, b, c\}$. In the ordered set $\mathbf{P}(E)$ the subset $J = \{\{a\}, \{b\}, \{c\}\}$ is totally unordered as is the subset $K = \{\{a, b\}, \{a, c\}, \{b, c\}\}$.

Let R be a binary relation on a set E and let R^t denote its converse, i.e. R^t is given by $xR^ty \Leftrightarrow yRx$. It is readily seen that if R is an ordering on E, then so also is R^t. We denote the converse of $\leq$ by $\geq$ and the converse of $<$ by $>$.

Many ordered sets can be conveniently represented by means of *Hasse diagrams*. In such a diagram we represent $x \leq y$ by

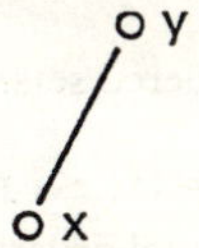

i.e. we join the point representing x to that representing y by an increasing line segment. In drawing Hasse diagrams we shall agree not to include any superfluous line segments which arise through the transitivity of $\leq$. This principle is illustrated in the following example.

EXAMPLE 1.8. Let E be the set of all positive factors of 12. If we order E according to Example 1.2 we obtain a chain. If we order E according to Example 1.4, the corresponding Hasse diagram is

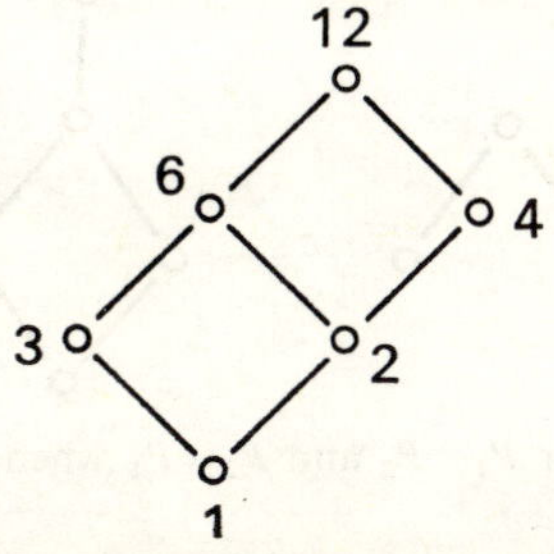

Note that in the above diagram we have not joined 2 and 12 by a direct line segment; for $2 \leq 6$ and $6 \leq 12$ imply that $2 \leq 12$ by transitivity, so such a line is superfluous.

By the *dual* of a Hasse diagram we mean the Hasse diagram associated with the converse ordering. It is clear that to obtain the dual diagram all we have to do is to turn the original upside down. By the *dual* of an ordered set we shall mean the same set equipped with the converse order. When we the need arises, we shall use the notation P^* to denote the dual of the ordered set P.

EXERCISES

1.1. Prove that every finite ordered set has a Hasse diagram.

1.2. Let E be the set of factors of 120, ordered by divisibility. Draw the Hasse diagram for E.

1.3. Draw the Hasse diagrams for all possible orderings on a set consisting of (a) 3, (b) 4, (c) 5 elements.

1.4. Let $(P_1, \leq_1)$, $(P_2, \leq_2)$ be ordered sets. Show that the relation $\leq$ defined on $P_1 \times P_2$ by

$$(x_1, x_2) \leq (y_1, y_2) \Leftrightarrow (x_1 \leq_1 y_1 \quad \text{and} \quad x_2 \leq_2 y_2)$$

is an ordering. Show also that $\leq$ is a total ordering if and only if $\leq_1$ and $\leq_2$ are total orderings and P_1 or P_2 consists of a single element.

1.5. Let $(P_1, \leq_1)$, $(P_2, \leq_2)$ be ordered sets. Prove that the relation $\leq$ defined on $P_1 \times P_2$ by

$$(x_1, x_2) \leq (y_1, y_2) \Leftrightarrow \begin{cases} \text{either} & x_1 <_1 y_1 \\ \text{or} & x_1 = y_1 \quad \text{and} \quad x_2 \leq_2 y_2 \end{cases}$$

is an ordering. This is known as the *lexicographic ordering* on $P_1 \times P_2$. Show that $\leq$ is a total ordering if and only if $\leq_1$ and $\leq_2$ are total orderings.

1.6. Let P_1 and P_2 be the ordered sets with respective Hasse diagrams

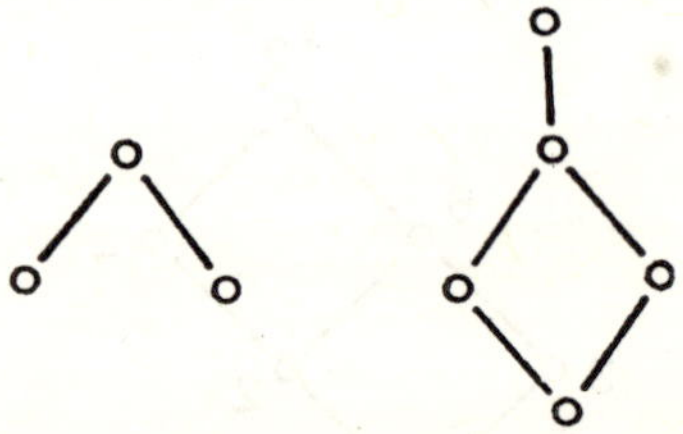

Draw the Hasse diagrams for $P_1 \times P_2$ and $P_2 \times P_1$ when ordered as in Examples 1.4 and 1.5.

1.7. Let $(P_1, \leq_1)$ and $(P_2, \leq_2)$ be disjoint ordered sets. Show that each of the following defines an ordering on $P = P_1 \cup P_2$:

(a) $x \leq y \Leftrightarrow x \leq_1 y$ or $x \leq_2 y$;

(b) $x \leq y \Leftrightarrow x \leq_1 y$, $x \leq_2 y$ or $x \in P_1$ and $y \in P_2$.

2. Mappings between ordered sets; residuated mappings

Let P be an ordered set. By an *(order) ideal* of P we shall mean any non-empty subset I of P satisfying the property

$$(x \in I \quad \text{and} \quad y \leq x) \Rightarrow y \in I.$$

By a *principal ideal* of P we shall mean any ideal of the form

$$[\leftarrow, x] = \{y \in P; y \leq x\}.$$

We define the dual notions of an *(order) filter* of P to be any non-empty subset J having the property

$$(x \in J \quad \text{and} \quad y \geq x) \Rightarrow y \in J,$$

and a *principal filter* of P to be any filter of the form

$$[x, \rightarrow] = \{y \in P; y \geq x\}.$$

If P, Q are ordered sets and $f: P \rightarrow Q$ is any mapping, then for each non-empty subset R of Q we define the *pre-image of R under f* to be the subset of P given by

$$f^{\leftarrow}(R) = \{x \in P; f(x) \in R\}.$$

Our first result shows how the above notions can be used to characterize an important type of mapping between ordered sets.

THEOREM 2.1. *If A, B are ordered sets and $f: A \rightarrow B$ is any mapping, the following conditions are equivalent:*

(1) $x \leq y \Rightarrow f(x) \leq f(y)$;

(2) *the pre-image of every principal ideal of B is either empty or is an ideal of A;*

(3) *the pre-image of every principal filter of B is either empty or is a filter of A.*

Proof. Note that we use the same symbol $\leq$ to denote the ordering in both A and B; no confusion will arise since the context will always make it clear to which set we are referring. We shall show that (1) $\Leftrightarrow$ (2); a dual argument will clearly yield (1) $\Leftrightarrow$ (3). Suppose then that f satisfies (1) and let $x \in B$ be such that $f^{\leftarrow}[\leftarrow, x] \neq \emptyset$ (where we write $f^{\leftarrow}[\leftarrow, x]$ in place of $f^{\leftarrow}([\leftarrow, x])$). Then if $y \in f^{\leftarrow}[\leftarrow, x]$ and $z \leq y$ we have, by (1), $f(z)$

$\leq f(y) \leq x$ so that $z \in f^{\leftarrow}[\leftarrow, x]$. This shows that (1) $\Rightarrow$ (2). Suppose, conversely, that f satisfies (2). For each $y \in A$ we have trivially $f(y) \leq f(y)$ and so $y \in f^{\leftarrow}[\leftarrow, f(y)]$. Since, by (2), $f^{\leftarrow}[\leftarrow, f(y)]$ is an ideal of A, it follows that

$$x \leq y \Rightarrow x \in f^{\leftarrow}[\leftarrow, f(y)] \Rightarrow f(x) \leq f(y).$$

We shall say that $f: A \rightarrow B$ is *isotone* if and only if it satisfies any of the mutually equivalent conditions of Theorem 2.1. We shall make frequent use of the fact that if $f, g, h: A \rightarrow B$ are mappings with $g \leq h$ then $g \circ f \leq h \circ f$ and, if f is isotone, $f \circ g \leq f \circ h$. There is, of course, a dual result which characterizes mappings which are *antitone*, namely:

THEOREM 2.1*. *If A, B are ordered sets and $f: A \rightarrow B$ is any mapping, the following conditions are equivalent:*

(1) $x \leq y \Rightarrow f(x) \geq f(y)$;

(2) *the pre-image of every principal ideal of B is either empty or is a filter of A;*

(3) *the pre-image of every principal filter of B is either empty or is an ideal of A.*

Suppose now that $f: A \rightarrow B$ is an isotone bijection. In general, the inverse map f^{-1} is not necessarily isotone. For example, consider the ordered sets $A = \{x, y, z\}$ and $B = \{\alpha, \beta, \gamma\}$ with Hasse diagrams

and consider the mapping $f: A \rightarrow B$ given by $f(x) = \beta, f(y) = \alpha, f(z) = \gamma$. Clearly f is an isotone bijection; but f^{-1} is not isotone, for $\beta \leq \gamma$ and $f^{-1}(\beta) = x \| z = f^{-1}(\gamma)$.

We shall say that the ordered sets A, B are *(order-)isomorphic* if and only if there is an isotone bijection $f: A \rightarrow B$ such that f^{-1} is isotone. It follows from this that A, B are order-isomorphic if and only if there is a surjection $f: A \to B$ such that $x \le y \Leftrightarrow f(x) \le f(y)$. In a similar way, we say that the ordered sets A, B are *dually(order-)isomorphic* if and only if there is a bijection $f: A \to B$ such that both f and f^{-1} are antitone, i.e. if and only if there is a surjection $f: A \to B$ such that $x \le y \Leftrightarrow f(x) \ge f(y)$. Ordered sets which are dually isomorphic to themselves are said to be *self-dual.*

Consider now the following problem: given the diagram of ordered sets and mappings

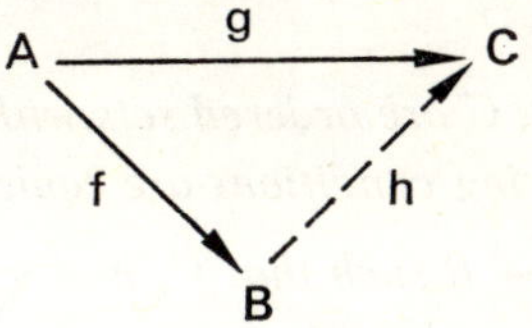

we wish to determine under what conditions there exists an isotone mapping $h: B \to C$ such that $h \circ f \ge g$ [resp. $h \circ f \le g$]. Though the next theorem does not solve the problem, it does provide some useful information.

THEOREM 2.2. *Let A, B, C be ordered sets with mappings $f: A \to B$ and $g: A \to C$. If $h: B \to C$ is isotone, the following are equivalent:*

(1) $h \circ f \ge g$;

(2) $(\forall x \in B) \qquad f^{\leftarrow}[\leftarrow, x] \subseteq g^{\leftarrow}[\leftarrow, h(x)]$.

Likewise, the following are equivalent:

(3) $h \circ f \le g$;

(4) $(\forall x \in B) \qquad f^{\leftarrow}[x, \to] \subseteq g^{\leftarrow}[h(x), \to]$.

Proof. (1) $\Rightarrow$ (2): If $f^{\leftarrow}[\leftarrow, x] = \emptyset$ there is nothing to prove; and i $f^{\leftarrow}[\leftarrow, x] \ne \emptyset$ then for each $y \in f^{\leftarrow}[\leftarrow, x]$ we have $f(y) \le x$ so that, h being isotone, $g(y) \le (h \circ f)(y) = h[f(y)] \le h(x)$ whence $y \in g^{\leftarrow}[\leftarrow, h(x)]$.

(2) $\Rightarrow$ (1): For each $y \in A$ we have $y \in f^{\leftarrow}[\leftarrow, f(y)] \subseteq g^{\leftarrow}[\leftarrow, h(f(y))]$ and so $g(y) \le h[f(y)]$ whence $g \le h \circ f$ as required.

The equivalence of (3) and (4) is proved similarly.

We shall now consider the associated problem in which all the arrows are reversed, namely given the diagram of ordered sets and mappings

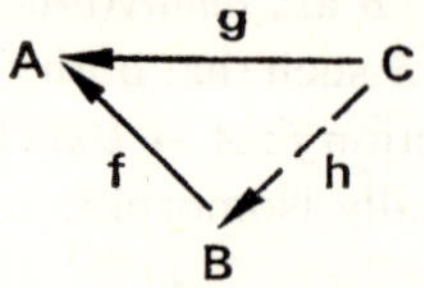

to determine under what conditions there exists a mapping $h : C \to B$ such that $f \circ h \leq g$ [resp. $f \circ h \geq g$]. Note that in this case we do not require h to be isotone.

THEOREM 2.3. *If A, B, C are ordered sets with mappings $f : B \to A$ and $g : C \to A$ then the following conditions are equivalent:*

(1) *there exists $h : C \to B$ such that $f \circ h \leq g$;*
(2) $(\forall x \in C)\ f^{\leftarrow} [\leftarrow, g(x)] \neq \emptyset$.

Likewise, the following conditions are equivalent:

(3) *there exists $h : C \to B$ such that $f \circ h \geq g$;*
(4) $(\forall x \in C)\ f^{\leftarrow} [g(x), \to] \neq \emptyset$.

Proof. Again we show that (1) $\Leftrightarrow$ (2), the proof of (3) $\Leftrightarrow$ (4) being similar. Suppose that (1) holds. Then from $(\forall x \in C) f[h(x)] \leq g(x)$ it follows that $(\forall x \in C)\ h(x) \in f^{\leftarrow} [\leftarrow, g(x)]$ whence (2) holds. Conversely, if (2) holds then we can define a mapping $h : C \to B$ by associating with each $x \in C$ a chosen element $h(x) \in f^{\leftarrow} [\leftarrow, g(x)]$. Clearly we have $(\forall x \in C)$ $(f \circ h)(x) = f[h(x)] \leq g(x)$, from which (1) follows.

In what follows we shall denote by id_E the identity map on a set E.

COROLLARY. *If $f : A \to B$ is isotone then the following conditions are equivalent:*

(1) *there exists $h : B \to A$ such that $f \circ h \leq \mathrm{id}_B$;*
(2) *for each principal ideal $[\leftarrow, x]$ of B, $f^{\leftarrow} [\leftarrow, x]$ is an ideal of A.*

Likewise, the following conditions are equivalent:

(3) *there exists $h : B \to A$ such that $f \circ h \geq \mathrm{id}_B$;*
(4) *for each principal filter $[x, \to]$ of B, $f^{\leftarrow} [x, \to]$ is a filter of A.*

Proof. That (1) and (2) are equivalent follows by applying Theorem 2.3, in the light of Theorem 2.1, to the diagram

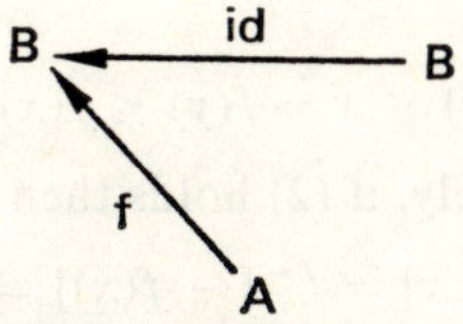

A similar proof establishes the equivalence of (3) and (4).

We shall say that $f: A \to B$ is *quasi-residuated* if it is isotone and satisfies either of the equivalent conditions (1), (2) of the above corollary. A more useful characterization of a quasi-residuated mapping is the following: *a mapping* $f: A \to B$ *is quasi-residuated if and only if it is isotone and such that* $(\forall y \in B)\, \{x \in A; f(x) \leq y\} \neq \emptyset$. In fact this latter condition is equivalent to saying that $(\forall y \in B)\, f^{\leftarrow}[\leftarrow, y] \neq \emptyset$. The result is therefore immediate from Theorem 2.3.

We say that $f: A \to B$ is *dually quasi-residuated* if it is isotone and satisfies either of the equivalent conditions (3), (4) of the above corollary. A particularly important type of dually quasi-residuated mapping which plays a prominent rôle in the theory of ordered algebraic structures is known as a *closure mapping*. By a closure mapping on an ordered set A we mean an isotone mapping $f: A \to A$ such that $f = f \circ f \geq \mathrm{id}_A$. In a dual manner we define a *dual closure mapping* on A to be an isotone mapping $f: A \to A$ such that $f = f \circ f \leq \mathrm{id}_A$ [*note:* f is isotone in each case]. A dual closure mapping is clearly a particular type of quasi-residuated mapping. As our next result shows, these mappings also admit characterizations in terms of pre-images of principal ideals and filters.

THEOREM 2.4. *If A is an ordered set and $f: A \to A$ is any mapping, the following conditions are equivalent:*

(1) *f is a dual closure mapping;*
(2) $(\forall x \in A)\, f^{\leftarrow}[\leftarrow, x] = f^{\leftarrow}[\leftarrow, f(x)]$.

Likewise, the following conditions are equivalent:

(3) *f is a closure mapping;*
(4) $(\forall x \in A)\, f^{\leftarrow}[x, \rightarrow] = f^{\leftarrow}[f(x), \rightarrow]$.

Proof. We prove that (1) $\Leftrightarrow$ (2); the proof of (3) $\Leftrightarrow$ (4) is similar. Suppose that (1) holds. It is evident that, for each $x \in A$, $x \in f^{\leftarrow}[\leftarrow, f(x)] \subseteq f^{\rightarrow}[\leftarrow, x]$. Moreover,

$$y \in f^{\leftarrow}[\leftarrow, x] \Rightarrow f(y) \leq x \Rightarrow f(y) \leq f(x) \Rightarrow y \in f^{\leftarrow}[\leftarrow, f(x)],$$

which yields (2). Conversely, if (2) holds then we have

$$(\forall x \in A) \quad f^{\leftarrow}[\leftarrow, x] = f^{\leftarrow}[\leftarrow, f(x)] = f^{\leftarrow}[\leftarrow, f(f(x))].$$

Now x is an element of the second of these sets. It therefore belongs to the other two and so

$$(\forall x \in A) \quad f(x) \leq x \quad \text{and} \quad f(x) \leq (f \circ f)(x),$$

giving $f \leq \mathrm{id}_A$ and $f \leq f \circ f$. Now f is isotone; for

$$y \leq x \Rightarrow f(y) \leq y \leq x \Rightarrow y \in f^{\leftarrow}[\leftarrow, x] = f^{\leftarrow}[\leftarrow, f(x)] \Rightarrow f(y) \leq f(x).$$

We therefore deduce from $f \leq \mathrm{id}_A$ that $f \circ f \leq f$. Collecting the above results, we see that f is an isotone map which is such that $f = f \circ f \leq \mathrm{id}_A$, i.e. is a dual closure mapping.

Our next result characterizes mappings of paramount importance in our future discussion.

THEOREM 2.5. *Let $f: A \to B$ be a mapping between the ordered sets A, B. The following conditions on f are equivalent:*

(1) *f is isotone and there exists an isotone mapping $h: B \to A$ such that $h \circ f \geq \mathrm{id}_A$ and $f \circ h \leq \mathrm{id}_B$;*

(2) *for each principal ideal $[\leftarrow, x]$ of B, $f^{\leftarrow}[\leftarrow, x]$ is a principal ideal of A.*

Proof. Suppose that (1) holds. Then, applying Theorem 2.2 and the corollary to Theorem 2.3, we have

$$(\forall x \in B) \quad \varnothing \subset f^{\leftarrow}[\leftarrow, x] \subseteq [\leftarrow, h(x)].$$

But if $y \in [\leftarrow, h(x)]$, then $y \leq h(x)$, and so we have $f(y) \leq f[h(x)] = (f \circ h)(x) \leq \mathrm{id}_B(x) = x$ whence $y \in f^{\leftarrow}[\leftarrow, x]$. Consequently,

$$(\forall x \in B) \quad \varnothing \subset f^{\rightarrow}[\leftarrow, x] = [\leftarrow, h(x)].$$

This establishes (2). Conversely, suppose that (2) holds, i.e. that

$$(\forall x \in B)(\exists y \in A) \quad \varnothing \subset f^{\leftarrow}[\leftarrow, x] = [\leftarrow, y].$$

It follows by Theorem 2.1 that f is isotone. Moreover, the element y defined above is clearly unique for each $x \in B$ so we can define a mapping $h: B \to A$ by setting $h(x) = y$. For this mapping h we have

$$(\forall x \in B) \quad (f \circ h)(x) = f[h(x)] \leq x,$$

since $h(x) \in [\leftarrow, h(x)] = f^{\leftarrow}[\leftarrow, x]$; and

$$(\forall z \in A) \quad (h \circ f)(z) = h[f(z)] \geq z,$$

since $z \in f^{\leftarrow}[\leftarrow, f(z)] = [\leftarrow, h(f(z))]$. This establishes (1).

We shall say that a mapping $f: A \to B$ is *residuated* if and only if it satisfies either of the equivalent conditions of Theorem 2.5; and *dually residuated* if it satisfies the dual theorem.

Let us note that if $f: A \to B$ is residuated then the mapping $h: B \to A$ satisfying $h \circ f \geq \mathrm{id}_A$ and $f \circ h \leq \mathrm{id}_B$ is *unique*. In fact, if h, h^* satisfy these properties, then

$$h = \mathrm{id}_A \circ h \leq (h^* \circ f) \circ h = h^* \circ (f \circ h) \leq h^* \circ \mathrm{id}_B = h^*,$$

and in a similar way $h^* \leq h$ whence we have $h = h^*$. We denote this unique mapping by f^+ and call it the *residual* of f. It is clear from the proof of Theorem 2.5 that a mapping $f: A \to B$ is residuated if and only if for each $y \in B$ the set $\{x \in A; f(x) \leq y\}$ is not empty and admits a greatest element. Moreover, when it exists, the residual f^+ of f is given by

$$(\forall y \in B) \quad f^+(y) = \max\{x \in A; f(x) \leq y\}.$$

Remark. Let us pause to note that when $f: A \to B$ is residuated, f and its residual f^+ are related by the inequalities $f^+ \circ f \geq \mathrm{id}_A$ and $f \circ f^+ \leq \mathrm{id}_B$. Until he becomes familiar with these inequalities, the reader should take care not to confuse them. It is also important to notice that if one regards f, f^+ as mappings between A^* and B^*, then $f^+: B^* \to A^*$ is residuated with f as its associated residual map.

At this point the reader may well ask just what there is about residuated mappings that makes then so important. As we shall soon see, the residuated mappings on a bounded ordered set E form a semigroup with a zero and an identity. What is more important, however, is that many important properties which E may enjoy can be characterized naturally in this semigroup. Residuated mappings crop up in a variety of situations.

Whilst we shall discuss this in some detail later, we mention here a few examples to whet the reader's appetite:

1. There is a bijection between the binary relations on a set E and the residuated mappings on the power set of E.

2. Every linear transformation f on a vector space V induces a residuated mapping on the lattice of subspaces of V, namely the mapping $M \to \{f(m); m \in M\}$.

3. Every bounded linear operator f on a Hilbert space H induces a residuated mapping on the lattice of closed subspaces of H, namely the mapping $M \to \{f(m); m \in M\}^{\perp\perp}$.

4. If A is a commutative ring with an identity element then, in the ordered semigroup of ideals of A, multiplication by a fixed ideal is a residuated mapping.

5. If X is a T_1-topological space and if R is a binary relation on X which is *continuous* in the sense that

$$A \text{ open} \Rightarrow \{x \in X; (\exists y \in A)\ xRy\} \text{ open}$$

then R induces a residuated mapping on the lattice $L(X)$ of closed subsets of X and *every* residuated mapping on $L(X)$ arises in this manner.

For the remainder of this section we shall look at some elementary properties of residuated mappings.

THEOREM 2.6. *If A, B are ordered sets and $f: A \to B$ is residuated, then*

(1) $f \circ f^+ \circ f = f$ *and* $f^+ \circ f \circ f^+ = f^+$;

(2) *the following conditions are equivalent:*

(a) $f^+ \circ f = id_A$;

(b) f *is injective;*

(c) f^+ *is surjective;*

(d) *if C is any set and $g, h: C \to A$ are any mappings then*

$$f \circ g = f \circ h \Rightarrow g = h;$$

(3) *the following conditions are equivalent:*

(α) $f \circ f^+ = id_B$;

(β) f *is surjective;*

(γ) *f^+ is injective;*

(δ) *if C is any set and $g, h : B \to C$ are any mappings then*

$$g \circ f = h \circ f \Rightarrow g = h.$$

Proof. Since f is isotone and $f^+ \circ f \geq \mathrm{id}_A$, $f \circ f^+ \leq \mathrm{id}_B$, we have $f \circ f^+ \circ f \geq f \circ \mathrm{id}_A = f$ and $f \circ f^+ \circ f \leq \mathrm{id}_B \circ f = f$. This yields the first equality of (1), the second being proved similarly. To prove (2), we show that (a) $\Leftrightarrow$ (c) and that (a) $\Rightarrow$ (b) $\Rightarrow$ (d) $\Rightarrow$ (a). It is clear that (a) $\Rightarrow$ (c); conversely, if (c) holds then for each $x \in A$ there exists $y \in B$ such that $f^+(y) = x$ so that, using (1),

$$x = f^+(y) = (f^+ \circ f \circ f^+)(y) = (f^+ \circ f)[f^+(y)] = (f^+ \circ f)(x),$$

whence (a) holds. If now (a) holds then

$$f(x) = f(y) \Rightarrow x = f^+[f(x)] = f^+[f(y)] = y,$$

so that (b) holds. If (b) holds then

$$\begin{aligned} f \circ g = f \circ h &\Rightarrow (\forall x \in C) \quad f[g(x)] = f[h(x)] \\ &\Rightarrow (\forall x \in C) \quad g(x) = h(x) \\ &\Rightarrow g = h, \end{aligned}$$

whence (d) holds. Finally, if (d) holds then from the equality $f \circ f^+ \circ f = f = f \circ \mathrm{id}_A$ we deduce that $f^+ \circ f = \mathrm{id}_A$ which is (a). The proof of (3) is dual to that of (2).

Using the previous result we can give the following characterization of closure mappings modulo residuated mappings.

THEOREM 2.7. *If A is an ordered set then $f : A \to A$ is a closure mapping if and only if there is an ordered set B and a residuated mapping $g : A \to B$ such that $f = g^+ \circ g$.*

Proof. Suppose first that $g : A \to B$ is residuated. Then, on the one hand, $g^+ \circ g \geq \mathrm{id}_A$; and, on the other, by Theorem 2.6, $g = g \circ g^+ \circ g$ so that $g^+ \circ g = (g^+ \circ g) \circ (g^+ \circ g)$. Thus $g^+ \circ g$ is a closure mapping, for being the composition of two isotone mappings it is also isotone.

Conversely, suppose that A is an ordered set with $f : A \to A$ a closure mapping. Let F be the equivalence relation associated with f, i.e. $x \equiv y(F) \Leftrightarrow f(x) = f(y)$. Define the relation $\preccurlyeq$ on A/F by

$$x/F \preccurlyeq y/F \Leftrightarrow f(x) \leq f(y).$$

It is readily seen that $\preccurlyeq$ is an ordering and, since f is isotone, the canonical surjection $\natural_F : A \to A/F$ is isotone. Now each equivalence class modulo F has a greatest element, the greatest element in the class of x modulo F being the element $f(x)$. We can therefore define a mapping $g : A/F \to A$ by setting $g\,(x/F) = f(x)$. We then have

$$\begin{cases} (g \circ \natural_F)\,(x) = g\,[\natural_F(x)] = g\,(x/F) = f(x) \geq x; \\ (\natural_F \circ g)\,(x/F) = \natural_F\,[f(x)] = [f(x)]/F = x/F, \end{cases}$$

from which it follows that $\natural_F$ is residuated with $g = \natural_F^+$ and that $f = \natural_F^+ \circ \natural_F$.

Remark. In the above proof we were concerned with an equivalence relation which was the equivalence associated with an isotone mapping. We shall be taking a very close look at such relations later.

THEOREM 2.8. *Let A, B, C be ordered sets and let $f: A \to B$ and $g: B \to C$ be residuated mappings. Then $g \circ f$ is residuated with $(g \circ f)^+ = f^+ \circ g^+$.*

Proof. Clearly $g \circ f$ and $f^+ \circ g^+$ are isotone. Moreover the isotonicity of f, g together with the relations $f^+ \circ f \geq \mathrm{id}_A$, $f \circ f^+ \leq \mathrm{id}_B$, $g^+ \circ g \geq \mathrm{id}_B$, $g \circ g^+ \leq \mathrm{id}_C$ yields

$$\begin{cases} (f^+ \circ g^+) \circ (g \circ f) \geq f^+ \circ \mathrm{id}_B \circ f = f^+ \circ f \geq \mathrm{id}_A; \\ (g \circ f) \circ (f^+ \circ g^+) \leq g \circ \mathrm{id}_B \circ g^+ = g \circ g^+ \leq \mathrm{id}_C, \end{cases}$$

from which we deduce, using the uniqueness of residuals, that $(g \circ f)^+$ exists and is none other than $f^+ \circ g^+$.

THEOREM 2.9. *If A is an ordered set and $f: A \to A$ is a residuated mapping, then*

(1) $(\forall n, p \in \mathbf{Z}_+)\, f^p = f^{p+n} \Leftrightarrow (f^+)^p = (f^+)^{p+n}$;
(2) $f \leq id_A \Leftrightarrow f^+ \geq id_A$;
(3) $f \geq id_A \Leftrightarrow f^+ \leq id_A$.

Proof. (1) We use the notation f^p to denote $f \circ f \circ \cdots \circ f$ (p factors). The result is in fact immediate on remarking that $(f^+)^p$ is the residual of f^p [to prove this, use Theorem 2.8 and induction] and that $(f^+)^{p+n}$ is the residual of f^{p+n}. (2) If $f \leq \mathrm{id}_A$ then $\mathrm{id}_A \leq f^+ \circ f \leq f^+ \circ \mathrm{id}_A = f^+$. (3) is proved similarly to (2).

THEOREM 2.10. *If A is an ordered set and $f: A \to A$ is residuated then the following conditions are equivalent:*

(a) *f is a closure mapping;*

(b) *f^+ is a dual closure mapping;*

(c) $f = f^+ \circ f$;

(d) $f^+ = f \circ f^+$.

Likewise, the following conditions are equivalent:

(α) *f is a dual closure mapping;*

(β) *f^+ is a closure mapping;*

(γ) $f = f \circ f^+$;

(δ) $f^+ = f^+ \circ f$.

Proof. That (a) and (b) are equivalent follows from Theorem 2.9, for $f = f \circ f \geq \mathrm{id}_A$ if and only if $f^+ = f^+ \circ f^+ \leq \mathrm{id}_A$. To establish the equivalence of (a), (b), (c), (d) we shall show that (a) $\Rightarrow$ (c) $\Rightarrow$ (d) $\Rightarrow$ (b). Suppose that (a) holds; then (c) follows from the inequalities

$$\begin{cases} f^+ \circ f = f^+ \circ f \circ f \geq \mathrm{id}_A \circ f = f; \\ f = f \circ f^+ \circ f \geq \mathrm{id}_A \circ f^+ \circ f = f^+ \circ f. \end{cases}$$

If now (c) holds then from $f = f^+ \circ f$ we deduce that $f \circ f^+ = f^+ \circ f \circ f^+ = f^+$ which is (d). Finally, if (d) holds, then $f^+ \circ f^+ = f \circ f^+ \circ f \circ f^+ = f \circ f^+ = f^+$ and $f^+ = f \circ f^+ \leq \mathrm{id}_A$, and hence (b) holds. The equivalence of (α), (β), (γ), (δ) is proved similarly.

The final result we shall prove in this section is a simple consequence of what has gone before. However, we require some additional terminology before formulating it.

Definition. By an *ordered semigroup* we shall mean a semigroup S on which there is defined an ordering $\leq$ in such a way that for each $x \in S$ the translations λ_x, ϱ_x given by the prescriptions $\lambda_x(y) = xy$ and $\varrho_x(y) = yx$

are isotone [in other words, S satisfies the property that $y \leq z \Rightarrow (\forall x \in S)$ $xy \leq xz$ and $yx \leq zx$].

EXAMPLE 2.1. $(\mathbf{R}, +)$, $(\mathbf{R}_+, \cdot)$ are ordered semigroups under the usual ordering, respectively.

EXAMPLE 2.2. For any set E, $(\mathbf{P}(E), \cap)$ and $(\mathbf{P}(E), \cup)$ are ordered semigroups under set inclusion.

EXAMPLE 2.3. For any ordered set E, the semigroup formed by the isotone mappings $f : E \to E$ is an ordered semigroup when ordered as in Example 1.5.

EXAMPLE 2.4. Let R be a commutative ring and let $I(R)$ denote its set of ideals. Define a multiplication on $I(R)$ by letting $\mathbf{ab}$ be the set (= ideal) of elements of R which can be expressed in the form $\sum_{i=1}^{n} a_i b_i$, where $a_i \in \mathbf{a}$ and $b_i \in \mathbf{b}$. With respect to this multiplication and set inclusion, $I(R)$ forms an ordered semigroup.

Definition. Let A, B be ordered semigroups. We say that A, B are *isomorphic* if and only if there is a semigroup homomorphism $f: A \to B$ which is an order isomorphism. We say that A, B are *anti-isomorphic* if and only if there is a semigroup anti-homomorphism $f: A \to B$ (i.e. for all $x, y \in A, f(xy) = f(y)f(x)$), which is a dual order isomorphism.

THEOREM 2.11. *If E is an ordered set then the set Res (E) of residuated mappings $f: E \to E$ forms an ordered semigroup and the set of their residuals forms an ordered semigroup Res$^+$ (E). Moreover, Res (E) and Res$^+$ (E) are anti-isomorphic.*

Proof. It is clear from Theorem 2.8 that Res (E) and Res$^+$ (E) form semigroups under composition of mappings. Moreover, these semigroups are ordered semigroups (under the ordering defined in Example 1.5) since all the mappings in question are isotone. Since $f \leq g \Leftrightarrow f \circ g^+ \leq \mathrm{id}_E$ $\Leftrightarrow g^+ \leq f^+$, it then follows from Theorem 2.8 and the uniqueness of residuals that the mapping $(+): \mathrm{Res}\,(E) \to \mathrm{Res}^+\,(E)$ described by $(+)(f) = f^+$ establishes an anti-isomorphism between Res (E) and Res$^+$ (E).

The following example is instructive.

EXAMPLE 2.5. Consider the set $E = \{1, 2, 3\}$ ordered in the usual way. There are ten isotone mappings from E to itself, namely:

$$\theta_0 = \mathrm{id}_E;$$
$$\theta_1: 1 \to 2, \quad 2 \to 3, \quad 3 \to 3;$$
$$\theta_2: 1 \to 1, \quad 2 \to 3, \quad 3 \to 3;$$
$$\theta_3: 1 \to 1, \quad 2 \to 2, \quad 3 \to 2;$$
$$\theta_4: 1 \to 2, \quad 2 \to 2, \quad 3 \to 3;$$
$$\theta_5: 1 \to 1, \quad 2 \to 1, \quad 3 \to 3;$$
$$\theta_6: 1 \to 1, \quad 2 \to 1, \quad 3 \to 2;$$
$$\theta_7: 1 \to 3, \quad 2 \to 3, \quad 3 \to 3;$$
$$\theta_8: 1 \to 2, \quad 2 \to 2, \quad 3 \to 2;$$
$$\theta_9: 1 \to 1, \quad 2 \to 1, \quad 3 \to 1.$$

Of these isotone mappings, those which are residuated are

$$\alpha_0 = \mathrm{id}_E; \quad \alpha_1 = \theta_2; \quad \alpha_2 = \theta_3; \quad \alpha_3 = \theta_5; \quad \alpha_4 = \theta_6; \quad \alpha_5 = \theta_9,$$

their residuals being respectively

$$\beta_0 = \mathrm{id}_E; \quad \beta_1 = \theta_5; \quad \beta_2 = \theta_2; \quad \beta_3 = \theta_4; \quad \beta_4 = \theta_1; \quad \beta_5 = \theta_7.$$

The respective semigroups are given by the following Cayley tables which exhibit the anti-isomorphism:

	α_0	α_1	α_2	α_3	α_4	α_5
α_0	α_0	α_1	α_2	α_3	α_4	α_5
α_1	α_1	α_1	α_1	α_3	α_3	α_5
α_2	α_2	α_2	α_2	α_4	α_4	α_5
α_3	α_3	α_1	α_5	α_3	α_5	α_5
α_4	α_4	α_2	α_5	α_4	α_5	α_5
α_5	α_5	α_5	α_5	α_5	α_5	α_5

	β_0	β_1	β_2	β_3	β_4	β_5
β_0	β_0	β_1	β_2	β_3	β_4	β_5
β_1	β_1	β_1	β_2	β_1	β_2	β_5
β_2	β_2	β_1	β_2	β_5	β_5	β_5
β_3	β_3	β_3	β_4	β_3	β_4	β_5
β_4	β_4	β_3	β_4	β_5	β_5	β_5
β_5	β_5	β_5	β_5	β_5	β_5	β_5

Remark. This example shows in particular that $\mathrm{Res}(E) \cup \mathrm{Res}^+(E)$ is not in general a semigroup; for example, $\alpha_2 \circ \beta_4 = \theta_8 \notin \mathrm{Res}(E) \cup \mathrm{Res}^+(E)$.

EXERCISES

2.1. Let E, F be sets. For any mapping $f: E \to F$ define the associated mappings $f^{\to}: \mathbf{P}(E) \to \mathbf{P}(F)$ and $f^{\leftarrow}: \mathbf{P}(F) \to \mathbf{P}(E)$ as follows

$$(\forall X \in \mathbf{P}(E)) \quad f^{\to}(X) = \{y \in F;\ (\exists x \in X)\ y = f(x)\};$$
$$(\forall Y \in \mathbf{P}(F)) \quad f^{\leftarrow}(Y) = \{x \in E;\ f(x) \in Y\}.$$

Prove that $f^{\to}$ is residuated and that $(f^{\to})^{+} = f^{\leftarrow}$.

2.2. Let $\mathbf{N}$ denote the set of non-negative integers, ordered in the usual way. Let $m \in \mathbf{N}$ $(m \neq 0)$ and define $f_m: \mathbf{N} \to \mathbf{N}$ by the prescription

$$(\forall n \in \mathbf{N}) \quad f_m(n) = mn.$$

Prove that f_m is residuated and determine f_m^{+}.

2.3. Let E be any set. For each subset A of E show that the mapping $t_A: \mathbf{P}(E) \to \mathbf{P}(E)$ given by

$$(\forall X \in \mathbf{P}(E)) \quad t_A(X) = A \cap X$$

is a residuated dual closure map on $\mathbf{P}(E)$ and determine t_A^{+}.

2.4. Let S be a semigroup with a zero element 0. Let $P_0(S)$ be the set of all subsets of S which contain 0, ordered by set inclusion. For each $A \in P_0(S)$ define the mappings $\lambda_A, \varrho_A: P_0(S) \to P_0(S)$ by setting $\lambda_A(X) = AX = \{ax;\ a \in A,\ x \in X\}$ and $\varrho_A(X) = XA = \{xa;\ a \in A,\ x \in X\}$. Prove that λ_A, ϱ_A are residuated and determine $\lambda_A^{+}, \varrho_A^{+}$.

2.5. With reference to Example 2.4, draw a conclusion analogous to that of Exercise 2.4.

2.6. If E is an ordered set and $f: E \to E$ is residuated, prove that the following conditions are equivalent: (a) $f = f^{+}$; (b) $f \circ f = \mathrm{id}_E$; (c) $f^{+} \circ f^{+} = \mathrm{id}_E$.

2.7. Let E be an ordered set and let T be the semigroup of isotone maps on E. For each subset S of T let $\langle S \rangle$ denote the subsemigroup generated by S; i.e., the set of all isotone mappings of the form $f_1 \circ f_2 \circ \cdots \circ f_n$, where each $f_i \in S$. If $f: E \to E$ is residuated, prove that the following conditions are equivalent:

(a) $f \neq f^{+}$ and $\langle \{f, f^{+}\} \rangle = \{f, f^{+}\}$;
(b) f is either a closure mapping or a dual closure mapping but not both.

2.8. Given ordered sets E, F and *antitone* mappings $f: E \to F$, $g: F \to E$ we say that the pair (f, g) establishes a *Galois connection* between E and F if and only if $f \circ g \geq \mathrm{id}_F$ and $g \circ f \geq \mathrm{id}_E$. Prove that if the antitone mappings $f: E \to F$, $g: F \to E$ set up a Galois connection between E and F, then f is a residuated mapping from $E \to F^{*}$ and a dually residuated mapping from $E^{*} \to F$. Show that an antitone mapping $f: E \to F$ admits a Galois connection with at most one antitone mapping $g: F \to E$ and that, when such an occasion arises,

(a) $f = f \circ g \circ f$ and $g = g \circ f \circ g$;
(b) $\{y \in F;\ y = (f \circ g)(y)\} = \mathrm{Im}\, f$;
(c) $\{x \in E;\ x = (g \circ f)(x)\} = \mathrm{Im}\, g$;
(d) the restriction of f to $\mathrm{Im}\, g$ is a dual isomorphism of $\mathrm{Im}\, g$ onto $\mathrm{Im}\, f$ whose inverse is the restriction of g to $\mathrm{Im}\, f$.

Remark. The reason for our emphasis on residuated mappings rather than Galois connections can be found in Theorem 2.8: two residuated mappings may be composed to yield a new residuated mapping; this is not the case with antitone mappings.

2.9. Let K, M be fields with K a subfield of M. Let G_K be the group consisting of all those automorphisms f on M which are such that $(\forall x \in K) f(x) = x$. Let $[K, M]$ denote the set of subfields contained between K and M and let $L(G_K)$ be the set of subgroups of G_K. Order $[K, M]$ and $L(G_K)$ by set inclusion. Define $f: [K, M] \to L(G_K)$ by $f(N) = G_N$ and $g: L(G_K) \to [K, M]$ by $g(H) = \{x \in M; (\forall h \in H)\, h(x) = x\}$. Show that the pair (f, g) establishes a Galois connection between $[K, M]$ and $L(G_K)$.

2.10. Let A be an ordered set and let $I(A)$ be the set of ideals of A, ordered by set inclusion. Let $f: A \to A$ be quasi-residuated. Extend f to a mapping $f^{\rightarrow}: I(A) \to I(A)$ by the prescription $f^{\rightarrow}(I) = \{y \in A; (\exists x \in I)\, y \leq f(x)\}$. Similarly, define $f^{\leftarrow}(I) = \{x \in A; f(x) \in I\}$. Show that $f^{\rightarrow}$ is residuated with $(f^{\rightarrow})^{+} = f^{\leftarrow}$.

2.11. Let X be a non-empty set, let E be a collection of subsets of X ordered by set inclusion and let $f: X \to X$ be such that for each $A \in E$ the set of elements of E containing $f^{\rightarrow}(A)$ is not empty and contains a smallest element denoted by E_A. Show that if ξ_f is defined by setting $\xi_f(A) = E_A$ for each $A \in E$ then ξ_f is residuated if and only if $f^{\leftarrow}(A) = \{x \in X; f(x) \in A\}$ contains a largest element of E. [*Hint*. If ξ_f is residuated, note that for each $A \in E$ we have $(f^{\rightarrow} \circ \xi_f^{+})(A) \subseteq (\xi_f \circ \xi_f^{+})(A) \subseteq A$ and $\xi_f^{+}(A) \in E$. If $B \in E$ and $B \subseteq f^{\leftarrow}(A)$, then $\xi_f(B) \subseteq A$ and $B \subseteq \xi_f^{+}(A)$. Thus $\xi_f^{+}(A)$ is the largest element of E contained in $f^{\leftarrow}(A)$. To obtain the converse, show that the mapping which sends A to the largest element of E contained in $f^{\leftarrow}(A)$ is effective as the residual mapping associated with ξ_f.] *Remark*. Note that the following are particular cases of this example: (a) Exercises 2.1, 2.4 and 2.9; (b) X any Λ-module, E the set of Λ-submodules of X and f any Λ-endomorphism.

2.12. Let E be an ordered set having a smallest element 0 (i.e. $0 \leq x$ for all $x \in E$). Show that an isotone mapping $f: E \to E$ is quasi-residuated if and only if $f(0) = 0$.

2.13. Let $E = \{1, 2, 3, \ldots, n\}$ under the natural order. Prove that an isotone mapping $f: E \to E$ is residuated if and only if $f(1) = 1$.

2.14. Given the diagram $A \xrightarrow{f} B \xrightarrow{g} C$ of ordered sets and isotone mappings in which f and $g \circ f$ are residuated, show that g is quasi-residuated but not in general residuated.

3. Directed sets; semilattices

If E is any ordered set and x is any element of E, it is clear that the canonical injection of $[\leftarrow, x]$ into E is an isotone mapping. If we insist that each such injection be quasi-residuated or residuated, this has important consequences as far as the structure of E is concerned.

THEOREM 3.1. *If E is an ordered set, the following are equivalent:*

(1) *for each $x \in E$ the canonical injection of $[\leftarrow, x]$ into E is quasi-residuated;*

(2) *the set intersection of any two principal ideals of E is not empty (and hence is an ideal of E);*

(3) *the set intersection of any two ideals of E is an ideal of E.*

Proof. Let $i_x : [\leftarrow, x] \to E$ be the canonical injection of $[\leftarrow, x]$ into E. By definition, i_x is quasi-residuated if and only if, for each $y \in E$, $i_x^{\leftarrow} [\leftarrow, y] \neq \emptyset$. This is equivalent to saying that for each $y \in E$ there exists $z \in [\leftarrow, x]$ such that $i_x(z) \leq y$. In other words, it is equivalent to saying that $[\leftarrow, x] \cap [\leftarrow, y] \neq \emptyset$. The theorem now follows.

Definition. If E is an ordered set which satisfies any of the equivalent conditions of Theorem 3.1, we shall say that E is *lower directed.* There is, of course, a dual result concerning filters and if E satisfies the dual propositions we say that E is *upper directed.* In this connection, let us note carefully that the dual of Theorem 3.1(1) is: for each $x \in E$ the canonical injection j_x: $[x, \to] \to E$ is dually quasi-residuated. Likewise, the dual of Theorem 3.1(2) is: the intersection of any two principal filters of E is not empty. Likewise, condition (3) becomes: the set intersection of any two filters of E is a filter.

From the result of Theorem 3.1, two questions arise: (a) What happens if we restrict each canonical injection to be residuated? (b) Under what conditions is the intersection of two principal ideals of E a principal ideal of E? As the next result shows, these problems are the same.

THEOREM 3.2. *If E is an ordered set then the following are equivalent:*

(1) *for each $x \in E$ the canonical injection of $[\leftarrow, x]$ into E is residuated;*

(2) *the set intersection of any two principal ideals of E is a principal ideal of E.*

Proof. It is clear that (1) holds if and only if, for any given $x, y \in E$, the set of elements $z \in [\leftarrow, x]$ such that $z = i_x(z) \leq y$ is not empty and admits a maximum element z^*; i.e. if and only if for any given $x, y \in E$; there exists $z^* \in E$ such that $[\leftarrow, x] \cap [\leftarrow, y] = [\leftarrow, z^*]$.

Definition. If an ordered set E satisfies either of the equivalent conditions of Theorem 3.2 we shall say that E is an *$\cap$-semilattice*. In this case we shall denote by $x \cap y$ the element z^* such that $[\leftarrow, x] \cap [\leftarrow, y] = [\leftarrow, z^*]$. Note that we are using the same symbol $\cap$ to mean two different things; no confusion will arise since the context will always make it clear to which operation we are referring. We call $x \cap y$ the *intersection* of x and y. There is, of course, a dual result which gives rise to the definition of a *$\cup$-semilattice* in which $[x, \rightarrow] \cap [y, \rightarrow] = [x \cup y, \rightarrow]$ and $x \cup y$ is called the *union* of x and y.

It is clear from the above definition that if E is an $\cap$-semilattice then $(x, y) \rightarrow x \cap y$ is a law of composition on E which is commutative and associative; it is also *idempotent* in the sense that $(\forall x \in E)\ x \cap x = x$. In fact, semilattices are characterized by these three properties as our next result shows.

THEOREM 3.3. *A set E can be given the structure of a semilattice if and only if it can be endowed with a law of composition $(x, y) \rightarrow x \top y$ which is commutative, associative and idempotent.*

Proof. In view of the preceding remarks, we need prove only sufficiency. This we shall do for $\cap$-semilattices; a dual proof will yield the result for $\cup$-semilattices. Suppose then that E is an abelian idempotent semigroup under the law of composition $(x, y) \rightarrow x \top y$. Define a relation R on E by

$$x\,R\,y \Leftrightarrow x \top y = x.$$

This relation R is an ordering on E. In fact, (1) since $x \top x = x$ we have xRx; (2) if xRy and yRx, then $x = x \top y = y \top x = y$; (3) if xRy and yRz, then $x = x \top y$ and $y = y \top z$, so that $x = x \top y = x \top (y \top z) = (x \top y) \top z = x \top z$, whence we have xRz. We shall therefore write $\leq$ in place of R. If now x, y are any two elements of E, we have $x \top y = x \top x \top y = x \top y \top x$ and so $x \top y \leq x$. Inverting the rôles of x, y we deduce that $x \top y \leq y$ and hence $x \top y \in [\leftarrow, x] \cap [\leftarrow, y]$ which is therefore not empty. Now

$$\begin{aligned} z \in [\leftarrow, x] \cap [\leftarrow, y] &\Rightarrow z \leq x \quad \text{and} \quad z \leq y \\ &\Rightarrow z = z \top x \quad \text{and} \quad z = z \top y \\ &\Rightarrow z = z \top y = z \top x \top y \\ &\Rightarrow z \leq x \top y. \end{aligned}$$

These observations show that $[\leftarrow, x] \cap [\leftarrow, y]$ has a maximum element, namely the element $x \top y$. It follows that E is an $\cap$-semilattice in which $x \cap y = x \top y$. A dual proof using the relation $x \equiv y(S) \Leftrightarrow x \top y = y$ yields the corresponding result for $\cup$-semilattices.

Definitions. If E is an ordered set and F is a non-empty subset of E, then $x \in E$ is said to be a *lower bound* of F if and only if $(\forall y \in F)\ x \leq y$; and the *greatest lower bound* of F if it is a lower bound of F and such that, for every lower bound z of F, $z \leq x$. In particular, if E is an $\cap$-semilattice then every two-element subset $\{x, y\}$ admits a greatest lower bound, namely the element $x \cap y$. Conversely, if E is an ordered set in which every two-element subset $\{x, y\}$ has a greatest lower bound, z say, then clearly $[\leftarrow, x] \cap [\leftarrow, y] = [\leftarrow, z]$ and so E is an $\cap$-semilattice with $x \cap y = z$. If E is an $\cap$-semilattice then it follows from the equality $[\leftarrow, x_1] \cap [\leftarrow, x_2] = [\leftarrow, x_1 \cap x_2]$ and simple induction that every finite subset $\{x_1, \ldots, x_n\}$ of E admits a greatest lower bound; and g.l.b. $\{x_1, \ldots, x_n\} = x_1 \cap \cdots \cap x_n$. There are, of course, the dual notions of *upper bound* and *least upper bound*; we leave the reader to formulate these.

EXAMPLE 3.1. Consider the set $E = \{1, 2, 3, 4, 5, 6\}$ ordered by divisibility. The corresponding Hasse diagram is

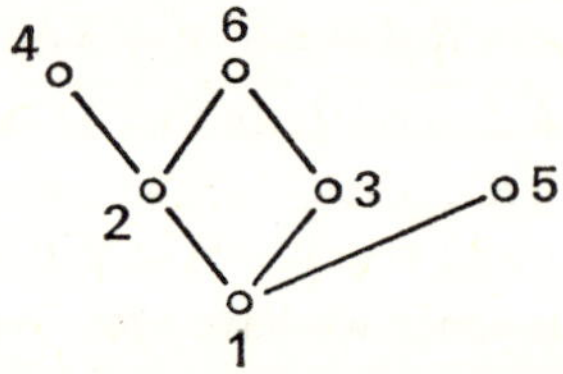

It is readily seen that E is an $\cap$-semilattice with respect to this ordering, with $m \cap n =$ h.c.f. $\{m, n\}$. E is not an upper directed set, however, for $[3, \rightarrow] \cap [5, \rightarrow] = \emptyset$ and so $\{3, 5\}$ has no upper bounds in E.

EXAMPLE 3.2. If R, S are equivalence relations on a set A, let us agree to write $R = S$ if and only if R, S are logically equivalent, in the sense that $xRy \Leftrightarrow xSy$. Under this definition of equality it is readily verified that the relation $\leq$ defined on the set E of equivalence relations on A by

$$R \leq S \quad \text{if and only if} \quad xRy \Rightarrow xSy$$

is an ordering on E. Moreover, with respect to this ordering E is an $\cap$-semilattice. Intersection in E is given by

$$x \equiv y\,(R \cap S) \Leftrightarrow (x \equiv y\,(R) \quad \text{and} \quad x \equiv y\,(S)).$$

As a third example of a semilattice we consider certain implications between properties of a residuated mapping. If E is an ordered set and $f: E \to E$ is a residuated mapping, then we say that f satisfies the property (p, n) if and only if $f^p = f^{p+n}$. In this context, p and n are integers with $p \geq 0$ and $n > 0$; we agree to write $f^0 = \mathrm{id}_E$.

THEOREM 3.4. *Consider the set $\mathscr{E}$ of all the conditions (p, n), I (injective), S (surjective), C (closure), DC (dual closure) which can be satisfied by a residuated mapping f on an ordered set E. When $\mathscr{E}$ is ordered by logical implication it forms an $\cap$-semilattice, part of the Hasse diagram of which is the following (in which t is a prime):*

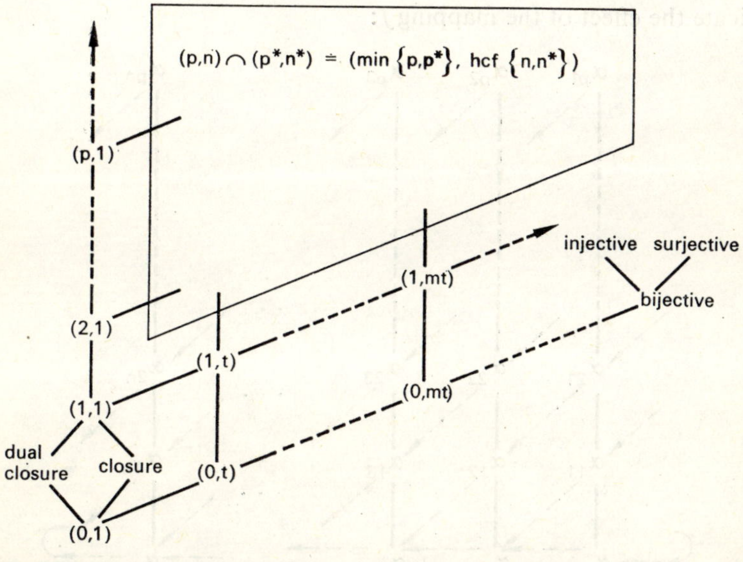

Proof. It is clear that $(p, n) \Rightarrow (p^*, n^*)$ whenever $p^* \geq p$ and n^* is a multiple of n; and that the properties of closure and dual closure each imply the condition $(1, 1)$. Just as clearly, any property of the form $(0, n)$ implies B which in turn implies I and S. In order to show that the properties in question are in general distinct, we consider the following four examples:

EXAMPLE 3.3. Let p, n be integers with $p \geq 0$ and $n > 0$. Let E_{pn} be a set consisting of $(p + 1)n$ elements labelled α_{ij}, where $i \in [0, p]$ and $j \in [1, n]$. Endow E_{pn} with the ordering defined by

$$\alpha_{ij} \leq \alpha_{kt} \Leftrightarrow (i \leq k \quad \text{and} \quad j = t).$$

Consider the mapping $f\colon E_{pn} \to E_{pn}$ described by

$$f(\alpha_{ij}) = \begin{cases} \alpha_{0,j+1} & \text{if} \quad i = 0, \quad j \neq n; \\ \alpha_{0,1} & \text{if} \quad i = 0, \quad j = n; \\ \alpha_{i-1,j+1} & \text{if} \quad i \neq 0, \quad j \neq n; \\ \alpha_{i-1,1} & \text{if} \quad i \neq 0, \quad j = n. \end{cases}$$

The Hasse diagram for E_{pn} is as follows, in which the dotted arrows indicate the effect of the mapping f:

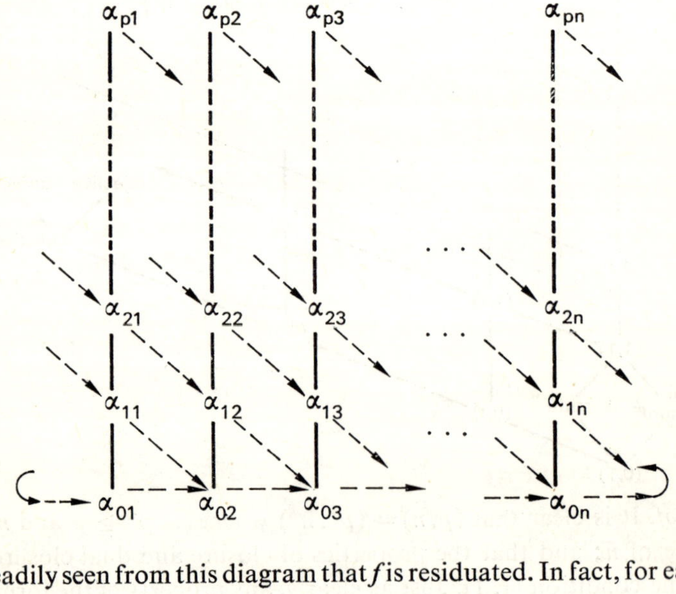

It is readily seen from this diagram that f is residuated. In fact, for each α_{ij},

$$\max \{\alpha_{kt};\ f(\alpha_{kt}) \leq \alpha_{ij}\}$$

exists and is given by

$$f^+(\alpha_{ij}) = \begin{cases} \alpha_{i+1,j-1} & \text{if } i \neq p, \ j \neq 1; \\ \alpha_{p,j-1} & \text{if } i = p, \ j \neq 1; \\ \alpha_{i+1,n} & \text{if } i \neq p, \ j = 1; \\ \alpha_{p,n} & \text{if } i = p, \ j = 1. \end{cases}$$

It is also readily seen from this diagram that f is such that $f^p = f^{p+n}$ and is such that $f^q = f^{q+r}$ if and only if $p \leq q$ and r is a multiple of n. Moreover, f is a closure mapping only in the cases $p = 0, n = 1$ and $p = 1, n = 1$; and is injective, surjective or bijective only in the case $p = 0$.

EXAMPLE 3.4. In Example 2.5 the mapping θ_3 is residuated and is such that $\theta_3 = \theta_3 \circ \theta_3 \leq \text{id}$. Thus θ_3 is a dual closure mapping. Clearly θ_3 is not a closure mapping, nor is it either injective or surjective.

EXAMPLE 3.5. Consider the mapping $f: \mathbf{Z}_+ \to \mathbf{Z}_+$ described by

$$f(n) = \begin{cases} 1 & \text{if } n = 1; \\ n - 1 & \text{otherwise.} \end{cases}$$

Clearly f is residuated; its residual is given by $f^+(n) = n + 1$. This mapping satisfies none of the properties (p, n), is surjective but not injective.

EXAMPLE 3.6. Taking the situation which is dual to that in Example 3.5 we obtain a residuated mapping $f^+ : \mathbf{Z}_+^* \to \mathbf{Z}_+^*$ which is injective, not surjective and satisfies none of the properties (p, n).

These examples establish that the conditions under consideration are in general all distinct and that the restriction of our ordering to the subset consisting of all properties of the form (p, n) yields an ordered set isomorphic to $\mathbf{N} \times \mathbf{Z}_+$, where $\mathbf{N}$ is ordered in the usual way and $\mathbf{Z}_+$ is ordered by divisibility. It follows immediately that

$$(p, n) \cap (p^*, n^*) = (\min\{p, p^*\}, \ \text{h.c.f.}\ \{n, n^*\}).$$

We leave the rest of the details to the reader.

It should be noted that in Examples 3.5 and 3.6 the ordered sets in question are infinite. This is not without purpose, for in the case of a finite set the notions injective, surjective and bijective are equivalent. This is the only modification to the diagram of Theorem 3.4 in the case of a finite ordered set, as is borne out by the fact that in Examples 3.3 and 3.4 we were dealing with finite sets.

The diagram of Theorem 3.4 is enormously simplified in certain circumstances. In the exercises for this section we shall impose further conditions on f and note the simplification which occurs.

EXERCISES

3.1. If $f: E \to E$ is residuated and such that $f^2 \leq f$, prove that for each integer $n \geq 2$ the property (p, n) is equivalent to the property $(p, 1)$.

3.2. Show that the mapping $f: \mathbf{Z} \to \mathbf{Z}$ described by $f(n) = n - 1$ is residuated, bijective and such that $f^2 \leq f$ but satisfies none of the conditions $(p, 1)$. Observing that the residuated mappings of Examples 3.4, 3.5, 3.6 all satisfy $f^2 \leq f$ and that if $n = 1$ in Example 3.3 this is also the case, deduce that if a residuated mapping f is such that $f^2 \leq f$, then the diagram of Theorem 3.4 simplifies as far as the following

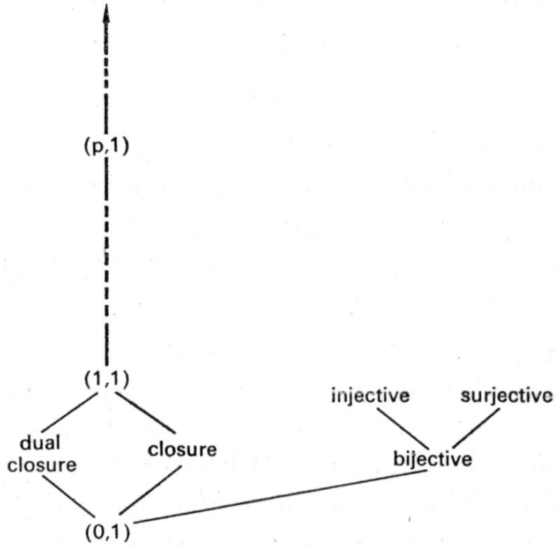

3.3. Let $f: E \to E$ be residuated and such that $f^2 \leq f$. Prove that if E satisfies the ascending chain condition (in that every ascending chain $x_1 \leq x_2 \leq \cdots \leq x_n \leq \ldots$ is finite), then the property $(0, 1)$ is equivalent to surjectivity. With the same hypothesis on f prove that if dually E satisfies the descending chain condition then the property $(0, 1)$ is equivalent to injectivity. [In the ascending chain case let f be surjective and consider the set $F = \{x \in E; f(x) < x\}$. Show that F is empty. In the descending chain case let

f be injective and consider $G = \{f(x) \in E; f[f(x)] > f(x)\}$. Show that G is empty and apply Theorem 2.6(d).]

3.4. Let $f: E \to E$ be residuated and such that $f \leq \mathrm{id}_E$. Prove that the property (0, 1) is equivalent to f being a closure mapping and that the property (1, 1) is equivalent to f being a dual closure mapping. Determine how far the diagram of Theorem 3.4 simplifies in this case.

4. Lattices; complete lattices

An ordered set which forms, with respect to its ordering, both a $\cup$-semilattice and an $\cap$-semilattice will be called a *lattice*. Thus an ordered set E is a lattice if and only if each canonical injection $i_x : [\leftarrow, x] \to E$ is residuated and each canonical injection $j_x : [x, \to] \to E$ is dually residuated. We can also characterize lattices in the following way.

THEOREM 4.1. *A set E can be given the structure of a lattice if and only if it can be endowed with two laws of composition* $(x, y) \to x \top y$ *and* $(x, y) \to x \perp y$ *such that*

(1) $(E, \top)$ *and* $(E, \perp)$ *are abelian semigroups;*

(2) *the following absorption laws hold:*

$$(\forall x, y \in E) \quad x \top (x \perp y) = x = x \perp (x \top y).$$

Proof. Suppose that E is a lattice; then E has two laws of composition which satisfy (1), namely $(x, y) \to x \cap y$ and $(x, y) \to x \cup y$. To show that (2) holds, we note that for all $x, y \in E$ we have $x \leq x \cup y$ and so $x \cap (x \cup y) = x$; similarly, $x \cap y \leq x$ yields $x \cup (x \cap y) = x$.

Conversely, suppose that E has two laws of composition $\top$ and $\perp$ satisfying (1) and (2). Using (2) twice we have

$$(\forall x \in E) \quad x \perp x = x \perp [x \top (x \perp x)] = x,$$

and, similarly, $x \top x = x$. This, together with Theorem 3.3 and its dual, shows that E can be given the structure of a semilattice with respect to each of $\top, \perp$. In order to show that E can be made into a lattice we have to show that, with $\top$ as $\cap$ and $\perp$ as $\cup$ for example, the orderings defined by them coincide; in other words, we must show that

$$x \top y = x \quad \text{is equivalent to} \quad x \perp y = y.$$

Now using (2) and (1) we have

$$\begin{cases} x \top y = x \Rightarrow y = (x \top y) \perp y = x \perp y; \\ x \perp y = y \Rightarrow x = x \top (x \perp y) = x \top y. \end{cases}$$

It therefore follows that E is a lattice in which the ordering is given by

$$x \leq y \Leftrightarrow x \top y = x \Leftrightarrow x \perp y = y.$$

It is also clear from results given previously for semilattices that an ordered set E is a lattice if and only if every two-element (and hence any finite) subset of E admits a greatest lower bound and a least upper bound.

EXAMPLE 4.1. For any set E, $(\mathbf{P}(E), \cap, \cup, \subseteq)$ is a lattice.

EXAMPLE 4.2. Every totally ordered set is a lattice.

EXAMPLE 4.3. The diagram of Example 1.8 is that of a lattice. In this example $m \cap n =$ h.c.f. $\{m, n\}$ and $m \cup n =$ l.c.m. $\{m, n\}$.

EXAMPLE 4.4. Let X, Y be arbitrary subgroups of a group G. The set theoretic intersection $X \cap Y$ is a subgroup of G. Denote by $X \curlyvee Y$ the subgroup generated by X and Y [i.e. the smallest subgroup of G to contain the set theoretic union $X \cup Y$]. With respect to the laws of composition $(X, Y) \rightarrow X \cap Y$, $(X, Y) \rightarrow X \curlyvee Y$, the set of all subgroups of G forms a lattice, known as the *subgroup lattice* of G.

EXAMPLE 4.5. Let L, M be lattices and let H denote the set of all isotone mappings from L to M. If, for each $f, g \in H$, we define the mappings $f \curlywedge g$ and $f \curlyvee g$ by

$$(\forall x \in L) \quad (f \curlywedge g)(x) = f(x) \cap g(x); \quad (f \curlyvee g)(x) = f(x) \cap g(x),$$

then $(f, g) \rightarrow f \curlywedge g$ and $(f, g) \rightarrow f \curlyvee g$ are laws of composition on H and $(H, \curlywedge, \curlyvee)$ is a lattice.

EXAMPLE 4.6. If $E_1, \ldots, E_n$ are lattices, then so also is $\mathop{\times}\limits_{i=1}^{n} E_i$ when ordered as in Example 1.6. A similar assertion holds for arbitrary direct products

Definitions. We say that a $\cup$-semilattice [resp. lattice] is $\cup$-*complete* if and only if *every* non-empty subset admits a least upper bound. It is clear that if L is $\cup$-complete then L contains a maximum element. We define the notion of $\cap$-completeness in a similar way. A lattice which is both $\cup$-complete and $\cap$-complete will be called simply *complete*. We say that a lattice is *bounded* if and only if it has both a maximum element and a minimum element. In particular, every complete lattice is bounded. By the notation $\bigcup_{\alpha \in A} x_\alpha$ we shall mean the least upper bound of the family $\{x_\alpha\}_{\alpha \in A}$ (whenever it exists). $\bigcap_{\alpha \in A} x_\alpha$ is defined similarly.

It is clear that every finite lattice is complete. The lattices of Examples 4.1 and 4.4 are complete; that of Example 4.5 is complete whenever M is; that of Example 4.2 is not in general complete, for if we consider the chain $\mathbf{Q}$ of rationals we see that the subset of rationals whose squares are less than 2 has no upper bound in $\mathbf{Q}$.

THEOREM 4.2. *A $\cup$-complete $\cup$-semilattice is a complete lattice if and only if it has a minimum element.*

Proof. Clearly, if L is a complete lattice, then L has a minimum element, namely the greatest lower bound of all the elements in L.

Conversely, suppose that L is a $\cup$-complete $\cup$-semilattice with minimum element 0_L. Let $X = \{x_\alpha\}_{\alpha \in A}$ be a non-empty subset of L and let $M = \{m_\beta\}_{\beta \in B}$ be the set of lower bounds of X. Clearly $M \neq \emptyset$ for $0_L \in M$. By hypothesis, the element

$$a = \bigcup_{\beta \in B} m_\beta$$

exists. Now by the definition of M we have

$$(\forall x_\alpha \in X)\,(\forall m_\beta \in M) \quad m_\beta \leq x_\alpha$$

and so

$$(\forall x_\alpha \in X) \quad a = \bigcup_{\beta \in B} m_\beta \leq x_\alpha,$$

whence a is a lower bound of X. By its definition, a is thus the greatest lower bound of X. Since X was chosen arbitrarily, it follows that L is also an $\cap$-complete $\cap$-semilattice.

There is, of course, a dual result to Theorem 4.2.

For the remainder of this section we shall be concerned with closure mappings and their relationship with complete lattices. The results discussed culminate in an important embedding theorem.

Definition. If E is an ordered set and $f: E \to E$ is a closure mapping, we say that $x \in E$ is *f-closed* if and only if $f(x) = x$.

THEOREM 4.3. *Let E be an ordered set and let F be any non-empty subset of E. The following conditions are equivalent:*

(1) *there exists a closure mapping $f: E \to E$ such that the set of f-closed elements is F;*

(2) *for each $x \in E$ the set $[x, \to] \cap F$ admits a minimum element.*

Proof. Suppose that (1) holds. Then for any $x \in E$ the set $[x, \to] \cap F$ is not empty, for it clearly contains the element $f(x)$. Moreover, if $z \in [x, \to] \cap F$, then $x \leq z$ and $f(x) \leq f(z) = z$. Consequently $[x, \to] \cap F$ admits a minimum element, namely $f(x)$. Conversely, suppose that (2) holds. Let x_* denote the minimum element of $[x, \to] \cap F$ and define a mapping $f: E \to E$ by the prescription $f(x) = x_*$. This mapping is isotone, for if $x \leq y$ then $[x, \to] \supseteq [y, \to]$ and so $[x, \to] \cap F \supseteq [y, \to] \cap F$ whence it follows that $x_* \leq y_*$ and $f(x) \leq f(y)$. Since $f(x) = x_* \geq x$ for each $x \in E$, we also have $f \geq \mathrm{id}_E$. Moreover, if $y \in F$, then clearly $y_* = y$ and so $f(y) = y$; but, in particular, $f(x) = x_* \in F$, and so it follows that $f[f(x)] = f(x)$. Thus $f \circ f = f$ and so f is a closure mapping.

Definition. A non-empty subset F of an ordered set E will be called a *closure subset* of E if and only if it satisfies the conditions of Theorem 4.3.

THEOREM 4.4. *If E is an ordered set and F, G are closure subsets of E associated with closure mappings f, g on E then the following conditions are equivalent:*

(a) $f \leq g$; (b) $G \subseteq F$; (c) $f \circ g = g$; (d) $g \circ f = g$.

Proof. If (a) holds, then $(\forall x \in E)\, f(x) \leq g(x)$. In particular, if $y \in G$, then $f(y) \leq g(y) = y$. But $f \geq \mathrm{id}_E$, and so $f(y) \geq y$. It follows that $f(y) = y$ and so $y \in F$. This shows that $(a) \Rightarrow (b)$. If now (b) holds, then for each $x \in E$ we have $g(x) \in G \subseteq F$ and so $f[g(x)] = g(x)$, giving $f \circ g = g$ which is (c). If now (c) holds, then from $g \geq \mathrm{id}_E$ we have $g = g \circ g = g \circ f \circ g \geq g \circ f \circ \mathrm{id}_E = g \circ f$, and from $f \geq \mathrm{id}_E$ we have $g \circ f \geq g$. Thus $g = g \circ f$ which is (d). Finally, if (d) holds then for each $x \in E$, we have $f(x) = (\mathrm{id}_E \circ f)(x) \leq (g \circ f)(x) = g(x)$ and (a) follows.

THEOREM 4.5. *Let E be an ordered set, let $K(E)$ denote its set of closure subsets and let $C(E)$ be its set of closure mappings. Then the ordered sets $K(E)$, $C(E)$ are dually isomorphic.*

Proof. This follows immediately from Theorem 4.4.

Definitions. A non-empty subset of a $\cup$-semilattice is called a *$\cup$-subsemilattice* if it is closed under the formation of furite unions. An *$\cap$-subsemilattice* is defined similarly. A *sublattice* of a lattice is a subset which is closed under both $\cup$ and $\cap$. A sublattice M of a lattice L is said to be *complete* if it is closed under the formation of arbitrary unions and intersections of nonempty subsets of M provided that the indicated unions and intersections exist in L. The notions of $\cup$-completeness and $\cap$-completeness are defined as one would expect.

THEOREM 4.6. *Let E be a complete lattice. Then every closure subset of E is an $\cap$-complete $\cap$-subsemilattice containing the greatest element of E, hence in its own right a complete lattice.*

Proof. Let C be any closure subset of E. Then there exists a closure mapping $f: E \to E$ such that $(\forall x \in C)\, f(x) = x$. Consider any collection $\{x_\alpha;\, \alpha \in A\}$ of elements of C. Since $f \geq \mathrm{id}_E$ we have

$$f\Big(\bigcap_{\alpha \in A} x_\alpha\Big) \geq \bigcap_{\alpha \in A} x_\alpha. \tag{*}$$

But, on the other hand, $(\forall \beta \in A) \bigcap_{\alpha \in A} x_\alpha \leq x_\beta$ and so $(\forall \beta \in A)\, f\Big(\bigcap_{\alpha \in A} x_\alpha\Big) \leq f(x_\beta) = x_\beta$, whence

$$f\Big(\bigcap_{\alpha \in A} x_\alpha\Big) \leq \bigcap_{\alpha \in A} x_\alpha. \tag{**}$$

From (*) and (**) we obtain

$$f\Big(\bigcap_{\alpha \in A} x_\alpha\Big) = \bigcap_{\alpha \in A} x_\alpha,$$

which shows that $\bigcap_{\alpha \in A} x_\alpha \in C$. Hence C is an $\cap$-complete $\cap$-subsemilattice of E. If π_E is the greatest element of E, then from $f \geq \mathrm{id}_E$ we deduce that $\pi_E = f(\pi_E)$ and hence that $\pi_E \in C$. The proof is completed by an application of the dual of Theorem 4.2.

THEOREM 4.7. *Any ordered set E can be embedded in a complete lattice L, any unions and intersections which may exist in E being conserved in L.*

Proof. If E does not already have a greatest element and a least element, we begin by adjoining whichever of these bounds are missing. Thus with no loss of generality we may assume that E is a bounded ordered set. Write $P = \mathbf{P}(E)$ and denote as usual by P^* the dual of P. We define mappings $g: P \to P^*$ and $h: P^* \to P$ as follows: if A is a non-empty subset of E, let $g(A)$ be the set of upper bounds of A and let $h(A)$ be the set of its lower bounds; moreover, let $g(\emptyset) = E = h(\emptyset)$. We leave to the reader the routine verification that $g \in \text{Res}\,(P, P^*)$ with $h = g^+$. By Theorem 2.7, $f = h \circ g$ is a closure map on P, and so, by Theorem 4.6, the closure subset F associated with f is a complete lattice. We observe that $(\forall x \in E)\ f(\{x\}) = [\leftarrow, x]$ and that $x \leq y \Leftrightarrow f(\{x\}) \subseteq f(\{y\})$. Thus $x \to f(\{x\})$ is an embedding of E in F. Suppose now that $a = \bigcap_{\alpha \in I} x_\alpha$ exists in E. Then $[\leftarrow, a]$ is the set-theoretic intersection of the family $\{[\leftarrow, x_\alpha];\ \alpha \in I\}$, thus showing that the embedding preserves any existing infima of subsets of E. On the other hand, if $b = \bigcup_{\alpha \in I} x_\alpha$ exists in E, note that $g(\{b\}) = g(\{x_\alpha;\ \alpha \in I\})$. Clearly $f(\{b\})$ is an upper bound for $\{f(\{x_\alpha\});\ \alpha \in I\}$ and if $A = f(A)$ is any other upper bound for this set in F then $g(A) \supseteq g(\{x_\alpha;\ \alpha \in I\}) = g(\{b\})$ whence

$$A = f(A) = (h \circ g)(A) \supseteq (h \circ g)(\{b\}) = f(\{b\}).$$

We deduce that in F we have $f(\{b\}) = \bigcup_{\alpha \in I} f(\{x_\alpha\})$, thus completing the proof of the theorem.

Remark. The complete lattice referred to in Theorem 4.7 will be referred to as the *MacNeille completion* of E.

EXERCISES

4.1. Let L, M be lattices and let $f, g \in \text{Res}\,(L, M)$, where $\text{Res}\,(L, M)$ denotes the set of all residuated mappings from L to M. Define $f \curlyvee g$ as in Example 4.5. Prove that $f \curlyvee g \in \text{Res}\,(L, M)$. If L and M are totally ordered, prove also that $f \curlywedge g \in \text{Res}\,(L, M)$. Is the latter true in general?

4.2. Let E, F be ordered sets and let $f \in \text{Res}\,(E, F)$. If $x = \bigcup_{\alpha \in A} x_\alpha$ exists in E, prove that $\bigcup_{\alpha \in A} f(x_\alpha)$ exists in F and is $f(x)$.

4.3. If L is a lattice and $p, q \in L$ are such that $p \leq q$, let $[p, q] = \{x \in L;\ p \leq x \leq q\}$. Given any $a, b \in L$, prove that the mapping $f: [a \cap b, b] \to [a, a \cup b]$ defined by $f(x) = x \cup a$ is residuated and determine f^+.

4.4. Give examples of two distinct residuated mappings from a lattice to itself which give rise to the same closure mapping (Theorem 2.7).

4.5. Let M be a left Λ-module and let $L(M)$ be the set of submodules of M. Prove that $(L(M), \cap, +)$ is a complete lattice.

4.6. If M_1, M_2 are left Λ-modules and $f: M_1 \to M_2$ is a Λ-homomorphism, prove that the induced mapping $f^{\rightarrow} : L(M_1) \to L(M_2)$ is residuated and that

$$(\forall H \in L(M_1)) \quad [(f^{\rightarrow})^{+} \circ f^{\rightarrow}](H) = H + \operatorname{Ker} f;$$

$$(\forall K \in L(M_2)) \quad [f^{\rightarrow} \circ (f^{\rightarrow})^{+}](K) = K \cap \operatorname{Im} f.$$

4.7. Let L_1, L_2 be bounded lattices. Denote their minimum elements by 0 and their maximum elements by π. For $i = 1, 2$ let the mappings $f_i : L_i \to L_1 \times L_2$ be given by $f_1(x) = (x, 0), f_2(x) = (0, x)$ and let $\mathrm{pr}_i : L_1 \times L_2 \to L_i$ be the projections $\mathrm{pr}_1(x, y) = x$, $\mathrm{pr}_2(x, y) = y$. Prove that $(i = 1, 2)$ $f_i \in \operatorname{Res}(L_i, L_1 \times L_2)$, $\mathrm{pr}_i \in \operatorname{Res}(L_1 \times L_2, L_i)$.

4.8. Let L, L_1 and L_2 be bounded lattices.

(a) Given $f_1 \in \operatorname{Res}(L, L_1)$ and $f_2 \in \operatorname{Res}(L, L_2)$ show that there is a unique $h \in \operatorname{Res}(L, L_1 \times L_2)$ such that the following diagram is commutative

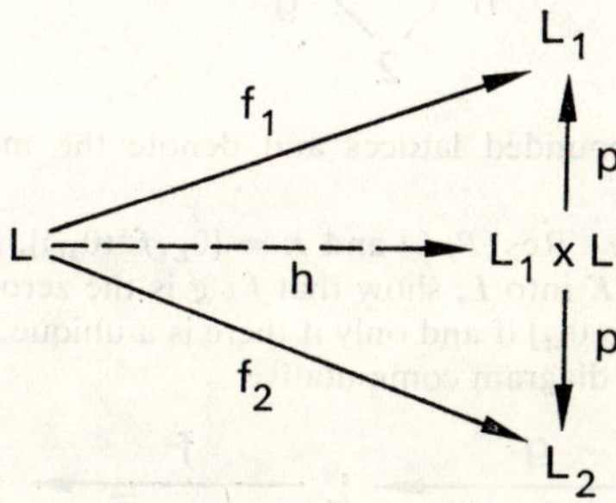

(b) Let $g_1 \in \operatorname{Res}(L_1, L)$ and $g_2 \in \operatorname{Res}(L_2, L)$. Show that there is a unique $h \in \operatorname{Res}(L_1 \times L_2, L)$ such that the following diagram is commutative

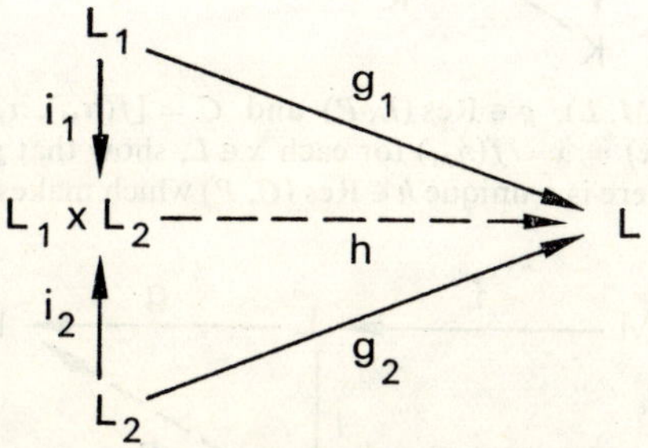

where i_1, i_2 denote the canonical injections.

4.9. Let 2 denote the two element lattice and suppose that L, M are bounded lattices.

(a) Given an injective element $f \in \text{Res}(L, M)$ prove that for every $g \in \text{Res}(L, 2)$ there is an $h \in \text{Res}(M, 2)$ such that the following diagram is commutative:

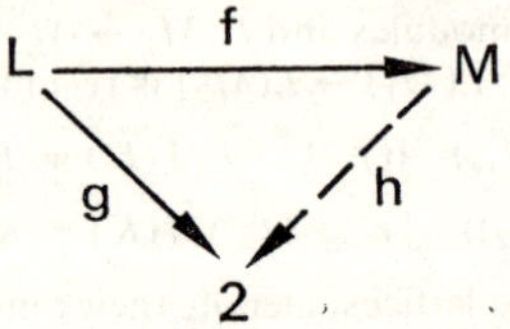

(b) Dually, if $f \in \text{Res}(L, M)$ is surjective, prove that for every $g \in \text{Res}(2, M)$ there is an $h \in \text{Res}(2, L)$ such that the following diagram is commutative:

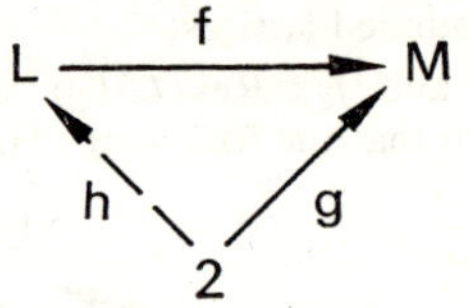

4.10. Let L, M, P be bounded lattices and denote the minimum (maximum) element of L by 0_L (π_L), etc.

(a) Let $f \in \text{Res}(L, M)$, $g \in \text{Res}(P, L)$ and $K = [0_L, f^+(0_M)]$. If i_K denotes the canonical injection of K into L, show that $f \circ g$ is the zero mapping [i.e. sends every element of P to 0_M] if and only if there is a unique $h \in \text{Res}(P, K)$ which makes the following diagram commutative

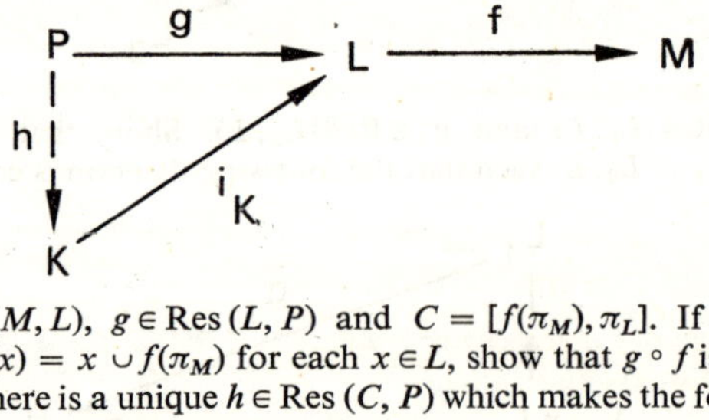

(b) Let $f \in \text{Res}(M, L)$, $g \in \text{Res}(L, P)$ and $C = [f(\pi_M), \pi_L]$. If $j \in \text{Res}(L, C)$ is defined by $j(x) = x \cup f(\pi_M)$ for each $x \in L$, show that $g \circ f$ is the zero map if and only if there is a unique $h \in \text{Res}(C, P)$ which makes the following diagram commutative

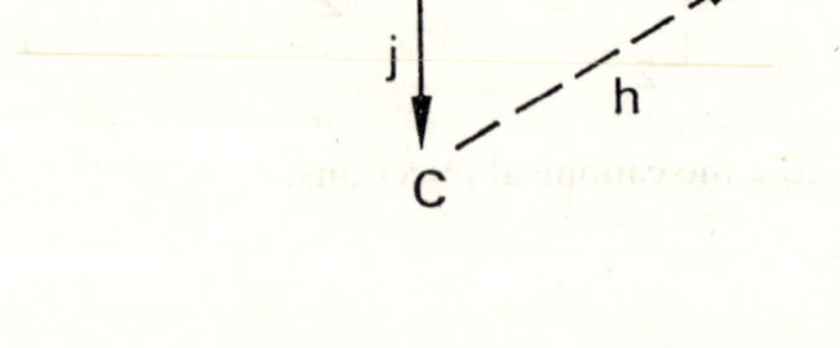

4.11. Let L, M be lattices and $f \in \text{Res}(L, M)$. Prove that $\text{Im} f$ is a lattice under the induced ordering and that the canonical injection i of $\text{Im} f$ into M is residuated. Prove further that there is a unique $g \in \text{Res}(L, \text{Im} f)$ making the following diagram commutative:

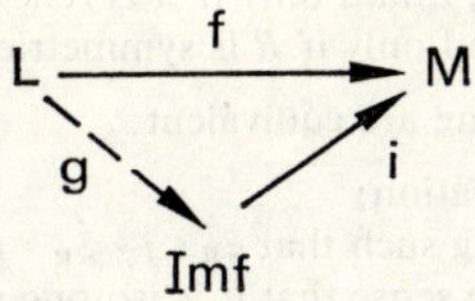

[*Hint.* Show that union and intersection in $\text{Im} f$ are given by $x \vee y = x \cup y$ and $x \wedge y = (f \circ f^+)(x \cap y)$.]

4.12. Consider the ordered set whose Hasse diagram is

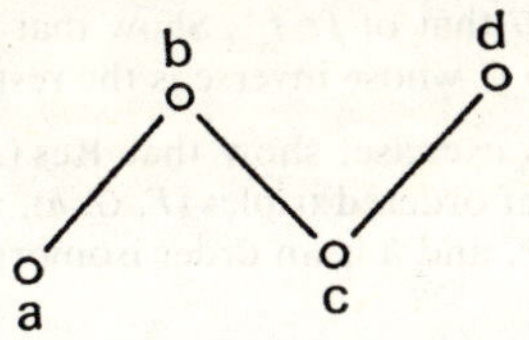

Embed this in a complete lattice L according to the method of Theorem 4.7 and draw the Hasse diagram for L.

4.13. Let E be an infinite set and let L be the lattice formed by E, $\emptyset$, and the finite subsets of E. Show that L is a sublattice of $\mathbf{P}(E)$ which is in its own right a complete lattice though infinite unions in L do not coincide with those in $\mathbf{P}(E)$.

4.14. Let E be a non-empty set. If R_1, R_2 are equivalence relations on E, show that the relation $R_1 \cup R_2$ given by

$$x \equiv y\,(R_1 \cup R_2) \Leftrightarrow (x \equiv y(R_1) \text{ or } x \equiv y(R_2))$$

is not in general an equivalence relation. If $\mathscr{E}(E)$ denotes the set of equivalence relations on E, order $\mathscr{E}(E)$ as in Example 3.2. Show that $\mathscr{E}(E)$ is a complete lattice in which intersection is given, for each family $\{R_\alpha\}_{\alpha \in I}$ of equivalence relations on E, by

$$x \equiv y\left(\bigcap_{\alpha \in I} R_\alpha\right) \Leftrightarrow (\forall \alpha \in I)\; x \equiv y(R_\alpha)$$

and union is given by the relation $\prod_{\alpha \in I} R_\alpha$ defined by

$$x \equiv y\left(\prod_{\alpha \in I} R_\alpha\right) \Leftrightarrow \begin{cases} (\exists a_1, \ldots, a_p \in E)\,(\exists \alpha_1, \ldots, \alpha_{p+1} \in I) \\ x \equiv a_1(R_{\alpha_1}), \ldots, a_i \equiv a_{i+1}(R_{\alpha_{i+1}}), \ldots, a_p \equiv y(R_{\alpha_{p+1}}). \end{cases}$$

4.15. Let E be any non-empty set and let R be a binary relation on E. Write the converse of R as R^t. Consider the mapping $\xi_R : \mathbf{P}(E) \to \mathbf{P}(E)$ described by

$$(\forall A \in \mathbf{P}(E)) \quad \xi_R(A) = \{y \in E;\, (\exists x \in A)\; xRy\}.$$

If $\jmath : \mathbf{P}(E) \to \mathbf{P}(E)$ is the (antitone) mapping which sends each subset A of E to its complement A' in E, prove that ξ_R is residuated with residual given by

$$\xi_R^+ = \jmath \circ \xi_{R^t} \circ \jmath.$$

Prove also that

(a) $\mathrm{id} \leq \xi_R$ if and only if R is reflexive;
(b) $\xi_R^2 \leq \xi_R$ if and only if R is transitive;
(c) ξ_R is a closure mapping if and only if R is reflexive and transitive;
(d) $\xi_R \circ \imath \circ \xi_R \circ \imath \leq \mathrm{id}$ if and only if R is symmetric.

Show also that the following are equivalent:

(i) R is an equivalence relation;
(ii) ξ_R is a closure mapping such that $\xi_R \circ \imath \circ \xi_R \circ \imath \leq \mathrm{id}$;
(iii) ξ_R is a *quantifier* in the sense that it is isotone and such that

$$(\forall X, Y \in \mathbf{P}(E)) \quad \xi_R\,[X \cap \xi_R(Y)] = \xi_R(X) \cap \xi_R(Y).$$

4.16. Let A, B be ordered sets and let $f \in \mathrm{Res}\,(A, B)$. By Theorem 2.7, $f^+ \circ f$ is a closure mapping on A and dually $f \circ f^+$ is a closure mapping on B^*. Let F denote the closure subset of $f^+ \circ f$ and G that of $f \circ f^+$. Show that the restriction of f to F is an order isomorphism of F onto G whose inverse is the restriction of f^+ to G.

4.17. Using the previous exercise, show that $\mathrm{Res}\,(A, B)$ can be put in one-one correspondence with the set of ordered triples (F, G, h), where F is a closure subset of A, G is a closure subset of B^*, and h is an order isomorphism of F onto G.

5. Morphisms

If L, M are $\cup$-semilattices, then a mapping $f: L \to M$ is called a *$\cup$-homomorphism* if and only if

$$(\forall x, y \in L) \quad f(x \cup y) = f(x) \cup f(y).$$

A $\cup$-homomorphism is necessarily isotone; for if $x \leq y$, then we have $f(y) = f(x \cup y) = f(x) \cup f(y)$ and so $f(x) \leq f(y)$. In a dual manner we define the notion of an *$\cap$-homomorphism*. If L, M are lattices, then we say that $f: L \to M$ is a *(lattice) homomorphism* if it is both a $\cup$-homomorphism and an $\cap$-homomorphism. We say that lattices L, M are *isomorphic* if they are isomorphic as ordered sets.

THEOREM 5.1. *A necessary and sufficient condition that the lattices L, M be isomorphic is that there exist a bijection $f: L \to M$ which is either a $\cup$-homomorphism or an $\cap$-homomorphism.*

Proof. Suppose that L, M are isomorphic, so that there is a bijection $f: L \to M$ such that $x \leq y \Leftrightarrow f(x) \leq f(y)$. Since f is surjective, each element of M is of the form $f(z)$ for some $z \in L$. Now $f(x) \cup f(y) = f(z)$ is equivalent to the properties

$$\begin{cases}\text{(a)} & f(x) \le f(z), \quad f(y) \le f(z); \\ \text{(b)} & (f(x) \le f(t) \text{ and } f(y) \le f(t)) \Rightarrow f(z) \le f(t).\end{cases}$$

Since f is an isomorphism, these properties are equivalent to

$$\begin{cases}(\alpha) & x \le z, \quad y \le z; \\ (\beta) & (x \le t \text{ and } y \le t) \Rightarrow z \le t,\end{cases}$$

i.e. to $x \cup y = z$. Hence $f(x) \cup f(y) = f(x \cup y)$, and so f is a $\cup$-homomorphism. Conversely, if f is a bijection which is a $\cup$-homomorphism then

$$x \le y \Leftrightarrow y = x \cup y \Leftrightarrow f(y) = f(x \cup y) = f(x) \cup f(y) \Leftrightarrow f(x) \le f(y),$$

and so f is an order-isomorphism. A similar proof holds for $\cap$-homomorphisms.

COROLLARY. *The lattices L, M are isomorphic if and only is there exists a bijective lattice homomorphism $f: L \to M$.*

Definition. If L, M are $\cup$-semilattices we say that $f: L \to M$ is a *complete $\cup$-homomorphism* if and only if, for each non-empty family $\{x_\alpha\}_{\alpha \in I}$ of elements of L such that $\bigcup_{\alpha \in I} x_\alpha$ exists, $\bigcup_{\alpha \in I} f(x_\alpha)$ exists and

$$f\Big(\bigcup_{\alpha \in I} x_\alpha\Big) = \bigcup_{\alpha \in I} f(x_\alpha).$$

The notion of complete $\cap$-homomorphism is defined similarly. We leave to the reader the routine verification that every lattice isomorphism is both a complete $\cup$-homomorphism and a complete $\cap$-homomorphism.

THEOREM 5.2. *Let L, M be $\cup$-semilattices. If $f: L \to M$ is any residuated mapping then f is a complete quasi-residuated $\cup$-homomorphism. If L is $\cup$-complete then f is residuated if and only if it is a complete quasi-residuated $\cup$-homomorphism.*

Proof. Assume first that L, M are $\cup$-semilattices with $f \in \operatorname{Res}(L, M)$. Let $\{x_\alpha\}_{\alpha \in I}$ be a family of elements of L and suppose that $x = \bigcup_{\alpha \in I} x_\alpha$ exists. Now if $(\forall \alpha \in I)\, y \ge f(x_\alpha)$, then $(\forall \alpha \in I)\, f^+(y) \ge f^+[f(x_\alpha)] \ge x_\alpha$ and so $f^+(y) \ge \bigcup_{\alpha \in I} x_\alpha = x$. But then $y \ge f[f^+(y)] \ge f(x)$ and so $\bigcup_{\alpha \in I} f(x_\alpha)$ exists and is none other than $f(x)$. This proves the first part of the theorem.

Now let L be $\cup$-complete and $f: L \to M$ a complete quasi-residuated $\cup$-homomorphism. For each $y \in M$ the set $\{x \in L;\ f(x) \le y\}$ is then nonempty and, making use of the completeness of f, we see that if $y^* = \bigcup \{x \in L; f(x) \le y\}$, then we must have $f(y^*) \le y$. It is immediate that $f^{\leftarrow}[\leftarrow, y] = [\leftarrow, y^*]$ and so f is residuated.

It should be noted that in the case where L is not complete, a complete quasi-residuated $\cup$-homomorphism need not be residuated, as the next two examples show.

EXAMPLE 5.1. The fields $\mathbf{Q}$, $\mathbf{R}$ form lattices with respect to their natural order in which $x \cup y = \max\{x, y\}$. Consider $f: \mathbf{Q}_+ \to \mathbf{R}_+$ given by setting $(\forall x \in \mathbf{Q}_+)\ f(x) = x^2$. If $x = \bigcup_{\alpha \in I} x_\alpha$ exists in $\mathbf{Q}_+$, then $x = \bigcup_{\alpha \in I} x_\alpha$ in $\mathbf{R}_+$. Clearly $(\forall \alpha \in I)\ x^2 \ge x_\alpha^2$, and if $(\forall \alpha \in I)\ y \ge x_\alpha^2$, then we have $(\forall \alpha \in I)$ $\sqrt{y} \ge x_\alpha$ so $\sqrt{y} \ge x = \bigcup_{\alpha \in I} x_\alpha$ and $y \ge x^2$. This shows that $f(x) = \bigcup_{\alpha \in I} f(x_\alpha)$ and so f is a complete $\cup$-homomorphism which is clearly quasi-residuated. However, f is not residuated since the set $\{x \in \mathbf{Q}_+;\ f(x) \le 2\}$ has no maximum element.

EXAMPLE 5.2. Let E be an infinite set and $\mathbf{P}_f(E)$ the set of finite subsets of E including $\varnothing$. If $\mathbf{P}_f(E)$ is ordered by set inclusion it clearly forms a lattice. For a fixed $A \in \mathbf{P}_f(E)$ the mapping λ_A given by the prescription $\lambda_A(B) = B \cap A$ is then seen to be a complete quasi-residuated $\cup$-homomorphism which is not residuated since the set of elements $B \in \mathbf{P}_f(E)$ such that $B \cap A = \varnothing$ has no maximum element.

If L is a lattice then Res(L) is always a $\cup$-semilattice (Exercise 4.1). If L is a chain then Res(L) is a lattice (Exercise 4.1). This also happens whenever L is a complete lattice (Exercise 5.4). On the other hand, the next example (due to C. Johnson) shows that Res(L) a lattice does not follow from the fact that L is a lattice.

EXAMPLE 5.3. Construct a lattice L as follows: take the four element lattice which has the following Hasse diagram:

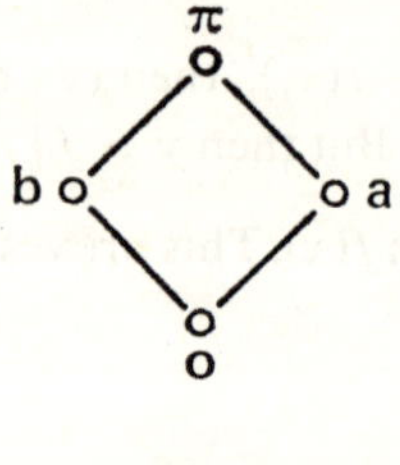

and insert three copies of the field of real numbers as suggested by the following diagram:

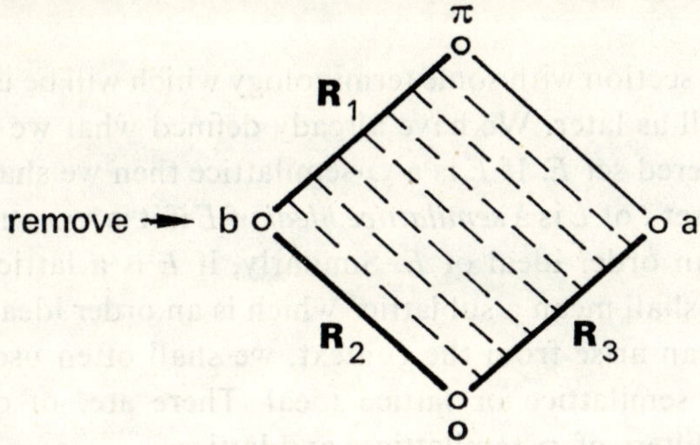

Remove the element b and enlarge the ordering as suggested by the dotted lines. To be more specific, for any $r \in \mathbf{R}_3$ let r^* denote the same real number in $\mathbf{R}_1$ and for $r, s \in \mathbf{R}_3$ define $r \leq s^*$ if and only if $r \leq s$ in the usual ordering of the reals. The remaining ordering is as suggested by the diagram. It is then easily verified that L is a lattice. Consider the mapping $f_a : L \to L$ defined by

$$f_a(x) = \begin{cases} x & \text{if } x \leq a; \\ a & \text{otherwise.} \end{cases}$$

This mapping is residuated; f_a^+ is given by

$$f_a^+(x) = \begin{cases} \pi & \text{if } x \geq a; \\ x \cap a & \text{otherwise.} \end{cases}$$

Now if $g \in \text{Res}(L)$ is such that $g \leq f_a$ and $g \leq \text{id}_L$, then for each $x \in \mathbf{R}_2$ we have $f_a(x) \cap \text{id}_L(x) = 0$ and so $g(x) = 0$. It follows that $g^+(0) \geq x$ for all $x \in \mathbf{R}_2$ and so $g^+(0) \in \mathbf{R}_1 \cup \{\pi\}$. It follows that there exists $c \in \mathbf{R}_1$ such that $c < g^+(0)$. Define $h_c : L \to L$ by

$$h_c(x) = \begin{cases} 0 & \text{if } x \leq c; \\ x \cap a & \text{otherwise.} \end{cases}$$

It is easily verified that $h_c \in \text{Res}(L)$ and that $h_c \leq f_a$ and $h_c \leq \text{id}_L$. For $x \leq g^+(0)$ we have $g(x) = 0 \leq h_c(x)$ and for $x \not\leq g^+(0)$ we have $g(x) \leq f_a(x) \cap \text{id}_L(x) \leq x \cap a = h_c(x)$. It therefore follows that $g \leq h_c$. Since

$g[g^+(0)] = 0 < h_c[g^+(0)]$ we even have $g < h_c$. This then shows that there cannot be a greatest lower bound for $\{f_a, \mathrm{id}_L\}$, and so Res (L) is not a lattice.

We end this section with some terminology which will be useful for the exercises as well as later. We have already defined what we mean by an ideal of an ordered set E. If E is a $\cup$-semilattice then we shall say that a non-empty subset I of E is a *semilattice ideal* of E if it is a $\cup$-subsemilattice which is also an order ideal of E. Similarly, if E is a lattice then by a *lattice ideal* we shall mean a sublattice which is an order ideal. Whenever no confusion can arise from the context, we shall often use simply the term *ideal* for semilattice or lattice ideal. There are, of course, dual definitions for filters of $\cap$-semilattices and lattices.

Ideals of $\cup$-semilattices with a minimum element can be characterized as kernels of $\cup$-homomorphisms; we defer a discussion of this until later (Exercise 6.6).

EXERCISES

5.1. Show that there are, up to lattice isomorphism, only five lattices having five elements, three of which are self-dual. [Draw Hasse diagrams.] Show also that there are, up to lattice isomorphism, only fifteen lattices having six elements, seven of which are self dual.

5.2. Let E be a $\cup$-semilattice and let $I(E)$ be its set of ideals. Order $I(E)$ by set inclusion. Show that $I(E)$ is a $\curlyvee$-semilattice in which union is given by

$$J \curlyvee K = \{x \in E; (\exists j \in J)(\exists k \in K)\, x \leq j \cup k\}.$$

Show further that if E has a smallest element then $I(E)$ is a complete lattice. If E is, in fact, a lattice, prove that the set of all principal ideals of E is a sublattice of $I(E)$ which is isomorphic to E.

5.3. Let E be a $\cup$-semilattice, $I(E)$ its semilattice of ideals and $f: E \to E$ a quasi-residuated $\cup$-homomorphism. Show that if $f^{\to}$ is defined on $I(E)$ by

$$f^{\to}(J) = \{y \in E; (\exists x \in J)\, y \leq f(x)\}$$

then $f^{\to}$ is residuated.

5.4. Prove that if L is a complete lattice then so also is Res (L).

5.5. Let G be a group. For each subset S of G let $\langle S \rangle$ be the subgroup generated by S. Show that the mapping $f: \mathbf{P}(G) \to L(G)$ described by $f(S) = \langle S \rangle$ is residuated.

5.6. Prove that a lattice is a chain if and only if every isotone mapping of L into any lattice M is a homomorphism.

5.7. Let L be a complete lattice. Let the maximum element of L be π_L and the minimum element be 0_L. If $f: L \to L$ is a closure mapping, prove that f is residuated if and only if its associated closure subset is a complete sublattice of L containing $0_L, \pi_L$.

5.8. Referring back to Exercise 4.15 for notation, prove that if E is any non-empty set then the following conditions concerning a mapping $f: \mathbf{P}(E) \to \mathbf{P}(E)$ are equivalent:

(a) f is residuated;
(b) f is a complete quasi-residuated $\cup$-homomorphism;
(c) $f = \xi_R$ for some binary relation R on E.

[*Hint*. (*b*) $\Rightarrow$ (*c*): note that f and ξ_R agree on singleton subsets, where R is given by $x \equiv y(R) \Leftrightarrow y \in f\{x\}$.]

5.9. Let E be a non-empty set and let $f: \mathbf{P}(E) \to \mathbf{P}(E)$ be a closure mapping with associated closure subset $\mathscr{L}$. Note by Theorem 4.6 that $\mathscr{L}$ is a complete lattice.

(a) For any mapping $g: E \to E$ let $\eta_g = f \circ g^{\rightarrow}$. Prove that the restriction of η_g to $\mathscr{L}$ is residuated if and only if, for each $A \in \mathscr{L}$, the set $g^{\leftarrow}(A)$ contains a largest element of $\mathscr{L}$.
(b) Using the notation of Exercise 4.15, let R be a binary relation on E. Let $\eta_R = f \circ \xi_R$. Prove that $\eta_R \in \operatorname{Res} \mathscr{L}$ if and only if, for each $A \in \mathscr{L}$, the set $(\imath \circ \xi_{R^t} \circ \imath)(A)$ contains a largest element of $\mathscr{L}$.
(c) Prove that a mapping $h: \mathscr{L} \to \mathscr{L}$ is residuated if and only if $h = \eta_R$ for some binary relation R on E satisfying the conditions in (b).

[*Hint*. (a) Use Exercise 2.11. (b) Suppose that A_R, the greatest element of $\mathscr{L}$ contained in $(\imath \circ \xi_{R^t} \circ \imath)(A)$, exists. Recall by Exercise 4.15 that $\xi_R \in \operatorname{Res}[\mathbf{P}(E)]$ with $\xi_R^+ = \imath \circ \xi_{R^t} \circ \imath$. Observe that $(\xi_R \circ \xi_R^+)(A) \subseteq A \Rightarrow (\eta_R \circ \xi_R^+)(A) \subseteq A \Rightarrow \eta_R(A_R) \subseteq A$ and that if $B \in \mathscr{L}$ with $B \subseteq A_R$ then $\eta_R(B) \subseteq A$. Hence $\eta_R \in \operatorname{Res}(\mathscr{L})$ with η_R^+ given by $\eta_R^+(A) = A_R$. For the converse, let η_R be residuated and show that, for each $A \in \mathscr{L}$, $\eta_R^+(A)$ is the largest element of $\mathscr{L}$ contained in $\xi_R^+(A)$. (c) Consider $x \equiv y(R) \Leftrightarrow y \in (f \circ g^{\rightarrow})(x)$ and proceed as in 5.8.]

6. Regular equivalences on an ordered set

Let E be an ordered set and let R be an equivalence relation on E. We shall say that R is *regular* on E if and only if there is an ordered set F and an isotone mapping $f: E \to F$ such that R is the equivalence associated with f in that $x \equiv y(R) \Leftrightarrow f(x) = f(y)$.

The above notion of regularity can be conveniently translated into a condition involving the ordering of E instead of the mapping f as the following result shows.

THEOREM 6.1. *An equivalence relation R defined on an ordered set E is regular on E if and only if it satisfies the property*

$$\left.\begin{array}{ll}(i = 1, \ldots, n) & a_i \equiv a_i^*(R) \\ (i = 1, \ldots, n-1) & a_i^* \leq a_{i+1} \\ & a_n^* \leq a_1\end{array}\right\} \Rightarrow (i = 1, \ldots, n-1)\ a_i \equiv a_{i+1}(R).$$

Before giving the proof of this result, we shall take a closer look at the property in question and give a particularly useful pictorial representation of it.

Definition. By a *closed bracelet* modulo *R* we shall mean a diagram of the form

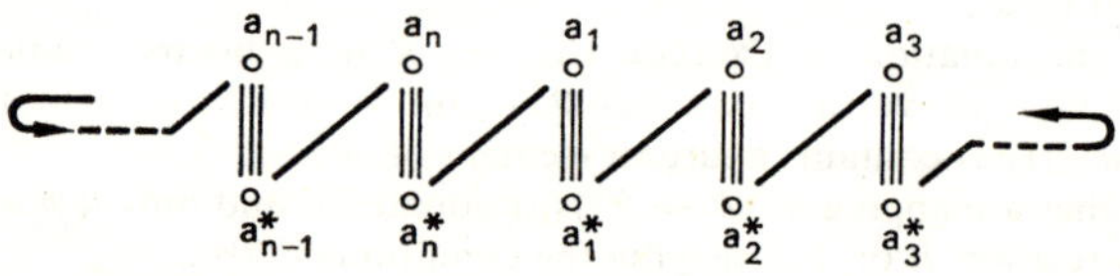

in which the three vertical lines denote equivalence modulo *R* and the other lines are interpreted as in a Hasse diagram. In a similar way, we define an *open bracelet* modulo *R* to be a diagram of the form

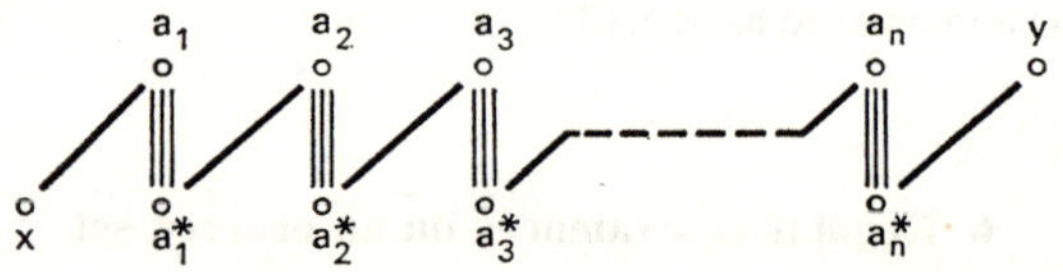

In such a diagram the element *x* will be called the *initial clasp* of the open bracelet and the element *y* will be called the *terminal clasp*.

Using these notions, we may re-phrase Theorem 6.1 as follows:

THEOREM 6.1. *An equivalence relation R defined on an ordered set E is regular on E if and only if every closed bracelet modulo R is contained in a single equivalence class modulo R.*

Proof. Suppose first that R is regular on E. Let there be a sequence of $2n$ elements $a_1, a_1^*, a_2, a_2^*, \ldots, a_n, a_n^*$ forming a closed bracelet modulo R, as above. If f is an associated isotone mapping, then we have

$$f(a_1) = f(a_1^*) \leq f(a_2) = f(a_2^*) \leq \cdots \leq f(a_n) = f(a_n^*) \leq f(a_1)$$

whence it follows that $f(a_1) = f(a_1^*) = \cdots = f(a_n) = f(a_n^*)$ and so the entire bracelet belongs to a single class modulo R.

Conversely, suppose that R satisfies the given property. On the quotient set E/R define the relation $\preccurlyeq$ by setting

$$x/R \preccurlyeq y/R \Leftrightarrow \begin{cases} \text{there is an open bracelet modulo } R \\ \text{with initial clasp } x \text{ and} \\ \text{terminal clasp } y. \end{cases}$$

The relation $\preccurlyeq$ is reflexive since for each $x \in E$ we have the trivial open bracelet

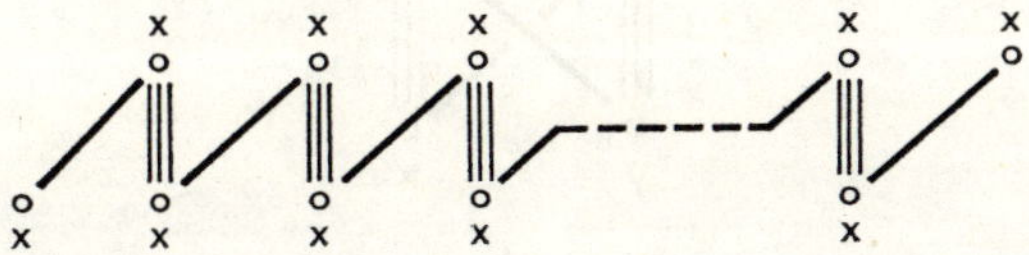

The relation $\preccurlyeq$ is also transitive since two open bracelets, the terminal clasp of one being equivalent modulo R to the initial clasp of the other, may clearly be joined to form a single open bracelet. Note that these two properties hold irrespective of the standing hypothesis that R satisfies the given property which we shall now use to show that $\preccurlyeq$ is anti-symmetric. Now if $x/R \preccurlyeq y/R$ and $y/R \preccurlyeq x/R$ we have open bracelets

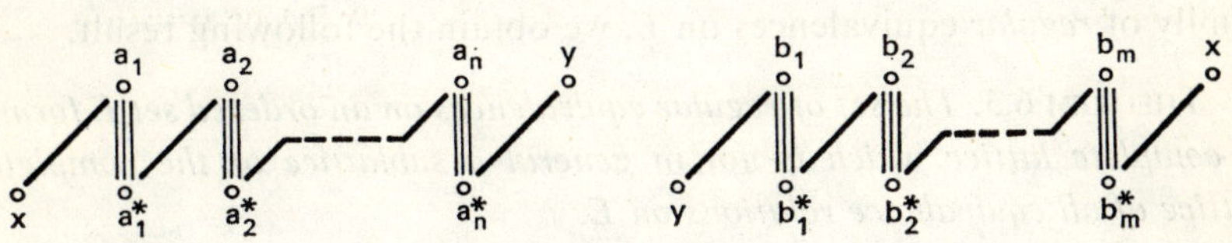

which we can clearly join together to form a closed bracelet, from which we deduce that $x \equiv y(R)$ and hence $x/R = y/R$. This then shows that $\preccurlyeq$ is an ordering on E/R. It is clear that $x \leq y \Rightarrow x/R \preccurlyeq y/R$ and so the canonical surjection $\natural_R : E \to E/R$ is isotone. Since it is such that $x \equiv y(R) \Leftrightarrow \natural_R(x) = \natural_R(y)$, it then follows that R is regular on E.

Our next result gives a very important property of the equivalence classes modulo a regular equivalence.

THEOREM 6.2. *If E is an ordered set and R is a regular equivalence on E then the equivalence classes modulo R are convex in the sense that*

$$\left.\begin{array}{r} x \leq y \leq z \\ x \equiv z(R) \end{array}\right\} \Rightarrow x \equiv y \equiv z(R).$$

Proof. The conditions $x \leq y \leq z$, $x \equiv z(R)$ may be expressed in the form of a closed bracelet modulo R, namely

from which it follows, by the regularity of R, that $x \equiv y \equiv z(R)$.

Suppose now that E is any set and let us consider the set of equivalence relations on E. By Exercise 4.14 this set forms a complete lattice. For any family $\{R_\alpha\}_{\alpha \in I}$ of equivalence relations on E, the union of this family in the lattice is the relation $\prod_{\alpha \in I} R_\alpha$ (refer to Exercise 4.14 for its definition). We call this the *transitive product* of the family.

Turning our attention to the case where E is *ordered* and $\{R_\alpha\}_{\alpha \in I}$ is a family of *regular* equivalences on E, we obtain the following result.

THEOREM 6.3. *The set of regular equivalences on an ordered set E forms a complete lattice which is not in general a sublattice of the complete lattice of all equivalence relations on E.*

Proof. It is clear that the relation of equality on E and the *universal equivalence* π_E on E [given by $x \equiv y(\pi_E) \Leftrightarrow x, y \in E$] both satisfy the bracelet property of Theorem 6.1 and are thus regular. The set of regular equivalences on E is therefore bounded. Now if $\{R_\alpha\}_{\alpha \in I}$ is any family of regular equivalences on E, then each R_α has the bracelet property of Theorem 6.1 and hence so also does $\bigcap_{\alpha \in I} R_\alpha$. This fact, together with the dual of Theorem 4.2, shows that the set of regular equivalences on E forms a complete lattice with minimum element equality and maximum element the universal equivalence on E. Note that intersection in this lattice coincides with intersection in the lattice of all equivalence relations on E. However, unions do not coincide (so that the lattice of regular equivalences is not a sublattice of the lattice of all equivalence relations). To demonstrate this, we shall show by means of a counter-example that *the transitive product of a family of regular equivalences is not in general regular*. For this purpose, consider the ordered set E with Hasse diagram

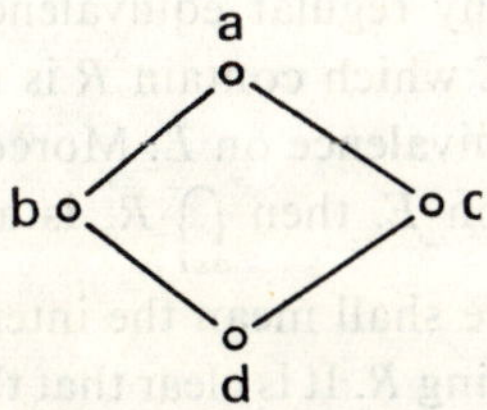

and let F, G be the ordered sets with Hasse diagrams

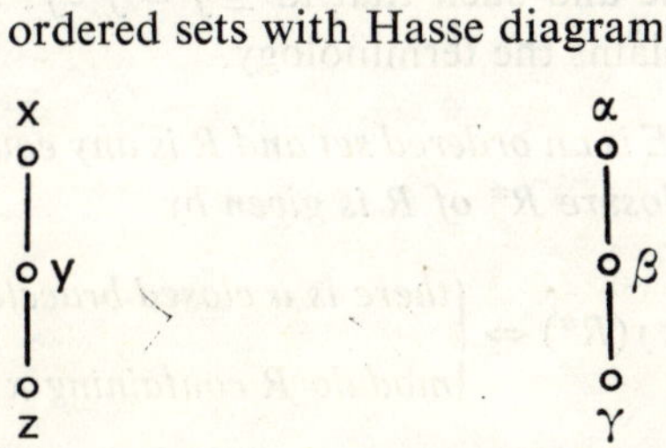

respectively. The mappings $f: E \to F$ and $g: E \to G$ described by

$$\begin{cases} f(a) = x = f(b); \quad f(c) = y; \quad f(d) = z; \\ g(a) = \alpha; \quad g(c) = \beta; \quad g(b) = \gamma = g(d) \end{cases}$$

are clearly isotone. The associated equivalence relations $\mathscr{F}, \mathscr{G}$ given by $p \equiv q(\mathscr{F}) \Leftrightarrow f(p) = f(q)$ and $p \equiv q(\mathscr{G}) \Leftrightarrow g(p) = g(q)$ are then regular, the corresponding partitions of E being $\{\{a, b\}, \{c\}, \{d\}\}$ and $\{\{a\}, \{c\}, \{b, d\}\}$. It is readily seen that the transitive product $\mathscr{F}\mathscr{G}$ partitions E into the classes $\{c\}, \{a, b, d\}$ so that, modulo $\mathscr{F}\mathscr{G}$, we have a closed bracelet of the form

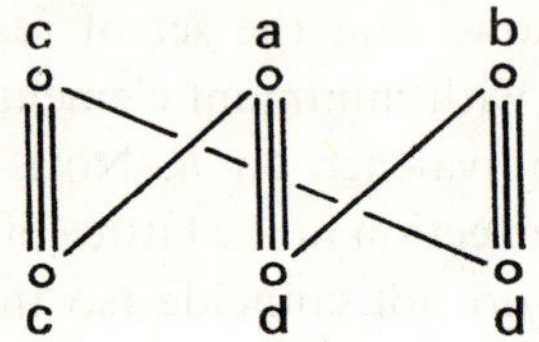

in which $c \not\equiv a\,(\mathscr{F}\mathscr{G})$. It follows by Theorem 6.1 that $\mathscr{F}\mathscr{G}$ is not regular. This completes the proof.

Our immediate aim now is to identify unions in the lattice of regular equivalences. Let R be any regular equivalence on E. Then the set of regular equivalences on E which contain R is not empty since it always contains the universal equivalence on E. Moreover, if $\{R_\alpha\}_{\alpha \in I}$ is a family of regular equivalences on E, then $\bigcap_{\alpha \in I} R_\alpha$ is also regular on E. By the *regular closure* R^* of R we shall mean the intersection of all the regular equivalences on E containing R. It is clear that the mapping f described by $f(R) = R^*$ is isotone and such that $\text{id} \leq f = f \circ f$; it is thus a closure mapping, which explains the terminology.

THEOREM 6.4. *If E is an ordered set and R is any equivalence relation on E then the regular closure R^* of R is given by*

$$x \equiv y(R^*) \Leftrightarrow \begin{cases} \text{there is a closed bracelet} \\ \text{modulo } R \text{ containing } x, y. \end{cases}$$

Proof. Let S denote the relation given by $x \equiv y(S)$ if and only if there is a closed bracelet modulo R containing both x, y. It is clear that $R \Rightarrow S$. Moreover, if T is any regular equivalence containing R then any bracelet modulo R is a bracelet modulo T. It follows by Theorem 6.1 that $x \equiv y(S) \Rightarrow x \equiv y(T)$ and hence that $S \Rightarrow R^*$. We thus have the implications

$R \Rightarrow S \Rightarrow R^*$. To establish the result, it therefore suffices to show that S is regular. Now if R is regular then so also is S, for in this case $R = R^*$ and so we must have $R = S$. Suppose then that R is not regular. By the proof of Theorem 6.1 the relation $\preccurlyeq_R$ defined on E/R is then reflexive and transitive but not anti-symmetric. Now the relation S is none other than the equivalence relation

$$x \equiv y(S) \Leftrightarrow (x/R \preccurlyeq_R y/R \quad \text{and} \quad y/R \preccurlyeq_R x/R),$$

a closed bracelet containing x, y being considered as made up of two open bracelets. To show that S is regular, it is clearly sufficient to show that the corresponding relation $\preccurlyeq_S$ defined on E/S *is* anti-symmetric, it being already reflexive and transitive. Now from $x/S \preccurlyeq_S y/S$ we deduce that there is an open bracelet modulo S with initial clasp x and terminal clasp y. Each "link" in this bracelet consists of a pair p, q with $p \equiv q(S)$ and, by the definition of S, can be replaced by an open bracelet modulo R with initial clasp p and terminal clasp q. By the transitivity of $\preccurlyeq_R$ on E/R we deduce that

$$x/S \preccurlyeq_S y/S \Rightarrow x/R \preccurlyeq_R y/R.$$

It follows that

$$\left.\begin{array}{l} x/S \preccurlyeq_S y/S \Rightarrow x/R \preccurlyeq_R y/R \\ y/S \preccurlyeq_S x/S \Rightarrow y/R \preccurlyeq_R x/R \end{array}\right\} \Rightarrow x/S = y/S,$$

whence $\preccurlyeq_S$ is anti-symmetric on E/S as required.

Definition. If R, S are equivalence relations such that $R \Rightarrow S$, we say that R is *finer* than S [resp. S is *coarser* than R]. This terminology may be conveniently remembered by thinking of the corresponding equivalence classes as determined by the mesh of a sieve.

THEOREM 6.5. *A non-empty subset C of an ordered set E is an equivalence class of at least one regular equivalence on E if and only if C is convex.*

Proof. The necessity follows by Theorem 6.2. Suppose conversely that C is convex and consider the relation R_C defined on E by

$$x \equiv y\,(R_C) \Leftrightarrow (x = y \quad \text{or} \quad x, y \in C).$$

It is clear that R_C is an equivalence relation on E. The equivalence classes modulo R_C are C itself and every single element subset $\{x\}$ where $x \notin C$. We shall show that R_C is regular on E whence the result will follow. Define the relation $\prec$ on E/R_C as follows:

$$\begin{cases} C \prec \{y\} \quad (y \notin C) \Leftrightarrow (\exists c \in C) \quad c < y; \\ \{y\} \prec C \ (y \notin C) \Leftrightarrow (\exists c \in C) \ \ y < c; \\ \{x\} \prec \{y\} \quad (x, y \notin C) \Leftrightarrow (x < y \quad \text{or} \quad (\exists c_1, c_2 \in C) \ x < c_1, c_2 < y). \end{cases}$$

It is clear that the relation $\prec$ is transitive. Moreover, since the equivalence classes modulo R_C are convex, the statements $C \prec \{y\}$, $\{y\} \prec C$ are incompatible, as are the statements $\{x\} \prec \{y\}$, $\{y\} \prec \{x\}$. It follows that the relation $\preccurlyeq$ defined on E/R_C by

$$x/R_C \preccurlyeq y/R_C \Leftrightarrow (x/R_C \prec y/R_C \quad \text{or} \quad x/R_C = y/R_C)$$

is an ordering of E/R_C. It follows from this that R_C is regular.

COROLLARY. *C being convex, R_C is the finest regular equivalence on E admitting C as a class.*

Proof. This is immediate from the definition of R_C.

Definition. A regular equivalence R on an ordered set E will be called *strongly upper regular* if and only if it satisfies the property

$$\left.\begin{matrix} a \equiv a^*(R) \\ a \leq b \end{matrix}\right\} \Rightarrow (\exists b^* \equiv b(R)) \quad a \leq b^*.$$

Pictorially, this condition says that any diagram modulo R of the form

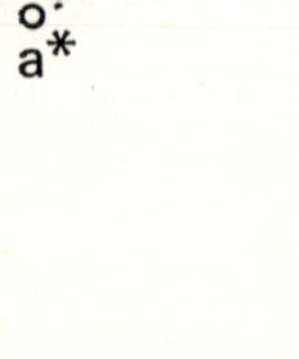

can be embedded in a diagram modulo R of the form

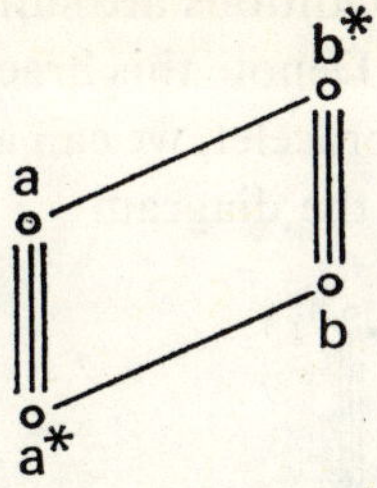

We shall refer to the above property as the *link property.*

Let us note that when R is strongly upper regular, we can apply the link property repeatedly to any open bracelet

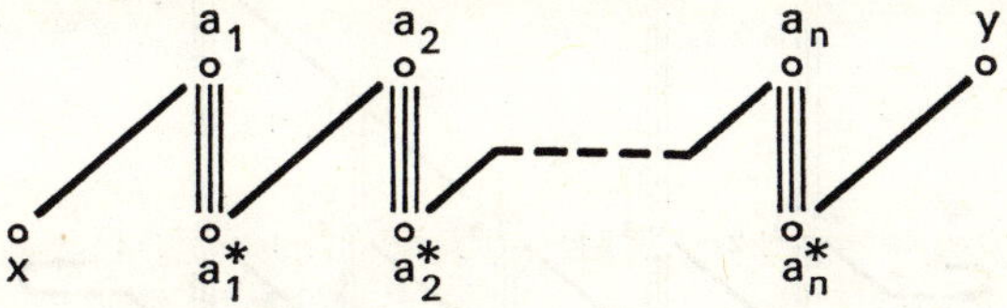

and thus reduce it to a diagram of the form

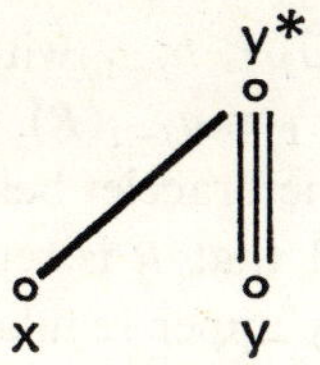

It follows from this that if R is strongly upper regular then the ordering defined on E/R as in Theorem 6.1 is given by

$$(X, Y \in E/R) \quad X \preccurlyeq Y \Leftrightarrow (\forall x \in X)\,(\exists y \in Y) \quad x \leq y.$$

THEOREM 6.6. *An equivalence relation R on an ordered set E is strongly upper regular if and only if it satisfies the properties*

(1) *R has convex classes;*

(2) *R satisfies the link property.*

Proof. The necessity of the conditions follows from what has gone before. To prove that the conditions are sufficient, suppose that we have a closed bracelet modulo R. Denote this bracelet by $[a_i; a_i^*]_i$. Now, starting with any given a_j in this bracelet, we can apply (2) repeatedly to obtain a chain of elements b_t as in the diagram

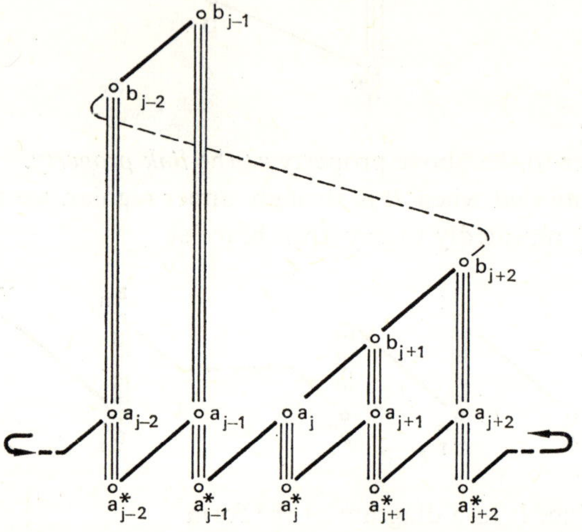

This process yields $a_{j-1}^* \leq a_j \leq b_{j-1}$ with $a_{j-1}^* \equiv b_{j-1}(R)$. The hypothesis (1) then gives $a_j \equiv a_{j-1}^* \equiv a_{j-1}(R)$. Since this holds for each j, it follows that all elements in the bracelet belong to the same class modulo R. It follows by Theorem 6.1 that R is regular. This, together with (2), then shows that R is strongly upper regular.

Remark. It is worthy of note at this juncture that neither of the conditions (1) and (2) of Theorem 6.6 is sufficient in itself to imply that R is regular. For example, let E be the ordered set with Hasse diagram

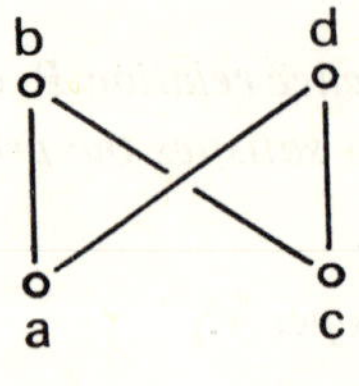

and consider the equivalence relation R on E whose partition is $\{\{a, b\}, \{c, d\}\}$. The classes modulo R are clearly convex, but R is not regular because of the following bracelet modulo R

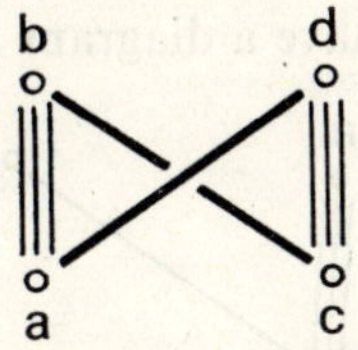

Also, if we consider **Z** ordered in the natural way and the equivalence relation S which partitions **Z** into two classes, one consisting of all the even integers and the other consisting of all the odd integers, then S is not regular since, for example, we have a bracelet

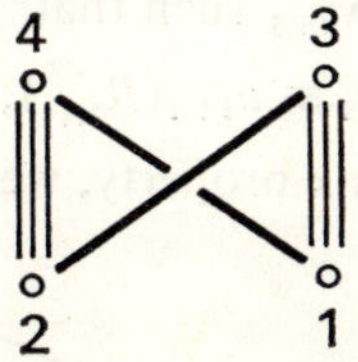

with $4 \not\equiv 3(S)$. However, S satisfies the link property; for any diagram of the form

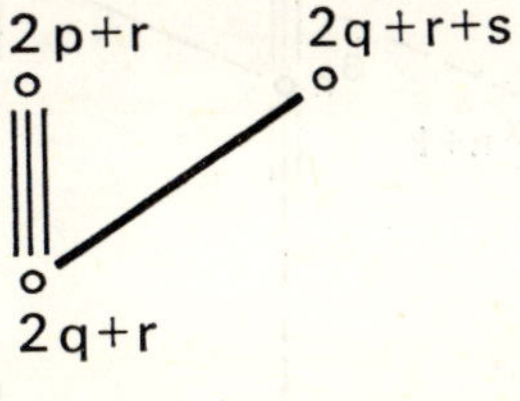

can be embedded in the diagram

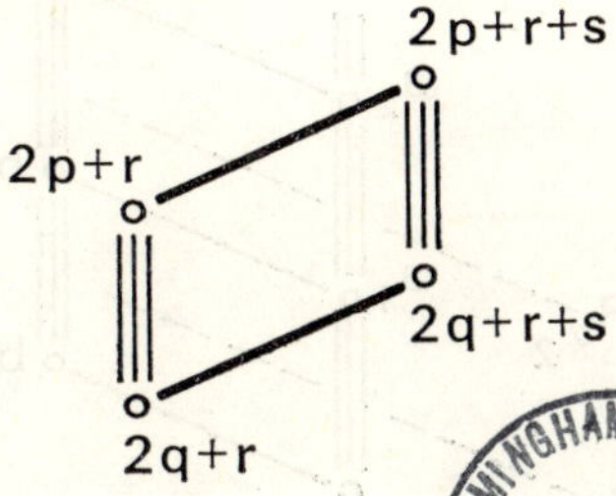

BIRMINGHAM UNIVERSITY LIBRARY

THEOREM 6.7. *If* $\{R_\alpha\}_{\alpha \in I}$ *is a family of equivalence relations on an ordered set E each of which satisfies the link property then so also does their transitive product* $\prod_{\alpha \in I} R_\alpha$.

Proof. Suppose that we have a diagram

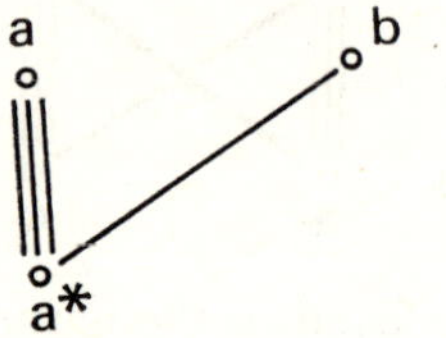

the equivalence being modulo the transitive product $\prod_{\alpha \in I} R_\alpha$. By the definition of $\prod_{\alpha \in I} R_\alpha$ there is a sequence of elements $a_1, \ldots, a_n$ and a sequence of suffices $\alpha_1, \ldots, \alpha_{n+1}$ such that

$$a^* \equiv a_1(R_{\alpha_1}), \quad \ldots, \quad a_i \equiv a_{i+1}(R_{\alpha_{i+1}}), \quad \ldots, \quad a_n \equiv a(R_{\alpha_{n+1}}).$$

Since each R_{α_i} satisfies the link property, we can build the diagram

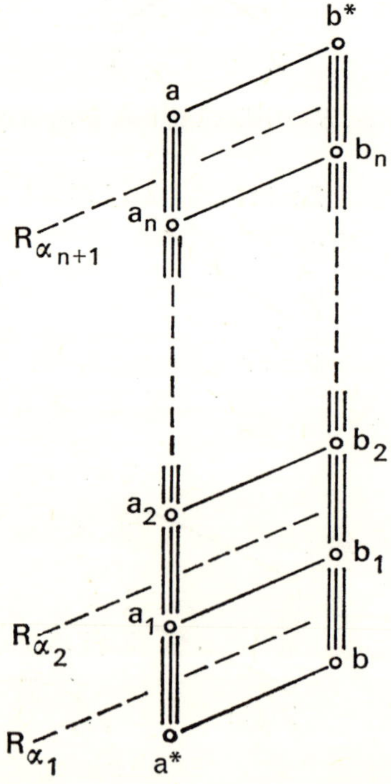

which, as a diagram modulo $\prod_{\alpha \in I} R_\alpha$, is

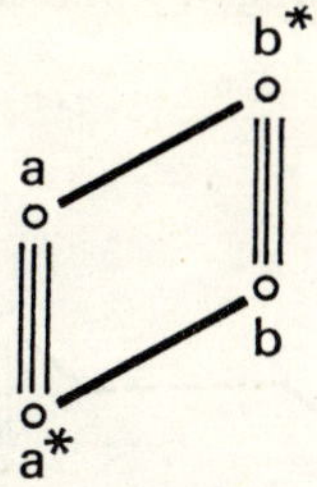

It follows that $\prod_{\alpha \in I} R_\alpha$ also satisfies the link property.

COROLLARY. *The transitive product of a family of strongly upper regular equivalences is strongly upper regular if and only if its classes are convex.*

Proof. This follows immediately from Theorem 6.6.

THEOREM 6.8. *If E is an ordered set then the set of strongly upper regular equivalences on E forms a complete lattice which is not in general a sublattice of the complete lattice of regular equivalences on E.*

Proof. The previous corollary shows that if unions exist then they are not in general transitive products. Given a family $\{R_\alpha\}_{\alpha \in I}$ of strongly upper regular equivalences on E, let us therefore consider the regular closure of the transitive product $\prod_{\alpha \in I} R_\alpha$. We know that $\left(\prod_{\alpha \in I} R_\alpha\right)^*$ has convex classes (Theorem 6.2). If, therefore, we can show that it satisfies the link property then it will be strongly upper regular by Theorem 6.6, whence the strongly upper regular equivalences on E will form a $\cup$-complete $\cup$-subsemilattice of the lattice of regular equivalences on E. For this purpose, suppose that we have a diagram of the form

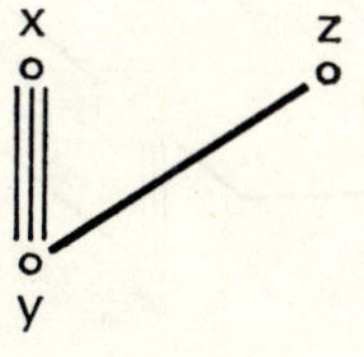

the equivalence being modulo $\left(\prod_{\alpha\in I} R_\alpha\right)^*$. By Theorem 6.4 there is a closed bracelet modulo $\prod_{\alpha\in I} R_\alpha$ containing x, y and so the above diagram becomes

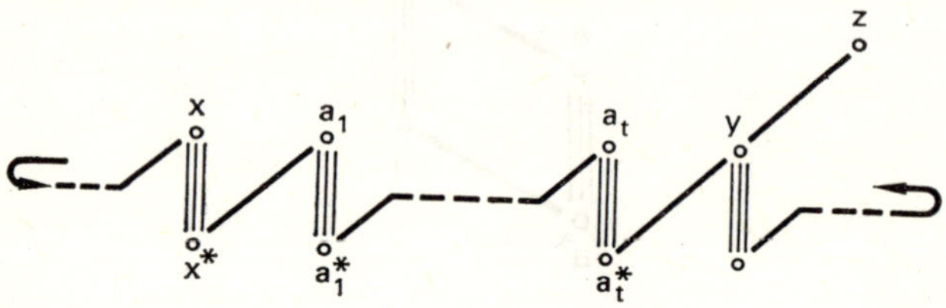

in which each equivalence is modulo $\prod_{\alpha\in I} R_\alpha$. Now we have shown in the previous theorem that $\prod_{\alpha\in I} R_\alpha$ satisfies the link property. Applying this fact repeatedly to the previous diagram, we can build the following diagram in which each equivalence is modulo $\prod_{\alpha\in I} R_\alpha$:

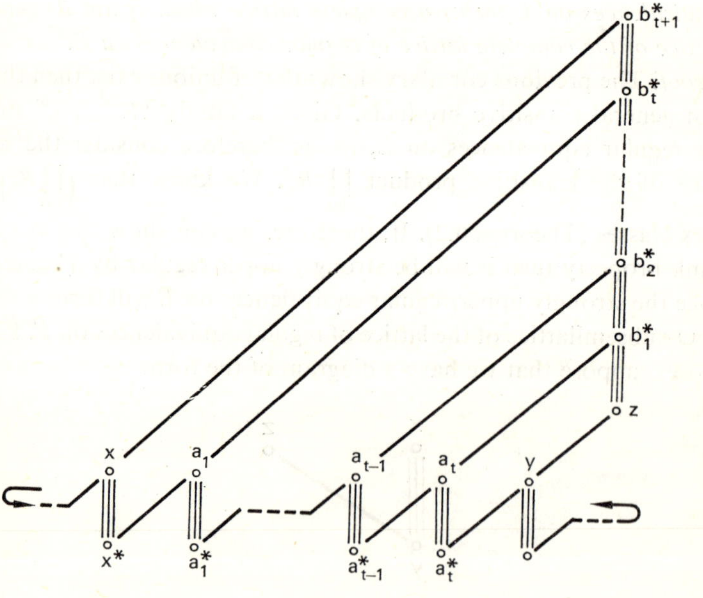

Since by definition $\prod_{\alpha \in I} R_\alpha \Rightarrow \left(\prod_{\alpha \in I} R_\alpha\right)^*$ there follows from this the diagram

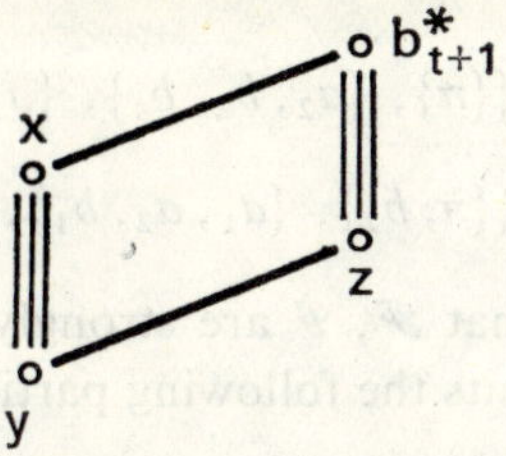

in which the equivalences are modulo $\left(\prod_{\alpha \in I} R_\alpha\right)^*$. This then shows that $\left(\prod_{\alpha \in I} R_\alpha\right)^*$ satisfies the link property. It follows that the set of strongly upper regular equivalences on E forms a $\bigcup$-complete $\cup$-subsemilattice of the complete lattice of regular equivalences on E. Since this semilattice contains a minimum element, namely equality (which is trivially strongly upper regular), it follows by Theorem 4.2 that it is a complete lattice. To show finally that it is not in general a sublattice of the complete lattice of regular equivalences on E, it suffices to show that *the intersection of two strongly upper regular equivalences is not in general strongly upper regular*. For this purpose, consider the ordered sets E, F, G with respective Hasse diagrams

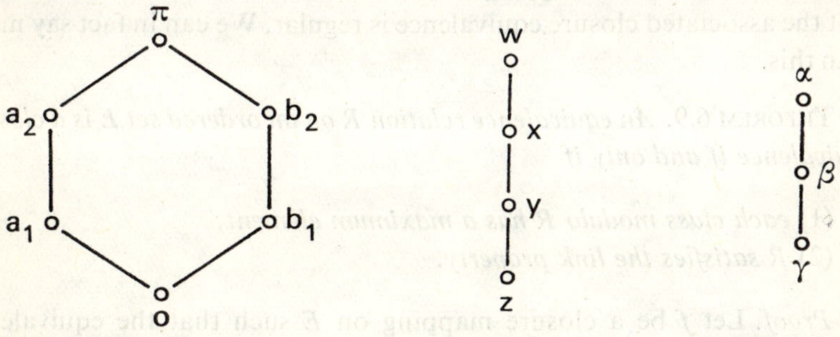

The mappings $f : E \to F$, $g : E \to G$ described by

$$\begin{cases} f(\pi) = w; \quad f(a_2) = f(b_2) = f(b_1) = x; \quad f(a_1) = y; \quad f(0) = z; \\ g(\pi) = g(b_2) = \alpha; \quad g(a_1) = g(a_2) = g(b_1) = \beta; \quad g(0) = \gamma; \end{cases}$$

are clearly isotone. The associated regular equivalences $\mathscr{F}$, $\mathscr{G}$ admit the following partitions of E:

$$\mathscr{F}:\quad \{\{\pi\},\ \{a_2, b_2, b_1\},\ \{a_1\},\ \{0\}\};$$

$$\mathscr{G}:\quad \{\{\pi, b_2\},\ \{a_1, a_2, b_1\},\ \{0\}\},$$

and it is readily seen that $\mathscr{F}$, $\mathscr{G}$ are strongly upper regular. Now the equivalence $\mathscr{F} \cap \mathscr{G}$ admits the following partition of E:

$$\mathscr{F} \cap \mathscr{G}:\quad \{\{\pi\},\ \{b_2\},\ \{a_2, b_1\},\ \{a_1\},\ \{0\}\}.$$

We thus have a diagram modulo $\mathscr{F} \cap \mathscr{G}$ of the form

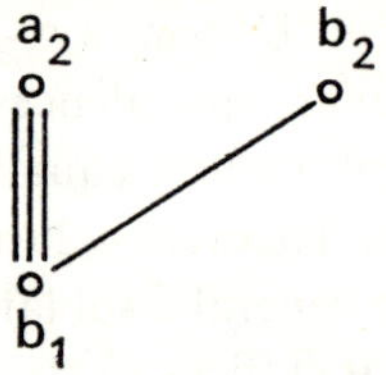

and since there is no element $x \in E$ such that $x \equiv b_2\ (\mathscr{F} \cap \mathscr{G})$ and $a_2 \leq x$, we conclude that $\mathscr{F} \cap \mathscr{G}$ is not strongly upper regular.

Since each closure mapping on an ordered set E is isotone, it is clear that the associated closure equivalence is regular. We can in fact say more than this.

THEOREM 6.9. *An equivalence relation R on an ordered set E is a closure equivalence if and only if*

(1) *each class modulo R has a maximum element;*
(2) *R satisfies the link property.*

Proof. Let f be a closure mapping on E such that the equivalence associated with f is R. It is clear that for each $x \in E$ the class x/R admits a maximum element, namely $f(x)$. To show that R satisfies the link property, we observe that since

$$a \leq b \Rightarrow (\forall a^* \equiv a(R)) \quad a^* \leq f(a) \leq f(b),$$

each diagram of the form

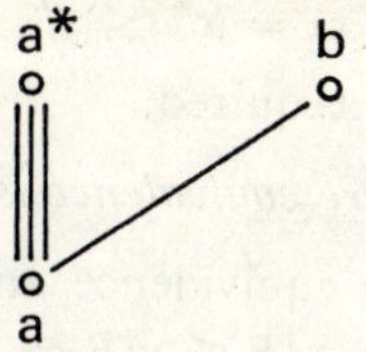

can be embedded in one of the form

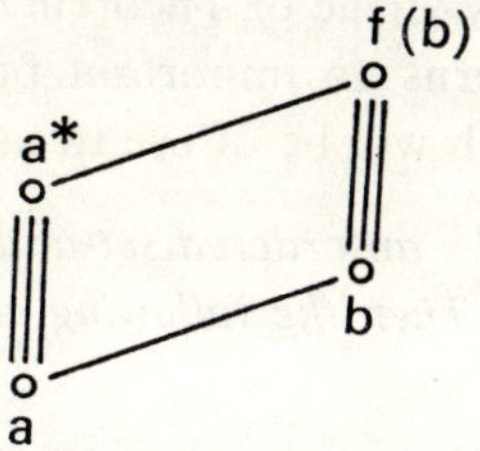

Conversely, suppose that R satisfies properties (1), (2). For each $x \in E$ let the maximum element in the class of x modulo R be x^* and consider the mapping $f: E \to E$ described by $(\forall x \in E)\, f(x) = x^*$. Since by definition $f(x) \in x/R$ it follows that $f \circ f = f$. As we have $\mathrm{id}_E \leq f$, it remains to show that f is isotone. Now since R satisfies the link property, the diagram

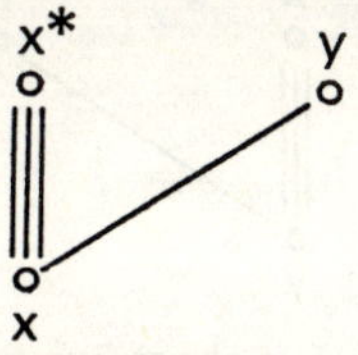

yields a diagram

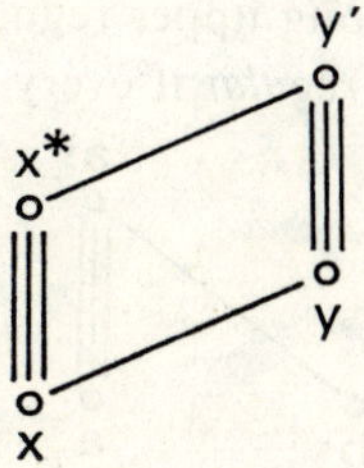

and since $y' \leq y^*$ by definition, we conclude that

$$x \leq y \Rightarrow f(x) = x^* \leq y' \leq y^* = f(y),$$

showing that f is isotone as required.

COROLLARY. *Every closure equivalence is strongly upper regular.*

Proof. If R is a closure equivalence and x^* denotes the maximum element of x/R, then clearly $x/R \preccurlyeq y/R \Leftrightarrow x^* \leq y^*$. It follows from this that the classes modulo R are convex. This, together with (2) of Theorem 6.9 gives the result by virtue of Theorem 6.6.

Our next result concerns an important property of strongly upper regular equivalences which will be of use to us later.

THEOREM 6.10. *Let E be an ordered set and let R be a strongly upper regular equivalence on E. Then the following conditions concerning $a \in E$ are equivalent:*

(1) $a/R \subseteq [\leftarrow, a]$;

(2) $(\forall x \in E)\ x/R \cap [\leftarrow, a] \neq \emptyset \Rightarrow x/R \subseteq [\leftarrow, a]$.

Proof. It is clear that (2) $\Rightarrow$ (1) since $a \in a/R \cap [\leftarrow, a]$. Suppose, conversely, that (1) holds and let $x \in E$ be such that $x/R \cap [\leftarrow, a] \neq \emptyset$. If $y \in x/R \cap [\leftarrow, a]$ then for each $x^* \in x/R$ we have, modulo R, the diagram

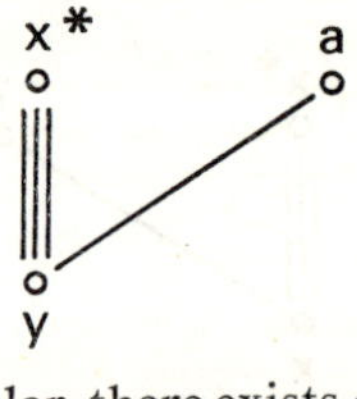

Since R is strongly upper regular, there exists $a^* \equiv a(R)$ such that $x^* \leq a^*$. It follows by (1) that $x^* \leq a$ and hence that $x/R \subseteq [\leftarrow, a]$.

Dual to the notion of strong upper regularity, we say that a regular equivalence is *strongly lower regular* if every diagram of the form

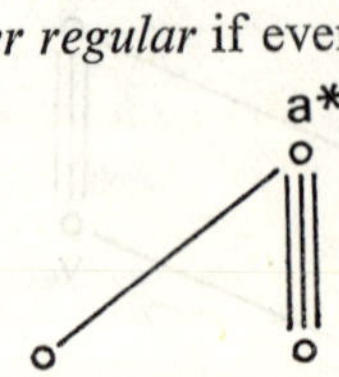

can be embedded in a diagram

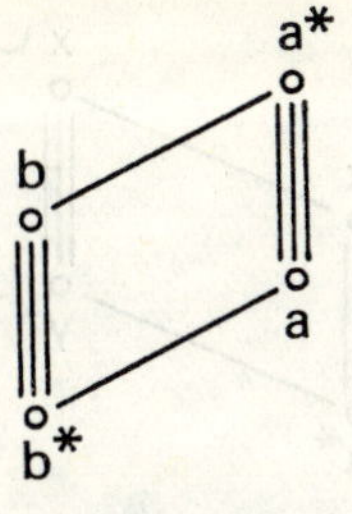

There are, of course, dual results to those above concerning strongly lower regular equivalences. A regular equivalence which is both strongly upper regular and strongly lower regular will be called *strongly regular*. In the particular case where the ordered set in question is a lattice, there is a particularly important type of strongly regular equivalence which we shall now describe.

If L is a $\cup$-semilattice, we shall say that an equivalence relation R on L is *compatible with* $\cup$ if and only if it is such that

$$x \equiv y(R) \Rightarrow (\forall z \in L) \quad z \cup x \equiv z \cup y(R).$$

When R is compatible with $\cup$, the quotient set L/R becomes a $\curlyvee$-semilattice under the induced law $x/R \curlyvee y/R = (x \cup y)/R$. In this case, the ordering $\leq_R$ of E/R is given by $x/R \leq_R y/R$ if and only if $y/R = x/R \curlyvee y/R$ which is equivalent to $y \equiv x \cup y(R)$.

THEOREM 6.11. *Let L be a $\cup$-semilattice. If R is an equivalence relation on L which is compatible with $\cup$ then R is strongly upper regular and the orderings $\leq_R$ and $\preccurlyeq_R$ coincide.*

Proof. We note first that the classes modulo R are convex; for if $x \leq y \leq z$ with $x \equiv z(R)$, then $y = x \cup y \equiv z \cup y = z(R)$. Moreover, R satisfies the link property; for from

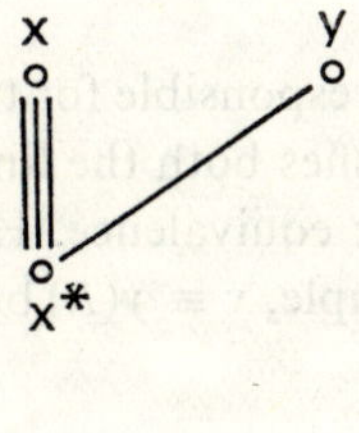

we deduce that $x \cup y \equiv x^* \cup y = y$, whence we have the diagram

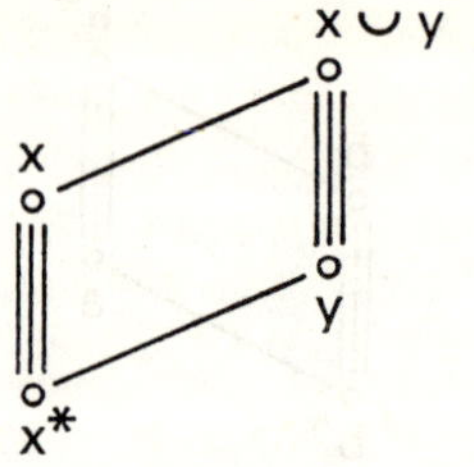

That R is strongly upper regular now follows by Theorem 6.6. Now let $x/R \leq_R y/R$, so that $y \equiv x \cup y(R)$. If $x^* \equiv x(R)$ then we have $x^* \cup y \equiv x \cup y \equiv y(R)$. In other words, for each x^* equivalent to x modulo R there is a y^* [$= x^* \cup y$] equivalent to y modulo R such that $x^* \leq y^*$. It follows that $x/R \preccurlyeq_R y/R$. But, conversely, if we have $x/R \preccurlyeq_R y/R$, then by the definition of $\preccurlyeq_R$ there exists y^* in the class of y modulo R such that $x \leq y^*$. This gives $y^* = x \cup y^*$ and so $y/R = y^*/R \geq_R x/R$. It follows that the orderings coincide.

Definition. Let L be a lattice. By a *congruence relation* on L we shall mean an equivalence relation on L which is compatible with both $\cup$ and $\cap$ in L.

It is immediate from the previous results that every congruence relation on a lattice L is strongly regular on L. The converse of this is not in general true. For example, consider the lattice with Hasse diagram

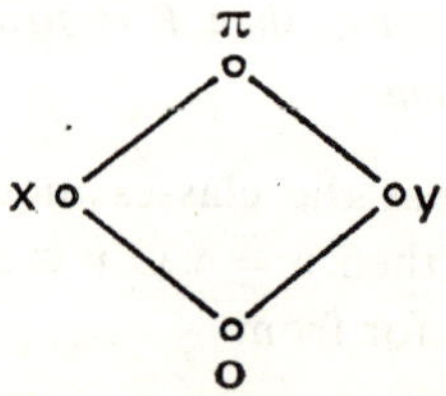

The equivalence relation R responsible for the partition $\{\{0\}, \{x, y\}, \{\pi\}\}$ has convex classes and satisfies both the link property and its dual. It is therefore a strongly regular equivalence. However, it is not compatible with either $\cup$ or $\cap$; for example, $x \equiv y(R)$ but $x = x \cup x \not\equiv x \cup y = \pi(R)$.

EXERCISES

6.1. Let E be an ordered set and let R be an equivalence relation on E. Define the relation $\preccurlyeq_R$ on E/R as follows:

$$x/R \preccurlyeq_R y/R \Leftrightarrow (\forall x^* \in x/R)\,(\exists y^* \in y/R)\; x^* \leq y^*.$$

Prove that $\preccurlyeq_R$ is an ordering on E/R if R has convex classes. Supposing that $\preccurlyeq_R$ is an ordering, let $\natural_R$ be the canonical surjection of E onto E/R. If F is any ordered set and $g: E/R \to F$ is such that $g \circ \natural_R$ is isotone, prove that g is isotone. Show also that $\natural_R$ is isotone if and only if R satisfies the link property. Deduce that $\preccurlyeq_R$ is an ordering and $\natural_R$ is isotone if and only if R is strongly upper regular and that $\natural_R$ is residuated if and only if R is a closure equivalence.

6.2. Let E, F be ordered sets and let $f: E \to F$ be isotone. If R_f is the associated equivalence and $f = g \circ \natural_{R_f}$ is the canonical decomposition of f, prove that $g: E/R_f \to \operatorname{Im} f$ is an order isomorphism if and only if

(a) $(x \leq y \quad \text{and} \quad f(x) = f(x^*)) \Rightarrow (\exists y^* \in E)\,(f(y^*) = f(y) \quad \text{and} \quad x^* \leq y^*)$;
(b) $f(x) \leq f(y) \Rightarrow (\exists x^*, y^* \in E)\,(f(x) = f(x^*), f(y) = f(y^*), x^* \leq y^*)$.

6.3. Let $(E_1, \leq_1)$, $(E_2, \leq_2)$ be ordered sets with E_2 upper directed. Let $E_1 \times E_2$ be ordered as in Example 1.6 and let R be the equivalence relation given by

$$(x_1, x_2) \equiv (y_1, y_2)\,(R) \Leftrightarrow x_1 = y_1.$$

Prove that R is strongly upper regular on $E_1 \times E_2$ and that the ordered sets $(E_1, \leq_1)$ and $((E_1 \times E_2)/R, \leq_R)$ are isomorphic.

6.4. Let E be an ordered set and let $\Delta = \{C_\alpha\}_{\alpha \in I}$ be a family of disjoint convex subsets of E. Prove that Δ is a family of equivalence classes of at least one regular equivalence on E if and only if Δ satisfies the following *class bracelet property*: any diagram of the form

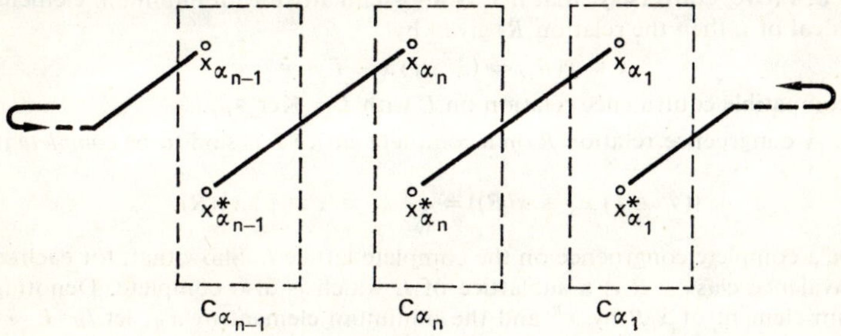

is contained entirely in a single C_α. [*Hint:* To prove necessity, use Theorem 6.1. As for sufficiency, consider the relation E_Δ given by

$$x \equiv y\,(E_\Delta) \Leftrightarrow (x = y \quad \text{or} \quad (\exists \alpha \in I)\; x, y \in C_\alpha).$$

Show that E_Δ is regular, having the C_α amongst its classes.]

6.5. A regular equivalence R on an ordered set E is said to be *totally regular* if and only if each diagram modulo R of the form

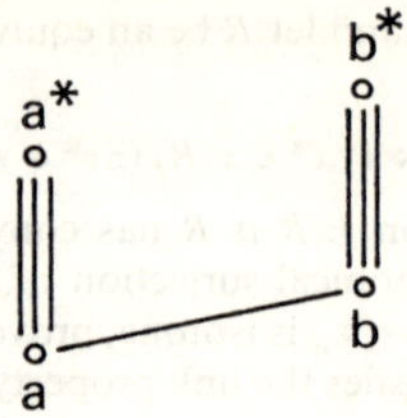

can be completed to a diagram

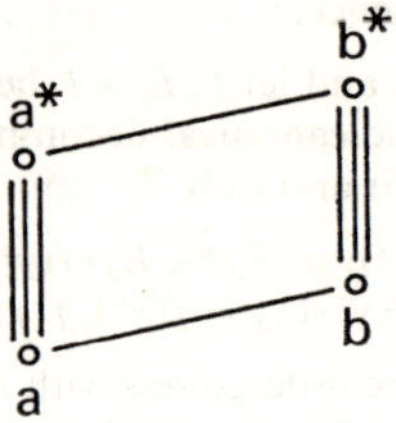

Prove that every totally regular equivalence R is strongly regular and that in this case the ordering $\preccurlyeq_R$ is given by

$$x/R \preccurlyeq_R y/R \Leftrightarrow (\forall x^* \in x/R)\,(\forall y^* \in y/R)\; x^* \leq y^*.$$

If $\{R_\alpha\}_{\alpha \in I}$ is a family of totally regular equivalences on E, prove that $\bigcap_{\alpha \in I} R_\alpha$ and $\prod_{\alpha \in I} R_\alpha$ are also totally regular. If E is a lattice, show by means of an example that a congruence relation on E is not in general totally regular.

6.6. Let L, M be $\cup$-semilattices, M having a minimum element 0. For any $\cup$-epimorphism $f: L \to M$ let $\operatorname{Ker} f = \{x \in L; f(x) = 0\}$. Show that $\operatorname{Ker} f$ is a semilattice ideal of L. Prove, conversely, that if L is a $\cup$-semilattice with minimum element and I is an ideal of L then the relation R_I given by

$$x \equiv y(R_I) \Leftrightarrow (\exists i \in I)\; x \cup i = y \cup i$$

is a $\cup$-compatible equivalence relation on L with $I = \operatorname{Ker} \natural_{R_I}$.

6.7. A congruence relation R on a complete lattice L is said to be *complete* if and only if

$$((\forall \alpha \in I)\; x_\alpha \equiv x(R)) \Rightarrow \bigcup_{\alpha \in I} x_\alpha \equiv x \equiv \bigcap_{\alpha \in I} x_\alpha(R).$$

Let R be a complete congruence on the complete lattice L. Show that, for each $x \in L$, the equivalence class x/R is a sublattice of L which is also complete. Denoting the maximum element of x/R by x^R and the minimum element by x_R, let $f_R : L \to L$ be given by the prescription $f_R(x) = x_R$. Prove that f_R is a residuated dual closure map with f_R^+ given by $f_R^+(x) = x^R$. Hence show that there is a bijection between the set of complete congruences on L and the set of residuated dual closure maps on L.

6.8. Let R be an equivalence relation on the ordered set E. Suppose that the relation $\preccurlyeq_R$ described in Exercise 6.1 is an ordering on E/R. Prove that the following conditions are equivalent:

(a) R is the equivalence relation associated with a residuated dual closure mapping on E;
(b) each class modulo R is bounded;
(c) the canonical surjection $\natural_R : E \to E/R$ is both residuated and residual.

6.9. If R is an equivalence relation on an ordered set E define the *transitive closure* of R to be the smallest transitive relation on E which contains R. If the relation $\preccurlyeq$ is defined on E/R by

$$x/R \preccurlyeq y/R \Leftrightarrow (\exists x^* \in x/R)\,(\exists y^* \in y/R) \quad x^* \leq y^*,$$

prove that R is regular if and only if $tc(\preccurlyeq)$, the transitive closure of $\preccurlyeq$, is anti-symmetric. Show also that if R is strongly upper regular then $\preccurlyeq$ and $tc(\preccurlyeq)$ coincide.

7. Complementation in lattices

In what follows we shall have frequent occasion to consider particular types of lattices. For this reason we devote § 7 → § 10 inclusively to a brief study of them together with properties which we shall require. In § 11 we shall discuss lattices which arise naturally in connection with a particular type of ring and in § 12 regain contact with residuated mappings, establishing a profound connection between lattices and the semigroup of residuated mappings on a bounded ordered set.

Unless otherwise specified, the symbol 0 will be used to denote the smallest element of an ordered set whereas π will be used to denote its greatest element (provided of course that such elements exist). An element b of a bounded lattice L is said to be a *complement* of $a \in L$ whenever $a \cup b = \pi$ and $a \cap b = 0$. A lattice L is said to be *complemented* if each element of L admits at least one complement. In a lattice L with 0 an element b is called a *semicomplement* of a whenever $a \cap b = 0$; and L is said to be *semicomplemented* if each $a \in L$ (with $a \neq \pi$ if π exists in L) admits at least one non-zero semicomplement. A lattice L with 0 is said to be *section complemented* if every interval sublattice $[0, a]$ is complemented and *section semicomplemented* if every interval $[0, a]$ is semicomplemented. A lattice L will be called *relatively complemented* whenever every interval $[a, b]$ is complemented.

We can also formulate the concept of a *dual semicomplemented*, a *dual section semicomplemented* or a *dual section complemented* lattice to denote the fact that the dual lattice has the corresponding property.

The following diagram, in which the ordering is given by logical implication, is designed to aid the reader's intuition:

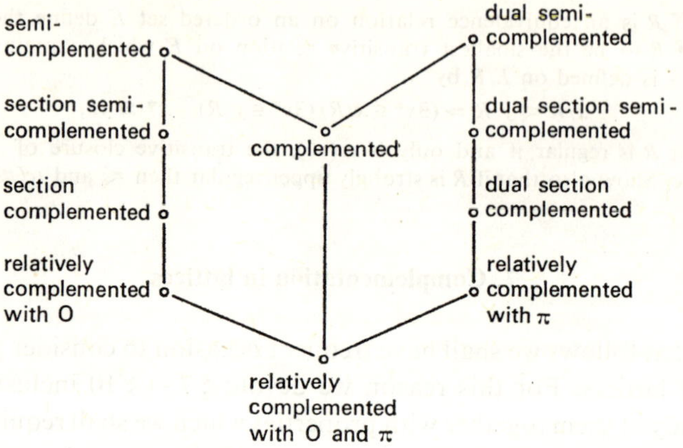

In order to see this, we begin by establishing the implications shown. Let L be a section complemented lattice. If $a < b$ and x is a complement of a in $[0, b]$ then $x \cap a = 0$ and $x \cup a = b$ forces $x \neq 0$ and so x is a non-zero semicomplement of a in $[0, b]$. Thus L is section semicomplemented. A similar argument shows that every complemented lattice is semicomplemented. The remaining implications follow from dual arguments or are immediate from the definitions.

Let us now show that each of the implications is strict. The lattice of all finite subsets of an infinite set is an example of a relatively complemented lattice with 0 having no greatest element. The following Hasse diagram describes a lattice which is section complemented but not relatively complemented:

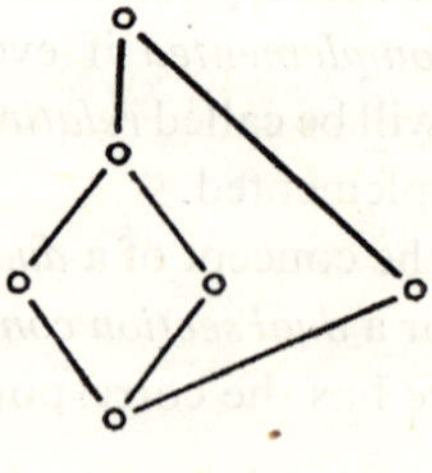

As an example of a lattice which is section semicomplemented but not section complemented, and semicomplemented without being complemented, we present the Hasse diagram

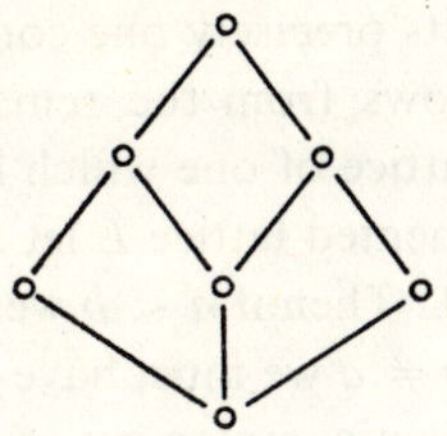

Finally we present an example of a complemented lattice which is not section semicomplemented:

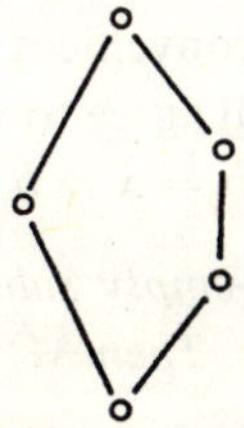

The remaining examples required are obtained by considering the duals of the above lattices.

While we are on the subject of examples and counter-examples, let us mention that Example 1.2 has no semicomplemented intervals, Example 1.4 is semicomplemented but not section semicomplemented while Example 1.3 is a relatively complemented lattice with 0 and π. Example 1.3, incidentally, also furnishes an example of what is known as a *pseudo-complemented lattice*; i.e. a lattice with 0 in which the semicomplements of each element form a principal ideal. Thus by a pseudo-complemented lattice we mean a lattice with 0 such that for each translation $\lambda_a: x \to x \cap a$ the element $\lambda_a^+(0) = \max \{y; a \cap y = 0\}$ exists. Closely related to this is the notion of a semilattice with 0 in which every translation is a residuated map. Such a semilattice is called a *Brouwer semilattice* and will be discussed later. We note that any bounded chain is a pseudo-complemented lattice (in fact Brouwerian) as is the last Hasse diagram of the preceding paragraph.

EXAMPLE 7.1. A bounded lattice L is said to be *uniquely complemented* if every element of L admits precisely one complement. The importance of this type of lattice follows from the remarkable fact (see [7], [10]) that *every* lattice is a sublattice of one which is uniquely complemented. Given a uniquely complemented lattice L let x' denote the unique complement of x for each $x \in L$. Then if $a < b$ we have $b \cup a' \geq a \cup a' = \pi$ and so $b \cup a' = \pi$. Since $b \neq a$ we must have $b' \neq a'$ and so $b \cap a' \neq 0$. Thus $b \cap a'$ is a non-zero semicomplement of a in $[0, b]$. This establishes the fact that L is section semicomplemented and a dual argument shows that L is also dual section semicomplemented.

Although we do not propose to develop here the theory of the lattices described above, it will prove convenient to establish a few useful facts. In connection with this, we shall agree to write $a \nabla b$ in a lattice with 0 to denote the fact that $(a \cup x) \cap b = x \cap b$ for all elements x.

THEOREM 7.1. *For each non-empty subset M of a lattice L with 0 let $M^\nabla = \{a \in L; (\forall m \in M)\ a \nabla m\}$. Then M^∇ is an ideal of L.*

Proof. Let $a \nabla m$ and let $b \leq a$. Then

$$(\forall x \in L) \quad (b \cup x) \cap m = (b \cup x) \cap (a \cup x) \cap m$$
$$= (b \cup x) \cap x \cap m = x \cap m$$

and so $b \nabla m$. Also, if $a_1 \nabla m$ and $a_2 \nabla m$, then

$$(\forall x \in L) \quad (a_1 \cup a_2 \cup x) \cap m = (a_2 \cup x) \cap m = x \cap m$$

and so $(a_1 \cup a_2) \nabla m$.

THEOREM 7.2. *Let L be a dual section semicomplemented lattice with 0. Then for $a, b \in L$ the following conditions are equivalent:*

(1) $a \nabla b$;
(2) $a \cup y = \pi \Rightarrow b \leq y$;
(3) $(\forall x \in L)\ x = (x \cup a) \cap (x \cup b)$.

Proof. (1) $\Rightarrow$ (2): If $a \nabla b$ and $a \cup y = \pi$, then $b = \pi \cap b = (a \cup y) \cap b = y \cap b$ and consequently $b \leq y$.

(2) $\Rightarrow$ (3): Let $x \in L$ and suppose that $x < (x \cup a) \cap (x \cup b)$. Using the fact that L is dual section semicomplemented we can produce an element y such that $x \leq y < \pi$ and $y \cup [(x \cup a) \cap (x \cup b)] = \pi$. Then

$$y \cup a = y \cup x \cup a \geq y \cup [(x \cup a) \cap (x \cup b)] = \pi$$

and so $y \cup a = \pi$. Similarly, we have $y \cup b = \pi$. By (2), $y \cup a = \pi$ implies $b \leq y$ so $y = y \cup b = \pi$, a contradiction. We conclude that (3) holds.

(3) $\Rightarrow$ (1): If $x = (x \cup a) \cap (x \cup b)$ then $x \cap b = (x \cup a) \cap (x \cup b) \cap b = (a \cup x) \cap b$.

COROLLARY. *If L is a dual section semicomplemented lattice with* 0, *then*

(1) $a \nabla b \Rightarrow b \nabla a$;
(2) *if* $x_\alpha \nabla b$ *for all* $\alpha \in I$ *and* $\bigcup_{\alpha \in I} x_\alpha$ *exists then* $\left(\bigcup_{\alpha \in I} x_\alpha\right) \nabla b$.

In sharp contrast to the above situation, we have:

EXAMPLE 7.2. Consider the lattice L whose ordering is indicated by the following diagram:

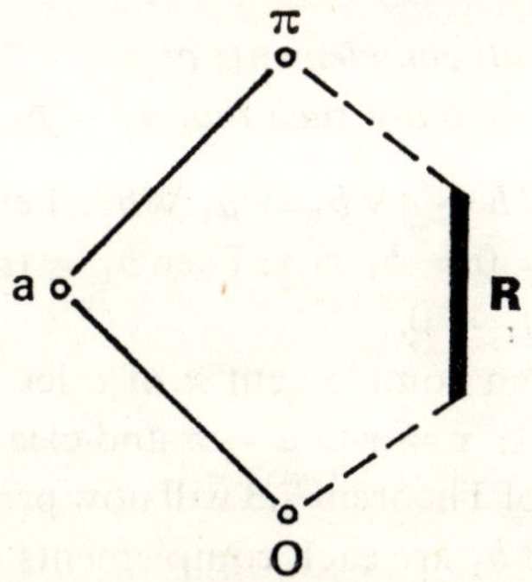

Specifically, let $L = \mathbf{R} \cup \{0, a, \pi\}$ where $0 < a < \pi$, $\mathbf{R}$ denotes the real numbers under their usual ordering and for each $r \in \mathbf{R}$ we agree that

$0 < r < \pi$. For $r, s \in \mathbf{R}$ with $r > s$ we have

$$(a \cup s) \cap r = \pi \cap r = r \quad \text{and} \quad s \cap r = s < r,$$

and so $a \nabla r$ fails. On the other hand, $r \nabla a$ is easily verified. If $(\forall \alpha \in I)\ r_\alpha \in \mathbf{R}$, and if $\{r_\alpha\}_{\alpha \in I}$ has no upper bound in $\mathbf{R}$ then clearly $\bigcup_{\alpha \in I} r_\alpha = \pi$ in L. Now $(\forall \alpha \in I)\ r_\alpha \nabla a$ whereas $\pi \nabla a$ fails. We thus have a complemented lattice in which both conditions of the previous corollary fail.

THEOREM 7.3. *In a section complemented lattice with π every dual semicomplement of an element b contains a complement of b.*

Proof. Let $a \cup b = \pi$ and choose x to be a complement of $a \cap b$ in $[0, a]$. Then $x \leq a, x \cap b = x \cap a \cap b = 0$ and $x \cup b = x \cup (a \cap b) \cup b = a \cup b = \pi$.

Definition. Two elements a, b of a lattice L with 0 will be called *perspective*, in symbols $a \sim b$, in case there is an element x such that $a \cup x = b \cup x$ while $a \cap x = 0 = b \cap x$. We shall say that a, b are *projective*, in symbols $a \approx b$, when there exist finitely many elements $a_1, a_2, \ldots, a_n$ such that $a \sim a_1 \sim a_2 \sim \cdots \sim a_n \sim b$.

THEOREM 7.4. *In a bounded relatively complemented lattice the following conditions are equivalent:*

(1) $a \nabla b$;

(2) *b is contained in all complements of a;*

(3) *if $a_1 \leq a$ and $b_1 \leq b$ are such that $a_1 \sim b_1$ then $a_1 = b_1 = 0$.*

Proof. (1) $\Rightarrow$ (3): $a \nabla b \Rightarrow a \nabla b_1 \Rightarrow a_1 \nabla b_1$. Let x be such that $a_1 \cup x = b_1 \cup x$ and $a_1 \cap x = 0 = b_1 \cap x$. Then $b_1 = (a_1 \cup x) \cap b_1 = x \cap b_1 = 0$; in a similar way $a_1 = 0$.

(3) $\Rightarrow$ (2): For a given complement x of a let y be a complement of $x \cup b$ in $[x, \pi]$. Then $y \geq x \Rightarrow y \cup a = \pi$ and clearly $y \cup b = y \cup x \cup b = \pi$. Two applications of Theorem 7.3 will now produce elements $a_1 \leq a$, $b_1 \leq b$ such that a_1 and b_1 are each complements of y. But then $a_1 \sim b_1$ and so by (3) we have $a_1 = b_1 = 0$ giving $y = \pi$ and $x = x \cup b \geq b$.

(2) $\Rightarrow$ (1): Let $a \cup x = \pi$. By Theorem 7.3, x contains a complement y of a. By (2) we then have $b \leq y \leq x$ from which we deduce that $a \nabla b$.

A useful characterization of both semicomplemented and section semicomplemented lattices may be given in terms of their associated filter lattices. For this purpose, we require the following notion.

Definition. A filter M of a lattice L which is such that $M \neq L$ and there is no filter F with $M \subset F \subset L$ will be called an *ultrafilter*. In other words, an ultrafilter is a maximal proper filter.

THEOREM 7.5. *In a lattice L with* 0 *let $a \cap b = 0$ with $b \neq 0$. Then there exists an ultrafilter M of L such that $b \in M$ but $a \notin M$.*

Proof. Let $\mathscr{F}$ be the family of all filters F such that $a \notin F$ but $b \in F$. Note that $\mathscr{F} \neq \varnothing$ since $[b, \rightarrow] \in \mathscr{F}$. Order $\mathscr{F}$ by set inclusion and note that by a simple application of Zorn's axiom $\mathscr{F}$ has a maximal element M. By the definition of M, $a \notin M$ but $b \in M$. Now if $M \subset F$ in the lattice of filters of L then by our choice of M we cannot have $F \in \mathscr{F}$. It follows that $a \in F$ and so $0 = a \cap b \in F$ whence $F = L$. This shows that M is an ultrafilter and completes the proof.

THEOREM 7.6. *A bounded lattice L is semicomplemented if and only if the intersection of its ultrafilters is $\{\pi\}$.*

Proof. Suppose first that the intersection of the ultrafilters of L is $\{\pi\}$. Then if $a < \pi$ there exists an ultrafilter M such that $a \notin M$. It follows that in the lattice of filters of L we have $[a, \rightarrow] \curlyvee M = L$. In particular $0 \in [a, \rightarrow] \curlyvee M$ and so $0 = a \cap x$ for some $x \in M$. Since M is an ultrafilter we must have $x \neq 0$. This shows that L is semicomplemented.

Suppose conversely that L is semicomplemented. If $a < \pi$ then a admits a non-zero semicomplement x. By Theorem 7.5 there exists an ultrafilter M such that $a \notin M$. It follows from this that the intersection of all the ultrafilters of L is $\{\pi\}$.

THEOREM 7.7. *A bounded lattice L is section semicomplemented if and only if every principal filter other than* $[0, \rightarrow]$ *is the intersection of a family of ultrafilters.*

Proof. Suppose first that every principal filter other than $[0, \rightarrow]$ is the intersection of a family of ultrafilters. Let $a < b$ in L. Then clearly $[b, \rightarrow] \subset [a, \rightarrow]$ and so there exists an ultrafilter M containing $[b, \rightarrow]$ but not $[a, \rightarrow]$. Then $[a, \rightarrow] \curlyvee M = L$, whence $0 \in [a, \rightarrow] \curlyvee M$ and so $0 = a \cap x$

for some $x \in M$. Now $b, x \in M$ with M an ultrafilter implies $b \cap x \neq 0$ since $b \cap x \in M$. It follows that $b \cap x$ is a non-zero semicomplement of a in $[0, b]$. Thus L is section semicomplemented.

Conversely, suppose that L is section semicomplemented. We must show that if $a \neq 0$, then $[a, \rightarrow]$ is the intersection of a family of ultrafilters. By Theorem 7.5 there exists an ultrafilter M such that $a \in M$. Let $\{F_\alpha; \alpha \in I\}$ denote the set of all ultrafilters containing $[a, \rightarrow]$. Note that $[a, \rightarrow] \subseteq \bigcap_{\alpha \in I} F_\alpha$. Now if $d \in \bigcap_{\alpha \in I} F_\alpha$ let us show that $d \geq a$. Suppose that $c = d \cap a < a$ and choose x to be a non-zero semicomplement of c in $[0, a]$. Then $x \cap d = x \cap a \cap d = x \cap c = 0$ and so, by Theorem 7.5, we can find an ultrafilter K such that $x \in K$ but $d \notin K$. Now $x \in K$ with $x \leq a$ implies $a \in K$; and by our choice of d we must then have $d \in K$, a contradiction. We conclude that $c = a$ and hence $a \leq d$. This completes the proof.

EXERCISES

7.1. Prove that in a lattice L with 0 the following conditions are equivalent:

(a) L is section semicomplemented;
(b) $a < b \Rightarrow (\exists x \in L)\ x \cap a = 0$ and $x \cap b \neq 0$;
(c) $\{x \in L; x \cap b = 0\} \subseteq \{x \in L; x \cap a = 0\} \Rightarrow a \leq b$.

7.2. Prove that the MacNeille completion of a lattice with 0 is semicomplemented (resp. section semicomplemented) if and only if the lattice itself is semicomplemented (resp. section semicomplemented). Deduce that the MacNeille completion of a bounded relatively complemented lattice is both section and dual section semicomplemented.

[*Hint*. Let $\bar{L}$ denote the MacNeille completion of L. Use the fact that L is a sublattice of $\bar{L}$ and that if $I < J$ in $\bar{L}$, then I must have an upper bound x in L such that x is not an upper bound for J.]

7.3. Prove that every pseudo-complemented lattice is bounded. Prove further that a pseudo-complemented lattice is complemented if and only if it is semicomplemented.

7.4. In an arbitrary lattice L define $a \nabla b$ to mean that $(\forall x \in L)\ (a \cup x) \cap b = x \cap b$. Show that L has a pair of elements a, b for which $a \nabla b$ holds if and only if L has a 0.

7.5. Let L be a dual section semicomplemented lattice with 0. Show that the mapping $I \rightarrow I^{\nabla}$ (see Theorem 7.1) induces a Galois connection in the sense of Exercise 2.8 on the lattice of ideals of L.

7.6. Prove that in a section semicomplemented lattice $a \nabla b$ is equivalent to the assertion that $b_1 \leq b$ and $b_1 \leq a \cup x$ with $b_1 \cap x = 0$ imply $b_1 = 0$.

7.7. An element a of a lattice with 0 is called an *atom* of L whenever $a \neq 0$ and there is no element x such that $0 < x < a$. L is said to be *atomic* if every non-zero element contains an atom; and *atomistic* if every non-zero element is the union of a family of atoms. Prove that

(a) a bounded atomic lattice is semicomplemented if and only if π is the union of its atoms;
(b) an atomic lattice is atomistic if and only if it is section semicomplemented;
(c) an atomic lattice is atomistic if and only if it is *relatively atomic* in the sense that $x < y$ implies the existence of an atom a such that $a \leq y$ but $a \nleq x$.

7.8. Prove that if a is an atom of a uniquely complemented lattice, then $a \nabla a'$ (a' denoting the unique complement of a). [*Hint*. Show that if $a \cup y = \pi$ then $a' \leq y$ and apply Theorem 7.2.]

8. Modularity in lattices

We shall say that an ordered pair (a, b) of elements of a lattice L form a *modular pair*, in symbols $M(a, b)$, if and only if, for all $c \in L$,

$$c \leq b \Rightarrow c \cup (a \cap b) = (c \cup a) \cap b.$$

Dually, (a, b) is called a *dual modular pair*, in symbols $M^*(a, b)$, if

$$c \geq b \Rightarrow c \cap (a \cup b) = (c \cap a) \cup b.$$

Thus $M^*(a, b)$ in L is equivalent to $M(a, b)$ in the dual of L. We say that a lattice L is *modular* if $M(a, b)$ holds for all $a, b \in L$.

In the following lattice

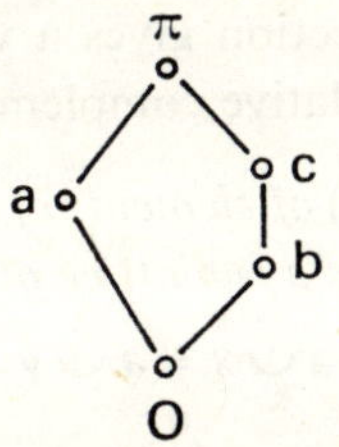

we note that $M(c, a)$ holds but not $M(a, c)$. This shows that the relation of being a modular pair is not symmetric. Since $M^*(a, c)$ is also true, we see that modular pairs need not be dual modular pairs. Despite this (see Exercise 8.1) it is true that L modular implies L^* modular.

EXAMPLE 8.1. Let G be a group and let $N(G)$ be the set of all normal subgroups of G. It is readily seen that $N(G)$ forms a lattice with respect to set inclusion in which intersection is simply set-theoretic intersection and union is given by

$$H \curlyvee K = HK = \{hk;\ h \in H,\ k \in K\}.$$

The lattice $(N(G), \cap, \curlyvee)$ is modular. In fact, in any lattice we have $x \leq z \Rightarrow x \cup (y \cap z) \leq (x \cup y) \cap (x \cup z) = (x \cup y) \cap z$ and so all we need do is show that

$$H \subseteq K \Rightarrow H(J \cap K) \supseteq HJ \cap K.$$

For this purpose, let $x \in HJ \cap K$; then we have $x \in HJ$ and $x \in K$. Consequently $(\exists y \in H)\,(\exists z \in J)\, x = yz$ and so $z = y^{-1}x \in HK \subseteq K^2 = K$ giving $z \in J \cap K$ and $x = yz \in H(J \cap K)$. A similar result holds for the lattice of ideals of a ring and, more generally, for the lattice of submodules of a module.

EXAMPLE 8.2. The set $L(V)$ of subspaces of a vector space V over a division ring D forms a complete modular lattice when ordered by set inclusion. This lattice is easily seen to be both atomistic and complemented. The atoms are, of course, the one-dimensional subspaces and a complement for a subspace M may be obtained in the following manner: construct a basis for M and extend this to a basis for V by means of vectors $\{x_\alpha\}_{\alpha \in I}$. The subspace generated by $\{x_\alpha\}_{\alpha \in I}$ will then serve as a complement for M.

Our first result of this section gives a very neat characterization of modular pairs in terms of relative complements:

THEOREM 8.1. *A pair (a, b) of elements of a lattice L is a modular pair if and only if L does not possess a sublattice of the form*

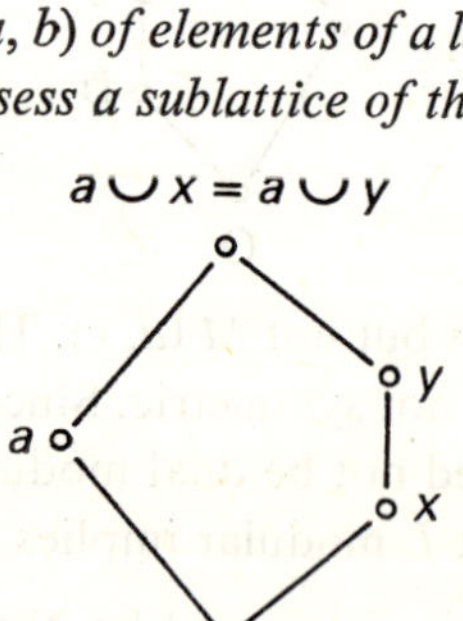

with $y \leq b$.

Proof. If $M(a, b)$ holds and there exists a sublattice of the indicated form then $x < y \leq b$ and so $(x \cup a) \cap b = x \cup (a \cap b) = x$ which gives $y = (x \cup a) \cap y = (x \cup a) \cap b \cap y = x \cap y = x$, a contradiction. If, on the other hand, $M(a, b)$ failed, then we could find an element $c < b$ such that $c \cup (a \cap b) < (c \cup a) \cap b$. Set $x = c \cup (a \cap b)$ and $y = (c \cup a) \cap b$. Note that $a \cap b \leq a \cap y = a \cap (c \cup a) \cap b = a \cap b$ and so $a \cap b = a \cap y = a \cap x$. Dually, $a \cup x = a \cup c \cup (a \cap b) = a \cup c \geq a \cup y \geq a \cup x$ shows that $a \cup x = a \cup y = a \cup c$. This produces a sublattice of the desired form.

COROLLARY 1. *$M(a, b)$ holds in L if and only if it holds in $[a \cap b, a \cup b]$.*

COROLLARY 2. *A lattice L is modular if and only if it has no sublattice of the form*

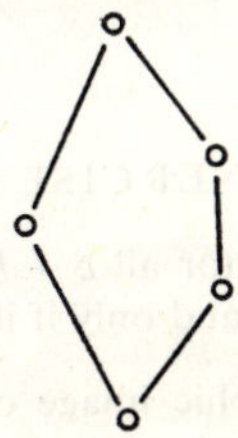

COROLLARY 3. *A lattice is modular if and only if no element admits distinct but comparable complements in an interval sublattice.*

Our next result is sometimes referred to as the *parallelogram law*:

THEOREM 8.2. *If $M(a, b)$ and $M^*(b, a)$ both hold in a lattice L then the interval sublattices $[a, a \cup b]$ and $[a \cap b, b]$ are isomorphic.*

Proof. Define $f: [a, a \cup b] \to [a \cap b, b]$ and $g: [a \cap b, b] \to [a, a \cup b]$ by the prescriptions $f(x) = x \cap b$ and $g(x) = x \cup a$. As can readily be seen, f and g are isotone and mutually inverse.

COROLLARY. *In a modular lattice with 0, $a \sim b$ implies that the intervals $[0, a]$ and $[0, b]$ are isomorphic.*

Proof. Let $a \cup x = b \cup x$ with $a \cap x = 0 = b \cap x$. Then by the theorem $[0, a] = [a \cap x, a]$ is isomorphic to $[x, x \cup a]$ which in turn is isomorphic to $[0, b]$.

Let us mention that the specific isomorphism called for in the previous corollary is given by $a_1 \to (a_1 \cup x) \cap b$ with $b_1 \to (b_1 \cup x) \cap a$ acting as its inverse.

In the presence of modularity several of the concepts of § 7 coincide, as is illustrated by the following result:

THEOREM 8.3. *Every complemented modular lattice is relatively complemented.*

Proof. Let $a \leq c \leq b$ and let a' denote a complement of a. Then by Theorem 8.2 the mapping $x \to x \cap a'$ is an isomorphism of $[a, b]$ onto $[0, b \cap a']$ whose inverse is given by $x \to x \cup a$. If w is a complement of $c \cap a'$ in L, then clearly $w \cap b \cap a'$ is a complement of $c \cap a'$ in the interval $[0, b \cap a']$. It is immediate that $(w \cap b \cap a') \cup a$ is a complement of c in $[a, b]$.

EXERCISES

8.1. Prove that if $M(a, c)$ holds for all $c > b$ in a lattice, then $M^*(a, b)$ holds. Deduce that a lattice L is modular if and only if its dual L^* is modular.

8.2. Prove that every homomorphic image of a modular lattice is modular and that $\times_{i \in I} L_i$ is modular if and only if each of the lattices L_i is modular.

8.3. Prove that the lattice of ideals of a lattice L with 0 is modular if and only if L is itself modular.

8.4. Prove that $M(a, b)$, $a_1 \in [a \cap b, a]$, $b_1 \in [a \cap b, b] \Rightarrow M(a_1, b_1)$.

8.5. Prove that $M(a, b)$, $M(c, a \cup b)$ with $c \cap (a \cup b) \leq a \Rightarrow M(c \cup a, b)$ and $(c \cup a) \cap b = a \cap b$.

8.6. Let L be a modular lattice with 0. Write $a \perp b$ to denote the fact that $a \cap b = 0$. Prove that if $a \perp b$ and $(a \cup b) \perp c$ then $a \perp (b \cup c)$.

8.7. Prove that in any modular lattice with 0 the properties $a \nabla b$ and $b \nabla a$ are equivalent.

8.8. Let L be a bounded relatively complemented lattice. Consider the following assertions concerning the elements $a, b \in L$:

(a) $a \sim b$ in $[0, a \cup b]$;
(b) $(\exists x \in L)$ $a \cup x = b \cup x$ and $a \cap x = b \cap x$;
(c) $a \sim b$;
(d) a and b have a common complement in L.

Show that (a) $\Rightarrow$ (b) $\Rightarrow$ (c) $\Rightarrow$ (d) and that in the presence of modularity (d) $\Rightarrow$ (a). Deduce from this that L is modular if and only if it has no sublattice of the form

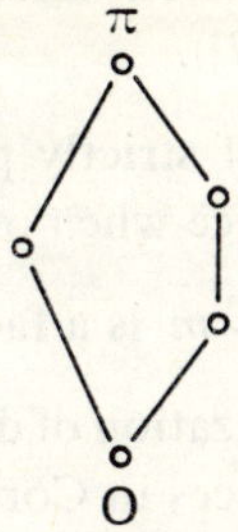

Deduce further that L is modular if and only if (d) $\Rightarrow$ (a).

8.9. Let L be a lattice with 0. An element b is called a *maximal* semicomplement of a in case $a \cap b = 0$ and $a \cap c \neq 0$ for all $c > b$. Prove that if L is a bounded semicomplemented modular lattice then every maximal semicomplement of a is in fact a complement of a. [*Hint:* use Exercise 8.6.]

8.10. Using Exercise 8.9, show that for a finite modular lattice the following conditions are equivalent:

(a) L is complemented;
(b) L is semicomplemented;
(c) L is dual semicomplemented.

9. Distributive lattices

An ordered triple (a, b, c) of elements of a lattice will be called a *distributive triple*, in symbols $D(a, b, c)$, whenever $(a \cup b) \cap c = (a \cap c) \cup (b \cap c)$. Dually it is known as a *dual distributive triple*, in symbols $D^*(a, b, c)$, when $(a \cap b) \cup c = (a \cup c) \cap (b \cup c)$. We shall say that a lattice L is *distributive* whenever every ordered triple of elements of L is a distributive triple.

EXAMPLE 9.1. Every chain is a distributive lattice.

EXAMPLE 9.2. The lattice of all subsets of a set is a complemented distributive lattice with respect to the usual set-theoretic operations of union and intersection. The lattice of all finite subsets of an infinite set is a relatively complemented distributive lattice which has no largest element.

EXAMPLE 9.3. The subgroups of a group G ordered by set inclusion form a lattice which is distributive if and only if every finitely generated subgroup of G is cyclic (see [27]).

EXAMPLE 9.4. The set $\mathbf{Z}_+$ of strictly positive integers forms a semi-complemented distributive lattice when ordered according to

$$m \preccurlyeq n \Leftrightarrow m \text{ is a factor of } n.$$

The following is a characterization of distributive lattices analogous to that provided for modular lattices in Corollary 3 of Theorem 8.1:

THEOREM 9.1. *A lattice L is distributive if and only if no element of L has two distinct complements in an interval sublattice.*

Proof. Suppose that L is distributive and that $c \cup x = c \cup y$ and $c \cap x = c \cap y$. Then $x = x \cap (c \cup x) = x \cap (c \cup y) = (x \cap c) \cup (x \cap y) = (y \cap c) \cup (y \cap x) = y \cap (c \cup x) = y \cap (c \cup y) = y$.

Suppose conversely that an element of L can have at most one complement in any interval sublattice. By Corollary 3 to Theorem 8.1 it follows that L is modular. Given elements $a, b, c \in L$ define

$$a^* = (b \cup c) \cap a, \quad b^* = (c \cup a) \cap b, \quad c^* = (a \cup b) \cap c.$$

Note that $a^* \cap c^* = a \cap c$, $b^* \cap c^* = b \cap c$ and $a^* \cap b^* = a \cap b$. Now let

$$d = (a \cup b) \cap (b \cup c) \cap (c \cup a).$$

We have

$$\begin{aligned} a^* \cup c^* = a^* \cup [(a \cup b) \cap c] &= (a^* \cup c) \cap (a \cup b) \\ &= \{[(b \cup c) \cap a] \cup c\} \cap (a \cup b) \\ &= (b \cup c) \cap (a \cup c) \cap (a \cup b) \\ &= d. \end{aligned}$$

By the symmetry of a, b, c we have $a^* \cup c^* = a^* \cup b^* = b^* \cup c^* = d$. We now note that

$$\begin{cases} c^* \cup [a^* \cup (b \cap c)] = d; \\ c^* \cap [a^* \cup (b \cap c)] = (c^* \cap a^*) \cup (b \cap c) = (a \cap c) \cup (b \cap c). \end{cases}$$

By the symmetry of *a*, *b* in the above expression, we also have

$$\begin{cases} c^* \cup [b^* \cup (a \cap c)] = d; \\ c^* \cap [b^* \cup (a \cap c)] = (a \cap c) \cup (b \cap c). \end{cases}$$

Applying our hypothesis we then deduce that

$$\begin{aligned} a^* \cup (b \cap c) = b^* \cup (a \cap c) &= a^* \cup (b \cap c) \cup b^* \cup (a \cap c) \\ &= b^* \cup a^* = d. \end{aligned}$$

We are able to conclude that

$$c^* = c^* \cap d = c^* \cap [b^* \cup (a \cap c)] = (a \cap c) \cup (b \cap c).$$

This is precisely the statement that $D(a, b, c)$. We thus have L distributive as claimed.

COROLLARY. *A lattice is distributive if and only if it has no sublattice of either of the following types:*

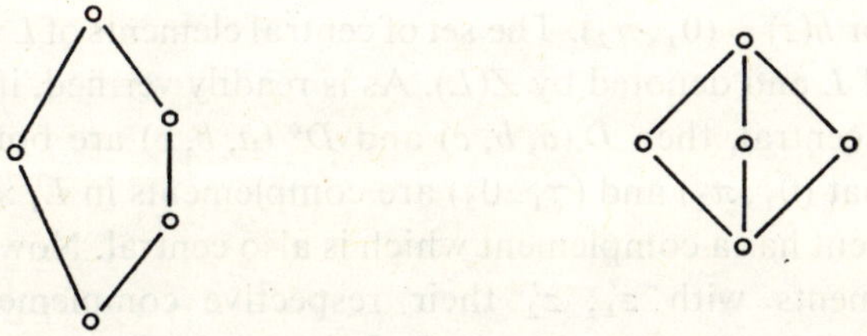

We shall also have occasion to consider the following *infinite distributive laws* in a lattice L:

(ID) If $\bigcup_{\alpha \in I} x_\alpha$ exists then, for each $y \in L$, $\bigcup_{\alpha \in I} (x_\alpha \cap y)$ exists and equals $\left(\bigcup_{\alpha \in I} x_\alpha\right) \cap y$.

(DID) If $\bigcap_{\alpha \in I} x_\alpha$ exists then, for each $y \in L$, $\bigcap_{\alpha \in I} (x_\alpha \cup y)$ exists and equals $\left(\bigcap_{\alpha \in I} x_\alpha\right) \cup y$.

Let us note that the law (ID) is equivalent to the assertion that for each $y \in L$ the translation $x \to x \cap y$ is a complete $\cup$-endomorphism, while (DID) is equivalent to $x \to x \cup y$ being a complete $\cap$-endomorphism.

We shall say that L is *infinitely distributive* whenever both (ID) and (DID) are valid. Clearly each of these implies distributivity.

Henceforth we shall agree that a complemented distributive lattice will be called a *Boolean lattice* or a *Boolean algebra.*

EXAMPLE 9.4. Any chain is infinitely distributive as is any Boolean lattice (see (Exercise 9.5).

EXAMPLE 9.5. Let E be an infinite set and take L to be the lattice formed by E together with its finite subsets, ordered by set inclusion. Then L is a complete distributive lattice. We claim that (ID) fails. To see this, let $x \in E$ and let $C(x) = \{M \in L; x \notin M\}$. Then we have, in L, $\bigcup_{M \in C(x)} M = E$ and $M \in C(x) \Rightarrow M \cap \{x\} = \emptyset$. Hence

$$\Big(\bigcup_{M \in C(x)} M\Big) \cap \{x\} = E \cap \{x\} = \{x\} \neq \emptyset = \bigcup_{M \in C(x)} (M \cap \{x\}).$$

EXAMPLE 9.6. *The centre of a bounded lattice.* An element z of a bounded lattice is called *central* whenever there exist (necessarily bounded) lattices L_1, L_2 and an isomorphism $h: L \rightarrow L_1 \times L_2$ such that $h(z) = (\pi_1, 0_2)$ or $h(z) = (0_1, \pi_2)$. The set of central elements of L will be called the *centre* of L and denoted by $Z(L)$. As is readily verified, if at least one of a, b, c is central, then $D(a, b, c)$ and $D^*(a, b, c)$ are both true. It is also clear that $(0_1, \pi_2)$ and $(\pi_1, 0_2)$ are complements in $L_1 \times L_2$ so every central element has a complement which is also central. Now let z_1, z_2 be central elements with z_1', z_2' their respective complements. Let $L_1 = [0, z_1 \cap z_2]$ and $L_2 = [0, z_1' \cup z_2']$. Define $h: L \rightarrow L_1 \times L_2$ by the prescription $h(x) = (x \cap z_1 \cap z_2, x \cap (z_1' \cup z_2'))$. Clearly h is isotone. For arbitrary $x \in L$, making use of the fact that z_1, z_2, z_1', z_2' are each central, we have

$$\begin{aligned}
x &= x \cap (z_1 \cup z_1') \\
&= (x \cap z_1) \cup (x \cap z_1') \\
&= [(x \cap z_1) \cup (x \cap z_1')] \cap (z_2 \cup z_2') \\
&= (x \cap z_1 \cap z_2) \cup (x \cap z_1 \cap z_2') \cup (x \cap z_1' \cap z_2) \cup (x \cap z_1' \cap z_2') \\
&= (x \cap z_1 \cap z_2) \cup [(x \cap z_1 \cap z_2') \cup (x \cap z_1' \cap z_2')] \\
&\qquad \cup [(x \cap z_1' \cap z_2) \cup (x \cap z_1' \cap z_2')] \\
&= (x \cap z_1 \cap z_2) \cup (x \cap z_2') \cup (x \cap z_1') \\
&= (x \cap z_1 \cap z_2) \cup [x \cap (z_1' \cup z_2')].
\end{aligned}$$

It follows from this that if $h(x) \leq h(y)$ then $x \leq y$. Suppose now that $(a, b) \in L_1 \times L_2$. Then $a \leq z_1 \cap z_2$ and $b \leq z_1' \cup z_2'$. Now

$$(a \cup b) \cap z_1 \cap z_2 = [(a \cap z_1) \cup (b \cap z_1)] \cap z_2$$
$$= (a \cap z_1 \cap z_2) \cup (b \cap z_1 \cap z_2).$$

If we observe that $(z_1' \cup z_2') \cap z_1 \cap z_2 = (z_1' \cap z_1 \cap z_2) \cup (z_2' \cap z_1 \cap z_2) = 0$ we see that $b \cap z_1 \cap z_2 = 0$ and so $(a \cup b) \cap z_1 \cap z_2 = a$. In a similar way we have $(a \cup b) \cap (z_1' \cup z_2') = b$ and hence $h(a \cup b) = (a, b)$. It follows that h is an isomorphism of L onto $L_1 \times L_2$. Since we have $h(z_1 \cap z_2) = (z_1 \cap z_2, 0)$ and $h(z_1' \cup z_2') = (0, z_1' \cup z_2')$ this proves that $z_1 \cap z_2$ and $z_1' \cup z_2'$ are both central. We conclude that $Z(L)$ is a Boolean sublattice of L.

We close this section by considering briefly the centre of a bounded relatively complemented lattice. Before doing so, however, we pause to present an extremely useful characterization of central elements.

THEOREM 9.2. *An element z of a bounded lattice L is central if and only if there exists an element z' such that*

$$(\forall x \in L) \quad x = (x \cap z) \cup (x \cap z') = (x \cup z) \cap (x \cup z').$$

Proof. If z is central, take z' to be the unique complement of z. Suppose conversely that the condition holds. Let $L_1 = [0, z]$, $L_2 = [0, z']$ and $h(x) = (x \cap z, x \cap z')$ for all $x \in L$. Then $h: L \to L_1 \times L_2$ is isotone. From our hypothesis we see that $h(x) \leq h(y)$ must imply $x \leq y$ so the proof will be complete if we can show that h is surjective. Accordingly, let $(a, b) \in L_1 \times L_2$. Then $a \leq (a \cup b) \cap z \leq (a \cup z') \cap z = (a \cup z') \cap (a \cup z) \cap z = a \cap z \leq a$ and so $(a \cup b) \cap z = a$. Similarly, we have $(a \cup b) \cap z' = b$ and $h(a \cup b) = (a, b)$.

THEOREM 9.3. *An element z of a bounded relatively complemented lattice is central if and only if it has a unique complement.*

Proof. Let z have a unique complement z'. Then by Theorem 7.4 we have $z \nabla z'$ and so, by Theorem 7.2, $x = (x \cup z) \cap (x \cup z')$ holds for all $x \in L$. The same argument applied to L^* yields $(\forall x \in L)\ x = (x \cap z) \cup (x \cap z')$. The converse is clear.

THEOREM 9.4. *The centre of a bounded relatively complemented lattice is a complete sublattice.*

Proof. Let $\{z_\alpha\}_{\alpha \in I}$ be a family of central elements such that $z = \bigcap_{\alpha \in I} z_\alpha$ exists in L. Let z' be any complement of z. Then

$$(\forall \alpha \in I) \quad z' = (z' \cup z_\alpha) \cap (z' \cup z'_\alpha) = \pi \cap (z' \cup z'_\alpha) = z' \cup z'_\alpha$$

gives $z' \geq z'_\alpha$. Suppose now that we could find an element x such that $(\forall \alpha \in I)\, z' > x \geq z'_\alpha$. Let y be a complement of x in $[0, z']$. Then $(\forall \alpha \in I)\, y \cap z'_\alpha \leq y \cap x = 0$ shows $y = (y \cap z_\alpha) \cup (y \cap z'_\alpha) = y \cap z_\alpha \leq z_\alpha$ and so $y \leq z = \bigcap_{\alpha \in I} z_\alpha$. But now $y \leq z'$ gives $y = y \cap z = 0$, a contradiction. This then shows that $z' = \bigcup_{\alpha \in I} z'_\alpha$. But this uniquely determines z' and so, by Theorem 9.3, z is central. To show that $Z(L)$ is stable under the formation of unions, we apply the above argument to L^*.

EXERCISES

9.1. Prove that a lattice is distributive if and only if its dual is distributive.

9.2. Prove that every homomorphic image as well as every sublattice of a distributive lattice is distributive. Prove further that the cartesian product of lattices is distributive if and only if each of the lattices is distributive.

9.3. Prove that a lattice L with 0 is distributive if and only if its lattice of ideals is distributive and, if this is so, then the infinite distributive law (ID) holds in the ideal lattice.

9.4. In a distributive lattice with 0 show that $a \nabla b$ is equivalent to $a \cap b = 0$.

9.5. Prove that every dual section semicomplemented distributive lattice satisfies the infinite distributive law (ID). [*Hint.* Assume $x = \bigcup_{\alpha \in I} x_\alpha$ exists and note that, for each $\alpha \in I$, $x \cap y \geq x_\alpha \cap y$. If $(\forall \alpha \in I)\, x \cap y > w \geq x_\alpha \cap y$, choose v such that $w \leq v < \pi$ and $v \cup (x \cap y) = \pi$. Conclude that $(\forall \alpha \in I)\, v \geq x_\alpha$ and arrive at a contradiction.]

9.6. Let L be a lattice which is both section and dual section semicomplemented. Prove that an element z of L is central if and only if there is an element z' such that

$$a \cap z = 0 = a \cap z' \Rightarrow a = 0;$$

$$a \cup z = \pi = a \cup z' \Rightarrow a = \pi.$$

9.7. Prove that an element z of a bounded lattice L is central if and only if z has a complement z' such that $M(z, z')$, $M(z', z)$ and $(\forall x \in L)\, x = (x \cap z) \cup (x \cap z')$.

9.8. Show that an element of a bounded distributive lattice is central if and only if it admits a complement.

9.9. Let L be a complemented lattice. Prove that an ideal I of L has a complement in the ideal lattice if and only if I is principal. Deduce that the centre of a bounded lattice need not be a complete sublattice. [*Hint*. Take L to be the lattice of all subsets of an infinite set E. The ideal formed by the finite subsets of E has no complement in the ideal lattice; yet it is the union of a family of central elements.]

9.10. Let L be a bounded lattice having the property that

$$(\forall x \in L)\ e(x) = \bigcap \{z \in Z(L);\ z \geq x\}$$

exists and is central. Show that the mapping $e : L \to L$ described by $x \to e(x)$ is a *quantifier* in the sense that

(1) $e(0) = 0$; (2) $(\forall x \in L)\ x \leq e(x)$; (3) $(\forall x, y \in L)\ e\,[x \cap e(y)] = e(x) \cap e(y)$.

9.11. Let L be a section semicomplemented lattice. Prove that L is distributive if and only if, for each $a \in L$, the semicomplements of a form an ideal of L. [*Hint*. Consider a semicomplement of $(a \cap c) \cup (b \cap c)$ in $[0, (a \cup b) \cap c]$.] Deduce that every pseudo-complemented, section semicomplemented lattice is Boolean. Give an example of a pseudo-complemented, semicomplemented lattice which is not distributive.

10. Congruence relations

Let R be a congruence relation on the lattice L. We have already noted in § 6 that the operation $x/R \curlyvee y/R = (x \cup y)/R$ turns L/R into a $\curlyvee$-semilattice. A dual argument shows that L/R is an $\curlywedge$-semilattice with respect to $x/R \curlywedge y/R = (x \cap y)/R$. Routine verification shows that

$$x/R = x/R \curlyvee (x/R \curlywedge y/R) = x/R \curlywedge (x/R \curlyvee y/R)$$

and so by Theorem 4.1 it follows that L/R is a lattice under these laws. We call L/R the *quotient lattice of L with respect to R*. Note that the canonical surjection $\natural_R : L \to L/R$ is a lattice epimorphism and that R is the equivalence relation associated with $\natural_R$. These results are important enough to warrant their formal presentation as a theorem:

THEOREM 10.1. *If R is a congruence relation on the lattice L then L/R is a lattice under the laws described by* $x/R \curlyvee y/R = (x \cup y)/R$ *and* $x/R \curlywedge y/R = (x \cap y)/R$ *and the canonical surjection* $\natural_R$ *is an epimorphism.*

We also have the following lattice-theoretic version of the "Fundamental Theorem of Homomorphisms":

THEOREM 10.2. *Let L, M be lattices, let* $f : L \to M$ *be an epimorphism and let R be the equivalence associated with f. Then R is a congruence rela-*

tion on L and the mapping $f^{\rightarrow}: L/R \rightarrow M$ *described by* $f^{\rightarrow}(x/R) = f(x)$ *is an isomorphism which is also the unique mapping which makes the following triangle commutative:*

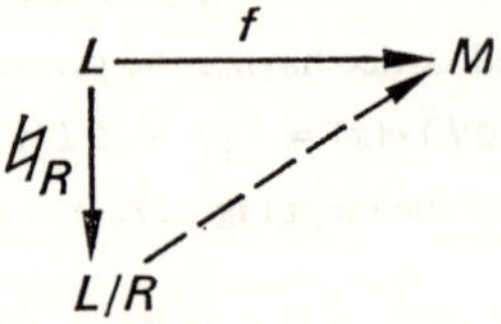

Proof. Since f is a homomorphism it is clear that R is a congruence on L. It is just as clear that the mapping $f^{\rightarrow}$ is well-defined. Since f is surjective, so also is $f^{\rightarrow}$. Also, if $x/R \preccurlyeq y/R$, then $y/R = x/R \curlyvee y/R = (x \cup y)/R$ and so $f(y) = f(x \cup y) = f(x) \cup f(y) \geq f(x)$. If $f^{\rightarrow}(x/R) \preccurlyeq f^{\rightarrow}(y/R)$ then $f(y) = f(y) \cup f(x) = f(x \cup y)$ and $y/R = (x \cup y)/R = x/R \curlyvee y/R \succcurlyeq x/R$, thus completing the proof that $f^{\rightarrow}$ is an isomorphism. We now merely note that $f^{\rightarrow} \circ \natural_R = f$ and that if $g \circ \natural_R = f$ then $g\,(x/R) = g\,[\natural_R(x)] = f(x)$ and so $g = f^{\rightarrow}$.

We shall often need to know just when an equivalence relation on a lattice is in fact a congruence relation. A useful set of necessary and sufficient conditions is given in the next result.

THEOREM 10.3. *Let R be a reflexive relation on the lattice L. Then R is a congruence relation on L if and only if R satisfies the following three conditions:*

(1) $a \equiv b(R) \Leftrightarrow (\forall x, y \in [a \cap b, a \cup b])\ x \equiv y(R)$;
(2) $a \cup b \equiv a(R) \Leftrightarrow b \equiv a \cap b(R)$;
(3) $a \equiv b(R),\ b \equiv c(R)$ *with* $a \geq b \geq c \Rightarrow a \equiv c(R)$.

Proof. If R is a congruence relation then (3) is clear. Let $a \equiv b(R)$ and let $x, y \in [a \cap b, a \cup b]$. Then

$$x = x \cap (a \cup b) \equiv x \cap (a \cap b) = a \cap b\ (R).$$

Similarly, we have $y \equiv a \cap b(R)$ and so $x \equiv y(R)$. This establishes (1). As for (2), we note that if $a \cup b \equiv a(R)$ then $b = b \cap (a \cup b) \equiv b \cap a(R)$ and conversely.

Suppose now that R is a reflexive relation on L satisfying conditions (1), (2), (3). That R is symmetric is immediate from (1). Let $a \equiv b(R)$ and let $t \in L$. Then $(a \cap b) \cup [t \cap (a \cup b)] \in [a \cap b, a \cup b]$ and so by (1) we have $a \cap b \equiv (a \cap b) \cup [t \cap (a \cup b)]$. Now take $x = (a \cup b) \cap t$ and $y = a \cap b$ and note that $x \cup y \equiv y(R)$ so that by (2) we obtain $x \equiv x \cap y(R)$ and hence

$$(a \cup b) \cap t \equiv (a \cup b) \cap t \cap (a \cap b) = a \cap b \cap t\,(R).$$

Since $a \cap t,\ b \cap t \in [a \cap b \cap t, (a \cup b) \cap t]$ we see that $a \cap t \equiv b \cap t(R)$. In a similar way we have $a \cup t \equiv b \cup t(R)$. We must still show transitivity. Let $a \equiv b(R)$ and $b \equiv c(R)$. Then $a \cup b \equiv b(R) \Rightarrow a \cup b \cup c \equiv b \cup c(R)$. Since $b \cup c \equiv c(R)$ we can apply (3) to obtain $a \cup b \cup c \equiv c(R)$. A dual argument produces $c \equiv a \cap b \cap c(R)$ and now (3) tells us that $a \cup b \cup c \equiv a \cap b \cap c(R)$. Since $a, c \in [a \cap b \cap c, a \cup b \cup c]$ we see that $a \equiv c(R)$, thus completing the proof that R is a congruence relation on L.

If R happens to be an equivalence relation on L then condition (3) of the previous theorem is of course superfluous.

Definition. We shall denote by $\mathrm{Con}(L)$ the set of congruence relations on a lattice L, this set being ordered in the usual way, namely

$$R \leqslant S \Leftrightarrow (x \equiv y\,(R) \Rightarrow x \equiv y\,(S)).$$

THEOREM 10.4. *For any lattice L, Con (L) forms a complete distributive lattice in which the infinite distributive law (ID) is valid.*

Proof. The congruence relation arising from equality is evidently the minimum element of $\mathrm{Con}\,(L)$ and the relation which identifies all the elements of L is clearly the greatest element of $\mathrm{Con}\,(L)$. If, for each $\alpha \in I$, R_α is a congruence relation on L, then so also is the relation $x \equiv y(R) \Leftrightarrow (\forall \alpha \in I)\ x \equiv y(R_\alpha)$. It is immediate that $\mathrm{Con}\,(L)$ is a complete lattice. We shall show that it is in fact a complete sublattice of the lattice of all equivalence relations on L. We have already dealt with the intersection operation, so we need only show that if E is the union [= transitive product] of $\{R_\alpha\}_{\alpha \in I}$ in the lattice of equivalence relations then $E = \bigvee_{\alpha \in I} R_\alpha$ in $\mathrm{Con}\,(L)$. This will follow if we can just show that $E \in \mathrm{Con}(L)$. Now if $x \equiv y(E)$, then there exist indices $\alpha_1, \alpha_2, \ldots, \alpha_n$ and elements $w_0, w_1, \ldots, w_n$ such that $w_0 = x$, $w_n = y$ and $w_{i-1} \equiv w_i(R_{\alpha_i})$ for $i = 1, 2, \ldots, n$. For arbitrary $t \in L$ we have $w_{i-1} \cup t \equiv w_i \cup t(R_{\alpha_i})$ for $i = 1, 2, \ldots, n$ from which it follows that $x \cup t \equiv y \cup t(E)$. In a similar way we have $x \cap t \equiv y \cap t(E)$ and so $E \in \mathrm{Con}(L)$ as required.

We are now ready to verify the infinite distributive law (ID). For this purpose, let $R = \bigvee_{\alpha \in I} R_\alpha$ and $S \in \mathrm{Con}(L)$. Then $(\forall \alpha \in I)\ R_\alpha \curlywedge S \preccurlyeq R \curlywedge S$ and so $R \curlywedge S \succcurlyeq \bigvee_{\alpha \in I} (R_\alpha \curlywedge S)$. Now if $x \equiv y\,(R \curlywedge S)$ then there exist indices $\alpha_1, \alpha_2, \ldots, \alpha_n$ and elements $w_0, w_1, \ldots, w_n$ such that $w_0 = x$, $w_n = y$ and $(i = 1, 2, \ldots, n)$ $w_{i-1} \equiv w_i(R_{\alpha_i})$. For each i, let $v_i = [(x \cap y) \cup w_i] \cap (x \cup y)$. Then $v_0 = x$, $v_n = y$ and for $i = 1, 2, \ldots, n$ we have

$$v_{i-1} = [(x \cap y) \cup w_{i-1}] \cap (x \cup y) \equiv [(x \cap y) \cup w_i] \cap (x \cup y) = v_i\,(R_{\alpha_i}).$$

Since $x \cap y \leq v_i \leq x \cup y$ and $x \cap y \equiv x \cup y(S)$, we have $v_{i-1} \equiv v_i(S)$ for all i so that $v_{i-1} \equiv v_i\,(R_{\alpha_i} \curlywedge S)$. It follows that $x \equiv y\left(\bigvee_{\alpha \in I} (R_\alpha \curlywedge S)\right)$ and hence that $R \curlywedge S = \bigvee_{\alpha \in I} (R_\alpha \curlywedge S)$.

We now pause to have a close look at congruence relations on a distributive lattice. In connection with this, we agree to call $0/R$ the *kernel* of the congruence relation R on the lattice L with 0. More generally, for an arbitrary lattice L, if L/R has a smallest element then this element is called the kernel of R. Clearly, if R has a kernel K then K is an ideal of L.

THEOREM 10.5. *Let L be a lattice. Then*

(1) *every ideal of L is the kernel of a congruence relation on L if and only if L is distributive;*

(2) *for an ideal I of a distributive lattice, the smallest congruence with kernel I is given by*

$$a \equiv b\,(R_I) \Leftrightarrow (\exists t \in I) \quad a \cup t = b \cup t$$

and the largest congruence with kernel I is given by

$$a \equiv b\,(R^I) \Leftrightarrow \{x;\, a \cap x \in I\} = \{x;\, b \cap x \in I\};$$

(3) *every ideal of a bounded lattice is the kernel of a unique congruence if and only if the lattice is Boolean.*

Proof. (1) Let L be distributive and let I be an ideal of L. Define R_I as in (2) above. Clearly, $a \equiv b(R_I) \Rightarrow (\forall c \in L)\ a \cup c \equiv b \cup c(R_I)$. Since L is distributive, if $a \cup t = b \cup t$ for some $t \in I$, then

$$(\forall c \in L) \quad (a \cap c) \cup (t \cap c) = (a \cup t) \cap c = (b \cup t) \cap c$$
$$= (b \cap c) \cup (t \cap c)$$

with $t \cap c \in I$ shows that $a \cap c \equiv b \cap c(R_I)$. The kernel of R_I is clearly I itself; and if I is the kernel of R then $a \cup t = b \cup t$ with $t \in I$ implies that $a \equiv a \cup t = b \cup t \equiv b(R)$ and so $R_I \preccurlyeq R$. If L fails to be distributive, then by the Corollary to Theorem 9.1 it has a sublattice of one of the following types:

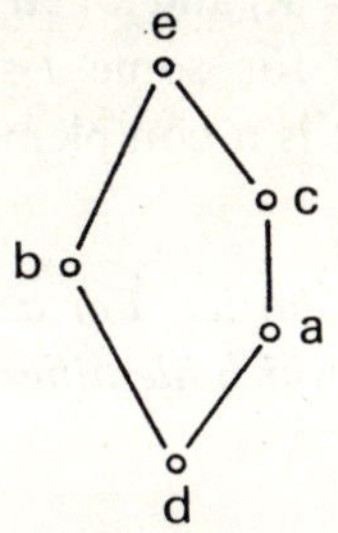

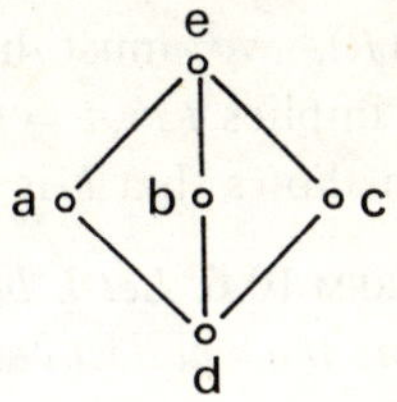

In either event, let $I = [\leftarrow, a]$. If I were the kernel of the congruence relation R, then $e = a \cup b \equiv b(R)$ implies $c = c \cap e \equiv c \cap b = d \equiv a(R)$, a contradiction.

(2) We have already established that if I is an ideal of a distributive lattice, then R_I is the smallest congruence with kernel I. Let us now consider R^I. If $a \equiv b(R^I)$, then

$$(a \cap c) \cap x \in I \Leftrightarrow a \cap (c \cap x) \in I \Leftrightarrow b \cap (c \cap x) \in I \Leftrightarrow (b \cap c) \cap x \in I$$

from which it follows that $a \cap c \equiv b \cap c(R^I)$. Moreover, if $(a \cup c) \cap x = (a \cap x) \cup (c \cap x) \in I$, then $a \cap x \in I \Rightarrow b \cap x \in I$ and so $(b \cup c) \cap x = (b \cap x) \cup (c \cap x) \in I$ and conversely. This establishes $a \cup c \equiv b \cup c(R^I)$ and hence that $R^I \in \mathrm{Con}(L)$. If R is a congruence with kernel I, then from $a \equiv b(R)$ and $a \cap x \in I$ we deduce that $b \cap x \in I$, and so we must have $R \preccurlyeq R^I$. The proof is completed on noting that the kernel of R^I is I.

(3) Let L be a Boolean algebra. If $R \in \mathrm{Con}(L)$ has kernel I, let $a \equiv b(R)$. Denoting by x' the complement of x, we must have $a \cap b' \equiv b \cap b' = 0(R)$ and $b \cap a' \equiv 0(R)$. It follows that $(a \cap b') \cup (b \cap a') \in I$.

Now if $(a \cap b') \cup (b \cap a') \in I$, then, as can easily be seen,

$$a \cup [(a \cap b') \cup (b \cap a')] = a \cup b = b \cup [(a \cap b') \cup (b \cap a')].$$

It follows that R is uniquely determined by its kernel. Suppose, conversely, that L is a bounded lattice in which every ideal is the kernel of a unique congruence relation. Then, by (1), L is distributive. Given $a \in L$, define R by the prescription

$$x \equiv y\,(R) \Leftrightarrow x \cap a = y \cap a.$$

Clearly, $R \in \mathrm{Con}(L)$. Let I be its kernel. Since $R = R_I$ and $a \cap a = \pi \cap a \Rightarrow a \equiv \pi(R)$, we must have $a \cup t = \pi \cup t = \pi$ for some $t \in I$. Then $t \equiv 0(R)$ implies $t \cap a = 0 \cap a = 0$ and hence t is a complement of a. This then shows that L is a Boolean algebra.

THEOREM 10.6. *Let L be a bounded distributive lattice. For a, b ∈ L let* $R_{a,b}$ *denote the smallest congruence relation on L which identifies a and b. Then*

(1) $x \equiv y(R_{a,0}) \Leftrightarrow x \cup a = y \cup a$;
(2) $x \equiv y(R_{a,\pi}) \Leftrightarrow x \cap a = y \cap a$;
(3) $x \equiv y(R_{a,b})$
$\Leftrightarrow (x \cup a \cup b = y \cup a \cup b$ *and* $x \cap a \cap b = y \cap a \cap b)$;
(4) *the centre of* $\mathrm{Con}(L)$ *is the* $\curlyvee$*-subsemilattice generated by* $\{R_{a,b};\, a, b \in L\}$;
(5) *there exists a Boolean algebra A such that* $\mathrm{Con}(L) \simeq \mathrm{Con}(A)$.

Proof. (1) This follows from Theorem 10.5 since, taking $I = [\leftarrow, a]$, we have, on the one hand, $R_{a,0} \preccurlyeq R_I$ and on the other

$$x \equiv y\,(R_I) \Rightarrow (\exists t \leq a) \quad x \cup t = y \cup t$$
$$\Rightarrow x \cup a = x \cup t \cup a = y \cup t \cup a = y \cup a$$
$$\Rightarrow x \equiv y\,(R_{a,0}).$$

(2) Apply (1) to the dual of L (which is also distributive by Exercise 9.1).
(3) Define the relation R on L by

$$x \equiv y\,(R) \Leftrightarrow (x \cup a \cup b = y \cup a \cup b \quad \text{and} \quad x \cap a \cap b = y \cap a \cap b).$$

That $R \in \mathrm{Con}(L)$ follows from the observation that $R = R_{a \cup b, 0} \curlywedge R_{a \cap b, \pi}$. Clearly, $a \equiv b(R)$. Suppose that $S \in \mathrm{Con}(L)$ with $a \equiv b(S)$. If $x \equiv y(R)$, then $x \cup a \cup b = y \cup a \cup b$, $x \cap a \cap b = y \cap a \cap b$ and $a \equiv b(S)$ imply that $x \cup a \equiv y \cup a(S)$ and $x \cap a \equiv y \cap a(S)$. Working in the distributive lattice L/S, this says that $x/S \curlyvee a/S = y/S \curlyvee a/S$ and $x/S \curlywedge a/S = y/S \curlywedge a/S$ from which it follows that $x/S = y/S$ and so $x \equiv y(S)$. We have thus shown that $R \preccurlyeq S$ and so $R = R_{a,b}$.

(4) Routine verification shows that $R_{a,0}$ and $R_{a,\pi}$ are complements in $\mathrm{Con}(L)$. Since $R_{a,b} = R_{a \cup b, 0} \curlywedge R_{a \cap b, \pi}$ it follows by Exercise 9.8 that $R_{a,b}$ is central. Consequently, if R is the union of a finite number of congruences of the form $R_{a,b}$ then R is central. Suppose conversely that R is central. If R' denotes the complement of R in $\mathrm{Con}(L)$, then $\pi \equiv 0\,(R \curlyvee R')$ implies the existence of $a_0, a_1, \ldots, a_n \in L$ such that $a_0 = 0$, $a_n = \pi$ and $(i = 1, 2, \ldots, n)$ $a_{i-1} \equiv a_i$ modulo R or R'. Denoting by Π the greatest element of $\mathrm{Con}(L)$, we thus have $\Pi = \bigvee_{i=1}^{n} R_{a_{i-1}, a_i}$ and consequently $R = \bigvee_{i=1}^{n} (R \curlywedge R_{a_{i-1}, a_i})$. Now for each i, either (1) $a_{i-1} \equiv a_i(R)$ in which case $R \curlywedge R_{a_{i-1}, a_i} = R_{a_{i-1}, a_i}$ or (2) $a_{i-1} \equiv a_i(R')$ in which case $R \curlywedge R_{a_{i-1}, a_i}$ reduces to equality. Thus $R = \curlyvee \{R_{a_{i-1}, a_i};\ a_{i-1} \equiv a_i(R)\}$.

(5) Let A denote the centre of $\mathrm{Con}(L)$. For each $R \in \mathrm{Con}(L)$ let $J(R)$ denote the set of central elements contained in R. Then $J(R)$ is an ideal of A. Clearly $R_1 \preccurlyeq R_2 \Rightarrow J(R_1) \preccurlyeq J(R_2)$; and if $J(R_1) \preccurlyeq J(R_2)$ then $a \equiv b(R_1) \Rightarrow R_{a,b} \preccurlyeq R_1 \Rightarrow R_{a,b} \preccurlyeq R_2$ which gives $a \equiv b(R_2)$ and so $R_1 \preccurlyeq R_2$. Let us now show that the map $R \to J(R)$ from $\mathrm{Con}(L)$ to the lattice $I(A)$ of ideals of A is surjective. Given any element $I \in I(A)$, let R denote the union in $\mathrm{Con}(L)$ of the elements of I. It is clear that $I \preccurlyeq J(R)$. If $R_{a,b} \in J(R)$ then $a \equiv b(R)$ implies the existence of finitely many elements R_{a_i, b_i} of I such that $a \equiv b\left(\bigvee_{i=1}^{n} R_{a_i, b_i}\right)$. This shows that $R_{a,b} \in I$ and so $I = J(R)$. We have thus established that the map $R \to J(R)$ is an isomorphism of $Z(\mathrm{Con}(L))$ onto $I(A)$. The proof is completed by noting that $I \to R_I$ is an isomorphism of $I(A)$ onto $\mathrm{Con}(A)$.

COROLLARY. *If L is a finite distributive lattice then $\mathrm{Con}(L)$ is a Boolean algebra.*

We have already noted (see Exercise 9.5) that every Boolean algebra is infinitely distributive. We leave the reader the routine verification that the infinite distributive law (ID) is inherited by every sublattice in which existing unions coincide with those in the Boolean algebra. A dual assertion applies to (DID). Suppose now that we are given a bounded distributive lattice L. Consider the mapping $k: L \to Z(\text{Con}(L))$ given by $k(a) = R_{a,0}$. This is evidently an isomorphism of L onto a sublattice of $Z(\text{Con}(L))$. If the embedding preserves any existing intersections then (DID) is inherited by L from $Z(\text{Con}(L))$. On the other hand, if (DID) holds in L and the intersection $b = \bigcap_{\alpha \in A} b_\alpha$ exists in L, let $x \equiv y \left(\bigwedge_{\alpha \in A} R_{b_\alpha,0}\right)$. Then $x \cup b_\alpha = y \cup b_\alpha$ for each $\alpha \in A$ and consequently

$$x \cup b = x \cup \left(\bigcap_{\alpha \in A} b_\alpha\right) = \bigcap_{\alpha \in A} (x \cup b_\alpha) = \bigcap_{\alpha \in A} (y \cup b_\alpha)$$
$$= y \cup \left(\bigcap_{\alpha \in A} b_\alpha\right) = y \cup b.$$

This shows that $R_{b,0} = \bigwedge_{\alpha \in A} R_{b_\alpha,0}$ in $Z(\text{Con}(L))$ and so the embedding k preserves existing intersections. If (ID) holds in L, let $b = \bigcup_{\alpha \in A} b_\alpha$. Then if $x \equiv y \left(\bigwedge_{\alpha \in A} R_{b_\alpha,\pi}\right)$ we see that $(\forall \alpha \in A)\ x \cap b_\alpha = y \cap b_\alpha$ and, by (ID), $x \cap b = y \cap b$. Thus $R_{b,\pi} = \bigwedge_{\alpha \in A} R_{b_\alpha,\pi}$ and since we are working in a Boolean algebra, we have $R_{b,0} = \bigvee_{\alpha \in A} R_{b_\alpha,0}$. Thus k preserves any existing unions. [Here, of course, we have made use of the fact that the mapping $x \to x'$ of a Boolean algebra to itself is a dual automorphism (Exercise 10.5).] We summarize the situation in the next theorem.

THEOREM 10.7. *Let L be a bounded distributive lattice. The infinite distributive law (ID) holds in L if and only if there is an isomorphism k of L onto a sublattice of a Boolean algebra such that*

(1) *$k(0) = 0$ and $k(\pi) = \pi$;*

(2) *k preserves any existing unions in L.*

The law (DID) is equivalent to the existence of a k satisfying (1) *and*

(2′) *k preserves any existing intersections in L.*

COROLLARY. *Every complete infinitely distributive lattice is isomorphic to a complete sublattice of a Boolean algebra.*

We shall now have a brief look at congruence relations on a complete lattice which is both section and dual section semicomplemented. Our goal is to show that the congruence relations on such a lattice form a *Stone lattice*; i.e. a pseudo-complemented distributive lattice in which the pseudo-complement of each element has a complement. We require some preliminary results.

THEOREM 10.8. *Let R be a congruence relation on a section semicomplemented lattice L. If b is disjoint from the kernel of R* (i.e. $b \cap x = 0$ *for each* $x \in Ker(R)$) *then $a \nabla b$ for each $a \in Ker(R)$.*

Proof. If $(a \cup x) \cap b > x \cap b$, choose d to be a non-zero semicomplement of $x \cap b$ in $[0, (a \cup x) \cap b]$. Then

$$d = d \cap (b \cup x) \equiv d \cap x = d \cap x \cap b = 0\,(R)$$

and so d is in the kernel of R. Since $d \leq b$ we must have $d = 0$ and this contradiction shows that $a \nabla b$.

Since a central element of a lattice behaves as if it were in a distributive lattice, the proof of the next result may be easily deduced from the pertinent portions of Theorem 10.6. It will therefore be omitted.

THEOREM 10.9. *Let z be a central element of a bounded lattice L and denote by z' its unique complement. Then $R_{z,0}$ and $R_{z',0}$ are complements in $Con(L)$. Furthermore, $a \equiv b(R_{z,0}) \Leftrightarrow a \cup z = b \cup z$.*

THEOREM 10.10. *If L is a complete lattice which is both section and dual section semicomplemented then $Con(L)$ is a Stone lattice.*

Proof. (1) Let I be the kernel of the congruence relation R, let z be the element $\bigcup \{x; x \in I\}$ and let $z^* = \bigcup \{x \in L; [0, x] \curlywedge I = \{0\}\}$. By Theorem 10.8 we have $a \in I$, $[0, b] \curlywedge I = \{0\} \Rightarrow a \nabla b$. Two applications of the corollary to Theorem 7.2 will now produce the fact that $z \nabla z^*$. If $(x \cap z) \cup (x \cap z^*) < x$, let y be a non-zero semicomplement of $(x \cap z) \cup (x \cap z^*)$ in $[0, x]$. Then $y \cap z = 0 \Rightarrow [0, y] \curlywedge I = \{0\} \Rightarrow y \leq z^*$ and so we have $y = y \cap z^* = 0$, a contradiction. Thus

$$(\forall x \in L) \quad x = (x \cap z) \cup (x \cap z^*) = (x \cup z) \cap (x \cup z^*).$$

It follows by Theorem 9.2 that z is central with z^* as its complement.

(2) Let $a \equiv b\,(R \curlywedge R_{z^*,0})$. If c is a semicomplement of $a \cap b$ in $[0, a \cup b]$ then $c \equiv 0(R)$. Since $a \cup b \cup z^* = (a \cap b) \cup z^*$ we see that

$$c = c \cap [(a \cap b) \cup z^*] = (c \cap a \cap b) \cup (c \cap z^*) = 0.$$

Thus $a = b$ and so $R \curlywedge R_{z^*,0}$ reduces to equality.

(3) Suppose now that equality is denoted by ω and that $R \curlywedge S = \omega$. If $a \equiv b\,(S \curlywedge R_{z,0})$ and if c is a semicomplement of $a \cap b$ in $[0, a \cup b]$ then $c \equiv 0(S)$, and since $a \cup b \cup z = (a \cap b) \cup z$ we must have

$$c = c \cap [(a \cap b) \cup z] = (c \cap a \cap b) \cup (c \cap z) = c \cap z \leq z.$$

But $c \equiv 0(S)$ and $R \curlywedge S = \omega$ imply that $[0, c] \curlywedge I = \{0\}$. By Theorem 10.8 we deduce that $x \nabla c$ for all $x \in I$ and by the corollary to Theorem 7.2 it follows that $z \nabla c$, so $c = 0$. This shows that $a = b$ and $S \curlywedge R_{z,0} = \omega$. Since $R_{z,0}$ and $R_{z^*,0}$ are complements in Con(L), we see that $S \preccurlyeq R_{z^*,0}$. This establishes that $R_{z^*,0}$ is the pseudo-complement of R in Con(L). We conclude by Theorem 10.9 that Con(L) is a Stone lattice.

COROLLARY. *If L is a complete relatively complemented lattice then Con(L) is a Stone lattice.*

We close this section by considering congruence relations on a section complemented lattice. We shall be especially interested in their kernels and shall give an intrinsic characterization of them.

THEOREM 10.11. *Let R be a congruence relation on the section complemented lattice L and let I be the kernel of R. The following conditions are then equivalent:*

(1) $a \equiv b(R)$;
(2) $(\exists s \in I) \quad a \cup b = (a \cap b) \cup s$;
(3) $(\exists t \in I) \quad a \cup t = b \cup t$.

Proof. (1) $\Rightarrow$ (2): Let s be a complement of $a \cap b$ in $[0, a \cup b]$. Then $s = s \cap (a \cup b) \equiv s \cap (a \cap b) = 0(R)$.

(2) $\Rightarrow$ (3): If $a \cup b = (a \cap b) \cup s$, then $a \cup b = a \cup (a \cup b) = a \cup (a \cap b) \cup s = a \cup s$ and, similarly, $a \cup b = b \cup s$.

(3) $\Rightarrow$ (1): If $a \cup t = b \cup t$ with $t \in I$, then $a \equiv a \cup t = b \cup t \equiv b(R)$.

THEOREM 10.12. *Let J be an ideal of the section complemented lattice L. The following conditions are equivalent:*

(1) *J is the kernel of a congruence relation on L;*

(2) $a \in J$, $b \leq a \cup x$ *with* $a \cap x = b \cap x = 0 \Rightarrow b \in J$.

Proof. (1) $\Rightarrow$ (2): If J is the kernel of the congruence R and if $a \in J$ and $b \leq a \cup x$, then $b = b \cap (a \cup x) \equiv b \cap x(R)$, and so if $b \cap x = 0$ we have $b \in J$.

(2) $\Rightarrow$ (1): Define the relation R by setting

$$a \equiv b(R) \Leftrightarrow (\exists t \in J)\, a \cup t = b \cup t.$$

It is clear that R is a $\cup$-compatible equivalence relation on L. By Theorem 7.3, a has a complement $t_1 \leq t$ in $[0, a \cup t]$. For any given $x \in L$ choose s_1 to be a complement of $a \cap x$ in $[0, (a \cup t) \cap x]$. Then $s_1 \cap a = s_1 \cap a \cap x = 0$, $s_1 \cup a \leq t_1 \cup a$ and $t_1 \cap a = 0$. It follows by the hypothesis (2) that $s_1 \in J$. We have thus shown that for each $x \in L$ there exists $s_1 \in J$ such that $(a \cup t) \cap x = (a \cap x) \cup s_1$. Similarly, we can show that there exists $s_2 \in J$ such that $(b \cup t) \cap x = (b \cap x) \cup s_2$. It follows that $(a \cap x) \cup s_1 \cup s_2 = (b \cap x) \cup s_1 \cup s_2$ and so $a \cap x \equiv b \cap x(R)$. Hence we have $R \in \operatorname{Con} L$. The proof is completed by noting that J is the kernel of R.

Suppose now that L is a relatively complemented lattice with 0. If an ideal J of L is stable under perspectivity, let $a \in J$ and $a \cup x \geq b \cup x$ with $a \cap x = b \cap x = 0$. By the dual of Theorem 7.3, x has a complement $b_1 \geq b$ in $[0, a \cup x]$. Then $b_1 \sim a$ puts b_1 and consequently b in J. This establishes the following:

COROLLARY 1. *An ideal J of a relatively complemented lattice with* 0 *is the kernel of a congruence relation if and only if J is stable under perspectivity.*

If a principal ideal $[0, z]$ of a bounded relatively complemented lattice is the kernel of a congruence relation then by Theorem 10.7 we have $z \nabla z'$ for *any* complement z' of z. It follows that z has a unique complement and so, by Theorem 9.3, z is central. In summary:

COROLLARY 2. *A principal ideal* $[0, z]$ *of a bounded relatively complemented lattice is the kernel of a congruence relation if and only if z is central.*

EXERCISES

10.1. Let R be a congruence relation on the lattice L and let $f: L \to M$ be a lattice homomorphism. Show that the following conditions are equivalent:

(a) there exists a (necessarily unique) homomorphism $g: L/R \to M$ such that the following triangle is commutative

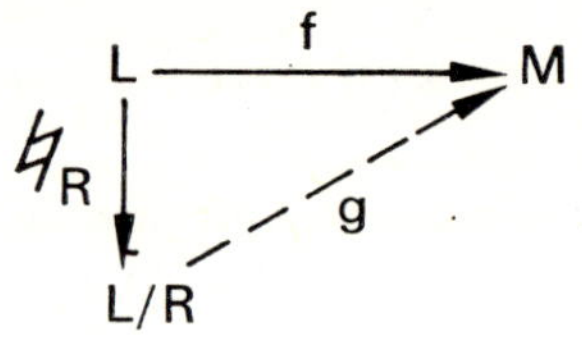

(b) the congruence associated with f is coarser than R.

10.2. Let R, S be congruence relations on the lattice L. If $R \preccurlyeq S$ show that there is a unique epimorphism $g: L/R \to L/S$ such that the following triangle is commutative

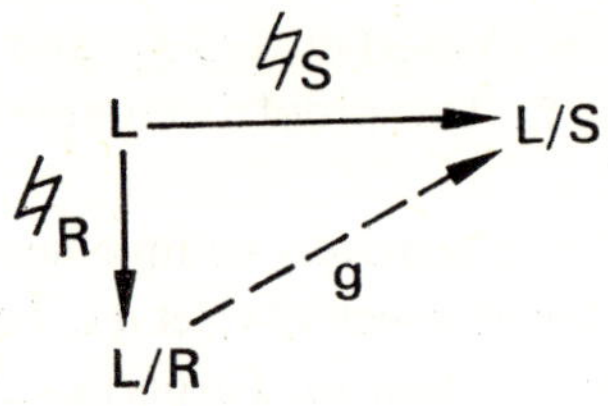

10.3. Show that if L has a zero element and $f: L \to M$ is an isotone surjection then M also has a zero.

10.4. Let L be an arbitrary lattice. Show that the set of congruences on L which have kernels forms a filter of Con (L). [*Hint*. Argue that Ker $(R \curlywedge S) =$ Ker (R) $\curlywedge$ Ker (S). If R admits a kernel and $R \preccurlyeq S$ use Exercises 10.2 and 10.3 to deduce that S admits a kernel.]

10.5. Let L be a Boolean algebra. For each $x \in L$ let x' denote the unique complement of x. Show that the mapping $x \to x'$ is a dual automorphism on L.

10.6. Let L be a lattice with 0. For each $R \in$ Con (L) let

$$k(R) = \curlywedge \{S \in \text{Con}(L);\ \text{Ker}(S) = \text{Ker}(R)\}.$$

Show that the map k is a residuated dual closure with k^+ given by

$$k^+(R) = \curlyvee \{S \in \text{Con}(L);\ \text{Ker}(S) = \text{Ker}(R)\}.$$

Deduce that we have defined a complete congruence on Con (L) and use this to prove that the set of congruence kernels of L, when ordered by set inclusion, forms a complete distributive lattice in which the infinite distributive law (ID) holds. [*Hint*. See Exercise 6.7.]

10.7. An ideal S of a lattice L is called *standard* if the relation $a \equiv b \Leftrightarrow a \cup b = (a \cap b) \cup s$ for some $s \in S$ is a congruence relation on L. Prove that the following conditions on the ideal S are equivalent:

(1) S is a standard ideal;
(2) $(\forall I, J \in I(L))\ (I \curlyvee S) \curlywedge J = (I \curlywedge J) \curlyvee (S \curlywedge J)$;
(3) $(\forall I \in I(L))\ I \curlyvee S = \{a \cup b;\ a \in I, b \in S\}$.

[*Hint*. (1) $\Rightarrow$ (2): if $x \in (I \curlyvee S) \curlywedge J$, then $x \in J$ and $x \leq a \cup s\ (a \in I,\ s \in S)$. Deduce that $x \equiv x \cap a$ so $x = (x \cap a) \cup s_1$ with $s_1 \in S$. This puts $x \in (I \curlywedge J) \curlyvee (S \curlywedge J)$.

(2) $\Rightarrow$ (3): note that if $b \leq a \cup s$ with $s \in S$, then b is an element of $([\leftarrow, a] \curlyvee S) \curlywedge [\leftarrow, b]$. Use this to deduce that $b = (a \cap b) \cup s_1$ with $s_1 \in S$.]

CHAPTER 2

COORDINATIZING BAER SEMIGROUPS

11. Baer rings

In this section we shall examine a class of lattices which arise in connection with certain rings. This example serves as a starting point for much of the material in the next few sections, and for this reason it is important that the reader consider it carefully.

It is, of course, assumed that the reader has a basic knowledge of ring theory. The letters e, f, g, h (with or without subscripts) will be used in this section to denote idempotent elements of the ring A. If $M \subseteq A$, then we define $R(M) = \{x \in A; (\forall m \in M)\ mx = 0\}$. The set $R(M)$ is called the *right annihilator of M* and is clearly a right ideal of A. In the case where $M = \{x\}$ we shall generally write $R(x)$ instead of $R(\{x\})$. *Left annihilators* are defined as one would expect and denoted by $L(M)$ or $L(x)$, whichever is appropriate. For each $x \in A$ let $xA = \{xy; y \in A\}$ and $Ax = \{yx; y \in A\}$. If A has an identity element 1, then $x \in xA$ and $x \in Ax$; it is also important to note that $R(x) = R(Ax)$ and $L(x) = L(xA)$. If the ring A has the property that for each $x \in A$ there exist idempotents e_x, f_x such that $R(x) = e_xA$ and $L(x) = Af_x$, then A is called a *Baer ring*.

We mention that this definition differs slightly from that of Kaplansky [18]. Before proceeding, we present some examples.

EXAMPLE 11.1. Any ring with an identity having no proper zero divisors (in particular, any division ring) is a Baer ring.

EXAMPLE 11.2. Let V be a vector space and let A be the ring of linear transformations on V. Given any $t \in A$ let e project onto the kernel (= null space) of t and let f project onto the image of t. As can readily be seen, $R(t) = e \circ A$ and $L(t) = A \circ (\mathrm{id}_V - f)$. Thus A is a Baer ring. Similarly, so is the ring of $n \times n$ matrices over a division ring.

EXAMPLE 11.3. Consider the ring $B(H)$ formed by the bounded operators of the Hilbert space H. Given $t \in B(H)$, let e be the orthogonal projection on the null space of t and let f be the projection onto the closure of the image of t. Clearly $e, f \in B(H)$, and we have $t \circ s = 0 \Leftrightarrow (\forall x \in H)$ $t[s(x)] = 0 \Leftrightarrow (\forall x \in H)\ s(x) = e[s(x)] \Leftrightarrow s = e \circ s$; $s \circ t = 0 \Leftrightarrow (\forall x \in H)$ $s[t(x)] = 0 \Leftrightarrow s \circ f = 0 \Leftrightarrow s = s \circ (\mathrm{id}_H - f)$. Thus $R(t) = e \circ B(H)$ and $L(t) = B(H) \circ (\mathrm{id}_H - f)$ and we have a Baer ring.

EXAMPLE 11.4. A ring A is said to be a *Boolean ring* if every element of A is idempotent. Every Boolean ring with an identity is a Baer ring.

EXAMPLE 11.5. The ring of all triangular 2×2 matrices $\begin{pmatrix} a & b \\ 0 & c \end{pmatrix}$ over a division ring is a Baer ring.

EXAMPLE 11.6. The complete direct sum of any family of Baer rings is a Baer ring.

In what follows, A will denote a Baer ring. Let $\mathscr{R} = \mathscr{R}(A)$ denote the set of right annihilators of elements of A and $\mathscr{L} = \mathscr{L}(A)$ the corresponding set of left annihilators. We also let PRI(A), PLI(A) denote the set of principal right, left ideals of A with all four sets ordered by set inclusion.

THEOREM 11.1. *With the notation as introduced above:*

(1) *A has a multiplicative identity element;*

(2) *the mappings $\hat{L}: \mathrm{PRI}(A) \to \mathrm{PLI}(A)$, $\hat{R}: \mathrm{PLI}(A) \to \mathrm{PRI}(A)$ given by the prescriptions $\hat{L}(xA) = L(x)$, $\hat{R}(Ax) = R(x)$ set up a Galois connection;*

(3) *$\hat{L} \circ \hat{R} \circ \hat{L} = \hat{L}$ and $\hat{R} \circ \hat{L} \circ \hat{R} = \hat{R}$;*

(4) *$xA \in \mathscr{R} \Leftrightarrow xA = (\hat{R} \circ L)(x)$ and $Ax \in \mathscr{L} \Leftrightarrow Ax = (\hat{L} \circ R)(x)$;*

(5) *the restriction $L^{\rightarrow}$ of $\hat{L}$ to $\mathscr{R}$ is a dual isomorphism of $\mathscr{R}$ onto $\mathscr{L}$ whose inverse is $R^{\rightarrow}$, the restriction of $\hat{R}$ to $\mathscr{L}$;*

(6) *for each idempotent e of A, $eA = R(1 - e) \in \mathscr{R}(A)$ and $Ae = L(1 - e) \in \mathscr{L}(A)$.*

Proof. (1) An idempotent generator of $A = R(0)$ will act as a left identity element (for if $A = eA$ then for each $x \in A$ we have the existence of a $y \in A$ such that $x = ey$ whence $ex = e^2y = ey = x$), while an idempotent generator of $A = L(0)$ acts as a right identity. It is immediate that A has a two-sided identity element, henceforth denoted by 1.

(2) If $xA \subseteq yA$, then $x = yw$ for some $w \in A$, so if $ay = 0$ we must have $ax = ayw = 0$. Thus $xA \subseteq yA \Rightarrow L(y) \subseteq L(x)$. If $a \in L(x)$, then $ax = 0$ puts $x \in R(a)$. This shows that $x \in (\hat{R} \circ L)(x)$ and so $\hat{R} \circ \hat{L} \geq \mathrm{id}_{\mathrm{PRI}(A)}$. A symmetric argument produces R antitone and $\hat{L} \circ \hat{R} \geq \mathrm{id}_{\mathrm{PLI}(A)}$. This then establishes the Galois connection.

(3) $xA \subseteq (\hat{R} \circ \hat{L})(xA) \Rightarrow \hat{L}(xA) \supseteq (\hat{L} \circ \hat{R} \circ \hat{L})(xA)$ and $\hat{L}(xA) \in \mathrm{PLI}(A) \Rightarrow \hat{L}(xA) \subseteq (\hat{L} \circ \hat{R})[\hat{L}(xA)] = (\hat{L} \circ \hat{R} \circ \hat{L})(xA)$. Thus $\hat{L} \circ \hat{R} \circ \hat{L} = \hat{L}$ and similarly $\hat{R} \circ \hat{L} \circ \hat{R} = \hat{R}$.

(4) If $xA = (\hat{R} \circ L)(x)$, let $Ae = L(x)$. Then $xA = R(e)$ puts $xA \in \mathscr{R}$. If $xA \in \mathscr{R}$ then $xA = R(y)$ for some $y \in A$ and so $(\hat{R} \circ \hat{L})(xA) = (\hat{R} \circ \hat{L})[R(y)] = (\hat{R} \circ \hat{L} \circ \hat{R})(Ay) = R(y) = xA$. A symmetric argument shows that $Ax \in \mathscr{L} \Leftrightarrow Ax = (\hat{L} \circ R)(x)$.

(5) By (4), $R^{\rightarrow} \circ L^{\rightarrow} = \mathrm{id}_{\mathscr{R}}$ and $L^{\rightarrow} \circ R^{\rightarrow} = \mathrm{id}_{\mathscr{L}}$. Since $L^{\rightarrow}, R^{\rightarrow}$ are each antitone, it is immediate that $L^{\rightarrow}$ is a dual isomorphism having $R^{\rightarrow}$ as its inverse.

(6) For each $x \in A$ we have $(1 - e)ex = ex - ex = 0$ whence $eA \subseteq R(1 - e)$. Conversely, if $(1 - e)x = 0$, then $x = ex \in eA$. The other equality is proved in a similar manner.

Remark. Much of the above proof could have been deduced from Exercise 2.8. However, we gave a direct proof in order to illustrate the annihilator properties of Baer rings.

THEOREM 11.2. *$\mathscr{L}$ and $\mathscr{R}$ form bounded dually isomorphic lattices.*

Proof. In view of Theorem 11.1(5) it suffices to prove that $\mathscr{L}, \mathscr{R}$ each form $\cap$-semilattices with a minimum element. By the obvious left/right duality present, we may concentrate our efforts on $\mathscr{R}$. Let $eA, fA \in \mathscr{R}$ and let $gA = R(f - ef)$. Then, since $(f - ef)(fg) = (f - ef)g = 0$ we have $fg \in gA$ and so $fg = gfg$. It follows that $fg = (fg)^2$, and so, by Theorem 11.1(6), $fgA \in \mathscr{R}(A)$. We claim that $fgA = eA \cap fA$. That $fgA \subseteq fA$ is clear. Note that $(1 - e)fg = (f - ef)g = 0$ and so $fg \in R(1 - e) = eA$. If now $x \in eA \cap fA$, then

$$(f - ef)x = (1 - e)fx = (1 - e)x = x - ex = 0$$

and so $x \in gA$. Then $x = gx$, $x = fx$ imply that $x = fgx$ and we have $eA \cap fA = fgA \in \mathscr{R}(A)$. Finally, we observe that $0A$ is the smallest element of $\mathscr{R}(A)$.

THEOREM 11.3. *Let $eA \subseteq fA$ in $\mathscr{R}$. Then*

(1) *there exists an idempotent e_0 such that $e_0A = eA$ and $e_0 = e_0f = fe_0$;*

(2) *there exists an idempotent f_0 such that $f_0A = fA$ and $e = ef_0 = f_0e$.*

Proof. (1) Since $eA \subseteq fA$ we have $e = fe$. Set $e_0 = ef$. Then $e_0e_0 = efef = e(fe)f = eef = ef = e_0$. Since $ee_0 = e_0$ and $e_0e = efe = ee = e$ we see that $eA = e_0A$. Finally, $e_0f = eff = ef = e_0$ and $fe_0 = fef = ef = e_0$.

(2) Set $f_0 = e + f - ef$. Then $ef_0 = f_0e = e$. Note also that $ff_0 = fe + f - fef = e + f - ef = f_0$ and $f_0f = ef + f - ef = f$ so $fA = f_0A$. To show that $f_0^2 = f_0$, we note that $f_0 = e + (1 - e)f$ and so

$$f_0f_0 = ef_0 + (1 - e)ff_0 = e + (1 - e)f_0 = f_0.$$

In the case where the idempotents e, f commute, we can produce a very nice explicit formula for the idempotent generators of the union and intersection of the corresponding principal right ideals. In order to emphasize the fact that the intersection operation is set-theoretic whereas the union operation most assuredly is not, we write these as $\cap$ and $\curlyvee$ respectively.

THEOREM 11.4. *If $ef = fe$ then $eA \cap fA = efA$ and $eA \curlyvee fA = (e + f - ef)A$.*

Proof. The fact that $eA \cap fA = efA$ is clear. Noting that $(e + f - ef)e = e + fe - efe = e$ and $(e + f - ef)f = f$, we see that $e + f - ef$ is an idempotent whose principal right ideal contains both eA and fA. If now gA contains both eA and fA, then, clearly, $g(e + f - ef) = e + f - ef$ and the result follows.

Making use of the above result, we are now able to show that $\mathscr{R}(A)$ is complemented. It is in fact relatively complemented, but we defer the proof of this to the exercises.

THEOREM 11.5. *For each idempotent $e \in A$ the ideals eA and $(1 - e)A$ are complements in $\mathscr{R}$ such that both $(eA, (1 - e)A)$ and $((1 - e)A, eA)$ form modular as well as dual modular pairs.*

Proof. Let $gA \subseteq eA$. By Theorem 11.3 we may assume that $g = eg = ge$. Then $g(1-e) = (1-e)g = 0$ and Theorem 11.4 gives $gA \curlyvee (1-e)A = (g+1-e)A$. Now since $e(g+1-e) = g = (g+1-e)e$ we can apply Theorem 11.4 a second time to conclude that $gA = (gA \curlyvee (1-e)A) \cap eA$. This establishes that $(1-e)A \cap eA = 0A$ and that $M((1-e)A, eA)$ holds. Similarly, $M(eA, (1-e)A)$ holds and a dual argument on $\mathscr{L}$ produces the fact that $Ae \cap A(1-e) = A0$ with $M(Ae, A(1-e))$ and $M(A(1-e), Ae)$ both true in $\mathscr{L}$. The fact that $\mathscr{L}$ and $\mathscr{R}$ are dually isomorphic then completes the proof.

We shall now show how the centre of $\mathscr{R}(A)$ is related to the centre of the ring A. We require first the following result:

THEOREM 11.6. *If* $eA \subseteq fA$ *and* $(1-e)A \subseteq (1-f)A$ *then* $e = f$.

Proof. $eA \subseteq fA$ implies $e = fe$ while $(1-e)A \subseteq (1-f)A$ implies $1-e = (1-f)(1-e) = 1-f-e+fe$ which gives $f = fe$. It follows that $e = f$.

THEOREM 11.7. eA *is in the centre of* $\mathscr{R}$ *if and only if* e *is in the centre of* A.

Proof. Suppose that e is in the centre of A and let $fA \in \mathscr{R}$. Then $fA \cap eA = efA$ and $fA \cap (1-e)A = (1-e)fA$. Since $f = ef + (1-e)f$ it follows from Theorem 11.4 that $fA = (fA \cap eA) \curlyvee [fA \cap (1-e)A]$. Also, $eA \curlyvee fA = (e+f-ef)A$ and $(1-e)A \curlyvee fA = [1-e+f-(1-e)f]A$. Since $e+f-ef$ commutes with $1-e+f-(1-e)f$ and their product is f we see that $fA = (fA \curlyvee eA) \cap [fA \curlyvee (1-e)A]$. It follows by Theorem 9.2 that eA is central in $\mathscr{R}$.

Suppose conversely that eA is central in $\mathscr{R}$. Then $(1-e)A$ is its unique complement therein. Let $x \in A$. Then $g = e + ex(1-e)$ is idempotent with $ge = e$ and $eg = g$. It follows that $eA = gA$. Then $(1-g)A$ is a complement of eA and so $(1-g)A = (1-e)A$. By Theorem 11.6 we obtain $e = g = e + ex(1-e)$. It follows that $ex(1-e) = 0$ and so $ex = exe$. In a similar way we have $(1-e)xe = 0$ and so $xe = exe$ from which it follows that $ex = xe$ and so e is in the centre of A.

We shall be very interested in just how the elements of a Baer ring A induce residuated mappings on $\mathscr{R}(A)$. Basically, the situation is as follows.

For a fixed element x of A we can induce a mapping $\varphi_x : \mathscr{R} \to \mathscr{R}$ by the prescription

$$\varphi_x(eA) = (R^{\rightarrow} \circ L)(xe).$$

Similarly, we can induce a mapping $\eta_x : \mathscr{L} \to \mathscr{L}$ by the prescription

$$\eta_x(Ae) = (L^{\rightarrow} \circ R)(ex).$$

The mappings φ_x, η_x are connected in the following way:

$$\varphi_x \in \mathrm{Res}(\mathscr{R}) \quad \text{with} \quad \varphi_x^+ = R^{\rightarrow} \circ \eta_x \circ L^{\rightarrow};$$
$$\eta_x \in \mathrm{Res}(\mathscr{L}) \quad \text{with} \quad \eta_x^+ = L^{\rightarrow} \circ \varphi_x \circ R^{\rightarrow}.$$

The following commutative diagrams illustrate the situation:

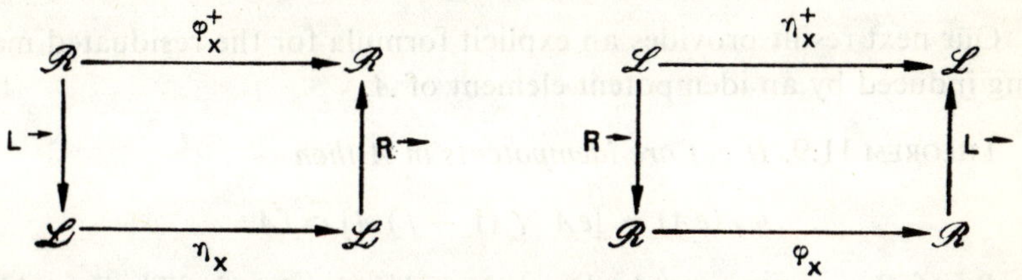

THEOREM 11.8. *For each* $x \in A$, $\varphi_x \in \mathrm{Res}(\mathscr{R})$ *with* $\varphi_x^+ = R^{\rightarrow} \circ \eta_x \circ L^{\rightarrow}$. *Dually,* $\eta_x \in \mathrm{Res}(\mathscr{L})$ *with* $\eta_x^+ = L^{\rightarrow} \circ \varphi_x \circ R^{\rightarrow}$.

Proof. (1) Let $eA \subseteq fA$. Then $e = fe$ and so if $yxf = 0$ we must have $yxe = yxfe = 0$ whence $L(xf) \subseteq L(xe)$. Thus $eA \subseteq fA \Rightarrow (R^{\rightarrow} \circ L)(xe) \subseteq (R^{\rightarrow} \circ L)(xf)$. This shows that the mapping φ_x is both well defined and isotone. In a similar way we can show that η_x is well-defined and isotone.

(2) The mapping $R^{\rightarrow} \circ \eta_x \circ L^{\rightarrow}$ is evidently isotone. If $Ag = L(xe)$ then

$$\begin{aligned}(R^{\rightarrow} \circ \eta_x \circ L^{\rightarrow} \circ \varphi_x)(eA) &= (R^{\rightarrow} \circ \eta_x \circ L^{\rightarrow})\,[(R^{\rightarrow} \circ L)(xe)]\\ &= (R^{\rightarrow} \circ \eta_x)\,[L(xe)]\\ &= (R^{\rightarrow} \circ \eta_x)(Ag)\\ &= (R^{\rightarrow} \circ L^{\rightarrow})\,[R(gx)]\\ &= R(gx)\\ &\supseteq eA,\end{aligned}$$

since $g \in L(xe) \Rightarrow e \in R(gx)$. Thus $R^{\rightarrow} \circ \eta_x \circ L^{\rightarrow} \circ \varphi_x \geq \mathrm{id}_{\mathscr{R}}$.

(3) A dual argument shows that $L^{\to} \circ \varphi_x \circ R^{\to} \circ \eta_x \geq \mathrm{id}_{\mathscr{L}}$ and so we have $L^{\to} \circ \varphi_x \circ R^{\to} \circ \eta_x \circ L^{\to} \geq L^{\to}$. Applying $R^{\to}$ to the left and using the fact that $R^{\to} \circ L^{\to} \circ \varphi_x = \varphi_x$, we see that $\varphi_x \circ R^{\to} \circ \eta_x \circ L^{\to} \leq R^{\to} \circ L^{\to} = \mathrm{id}_{\mathscr{R}}$. We conclude that $\varphi_x \in \mathrm{Res}(\mathscr{R})$ with $\varphi_x^+ = R^{\to} \circ \eta_x \circ L^{\to}$.

COROLLARY. *For each* $x \in A$, $\varphi_x^+ (eA) = R(x - ex)$.

Proof. Applying the above formula we have

$$\begin{aligned}\varphi_x^+ (eA) = (R^{\to} \circ \eta_x \circ L^{\to})(eA) &= (R^{\to} \circ \eta_x)[A(1-e)] \\ &= (R^{\to} \circ L^{\to})\{R[(1-e)x]\} \\ &= R(x - ex).\end{aligned}$$

Our next result provides an explicit formula for the residuated mapping induced by an idempotent element of A.

THEOREM 11.9. *If* e, f *are idempotents in* A *then*

$$\varphi_f(eA) = [eA \curlyvee (1-f)A] \cap fA.$$

Proof. By an argument dual to that used in the proof of Theorem 11.2, if $Ag = L(fe)$ then $gf = gfg$ and $A(1-e) \cap Af = Agf$. Clearly $gf = gfg$ implies that $Agf = Ag \cap Af$. Taking right annihilators, we see that

$$(R^{\to} \circ L)(fe) \curlyvee (1-f)A = eA \curlyvee (1-f)A.$$

Taking the intersection with fA and using the fact that $M((1-f)A, fA)$ holds, we see that

$$\begin{aligned}\varphi_f(eA) = (R^{\to} \circ L)(fe) &= [(R^{\to} \circ L)(fe) \curlyvee (1-f)A] \cap fA \\ &= [eA \curlyvee (1-f)A] \cap fA.\end{aligned}$$

All of this will be of considerable interest because of:

THEOREM 11.10. *The mapping described by* $x \to \varphi_x$ *is a semigroup homomorphism of* A *into* $\mathrm{Res}(\mathscr{R})$.

Proof. Given $x, y \in A$, let $eA \in \mathscr{R}$ and $gA = (R^{\to} \circ L)(ye)$. Then $L(g) = L(ye)$ and so

$$a(xg) = 0 \Leftrightarrow ax \in L(g) = L(ye) \Leftrightarrow a(xye) = 0.$$

Thus $L(xg) = L(xye)$ and so

$$\varphi_x[\varphi_y(eA)] = \varphi_x(gA) = (R^{\rightarrow} \circ L)(xg) = (R^{\rightarrow} \circ L)(xye) = \varphi_{xy}(eA).$$

It follows immediately from this that $x \rightarrow \varphi_x$ is a homomorphism.

We close this section by having a careful look at Example 11.2, our goal being to give a concrete interpretation to some of the above results. Let V be a (left) vector space over a division ring D, let $A = \mathrm{Hom}(V)$ be the ring of linear transformations on V and let $L = L(V)$ be the lattice of all subspaces of V. Recall that by Example 8.2 the lattice L is atomic, complemented and modular. We break our discussion into several parts.

I. *L is isomorphic to $\mathscr{R}(A)$*. For each idempotent (= projection) e in A let $M_e = \mathrm{Im}(e) = \{x \in V;\, x = e(x)\}$. Clearly M_e is a subspace of V. If $e \circ A \subseteq f \circ A$, then $e = f \circ e$ and so $x = e(x) \Rightarrow f(x) = f[e(x)] = (f \circ e)(x) = e(x) = x$ whence $M_e \subseteq M_f$. This shows that the mapping $M : \mathscr{R}(A) \rightarrow L$ given by the prescription $M(e \circ A) = M_e$ is both well-defined and isotone. If, on the other hand, $M_e \subseteq M_f$, then $(\forall x \in V)$ $e(x) \in M_e \subseteq M_f \Rightarrow (\forall x \in V)$ $e(x) = f[e(x)]$ whence $e = f \circ e$ and $e \circ A \subseteq f \circ A$. The proof would be complete if we could just show that M mapped $\mathscr{R}$ onto L. Accordingly let $Y \in L$ and let Z be a complement (= supplement) of Y in L. Then each $x \in V$ has a unique representation in the form $x = y + z$ where $y \in Y$ and $z \in Z$. If we define $e(x)$ to be this unique vector y then it is easily seen that $e = e \circ e \in A$ and $M_e = Y$.

II. We know by Exercise 2.10 that each $t \in A$ induces a residuated mapping $t^{\rightarrow}$ on L with residual $t^{\leftarrow}$. We also have by Theorem 11.8 that t induces a residuated mapping φ_t on $\mathscr{R}(A)$ given by the prescription $\varphi_t(e \circ A) = (R^{\rightarrow} \circ L)(t \circ e)$ with φ_t^+ given by $\varphi_t^+(e \circ A) = R(t - e \circ t)$. We claim that if g is an idempotent generator of $(R^{\rightarrow} \circ L)(t \circ e)$, then $M_g = t^{\rightarrow}(M_e)$. Also, if h is an idempotent generator of $R(t - e \circ t)$, then $M_h = t^{\leftarrow}(M_e)$.

Proof. Let g project onto $t^{\rightarrow}(M_e)$. We shall show that $g \circ A = (R^{\rightarrow} \circ L)(t \circ e)$. Note that $t^{\rightarrow}(M_e)$ is none other than $\mathrm{Im}(t \circ e)$, so by Example 11.2 we have $L(t \circ e) = A \circ (\mathrm{id} - g)$ and hence $(R^{\rightarrow} \circ L)(t \circ e) = R(\mathrm{id} - g) = g \circ A$. Note also that $x \in t^{\leftarrow}(M_e) \Leftrightarrow t(x) \in M_e \Leftrightarrow t(x) = e[t(x)] \Leftrightarrow (t - e \circ t)(x) = 0 \Leftrightarrow x$ is in the kernel (= null space) of $t - e \circ t$.

If h projects onto $t^{\leftarrow}(M_e)$, then by Example 11.2 we have $R(t - e \circ t) = h \circ A$ and $M_h = t^{\leftarrow}(M_e)$.

This shows that each of the following rectangles is commutative:

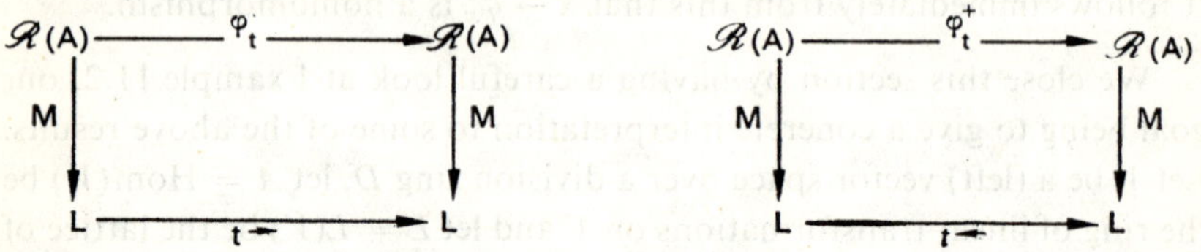

III. Suppose now that the division ring D is in fact a field. Two linear transformations s, t then induce the same residuated mapping on L if and only if there is a non-zero scalar $\lambda \in D$ such that $s = \lambda t$.

Proof. If $s = \lambda t$ with $\lambda \neq 0$, then the assertion is clear. Suppose then that $s^{\rightarrow} = t^{\rightarrow}$. Denoting by $[x]$ the subspace generated by $\{x\}$, we see that $s^{\rightarrow}([x]) = \{0\} \Leftrightarrow t^{\rightarrow}([x]) = \{0\}$ and so $s(x) = 0 \Leftrightarrow t(x) = 0$. Assume that $s(x) \neq 0$. Then $s^{\rightarrow}([x]) = t^{\rightarrow}([x]) \Rightarrow s(x) = \lambda_x t(x)$ for some non-zero λ_x in D. Similarly, if $s(y) \neq 0$, then $s(y) = \lambda_y t(y)$ with $\lambda_y \in D$ and $\lambda_y \neq 0$. We must show that $\lambda_x = \lambda_y$.

Case 1. $t(x) = \alpha t(y)$. In this case $t(x - \alpha y) = t(x) - \alpha t(y) = 0$ and so $s(x - \alpha y) = 0$ whence $s(x) = \alpha s(y)$. But then $\lambda_x t(x) = \alpha \lambda_y t(y)$ and $\lambda_x t(x) = \lambda_x \alpha t(y)$ and so $\alpha \lambda_y = \lambda_x \alpha$ whence we have $\lambda_x = \lambda_y$.

Case 2. $t(x)$, $t(y)$ linearly independent. In this case we have $s(x) = \lambda_x t(x)$, $s(y) = \lambda_y t(y)$ and we may certainly write $s(x + y) = \lambda t(x + y)$. Using linearity, we then have

$$\begin{cases} s(x + y) = \lambda t(x + y) = \lambda t(x) + \lambda t(y); \\ s(x + y) = s(x) + s(y) = \lambda_x t(x) + \lambda_y t(y), \end{cases}$$

from which we deduce that $(\lambda - \lambda_x)\, t(x) + (\lambda - \lambda_y)\, t(y) = 0$. The linear independence of $t(x)$, $t(y)$ then gives $\lambda_x = \lambda = \lambda_y$.

Combining the above arguments, we see that if there exists an x such that $s(x) \neq 0$, then $s = \lambda_x t$ as desired, and otherwise $s = t = 0$.

Remark. If the division ring D is not commutative, then an obvious modification of the argument given in the case 2 will still establish III for linear transformations s, t of rank >1. The result fails for transformations of rank 1. To see this, let D be a non-commutative division ring and consider D as a left vector space over itself. Choose an element α *not* in the centre of D. Define $t: D \to D$ by $t(x) = x\alpha$. Then t is evidently a linear transformation and t induces the same residuated map as does the identity map. If $t = \lambda \mathrm{id}$ then from $1\alpha = \lambda 1$ we have $\alpha = \lambda$ and so $(\forall x \in D)\ \alpha x = x\alpha$, a contradiction.

EXERCISES

11.1. Show that if e is an idempotent in the Baer ring A then eAe is a Baer ring with $\mathscr{R}(eAe)$ isomorphic to the interval in $\mathscr{R}(A)$ from $0A$ to eA. [*Hint*. If $x \in eAe$ and $R(x) = fA$, then $x(1-e) = 0 \Rightarrow 1 - e = f(1-e) \Rightarrow ef = efe$. Show that ef is the idempotent generator of the right annihilator of x in eAe and similarly for left annihilators. The mapping described by $f(eAe) \to fA$ is then the desired lattice isomorphism.]

11.2. Let e, f be idempotents in the Baer ring A and let $Ag = L(f - fe)$. Prove that $gf = gfg$ and $Ae \cap Af = Agf$.

11.3. Prove that for a Baer ring A the lattice $\mathscr{R}(A)$ is relatively complemented. [*Hint*. Use Theorem 11.5 to show that $\mathscr{R}$ is section complemented. Use it again to show that every interval $[eA, fA]$ is isomorphic to one of the form $[0A, gA]$.]

11.4. Show that for idempotents e, f of a Baer ring A,

$$\varphi_f^+(eA) = (eA \cap fA) \curlyvee (1 - f)A.$$

11.5. Prove that eA is central in $\mathscr{R}(A)$ if and only if $ef = fef$ for all idempotents $f \in A$. [*Hint*. If $ef = fef$, prove that $eA \cap fA = efA$. Deduce that if fA is a complement of eA then $ef = 0$ and so $fA = (1 - e)A$. Now apply Theorem 11.3 and Theorem 9.3.]

11.6. Prove that $\mathscr{R}(A)$ is a Boolean algebra if and only if every idempotent of A is central.

11.7. Prove that the centre Z of the Baer ring A is a Baer ring with $\mathscr{R}(Z)$ isomorphic to the centre of $\mathscr{R}(A)$. [*Hint*. If $x \in Z$ let $eA = R(x)$ and $Af = L(x)$. Argue that, for $y \in A$, $ey \in L(x)$ and so $ey = eyf$. Likewise show that $yf = eyf$. Deduce that $e = f$ and $ey = ye$ so that $e \in Z$.]

11.8. A Baer ring A is said to be *complete* if the right annihilator of each subset of A is a principal right ideal generated by an idempotent. Prove that the following statements are equivalent:

(1) A is complete;
(2) the left annihilator of each subset is a principal left ideal generated by an idempotent;
(3) $\mathscr{R}(A)$ is a complete lattice.

[*Hint*. Observe that for $M \subseteq A$ we have $R(M) = \bigcap_{m \in M} R(m)$.]

12. Baer semigroups

The crucial annihilator properties of a Baer ring are essentially properties of its multiplicative semigroup. For this reason it is natural to ask just how far one can go with some sort of semigroup analogue of a Baer ring. In the next few sections such a theory will be introduced. We begin by giving some definitions.

A non-empty subset M of a semigroup S is called a *right ideal* of S if and only if $x \in M \Rightarrow (\forall y \in S)\ xy \in M$, a *left ideal* if $x \in M \Rightarrow (\forall y \in S)$ $yx \in M$ and an *ideal* in case it is both a right and a left ideal. For each $x \in S$ and each $M \subseteq S$ we agree to write $xM = \{xy; y \in M\}$ and $Mx = \{yx; y \in M\}$. For each $x \in S$ we define xS to be the *principal right ideal generated by* x and likewise Sx to be the *principal left ideal generated by* x. We let PLI(S), PRI(S) denote the set of principal left, right ideals of S with both sets ordered by set inclusion.

Suppose now that K is a distinguished ideal of the semigroup S. If $M \subseteq S$, then we define the *left K-annihilator of M* by

$$L_K(M) = \{y \in S;\ (\forall m \in M)\ ym \in K\}.$$

Similarly, the *right K-annihilator of M* is defined to be

$$R_K(M) = \{y \in S;\ (\forall m \in M)\ my \in K\}.$$

In the case where $M = \{x\}$ we shall usually write $L_K(x)$ instead of $L_K(\{x\})$ and $R_K(x)$ instead of $R_K(\{x\})$. Clearly every left K-annihilator is a left ideal and every right K-annihilator is a right ideal of S.

Definition. A pair $\langle S; K\rangle$ is called a *Baer semigroup* if S is a semigroup and K is an ideal of S having the property that for each $x \in S$ there exist idempotents $e, f \in S$ such that $R_K(x) = eS$ and $L_K(x) = Sf$.

It is important to note that *uniqueness* of the idempotents is *not* being postulated. We need not have $e = f$ and there could well exist idempotents g, h such that $e \neq g, f \neq h$ but $eS = gS$ and $Sf = Sh$. However, it will be very useful to note that for idempotents e, f we have $y \in eS \Leftrightarrow y = ey$ and $y \in Sf \Leftrightarrow y = yf$.

Suppose now that $\langle S; K\rangle$ is a Baer semigroup and let $x \in K$. Then there exist idempotents e, f such that $R_K(x) = eS$ and $L_K(x) = Sf$. Since K is an ideal it is immediate that $S = eS = Sf$. Thus e is a left identity and f is a right identity for S. It follows easily from this that $e = f$ and is a two-sided identity for S; this we shall denote henceforth by 1. Note that $1x \in K \Leftrightarrow x1 \in K \Leftrightarrow x \in K$. It follows that if $R_K(1) = gS$ and $L_K(1) = Sh$, then $K = gS = Sh$. It is immediate that $g = h$ is an identity for K. Let us denote this by k so that we have $k = k^2$ and $K = kS = Sk$. Now $(\forall x \in S)$ $xk \in K \Rightarrow xk = kxk$ and likewise $kx \in K \Rightarrow kx = kxk$. We thus have $(\forall x \in S)\, kx = xk$. This proves that K is a principal ideal of S generated by an idempotent k which is *central* in the sense that it commutes with every element of S. For this reason, we shall henceforth speak of a Baer semigroup as being a pair $\langle S; k\rangle$ where S is a semigroup and k is a central idempotent of S having the property that for each $x \in S$ there exist idempotents e, f such that $R_k(x) = eS$ and $L_k(x) = Sf$ where we write $R_k(x)$ instead of $R_{kS}(x)$ and $L_k(x)$ instead of $L_{Sk}(x)$. The element k will be called the *focus* of S and the ideal kS the *focal ideal*. It will prove convenient to let $\mathscr{L}_k = \mathscr{L}_k(S) = \{L_k(x); x \in S\}$ and $\mathscr{R}_k = \mathscr{R}_k(S) = \{R_k(x); x \in S\}$ with both sets ordered by set inclusion. The symbols e, f, g, h with or without subscripts or superscripts will be used exclusively in connection with Baer semigroups to denote idempotents. It will at times prove useful to let e' denote an idempotent generator of $R_k(e)$ and $e^{\#}$ an idempotent generator of $L_k(e)$.

Before proceeding, we give some examples of Baer semigroups.

EXAMPLE 12.1. The multiplicative semigroup of any Baer ring; more generally, any subsemigroup M of the multiplicative semigroup of a Baer ring, provided that M contains all of the idempotents. In this case we have a Baer semigroup with focus 0.

EXAMPLE 12.2. Any semigroup with 0 and 1 having no proper zero divisors.

EXAMPLE 12.3. Let S be a pseudo-complemented semilattice. Then $\langle S; 0\rangle$ forms an abelian Baer semigroup with respect to multiplication defined by $xy = x \cap y$. Here every element is a central idempotent and for each $x \in S$ we have $R_0(x) = L_0(x) = x^*S$, where x^* denotes the pseudo-complement of x. This class of Baer semigroups will prove to be a useful source of examples and counter-examples.

EXAMPLE 12.4. Let X be a non-empty set and let $\mathrm{Rel}(X)$ denote the set of binary relations on X. Given $S, T \in \mathrm{Rel}(X)$, define $S \circ T$ by the prescription $x(S \circ T)y \Leftrightarrow (\exists z \in X)\, xTz$ and zSy. If $S \in \mathrm{Rel}(X)$ and $M \subseteq X$, define $S(M) = \{y \in X; (\exists x \in M)\, xSy\}$. We define the *domain* and *image* of a relation S by $\mathrm{Dom}\, S = S^t(X)$ and $\mathrm{Im}\, S = S(X)$, where S^t denotes the converse of S. For each subset M of X define I_M by $xI_My \Leftrightarrow x = y \in M$. Note that $I_M = I_M \circ I_M \in \mathrm{Rel}(X)$. Given S, T in $\mathrm{Rel}(X)$ and $M \subseteq X$, we point out that $(S \circ T)(M) = S[T(M)]$. We leave to the reader the routine verification that this operation turns $\mathrm{Rel}(X)$ into a semigroup whose zero element is the empty relation on X while we concentrate our efforts on showing that it is a Baer semigroup. Suppose first that $S \circ T = \emptyset$. If $z \in \mathrm{Im}\, T$ then we cannot have $z \in \mathrm{Dom}\, S$ and so $\mathrm{Im}\, T \subseteq [\mathrm{Dom}\, S]'$, the complement of the domain of S. If, on the other hand, $\mathrm{Im}\, T \subseteq [\mathrm{Dom}\, S]'$, it is clear that there can be no elements x, y such that $x(S \circ T)y$ and so $S \circ T = \emptyset$. Let us now observe that if $T = I_A \circ T$ then $\mathrm{Im}\, T = T(X) = I_A[T(X)] \subseteq I_A(X) = A$ while if $\mathrm{Im}\, T \subseteq A$ then $xTy \Rightarrow yI_Ay$ and so $T = I_A \circ T$. It is immediate that $R_\emptyset(S) = I_A \circ \mathrm{Rel}(X)$ with $A = [\mathrm{Dom}\, S]'$. Making use of the fact that $T \circ S = \emptyset \Leftrightarrow S^t \circ T^t = \emptyset$, a dual argument produces the fact that $L_\emptyset(S) = \mathrm{Rel}(X) \circ I_B$, where $B = [\mathrm{Dom}\, S^t]' = [\mathrm{Im}\, S]'$. Thus $\langle \mathrm{Rel}(X); \emptyset \rangle$ is a Baer semigroup.

We are now ready to develop some of the theory of Baer semigroups. *Until further notice, we shall be dealing with a Baer semigroup* $\langle S; k \rangle$. The proof of the first result is so similar to that of Theorem 11.1 that it will be omitted.

THEOREM 12.1. (1) *The mappings* $\hat{L}_k : \mathrm{PRI}(S) \to \mathrm{PLI}(S)$, $\hat{R}_k : \mathrm{PLI}(S) \to \mathrm{PRI}(S)$ *given by* $\hat{L}_k(xS) = L_k(x)$, $\hat{R}_k(Sx) = R_k(x)$ *set up a Galois connection;*

(2) $\hat{L}_k \circ \hat{R}_k \circ \hat{L}_k = \hat{L}_k$ *and* $\hat{R}_k \circ \hat{L}_k \circ \hat{R}_k = \hat{R}_k$;

(3) $xS \in \mathscr{R}_k \Leftrightarrow xS = (\hat{R}_k \circ L_k)(x)$ *and* $Sx \in \mathscr{L}_k \Leftrightarrow Sx = (\hat{L}_k \circ R)(x)$;

(4) $L_k^{\rightarrow}$, *the restriction of* $\hat{L}_k$ *to* $\mathscr{R}_k$, *is a dual isomorphism of* $\mathscr{R}_k$ *ontc* $\mathscr{L}_k$ *whose inverse is* $R_k^{\rightarrow}$, *the restriction of* $\hat{R}_k$ *to* $\mathscr{L}_k$.

It is important to note that the semigroup analogue of Theorem 11.1(6) is not true. A counter-example is provided by the three element chain $S = \{0, a, \pi\}$ with $0 < a < \pi$. As in Example 12.3, $\langle S; 0\rangle$ is a Baer semigroup. In this case we have $\mathscr{R}_0(S) = \{0S, \pi S\}$ and $a = a^2$ is an idempotent such that $aS \notin \mathscr{R}_0(S)$.

THEOREM 12.2. *Let* $eS, fS \in \mathscr{R}_k$, $Se^{\#} = L_k(e)$, $Sf^{\#} = L_k(f)$ *and* $gS = R_k(f^{\#}e)$. *Then* $eg = (eg)^2$ *and* $egS = R_k(\{e^{\#}, f^{\#}\})$.

Proof. Note first that $(f^{\#}e)(eg) = f^{\#}eg \in kS$ implies $eg \in R_k(f^{\#}e) = gS$ whence $eg = geg$ and so $eg = (eg)^2$. If $x \in R_k(\{e^{\#}, f^{\#}\})$, then $e^{\#}x \in kS \Rightarrow x \in R_k(e^{\#}) = (R_k^{\rightarrow} \circ L_k)(e) = eS \Rightarrow x = ex$ and so $f^{\#}ex = f^{\#}x \in kS$ puts x in $R_k(f^{\#}e) = gS$ and consequently $x = gx = egx$. If conversely $x = egx$ then $e^{\#}x = e^{\#}egx \in kS$ and $f^{\#}x = f^{\#}egx \in kS$ whence we have $x \in R_k(\{e^{\#}, f^{\#}\})$.

THEOREM 12.3. $\mathscr{R}_k(S)$ *and* $\mathscr{L}_k(S)$ *are bounded dually isomorphic lattices.*

Proof. kS is clearly the smallest element of both $\mathscr{R}_k$ and $\mathscr{L}_k$. With the same notation as in Theorem 12.2, it is clear that $eS, fS \in \mathscr{R}_k$ imply that $egS = R_k(\{e^{\#}, f^{\#}\})$ is the set-theoretic intersection of eS and fS. Now $egS \subseteq eS$ implies that $(R_k^{\rightarrow} \circ L_k)(eg) \subseteq (R_k^{\rightarrow} \circ L_k)(e) = eS$ and similarly $(R_k^{\rightarrow} \circ L_k)(eg) \subseteq fS$ forces $(R_k^{\rightarrow} \circ L_k)(eg) \subseteq egS$. It follows that $(R_k^{\rightarrow} \circ L_k)(eg) = egS$ so $egS = eS \cap fS$ in $\mathscr{R}_k(S)$. This shows that $\mathscr{R}_k$ is an $\cap$-semilattice with 0. A dual argument produces the fact that $\mathscr{L}_k$ is an $\cap$-semilattice with 0 and the theorem now follows by Theorem 12.1(4).

Remarks. (1) Note that while the intersection operation in $\mathscr{R}_k$ is set-theoretic, the union operation is generally *not* set-theoretic. Indeed, we have $eS \curlyvee fS = R_k(Se^{\#} \cap Sf^{\#})$. With notation as in Theorem 12.2, if $hS = R_k(e^{\#}f)$, then a symmetric argument will yield $fh = (fh)^2$ and $fhS = fS \cap eS$. We shall also have occasion to make use of the fact that $egS = eS \cap gS$ and $fhS = fS \cap hS$. This follows immediately from the equations $eg = geg$, $fh = hfh$.

(2) If $\langle S; k\rangle$ is a Baer semigroup and if the law of composition $\odot$ is defined on S by $x \odot y = yx$, then there results a new Baer semigroup $\langle S^*; k\rangle$ which we call the *dual* of $\langle S; k\rangle$. It is obvious that there exists a

natural isomorphism between $\mathscr{L}_k(S^*)$ and $\mathscr{R}_k(S)$ as well as between $\mathscr{R}_k(S^*)$ and $\mathscr{L}_k(S)$. Making use of this, we can dualize theorems involving $\mathscr{R}_k$ to corresponding results involving $\mathscr{L}_k$ by interchanging the rôles of the left and right annihilators and reversing all multiplications. As an example of this, we may dualize the above remarks as follows: let $Se, Sf \in \mathscr{L}_k$, $e'S = R_k(e), f'S = R_k(f)$, $Sg = L_k(ef')$ and $Sh = L_k(fe')$; then ge, hf are idempotents with

$$Se \cap Sf = Sg \cap Se = Sge = Sh \cap Sf = Shf.$$

We saw in the previous section that if A is a Baer ring, then $\mathscr{R}(A)$ is a bounded relatively complemented lattice. We now ask what properties are enjoyed by the lattice of right k-annihilators of a Baer semigroup $\langle S; k\rangle$. The answer is quite startling: *any bounded lattice is isomorphic to the lattice of right k-annihilators of some Baer semigroup* $\langle S; k\rangle$*!* In connection with this, it will prove convenient to say that the lattice L is *coordinatized* by the Baer semigroup $\langle S; k\rangle$, or that $\langle S; k\rangle$ is a *coordinatizing* Baer semigroup for L, in case L is isomorphic to $\mathscr{R}_k(S)$. It is at this point that we must return to a consideration of residuated mappings.

Let E be a bounded ordered set. Given $e \in E$ we leave to the reader the routine verification that the mappings $\alpha_e, \beta_e : E \to E$ described by

$$\alpha_e(x) = \begin{cases} e & \text{if } x \neq 0; \\ 0 & \text{if } x = 0, \end{cases} \qquad \beta_e(x) = \begin{cases} \pi & \text{if } x \nleq e; \\ 0 & \text{if } x \leq e, \end{cases}$$

are idempotent elements of Res(E) with associated residual maps given by

$$\alpha_e^+(x) = \begin{cases} \pi & \text{if } x \geq e; \\ 0 & \text{if } x \ngeq e, \end{cases} \qquad \beta_e^+(x) = \begin{cases} e & \text{if } x \neq \pi; \\ \pi & \text{if } x = \pi. \end{cases}$$

Likewise, if E is a lattice then the maps $\theta_e, \psi_e : E \to E$ described by

$$\theta_e(x) = \begin{cases} x & \text{if } x \leq e; \\ e & \text{if } x \nleq e, \end{cases} \qquad \psi_e(x) = \begin{cases} 0 & \text{if } x \leq e; \\ x \cup e & \text{if } x \nleq e, \end{cases}$$

are idempotent elements of Res(E) with associated residual maps given by

$$\theta_e^+(x) = \begin{cases} \pi & \text{if } x \geq e; \\ x \cap e & \text{if } x \ngeq e, \end{cases} \qquad \psi_e^+(x) = \begin{cases} x & \text{if } x \geq e; \\ e & \text{if } x \ngeq e. \end{cases}$$

For an arbitrary bounded ordered set E we have, by Theorem 2.11, that Res (E) is an ordered semigroup. The identity map serves as the multiplicative identity element and the zero map is the multiplicative zero element. When working with 0-annihilators in a semigroup with 0, we shall often omit the subscripts and write R in place of R_0, etc. Our immediate goal is to decide what it means for $\langle \mathrm{Res}(E); 0 \rangle$ to be a Baer semigroup.

THEOREM 12.4. *Let E be a bounded ordered set. Then in $S = \mathrm{Res}(E)$*

(1) $\theta \circ \varphi = 0$ *if and only if* $\varphi(\pi) \leq \theta^+(0)$;

(2) *if* $R(\theta) = \varphi \circ S$ *with* $\varphi = \varphi^2$ *then* $\varphi(\pi) = \theta^+(0)$.

Proof. (1) Since θ, φ are isotone $\theta \circ \varphi = 0$ if and only if $\theta\,[\varphi(\pi)] = 0$. It is clear from the definition of a residuated mapping that this is equivalent to $\varphi(\pi) \leq \theta^+(0)$.

(2) If $R(\theta) = \varphi \circ S$ with $\varphi = \varphi^2$, then by (1) we have $\varphi(\pi) \leq \theta^+(0)$. Now let $\alpha = \alpha_{\theta^+(0)}$ defined as above. We see that $\theta \circ \alpha = 0$ and so $\alpha = \varphi \circ \alpha$ whence $\theta^+(0) = \alpha(\pi) = \varphi\,[\alpha(\pi)] \leq \varphi(\pi)$ and hence $\varphi(\pi) = \theta^+(0)$.

THEOREM 12.5. *Let E be a bounded ordered set. If $\langle \mathrm{Res}(E); 0 \rangle$ is a Baer semigroup then E is a lattice and $\langle \mathrm{Res}(E); 0 \rangle$ coordinatizes E.*

Proof. Let $S = \mathrm{Res}(E)$ and let $L = \mathscr{R}(S)$. Then by Theorem 12.3 we know that L is a lattice. By the result of Theorem 12.4, we can define a mapping $f: L \to E$ by the prescription $f(\xi \circ S) = \xi(\pi)$, where ξ is an idempotent generator of $\xi \circ S$. Note that $\xi \circ S \leq \eta \circ S \Rightarrow \xi = \eta \circ \xi$ and so $\xi(\pi) = \eta\,[\xi(\pi)] \leq \eta(\pi)$. If, on the other hand, $\xi(\pi) \leq \eta(\pi)$ and if $\eta \circ S = R(\theta)$, then $\xi(\pi) \leq \eta(\pi) = \theta^+(0)$ implies $\xi \in R(\theta)$ and so $\xi \circ S \leq \eta \circ S$. We thus have $f(\xi \circ S) \leq f(\eta \circ S) \Leftrightarrow \xi \circ S \leq \eta \circ S$. It remains to show that f is surjective. Accordingly, let $x \in E$. Then $\beta_x \in S$ and if $R(\beta_x) = \varphi \circ S$ with $\varphi = \varphi^2$, then, by Theorem 12.4, $f(\varphi \circ S) = \varphi(\pi) = \beta_x^+(0) = x$.

THEOREM 12.6. *For a bounded ordered set E the following conditions are equivalent:*

(1) *E is a lattice;*

(2) $\mathrm{Res}(E)$ *is a Baer semigroup with focus* 0;

(3) *E can be coordinatized by a Baer semigroup.*

Proof. (1) ⇒ (2): If E is a lattice, then $(\forall x \in E)\ \theta_x, \psi_x \in \text{Res}(E)$. Given $\theta \in \text{Res}(E)$, recall that $\theta \circ \varphi = 0$ if and only if $\varphi(\pi) \leq \theta^+(0)$. If we let $x = \theta^+(0)$, then we see that $\varphi(\pi) \leq x \Rightarrow \varphi = \theta_x \circ \varphi$; and if $\varphi = \theta_x \circ \varphi$, then $\varphi(\pi) = \theta_x[\varphi(\pi)] \leq \theta_x(\pi) = x$. It follows immediately from this that $R(\theta) = \theta_x \circ \text{Res}(E)$. A dual argument in the semigroup $\text{Res}^+(E)$ will show that $R(\theta^+) = \psi_y^+ \circ \text{Res}^+(E)$ with $y = \theta(\pi)$. It follows from this that, in $\text{Res}(E)$, $L(\theta) = \text{Res}(E) \circ \psi_y$.

(2) ⇒ (3): immediate from Theorem 12.5.

(3) ⇒ (1): immediate from Theorem 12.3.

Although the coordinatization of a lattice by a Baer semigroup is highly non-unique, we shall show that $\text{Res}(L)$ is "universal" in the sense that if $\langle S; k\rangle$ is a Baer semigroup which coordinatizes L then $\text{Res}(L)$ contains a homomorphic image of $\langle S; k\rangle$ which is itself a Baer semigroup which coordinatizes L. The next few results serve to establish this. In order to simplify notation, we agree to identify L with $\mathscr{R}_k(S)$ when $\langle S; k\rangle$ coordinatizes L.

Let $\langle S; k\rangle$ be a Baer semigroup and let $L = \mathscr{R}_k(S)$. As we shall see, for each $x \in S$, we can define mappings $\varphi_x : L \to L$ and $\eta_x : \mathscr{L}_k(S) \to \mathscr{L}_k(S)$ by the prescriptions

$$\varphi_x(eS) = (R_k^{\rightarrow} \circ L_k)(xe) \quad (eS \in L);$$

$$\eta_x(Sf) = (L_k^{\rightarrow} \circ R_k)(fx) \quad (Sf \in \mathscr{L}_k(S)).$$

As in § 11, the mappings φ_x, η_x are related in the following way:

THEOREM 12.7. *For each* $x \in S$, $\varphi_x \in \text{Res}(L)$ *with* $\varphi_x^+ = R_k^{\rightarrow} \circ \eta_x \circ L_k^{\rightarrow}$ *and* $\eta_x \in \text{Res}(\mathscr{L})$ *with* $\eta_x^+ = L_k^{\rightarrow} \circ \varphi_x \circ R_k^{\rightarrow}$.

Proof. Let $eS \subseteq fS$ in L. Then $e = fe$, so if $yxf \in kS$ we must have $yxe = yxfe \in kS$ and $L_k(xe) \supseteq L_k(xf)$. It follows from this that the mapping φ_x is both well-defined and isotone. The remainder of the proof follows almost identically that of Theorem 11.8 and we leave it to the reader.

COROLLARY. *For each* $x \in S$, $\varphi_x \in \text{Res}(L)$ *with* $\varphi_x^+(eS) = R_k(e^{\#}x)$ *where* $eS \in L$ *and* $Se^{\#} = L_k(e)$.

Proof. $\varphi_x^+(eS) = (R_k^{\rightarrow} \circ \eta_x \circ L_k^{\rightarrow})(eS) = (R_k^{\rightarrow} \circ \eta_x)[L_k(e)] = (R_k^{\rightarrow} \circ \eta_x)(Se^{\#}) = R_k^{\rightarrow}[(L_k^{\rightarrow} \circ R_k)(e^{\#}x)] = R_k(e^{\#}x)$.

If S, T are semigroups and $f: S \to T$ is a homomorphism, then whenever T has a 0 we define the *kernel* of f to be the set $f^{\leftarrow}(0)$. Evidently, the kernel of f is an ideal of S.

THEOREM 12.8. *With notation as in Theorem 12.7, the mapping $x \to \varphi_x$ is a semigroup homomorphism from S to* $\mathrm{Res}(L)$ *with kernel kS. Furthermore, $\bar{S} = \{\varphi_x;\ x \in S\}$ is a Baer semigroup with focus* 0 *which coordinatizes L.*

Proof. (1) Let $eS \in L$, $x, y \in S$ and $gS = (R_k^{\rightarrow} \circ L_k)(ye)$. Then $L_k(g) = (L_k^{\rightarrow} \circ R_k \circ L_k)(ye) = L_k(ye)$ and so

$$axg \in kS \Leftrightarrow ax \in L_k(g) = L_k(ye) \Leftrightarrow a(xye) \in kS.$$

Thus $L_k(xg) = L_k(xye)$ and so

$$\begin{aligned}\varphi_x[\varphi_y(eS)] &= \varphi_x[(R_k^{\rightarrow} \circ L_k)(ye)] = \varphi_x(gS) = (R_k^{\rightarrow} \circ L_k)(xg)\\ &= (R_k^{\rightarrow} \circ L_k)(xye) = \varphi_{xy}(eS).\end{aligned}$$

We deduce from this that $\varphi_x \circ \varphi_y = \varphi_{xy}$ and so $x \to \varphi_x$ is indeed a semigroup homomorphism.

(2) We shall now show that kS is the kernel of $x \to \varphi_x$. Note first that if $x \in kS$ then $L_k(x) = S$ and so $(R_k^{\rightarrow} \circ L_k)(x) = kS$. Since $\varphi_x(eS) \subseteq \varphi_x(1S) = (R_k^{\rightarrow} \circ L_k)(x1) = (R_k^{\rightarrow} \circ L_k)(x) = kS$, it is immediate that φ_x is the zero mapping on L. If, conversely, $\varphi_x = 0$, then $\varphi_x(1S) = (R_k^{\rightarrow} \circ L_k)(x1) = (R_k^{\rightarrow} \circ L_k)(x) = kS$ puts $x \in kS$.

(3) Finally, let us show that $\langle \bar{S}; 0\rangle$ is a Baer semigroup which coordinatizes L. Let $\varphi_x \in \bar{S}$ with $eS = R_k(x)$ in $\langle S; k\rangle$. Then $\varphi_x \circ \varphi_y = 0 \Rightarrow \varphi_{xy} = 0 \Rightarrow xy \in kS \Rightarrow y = ey \Rightarrow \varphi_y = \varphi_e \circ \varphi_y$ in S. If, on the other hand, $\varphi_y = \varphi_e \circ \varphi_y$, then $\varphi_x \circ \varphi_y = \varphi_x \circ \varphi_e \circ \varphi_y = \varphi_{xey} = 0$ since $xey \in kS$. Hence in $\bar{S}$ we have $R(\varphi_x) = \varphi_e \circ \bar{S}$. A similar argument applies for left annihilators and so $\langle \bar{S}; 0\rangle$ is a Baer semigroup. To show that it coordinatizes L, it suffices to show that the mapping $eS \to \varphi_e \circ \bar{S}$ is an isomorphism of L onto $\mathscr{R}(\bar{S})$. If $eS \subseteq fS$ in L, then $e = fe$ and so $\varphi_e = \varphi_f \circ \varphi_e$ whence $\varphi_e \circ \bar{S} \subseteq \varphi_f \circ \bar{S}$. If now $\varphi_e \circ \bar{S} \subseteq \varphi_f \circ \bar{S}$, then $\varphi_e = \varphi_f \circ \varphi_e$ and so

$$(R_k^{\rightarrow} \circ L_k)(e) = \varphi_e(1S) = (\varphi_f \circ \varphi_e)(1S) \subseteq \varphi_f(1S) = (R_k^{\rightarrow} \circ L_k)(f).$$

Since $eS, fS \in L$ we deduce that $eS = (R_k^{\rightarrow} \circ L_k)(e) \subseteq (R_k^{\rightarrow} \circ L_k)(f) = fS$. Since we have already shown that for $\varphi_x \in \bar{S}$, $R(\varphi_x) = \varphi_e \circ \bar{S}$ where $eS = R_k(x)$ in $\langle S; k \rangle$, the mapping $eS \rightarrow \varphi_e \circ \bar{S}$ is indeed surjective. We conclude that it is an isomorphism.

By Theorem 12.6, *every* bounded lattice may be coordinatized by a Baer semigroup, while by Theorem 11.5 the lattice of right annihilators of elements of a Baer ring is complemented (indeed relatively complemented). It is natural to ask just what there is about a Baer ring that forces this difference. Our next result provides the answer: *for an idempotent e of a Baer ring A, $eA \in \mathscr{R}(A)$ and $Ae \in \mathscr{L}(A)$; this need not hold in a Baer semigroup.*

THEOREM 12.9. *Let $\langle S; k \rangle$ be a Baer semigroup, let $fS \in \mathscr{R}_k(S)$ and let $Sf \in \mathscr{L}_k(S)$. If $f'S = R_k(f)$ then fS and $f'S$ are complements in $\mathscr{R}_k(S)$ with $M(f'S, fS)$ and $M^*(fS, f'S)$ both true. Furthermore, for all $eS \in \mathscr{R}_k(S)$,*

$$\varphi_f(eS) = (eS \curlyvee f'S) \cap fS.$$

Proof. (1) Let $eS \subseteq fS$ so that $e = fe$. Setting $Se^{\#} = L_k(e)$ we see that $e^{\#}fe = e^{\#}e \in kS$ implies $e^{\#}f = e^{\#}fe^{\#}$. It follows that $e^{\#}f = (e^{\#}f)^2$ and $Se^{\#} \cap Sf = Se^{\#}f$. If $hS = R_k(e^{\#}f)$, then by Theorem 12.2 we have $fh = (fh)^2$ and $fhS = fS \cap hS = eS \cap fS$ [see the remarks following Theorem 12.3]. Hence

$$eS = eS \cap fS = hS \cap fS = R_k(e^{\#}f) \cap fS = [R_k^{\rightarrow}(Se^{\#} \cap Sf)] \cap fS$$
$$= (eS \curlyvee f'S) \cap fS.$$

Setting $e = 0$ we obtain $f'S \cap fS = 0S$ and $M(f'S, fS)$ follows.

(2) Setting $Sf^{\#} = L_k(f)$, a dual argument on $\mathscr{L}_k(S)$ will yield the fact that $Sf^{\#} \cap Sf = S0$ with $M(Sf^{\#}, Sf)$. Making use of the fact that $R_k^{\rightarrow}$ is a dual isomorphism of $\mathscr{L}_k$ onto $\mathscr{R}_k$ such that $R_k^{\rightarrow}(Sf^{\#}) = fS$ and $R_k^{\rightarrow}(Sf) = f'S$, it is immediate that $fS \curlyvee f'S = 1S$ with $M^*(fS, f'S)$.

(3) Recall that $\varphi_f(eS) = (R_k^{\rightarrow} \circ L_k)(fe)$. Let $Sg = L_k(fe)$, $Sf^{\#} = L_k(f)$ and $Se^{\#} = L_k(e)$. Then by the remarks following Theorem 12.3 we have $gf = gfg = (gf)^2$ and $Se^{\#} \cap Sf = Sg \cap Sf = Sgf$. Now $f^{\#}fe \in kS$ implies $f^{\#} \in Sg$ and so $Sf^{\#} \subseteq Sg$ and $g'S = R_k(g) \subseteq fS$. Using $M(f'S, fS)$

we conclude that

$$g'S = (g'S \curlyvee f'S) \cap fS = R_k^{\rightarrow}(Sg \cap Sf) \cap fS = R_k^{\rightarrow}(Se^{\#} \cap Sf) \cap fS$$
$$= (eS \curlyvee f'S) \cap fS.$$

Our next item of business is to investigate the various possible focal ideals of a Baer semigroup. In connection with this, the next result will be used often enough to warrant its presentation as a theorem.

THEOREM 12.10. *Let e be an idempotent element of the Baer semigroup* $\langle S; k \rangle$. *If* $R_k(xe) = fS$ *then* $ef = fef$. *Dually, if* $L_k(ex) = Sg$ *then* $ge = geg$.

Proof. $(xe)(ef) = xef \in kS \Rightarrow ef \in R_k(xe) = fS \Rightarrow ef = fef$.

THEOREM 12.11. *If* $\langle S; j \rangle$ *and* $\langle S; k \rangle$ *are Baer semigroups then so also is* $\langle S; jk \rangle$.

Proof. For $x \in S$ let $R_j(x) = eS$ and $R_k(xe) = fS$. Then by Theorem 12.10 we have $ef = fef$ and so ef is idempotent. If $y = efy$ then $y = ey$ and $xy = xey \in jS$ since $xe \in jS$. But now $xy = xefy \in kS$ since $fy \in R_k(xe)$. Hence $xy \in jkS$. If $xy \in jkS$, then $xy \in jS$ and $xy \in kS$. Now $xy \in jS$ implies $y = ey$ and then $xy = xey \in kS$ implies $y = fy$ and so $y = efy$. Hence we have $R_{jk}(x) = efS$ with $ef = (ef)^2$. A dual argument applies for left annihilators.

We now present the semigroup analogue of Exercise 11.1.

THEOREM 12.12. *Let e be an idempotent element of the Baer semigroup* $\langle S; k \rangle$. *Then* $\langle eSe; ek \rangle$ *is a Baer semigroup with* $\mathcal{R}_{ek}(eSe)$ *isomorphic to the set of fixed points of the residuated map* φ_e *induced on* $\mathcal{R}_k(S)$ *by e.*

Proof. (1) Let $T = eSe$, let $x \in T$ and let $R_k(x) = fS$. Note that for $y \in T$,

$$xy \in ekT \Rightarrow xy \in kS \Rightarrow y = fy \Rightarrow y = efey;$$

$$y = efey \Rightarrow xy = xefey = xfey \in kS \Rightarrow xy \in ekT.$$

Since $xefe = xfe \in ekT$, it is immediate that, in T,

$$R_{ek}(x) = efeT \quad \text{with} \quad efe = (efe)^2.$$

Dually, if $L_k(x) = Sg$, then $L_{ek}(x) = Tege$ with $ege = (ege)^2$. Thus $\langle T; ek \rangle$ is a Baer semigroup.

(2) Let $fT \in \mathscr{R}_{ek}(T)$ and $hS = (R_k^{\rightarrow} \circ L_k)(f)$ in S. Then $L_k(f) = L_k(h)$ and so

$$xh \in kS \Leftrightarrow xf \in kS \Leftrightarrow xef \in kS \Leftrightarrow xeh \in kS.$$

Thus $L_k(h) = L_k(eh)$ and $\varphi_e(hS) = (R_k^{\rightarrow} \circ L_k)(eh) = (R_k^{\rightarrow} \circ L_k)(h) = hS$. Thus hS is a fixed point of φ_e. If $fT \subseteq gT$ then $f = gf$ implies $L_k(g) \subseteq L_k(f)$ and so $(R_k^{\rightarrow} \circ L_k)(f) \subseteq (R_k^{\rightarrow} \circ L_k)(g)$. If, conversely, $fT, gT \in \mathscr{R}_{ek}(T)$ with $(R_k^{\rightarrow} \circ L_k)(f) \subseteq (R_k^{\rightarrow} \circ L_k)(g)$ then $L_k(g) \subseteq L_k(f)$ in S and so, for $y \in T$, $yg \in ekT \Rightarrow yf \in kS \Rightarrow yf \in kT$. Thus, in T, $L_{ek}(g) \subseteq L_{ek}(f)$ and so $fT = (R_{ek}^{\rightarrow} \circ L_{ek})(f) \subseteq (R_{ek}^{\rightarrow} \circ L_{ek})(g) = gT$.

(3) The proof would be complete if we could show that the mapping described by $fT \rightarrow (R_k^{\rightarrow} \circ L_k)(f)$ is *onto* the set of fixed points of φ_e. For this purpose, let $\varphi_e(fS) = (R_k^{\rightarrow} \circ L_k)(ef) = fS$. Then $ef \subseteq fS$ implies $ef = fef$ and $L_k(ef) = L_k(f)$. Let $Sf^{\#} = L_k(f)$. Then $f^{\#}ef = f^{\#}fef \in kS$ implies $f^{\#}e = f^{\#}ef^{\#}$. We claim that in T we have $R_{ek}(ef^{\#}e) = efeT$. To see this, note that for $y \in T$,

$$\begin{aligned} ef^{\#}ey \in ekT \Rightarrow ef^{\#}y \in ekT \Rightarrow f^{\#}ef^{\#}y = f^{\#}\ ey = f^{\#}y \in kS \\ \Rightarrow y \in R_k(f^{\#}) = fS \\ \Rightarrow y = fy = efey. \end{aligned}$$

Since $(ef^{\#}e)(efe) = e(f^{\#}e)(fe) = ef^{\#}ef^{\#}fe \in ekT$, we see that $efe = (efe)^2$ and $R_{ek}(ef^{\#}e) = efeT$, so $efeT \in \mathscr{R}_{ek}(T)$. Now for $y \in S$,

$$yf \in kS \Rightarrow yef \in kS \Rightarrow yefe \in kS;$$

$$yefe \in kS \Rightarrow yefef \in kS \Rightarrow yeef = yef \in kS \Rightarrow yf \in kS.$$

Hence

$$fS = (R_k^{\rightarrow} \circ L_k)(fS) = (R_k^{\rightarrow} \circ L_k)(efe).$$

We close this section by presenting two final examples of Baer semigroups.

EXAMPLE 12.5. Let V be a left vector space over a division ring D. By a *semilinear transformation* of V we shall mean a pair (s', s'') where

(1) s' is an automorphism of D;
(2) $s'' : V \to V$;
(3) $(\forall x, y \in V)\ s''(x + y) = s''(x) + s''(y)$;
(4) $(\forall \lambda \in D)\ (\forall x \in V)\ s''(\lambda x) = s'(\lambda)\, s''(x)$.

If $s = (s', s'')$ and $t = (t', t'')$ are semilinear transformations on V, we define their product by $st = (s' \circ t', s'' \circ t'')$. Note that $k = (\mathrm{id}, 0)$ is a central idempotent element for this law. Note also that every linear transformation s may be identified naturally with the semilinear transformation (id, s); and that if $t = (t', t'')$ is any semilinear transformation then for any subspace M of V both $t''^{\rightarrow}(M)$ and $t''^{\leftarrow}(M)$ are subspaces. By an argument similar to that given in Example 11.3, we can show that the set of semilinear transformations of V forms with respect to the focus k a Baer semigroup which coordinatizes the lattice of all subspaces of V.

As a preliminary to the next example, we consider a T_1-topological space $(X, \mathscr{T})$. The reader will no doubt recall that a T_1-topological space is one in which every singleton subset is closed. It is easy to show that the set $L(X)$ of closed subsets of X, when ordered by set inclusion, forms a complete atomistic distributive lattice; furthermore, the union and intersection operations in $L(X)$ are both set-theoretic [for finite subsets of $L(X)$]. Given $A \subseteq X$ let us agree to write A^- for the closure of A. If R is a binary relation on X we can define a mapping $\eta_R : L(X) \to L(X)$ by the prescription $\eta_R(M) = [\xi_R(M)]^-$, where $\xi_R(M)$ is defined as in Exercise 4.15. By Exercise 5.9, η_R is residuated if and only if, for each $A \in L(X)$, the set $(\imath \circ \xi_{R^t} \circ \imath)(A)$ contains a largest closed subset of X. By the T_1 axiom, this clearly forces $(\imath \circ \xi_{R^t} \circ \imath)(A)$ to be closed. We thus have

$$\begin{aligned} \eta_R \text{ residuated} &\Leftrightarrow \{A \text{ closed} \Rightarrow (\imath \circ \xi_{R^t} \circ \imath)(A) \text{ closed}\} \\ &\Leftrightarrow \{B \text{ open} \Rightarrow (\imath \circ \xi_{R^t})(B) \text{ closed}\} \\ &\Leftrightarrow \{B \text{ open} \Rightarrow R^t(B) \text{ open}\}. \end{aligned}$$

This suggests that relations R having the property that B open $\Rightarrow R^t(B)$ open might be of some interest and leads us to:

EXAMPLE 12.6. Let $(X, \mathscr{T})$ be a topological space. We shall call a relation R on X *continuous* if it satisfies the property B open $\Rightarrow R^t(B)$ open. Let $\mathrm{CR}(X)$ denote the set of all continuous relations on X. With respect to the law of composition introduced in Example 12.4, $\mathrm{CR}(X)$ clearly forms a semigroup whose zero element is the empty relation $\emptyset$. For an arbitrary subset A of X, it will prove convenient to denote the closure mapping $A \to A^-$ by writing $\mathrm{Cl}(A)$ for A^-. Then, with notation as in Example 12.4 we see that for $S, T \in \mathrm{CR}(X)$,

$$S \circ T = \emptyset \Leftrightarrow \mathrm{Im}\, T \subseteq \text{¡}(\mathrm{Dom}\, S) \Leftrightarrow \mathrm{Cl}(\mathrm{Im}\, T) \subseteq \text{¡}(\mathrm{Dom}\, S)$$

$$\Leftrightarrow \mathrm{Dom}\, S \subseteq (\text{¡} \circ \mathrm{Cl})(\mathrm{Im}\, T).$$

Note that for A open, I_A is continuous and

$$\mathrm{Dom}\, S \subseteq A \Leftrightarrow (xSy \Rightarrow x \in A) \Leftrightarrow S = S \circ I_A.$$

Thus with $A = (\text{¡} \circ \mathrm{Cl})(\mathrm{Im}\, T)$ we have $S \circ T = \emptyset \Leftrightarrow S = S \circ I_A$ and so $L_\emptyset(T) = \mathrm{CR}(X) \circ I_A$.

Before examining the right $\emptyset$-annihilator of T it will prove convenient to introduce another class of continuous relations. If B is open, define J_B by

$$xJ_By \Leftrightarrow \begin{cases} \text{either} & x \notin B \quad \text{and} \quad x = y \\ \text{or} & x \in B \quad \text{and} \quad y \notin B. \end{cases}$$

Note that $\mathrm{Dom}\, J_B = X$ and $\mathrm{Im}\, J_B = \text{¡}(B)$. If M is open and $M \subseteq B$ then $J_B^t(M) = \emptyset$; and if there is an element $y \in M \cap \text{¡}(B)$, then xJ_By for all $x \in B$ and yJ_By. It follows that $J_B^t(M) = [M \cap \text{¡}(B)] \cup B = M \cup B$ which is open. [Note that the operations here are set-theoretic union and intersection.] This shows that $J_B \in \mathrm{CR}(X)$. The most important fact that we shall require about J_B is that

$$S = J_B \circ S \Leftrightarrow \mathrm{Im}\, S \subseteq \text{¡}(B). \qquad (*)$$

To see this, we first assume that $\mathrm{Im}\, S \subseteq \text{¡}(B)$. Then $xSy \Rightarrow y \notin B \Rightarrow yJ_By \Rightarrow x\,(J_B \circ S)\,y$, and if $x\,(J_B \circ S)\,y$, then for some $z \in X$ we must have xSz and zJ_By. But xSz implies $z \notin B$ and then zJ_By forces $z = y$ and so xSy. Hence if $\mathrm{Im}\, S \subseteq \text{¡}(B)$, then $S = J_B \circ S$. On the other hand, if $S = J_B \circ S$, then

$$\operatorname{Im} S = S(X) = (J_B \circ S)(X) = J_B[S(X)] \subseteq J_B(X) = \operatorname{Im} J_B = ¡(B).$$

Since $\operatorname{Im} J_B = ¡(B)$, it is immediate that $J_B = J_B \circ J_B$.

Let us now return to our continuous relation T. We know that $T \circ S = \emptyset$ if and only if $\operatorname{Im} S \subseteq ¡\,(\operatorname{Dom} T)$. Set $B = \operatorname{Dom} T$, which is open since T is continuous. Then by (*) we have

$$T \circ S = \emptyset \Leftrightarrow \operatorname{Im} S \subseteq ¡(B) \Leftrightarrow S = J_B \circ S$$

and so $R_\emptyset(T) = J_B \circ \mathrm{CR}\,(X)$. We have thus shown that $\langle \mathrm{CR}\,(X); \emptyset \rangle$ is a Baer semigroup.

Our final goal is to show that $\langle \mathrm{CR}\,(X); \emptyset \rangle$ coordinatizes $L(X)$, the lattice of closed subsets of X. We define $f : \mathscr{R}_\emptyset \to L(X)$ by the prescription $f(J_B \circ \mathrm{CR}\,(X)) = ¡(B)$ and note that, by (*),

$$J_B \circ \mathrm{CR}\,(X) \subseteq J_A \circ \mathrm{CR}\,(X) \Leftrightarrow J_B = J_A \circ J_B \Leftrightarrow ¡(B) \subseteq ¡(A).$$

We would therefore be done if we could show that f mapped $\mathscr{R}_\emptyset$ onto $L(X)$. Now if $M \in L(X)$ and $B = ¡(M)$, then $I_B \in \mathrm{CR}\,(X)$ with $R_\emptyset(I_B) = J_B \circ \mathrm{CR}\,(X)$ and $f(J_B \circ \mathrm{CR}\,(X)) = ¡(B) = M$. This completes the proof.

EXERCISES

12.1. Let E be a bounded ordered set. Show that the right 0-annihilator of every element of Res (E) is a principal order ideal of Res (E). [*Hint.* use Theorem 12.4(1).]

12.2. Let E be a bounded ordered set. Show that the mapping of Res (E) to E given by $\varphi \to \varphi(\pi)$ is residuated with $x \to \alpha_x$ the associated residual map.

12.3. Call a Baer semigroup $\langle S; k \rangle$ *complete* if the right k-annihilator of every subset of S is a principal right ideal generated by an idempotent. Show that if $\langle S; k \rangle$ is complete then the left k-annihilator of every subset of S is a principal left ideal generated by an idempotent. [*Hint.* Use the fact that $L_k^{\rightarrow} = L_k^{\rightarrow} \circ R_k^{\rightarrow} \circ L_k^{\rightarrow}$ and $R_k^{\rightarrow} = R_k^{\rightarrow} \circ L_k^{\rightarrow} \circ R_k^{\rightarrow}$.] Show further that the following three conditions are equivalent:

(1) E is a complete lattice;
(2) $\langle \mathrm{Res}\,(E); 0 \rangle$ is a complete Baer semigroup;
(3) E can be coordinatized by a complete Baer semigroup.

[*Hint*. It is useful to observe that for a subset M of a Baer semigroup S, $x \in R_k(M) \Leftrightarrow (\forall m \in M)\ x \in R_k(m)$.]

12.4. Let $\langle S; k \rangle$ be a Baer semigroup. Define a relation R on S by setting $xRy \Leftrightarrow (x = y$ or $x, y \in kS)$. Show that R is an equivalence relation on S which is compatible with multiplication. Show also that S/R has a zero element and that $\langle S/R; 0 \rangle$ is a Baer semigroup whose lattice of right 0-annihilators is isomorphic to $\mathscr{R}_k(S)$.

12.5. Let e, f be idempotent elements of the semigroup S and suppose that $ef = fe$. Show that if $\langle eSe; j \rangle$ and $\langle fSf; k \rangle$ are each Baer semigroups then so also is $\langle efSef; jk \rangle$. [*Hint*. Use Theorems 12.11 and 12.12.]

12.6. Let $(X, \mathscr{T})$ be a T_1-topological space. With notation as in the remark preceding Example 12.6, show that the mapping $R \to \eta_R$ is a semigroup homomorphism of CR (X) *onto* Res $[L(X)]$. [*Hint*. To show that the mapping is a homomorphism, it may be more convenient to work with the associated residual maps. To show that the mapping is onto, let $\varphi \in$ Res $[L(X)]$ and define R by $xRy \Leftrightarrow y \in \varphi^{\to}(\{x\})$. Argue that for A open, $R^t(A) = (\imath \circ \varphi^+ \circ \imath)(A)$ and so R is continuous. Finally, use the fact that η_R and φ agree on the atoms of $L(X)$ to deduce that they are equal.]

12.7. Let $\langle S; k \rangle$ be a Baer semigroup with $L = \mathscr{R}_k(S)$. Then the set $\mathscr{L} = \{R_k^{\to}(M); M \subseteq S\}$ is a complete lattice when ordered by set inclusion. Show that $\mathscr{L}$ is isomorphic to $\bar{L}$ the MacNeille completion of L. [*Hint*. Given $M \in \mathscr{L}$ define $\varphi(M) = \{(R_k^{\to} \circ L_k)(x); x \in M\}$. Then $\varphi : \mathscr{L} \to \bar{L}$ is the desired isomorphism with φ^{-1} given by $\varphi^{-1}(J) = \{x \in S; (R_k^{\to} \circ L_k)(x) \in J\}$ for all $J \in \bar{L}$. The key item in proving this is the observation that, for $x, y \in S$,

$$yx \in kS \Leftrightarrow \varphi_y \circ \varphi_x = 0 \Leftrightarrow \varphi_x(\pi) \leq \varphi_y^+(0) \Leftrightarrow (R_k^{\to} \circ L_k)(x) \subseteq R_k(y).$$

Hence $y \in L_k(M) \Leftrightarrow R_k(y)$ is an upper bound for $\varphi(M)$.]

13. Range-closed residuated mappings

We turn now to the study of an extremely important class of residuated mappings, the consideration of which will be intimately related to the notions of modularity in a lattice. Let P, Q be ordered sets. A mapping $f \in$ Res (P, Q) will be called *range-closed* if Im f is an (order) ideal of Q. Dually, we say that f is *dually range-closed* if Im f^+ is a filter of P. Finally, we shall say that f is *weakly regular* if it is both range-closed and dually range-closed.

We begin with a characterization of range-closed residuated mappings between bounded ordered sets, the unbounded case being left for consideration in the exercises.

THEOREM 13.1. *Let P, Q be bounded ordered sets. For $f \in \text{Res}(P, Q)$ the following conditions are equivalent:*

(1) *f is range-closed;*
(2) *the restriction of f to $[f^+(0), \pi]$ is a surjection onto $[0, f(\pi)]$;*
(3) *$(\forall q \in Q)\ q \cap f(\pi)$ exists and equals $(f \circ f^+)(q)$;*
(4) *the restriction of f^+ to $[0, f(\pi)]$ is injective.*

Proof. (1) ⇒ (2): Let f be range-closed. Then if $q \leq f(\pi)$ we have $q = f(p)$ for some $p \in P$ and so $q = f(p) = (f \circ f^+ \circ f)(p) = f[(f^+ \circ f)(p)]$ with $(f^+ \circ f)(p) \geq f^+(0)$.

(2) ⇒ (3): Clearly $(f \circ f^+)(q) \leq q$ and $(f \circ f^+)(q) \leq f(\pi)$. Suppose that $q_1 \leq q$ and $q_1 \leq f(\pi)$, then $q_1 = f(p_1)$ for some $p_1 \in P$ and

$$q_1 = f(p_1) = (f \circ f^+ \circ f)(p_1) = (f \circ f^+)[f(p_1)] \leq (f \circ f^+)(q)$$

since $f(p_1) = q_1 \leq q$.

(3) ⇒ (4): Suppose that $q_1, q_2 \leq f(\pi)$ and $f^+(q_1) = f^+(q_2)$. Then

$$q_1 = q_1 \cap f(\pi) = (f \circ f^+)(q_1) = (f \circ f^+)(q_2) = q_2 \cap f(\pi) = q_2.$$

(4) ⇒ (1): Let $q \leq f(\pi)$. Then $f^+(q) = f^+[(f \circ f^+)(q)]$ implies that $q = (f \circ f^+)(q)$ and so $q \in \text{Im} f$.

The dual of the previous result is as follows:

THEOREM 13.1*. *Let P, Q be bounded ordered sets. For $f \in \text{Res}(P, Q)$ the following conditions are equivalent:*

(1) *f is dually range-closed;*
(2) *the restriction of f^+ to $[0, f(\pi)]$ is a surjection onto $[f^+(0), \pi]$;*
(3) *$(\forall p \in P)\ p \cup f^+(0)$ exists and equals $(f^+ \circ f)(p)$;*
(4) *the restriction of f to $[f^+(0), \pi]$ is injective.*

Before proceeding, we give our usual consideration to a few examples.

EXAMPLE 13.1. If L is a bounded lattice then for each $e \in L$ the mapping θ_e is range-closed while ψ_e is dually range-closed (see the definitions immediately preceding Theorem 12.4). Thus in $\text{Res}(E)$ we see that the right annihilator of each element is a principal right ideal generated by a range-closed idempotent, while its left annihilator is a principal left ideal generated by a dually range-closed idempotent.

EXAMPLE 13.2. Let a, b denote fixed elements of a lattice L with $a \neq b$. Define $f: [a \cap b, b] \to [a, a \cup b]$ by the prescription $f(x) = x \cup a$. Then f is residuated with $f^+ : [a, a \cup b] \to [a \cap b, b]$ given by $f^+(y) = y \cap b$. To see this, one merely notes that

$$(\forall x \in [a \cap b, b]) \quad (f^+ \circ f)(x) = (x \cup a) \cap b \geq x;$$

$$(\forall y \in [a, a \cup b]) \quad (f \circ f^+)(y) = (y \cap b) \cup a \leq y.$$

Note now that if $M^*(a, b)$ holds then for each $y \in [a, a \cup b]$ we have $(f \circ f^+)(y) = y$ and so f is range-closed. Conversely, if f is range-closed, then for $y \in [a, a \cup b]$ we have $(f \circ f^+)(y) = y \cap f(b) = y$ and so $y = (y \cap b) \cup a$. Then if $w \geq a$ we have $w \cap (a \cup b) \in [a, a \cup b]$ and $w \cap (a \cup b) = [w \cap (a \cup b) \cap b] \cup a = (w \cap b) \cup a$, thus showing that $M^*(b, a)$ holds. Dually, we can show that f is dually range-closed if and only if $M(a, b)$.

EXAMPLE 13.3. Let V be a left vector space over a division ring D. Let $s = (s', s'')$ be a semilinear transformation of V. As in Exercise 2.11, the induced map $s''^{\to} : L(V) \to L(V)$ is residuated with residual given by $s''^{\leftarrow}$. We leave to the reader the routine verification that

$$(s''^{\leftarrow} \circ s''^{\to})(M) = M + s''^{\leftarrow}(0) \quad \text{and} \quad (s''^{\to} \circ s''^{\leftarrow})(M) = M \cap S''^{\to}(V)$$

for each subspace M of V. This shows that $s''^{\to}$ is weakly regular.

EXAMPLE 13.4. Let V be as in the preceding example but suppose now that there is a closure map f on $L(V)$ such that every subspace of dimension at most one is closed. Let L be the lattice formed by the "closed" subspaces of V; i.e. those subspaces M such that $f(M) = M$. Suppose that the semilinear transformation $s = (s', s'')$ is *continuous* in the sense that M closed implies $s''^{\leftarrow}(M)$ closed. By Exercise 5.9(a) the mapping $\xi_s : L \to L$ defined by $\xi_s(M) = (f \circ s''^{\to})(M)$ is residuated. We claim that ξ_s is range-closed if and only if the image of s [in other words $s''^{\to}(V)$] is closed. [*Remark*. It is essentially from this example that the terminology "range-closed" originated.] To see this, assume first that $s''^{\to}(V)$ is closed. Then for $M \in L$,

$$(\xi_s \circ \xi_s^+)(M) = (f \circ s''^{\rightarrow} \circ s''^{\leftarrow})(M) = f[M \cap s''^{\rightarrow}(V)] = M \cap s''^{\rightarrow}(V)$$
$$= M \cap (f \circ s''^{\rightarrow})(V)$$
$$= M \cap \xi_s(V),$$

and so the mapping ξ_s is range-closed. Assume next that $s''^{\rightarrow}(V)$ is not closed. Choose x such that $x \in \xi_s(V)$ but $x \notin s''^{\rightarrow}(V)$. Then there is no element y such that $s''(y) = x$ and so if M is the subspace generated by x we cannot have $\xi_s(N) = M$ for any $N \in L$. This shows that ξ_s is not range closed.

Returning now to the development of the theory of these mappings, we have as an immediate consequence of Theorems 13.1 and 13.1* the following:

THEOREM 13.2. *Let P, Q be bounded ordered sets. If f is a weakly regular element of* Res (P, Q) *then the restriction of f to $[f^+(0), \pi]$ is an isomorphism onto $[0, f(\pi)]$; furthermore, $(\forall p \in P)\ p \cup f^+(0)$ exists and $(\forall q \in Q)\ q \cap f(\pi)$ exists.*

Remark. The converse of the above theorem is also true. Suppose that $x \in P$, $y \in Q$ are such that $(\forall p \in P)\ (\forall q \in Q)$ both $p \cup x$ and $q \cap y$ exist. Suppose further that $f\colon [x, \pi] \to [0, y]$ is an isomorphism. Define mappings $g : P \to Q$, $h : Q \to P$ by the prescriptions $g(p) = f(x \cup p)$, $h(q) = f^{-1}(y \cap q)$. Note now that

$$(\forall p \in P)\ \ (h \circ g)(p) = h[f(x \cup p)] = (f^{-1} \circ f)(x \cup p)$$
$$= x \cup p \geq x;$$
$$(\forall q \in Q)\ \ (g \circ h)(q) = g[f^{-1}(y \cap q)] = (f \circ f^{-1})(y \cap q)$$
$$= y \cap q \leq y.$$

It follows that g is a weakly regular element of Res (P, Q) with $h = g^+$.

Let us now turn our attention to idempotent range-closed residuated maps.

THEOREM 13.3. *Let P be a bounded lattice and let $f \in \mathrm{Res}(P)$ be a range-closed idempotent. Then $f^+(0) \cap f(\pi) = 0$ and $M(f^+(0), f(\pi))$ holds.*

Proof. We note that for $x \leq f(\pi)$ we have $f(x) = x$ and so

$$x = f(x) = (f \circ f^+ \circ f)(x) = (f \circ f^+ \circ f^+ \circ f)(x) \geq (f \circ f^+)[x \cup f^+(0)]$$
$$= [x \cup f^+(0)] \cap f(\pi) \geq x.$$

Thus $x \leq f(\pi)$ implies $x = [x \cup f^+(0)] \cap f(\pi)$. With $x = 0$ this establishes $0 = f^+(0) \cap f(\pi)$ and consequently $M(f^+(0), f(\pi))$.

Remark. If P is a bounded ordered set and $f \in \mathrm{Res}(P)$ has the property that $f(\pi)$ is an atom then f is clearly range-closed. This observation suffices to yield examples showing that for a range-closed idempotent map f in $\mathrm{Res}(P)$ none of the following conditions need hold:

$$M(f(\pi), f^+(0)); \quad M^*(f(\pi), f^+(0)); \quad M^*(f^+(0), f(\pi)).$$

For example, consider the lattice L described by the following Hasse diagram

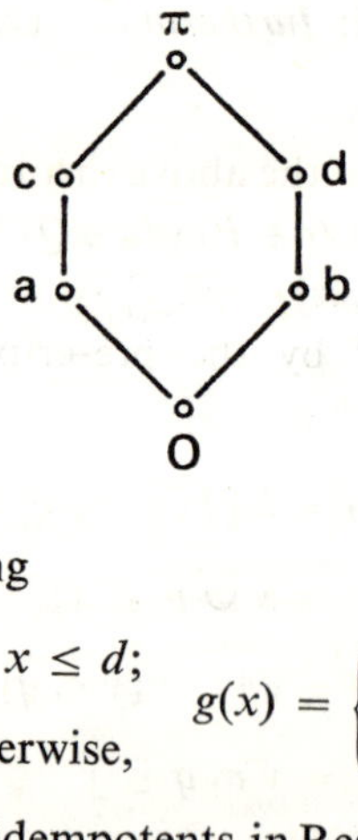

Define $f, g : L \to L$ by setting

$$f(x) = \begin{cases} 0 & \text{if } x \leq d; \\ a & \text{otherwise,} \end{cases} \qquad g(x) = \begin{cases} 0 & \text{if } x \leq b; \\ a & \text{otherwise.} \end{cases}$$

Then f, g are range-closed idempotents in $\mathrm{Res}(L)$ with $f(\pi) = g(\pi) = a$, $f^+(0) = d$ and $g^+(0) = b$. Note, however, that $M(a, d)$, $M^*(a, b)$ and $M^*(b, a)$ all fail to hold. For the weakly regular case, the following theorem provides a more gratifying result.

THEOREM 13.4. Let L *be a bounded lattice and let* $f \in \mathrm{Res}(L)$. *The following are necessary and sufficient conditions that* f *be a weakly regular idempotent:*

(1) $f^+(0)$ *and* $f(\pi)$ *are complements in* L;

(2) $M(f^+(0), f(\pi))$ *and* $M^*(f(\pi), f^+(0))$ *hold;*

(3) $(\forall x \in L)\, f(x) = [x \cup f^+(0)] \cap f(\pi)$.

Proof. Suppose first that $a, b \in L$ are such that $a \cup b = \pi$ and $a \cap b = 0$ with $M(a, b)$ and $M^*(b, a)$ both true. Define f and g by setting $f(x) = (x \cup a) \cap b$ and $g(x) = (x \cap b) \cup a$. Then by $M^*(b, a)$ we have

$$(g \circ f)(x) = g[(x \cup a) \cap b] = [(x \cup a) \cap b] \cup a = (x \cup a) \cap (b \cup a)$$
$$= x \cup a \geq a$$

and by $M(a, b)$ we have

$$(f \circ g)(x) = f[(x \cap b) \cup a] = [(x \cap b) \cup a] \cap b = (x \cap b) \cup (a \cap b)$$
$$= x \cap b \leq x.$$

It follows that $f \in \mathrm{Res}(L)$ with $g = f^+$. Also, by Theorems 13.1 and 13.1*, f is weakly regular. Since $x \leq b$ implies that $x = f(x)$, we see that f is idempotent.

Suppose now that $f \in \mathrm{Res}(L)$ is a weakly regular idempotent. Then, by Theorem 13.3, $f^+(0) \cap f(\pi) = 0$ with $M(f^+(0), f(\pi))$. By the dual of Theorem 13.3 we also have $f(\pi) \cup f^+(0) = \pi$ and $M^*(f(\pi), f^+(0))$. Note finally that

$$(\forall x \in L) \quad f(x) = (f \circ f^+ \circ f)(x) = (f \circ f^+ \circ f^+ \circ f)(x)$$
$$= (f \circ f^+)[x \cup f^+(0)]$$
$$= [x \cup f^+(0)] \cap f(\pi).$$

Here we have invoked Theorems 13.1 and 13.1*.

We shall now introduce a strengthened version of the range-closed notion. We shall say that $f \in \mathrm{Res}(P, Q)$ is *totally range-closed* if and only if the image under f of every principal ideal of P is a principal ideal of Q. Similarly, we say that $f \in \mathrm{Res}(P, Q)$ is *dually totally range-closed* if the image under f^+ of every principal filter of Q is a principal filter of P. Finally, we shall say that $f \in \mathrm{Res}(P, Q)$ is *strongly range-closed* whenever it is both totally and dually totally range-closed. Once again we consider the bounded case, leaving the unbounded case to the exercises.

THEOREM 13.5. *Let* L *be a bounded lattice and let* $f \in \mathrm{Res}(L)$. *The following conditions are then equivalent:*

(1) *f is totally range-closed;*
(2) *g range-closed $\Rightarrow f \circ g$ range-closed;*
(3) *for each $x \in L$ there exists a range-closed idempotent $g_x \in \mathrm{Res}(L)$ such that $g_x(\pi) = x$ and $f \circ g_x$ is range-closed;*
(4) *for each $x \in L$ there exists a range-closed element $g_x \in \mathrm{Res}(L)$ such that $g_x(\pi) = x$ and $f \circ g_x$ is range-closed;*
(5) $(\forall x, y \in L)\, f[f^+(x) \cap y] = x \cap f(y)$.

Proof. (1) $\Rightarrow$ (2): Let $g \in \mathrm{Res}(L)$ be range-closed and let $x = g(\pi)$. Then $f^{\rightarrow}[0, x] = [0, f(x)] = [0, (f \circ g)(\pi)]$. Now if $y \leq (f \circ g)(\pi) = f(x)$ then we must have $y = f(w)$ for some $w \leq x$. Since g is range-closed, $w \leq x = g(\pi)$ implies that $w = g(v)$ for some $v \in L$. Hence $y = (f \circ g)(v)$ and so $f \circ g$ is range-closed.

(2) $\Rightarrow$ (3): Take $g_x = \theta_x$ (defined immediately before Theorem 12.4).

(3) $\Rightarrow$ (4): Clear.

(4) $\Rightarrow$ (5): Let $g_y \in \mathrm{Res}(L)$ be range-closed with $g_y(\pi) = y$. Making use of Theorem 13.1, we may then write

$$\begin{aligned} f[f^+(x) \cap y] = f[f^+(x) \cap g_y(\pi)] &= (f \circ g_y \circ g_y^+ \circ f^+)(x) \\ &= [(f \circ g_y) \circ (f \circ g_y)^+](x) \\ &= x \cap (f \circ g_y)(\pi) \\ &= x \cap f(y). \end{aligned}$$

(5) $\Rightarrow$ (1): If $x \leq f(y)$, then $x = x \cap f(y) = f[f^+(x) \cap y]$. Hence we have $f^{\rightarrow}[0, y] = [0, f(y)]$ and so f is totally range-closed.

Combining Theorem 13.5 and its dual, we deduce:

THEOREM 13.6. *A residuated mapping f on a bounded lattice L is strongly range-closed if and only if it satisfies the following two conditions:*

(1) $(\forall x, y \in L)\, f[f^+(x) \cap y] = x \cap f(y)$;
(2) $(\forall x, y \in L)\, f^+[f(x) \cup y] = x \cup f^+(y)$.

It is worth mentioning that by Theorem 13.6 all the mappings mentioned in Example 13.3 are strongly range-closed. This fact could of course be verified directly. Here is another example of some interest.

EXAMPLE 13.5. Let Λ be a commutative ring with identity and let $I(\Lambda)$ be the set of ideals of Λ ordered by set inclusion. Then $I(\Lambda)$ forms a complete lattice whose intersection operation is set-theoretic and whose union operation is given by

$$\mathbf{a} \curlyvee \mathbf{b} = \mathbf{a} + \mathbf{b} = \{a + b; a \in \mathbf{a}, b \in \mathbf{b}\}.$$

For each $\mathbf{a} \in I(\Lambda)$ define a map $f_{\mathbf{a}} : I(\Lambda) \to I(\Lambda)$ by setting $f_{\mathbf{a}}(\mathbf{b}) = \mathbf{a} \cdot \mathbf{b} =$ the set of all finite sums of the form $\sum_{i=1}^{n} a_i b_i$, where $a_i \in \mathbf{a}$ and $b_i \in \mathbf{b}$ for each i. It is readily verified that $f_{\mathbf{a}}$ is residuated with $f_{\mathbf{a}}^{+}$ given by $f_{\mathbf{a}}^{+}(\mathbf{b}) = \{x \in \Lambda; (\forall a \in \mathbf{a})\ xa \in \mathbf{b}\}$. Suppose now that $\mathbf{a}$ is a principal ideal. We claim that $f_{\mathbf{a}}$ is strongly range-closed. Suppose in fact that $\mathbf{a} = \Lambda x$. We note first that $f_{\mathbf{a}}\,[f_{\mathbf{a}}^{+}(\mathbf{b}) \cap \mathbf{c}]$ is always contained in $\mathbf{b} \cap f_{\mathbf{a}}(\mathbf{c})$; we show the converse inclusion. Let $y \in \mathbf{b} \cap f_{\mathbf{a}}(\mathbf{c})$. Then $y \in \mathbf{b}$ and $y = \sum_{i=1}^{n} a_i c_i$ with $a_i \in \mathbf{a}$ and $c_i \in \mathbf{c}$ for each i. Now $a_i \in \mathbf{a} = \Lambda x$ implies that $a_i = x d_i$ for some $d_i \in \Lambda$. Hence $y = \sum_{i=1}^{n} a_i c_i = \sum_{i=1}^{n} x d_i c_i = \left(\sum_{i=1}^{n} c_i d_i\right) x$. Since $y \in \mathbf{b}$ it follows that $\sum_{i=1}^{n} d_i c_i \in f_{\mathbf{a}}^{+}(\mathbf{b})$. Now clearly $c_i \in \mathbf{c}$ implies that $\sum_{i=1}^{n} d_i c_i \in \mathbf{c}$. We have thus shown that $\sum_{i=1}^{n} d_i c_i \in f_{\mathbf{a}}^{+}(\mathbf{b}) \cap \mathbf{c}$ whence it follows that $y = \left(\sum_{i=1}^{n} d_i c_i\right) x \in f_{\mathbf{a}}\,[f_{\mathbf{a}}^{+}(\mathbf{b}) \cap \mathbf{c}]$ as desired. This shows that $f_{\mathbf{a}}$ is totally range-closed. Likewise, we note that the set $f_{\mathbf{a}}^{+}\,[f_{\mathbf{a}}(\mathbf{b}) + \mathbf{c}]$ always contains $\mathbf{b} + f_{\mathbf{a}}^{+}(\mathbf{c})$. Let us now establish the reverse inclusion when $\mathbf{a} = \Lambda x$. Let $y \in f_{\mathbf{a}}^{+}\,[f_{\mathbf{a}}(\mathbf{b}) + \mathbf{c}]$. Then clearly there exist $b \in \mathbf{b}$ and $c \in \mathbf{c}$ such that $yx = bx + c$. It follows that $(y - b)\,x = c$ and so $y - b \in f_{\mathbf{a}}^{+}(\mathbf{c})$ and consequently $y \in \mathbf{b} + f_{\mathbf{a}}^{+}(\mathbf{c})$ as desired. This shows that $f_{\mathbf{a}}$ is strongly range-closed.

We shall now tie all of this in more closely with notions of modularity. The key item is provided by the next result.

THEOREM 13.7. *Let L be a bounded lattice and let $f, g \in \text{Res}(L)$. Then*

(1) *if g is dually range-closed we have*

$$g \circ f \text{ range-closed} \Rightarrow M^*(f(\pi), g^+(0));$$

(2) *if f is range closed and g is weakly regular we have*

$$g \circ f \text{ range-closed} \Leftrightarrow M^*(f(\pi), g^+(0)).$$

Proof. (1) Let $a \geq g^+(0)$. Then $a = g^+(b)$ for some $b \in L$ and so

$$\begin{aligned} a \cap [f(\pi) \cup g^+(0)] &= a \cap (g^+ \circ g \circ f)(\pi) \\ &= g^+(b) \cap (g^+ \circ g \circ f)(\pi) \\ &= g^+ [b \cap (g \circ f)(\pi)] \\ &= [g^+ \circ (g \circ f) \circ (g \circ f)^+](b) \\ &= (g^+ \circ g \circ f \circ f^+ \circ g^+)(b) \\ &= (g^+ \circ g \circ f \circ f^+)(a) \\ &= (g^+ \circ g)[a \cap f(\pi)] \\ &= [a \cap f(\pi)] \cup g^+(0). \end{aligned}$$

(2) Suppose now that f is range-closed and that g is weakly regular. In view of (1), we need only show that $M^*(f(\pi), g^+(0))$ implies that $g \circ f$ is range-closed. For this purpose, let $x \in L$ be arbitrary; then

$$\begin{aligned} x \cap (g \circ f)(\pi) &= [x \cap (g \circ f)(\pi)] \cap g(\pi) \\ &= (g \circ g^+)[x \cap (g \circ f)(\pi)] \\ &= g[g^+(x) \cap (g^+ \circ g \circ f)(\pi)] \\ &= g\{g^+(x) \cap [f(\pi) \cup g^+(0)]\} \\ &= g\{[g^+(x) \cap f(\pi)] \cup g^+(0)\} \\ &= g[g^+(x) \cap f(\pi)] \\ &= (g \circ f \circ f^+ \circ g^+)(x) \\ &= [(g \circ f) \circ (g \circ f)^+](x). \end{aligned}$$

Working in L^*, the dual of L, and regarding f^+, g^+ as elements of Res (L^*), we have that g^+ dually range-closed and $g^+ \circ f^+$ range-closed imply that $M^*(f^+(0), g(\pi))$ holds in L^*. Translating this assertion into one involving f, g and L we see that g range-closed and $f \circ g$ dually range-closed imply that $M(f^+(0), g(\pi))$ holds in L. Thus the dual of the above result reads:

THEOREM 13.7*. *Let L be a bounded lattice and let* $f, g \in \text{Res}(L)$. *Then*

(1) *if g is range-closed we have*
$$f \circ g \text{ dually range-closed} \Rightarrow M(f^+(0), g(\pi));$$
(2) *if f is dually range-closed and g is weakly regular we have*
$$f \circ g \text{ dually range-closed} \Leftrightarrow M(f^+(0), g(\pi)).$$

Making use of Theorem 13.5 and its dual, we have:

COROLLARY 1. *Let g be a weakly regular residuated mapping on the bounded lattice L. Then*

(1) *g is totally range-closed* $\Leftrightarrow (\forall a \in L)\ M^*(a, g^+(0))$;
(2) *g is dually totally range-closed* $\Leftrightarrow (\forall b \in L)\ M(b, g(\pi))$.

COROLLARY 2. *Every weakly regular residuated mapping on a bounded modular lattice is strongly range-closed.*

We now consider these ideas in an arbitrary Baer semigroup $\langle S; k\rangle$. We shall say that an element $y \in S$ is *range-closed, dually range-closed*, etc., if and only if the associated residuated map $\varphi_y \in \text{Res}(\mathscr{R}_k)$ has the indicated property. Thus, to say that $y \in S$ is range-closed is equivalent to

$$(\forall eS \in \mathscr{R}_k) \quad (\varphi_y \circ \varphi_y^+)(eS) = eS \cap (R_k^{\rightarrow} \circ L_k)(y).$$

To say that $y \in S$ is dually range-closed is equivalent to

$$(\forall eS \in \mathscr{R}_k) \quad (\varphi_y^+ \circ \varphi_y)(eS) = eS \curlyvee R_k(y).$$

The second of these says that

$$(R_k^{\rightarrow} \circ \eta_y \circ L_k^{\rightarrow} \circ \varphi_y)(eS) = eS \curlyvee R_k(y).$$

Taking left k-annihilators and letting $Se^{\#} = L_k(e)$, we obtain

$$(\eta_y \circ \eta_y^+)(Se^{\#}) = (\eta_y \circ L_k^{\rightarrow} \circ \varphi_y \circ R_k^{\rightarrow})(Se^{\#}) = Se^{\#} \cap (L_k^{\rightarrow} \circ R_k)(y).$$

Thus y is dually range-closed if and only if the mapping η_y is a range-closed element of Res $(\mathscr{L}_k)$.

We agree to call the Baer semigroup $\langle S; k\rangle$ *range-closed*, etc., if and only if every element of S has the property in question.

THEOREM 13.8. *Let $\langle S; k\rangle$ be a Baer semigroup and let $T =$ Res $(\mathscr{R}_k)$. If $yS \in \mathscr{R}_k(S)$ then y is range-closed. If $e = e^2 \in S$ then e is range-closed if and only if $\varphi_e \circ T \in \mathscr{R}(T)$.*

Proof. Let $yS = R_k(x)$. Then if $gS \subseteq (R_k^{\rightarrow} \circ L_k)(y) = (R_k^{\rightarrow} \circ L_k^{\rightarrow} \circ R_k)(x) = R_k(x) = yS$ we have $g = yw$ for some $w \in S$. If $hS = (R_k^{\rightarrow} \circ L_k)(w)$ it follows that

$$gS = (R_k^{\rightarrow} \circ L_k)(g) = (R_k^{\rightarrow} \circ L_k)(yw) = (R_k^{\rightarrow} \circ L_k)(yh) = \varphi_y(hS)$$

and so y is range-closed. To prove the second assertion, we need only note that for φ a range-closed idempotent in T, $\varphi = \theta_{\varphi(1S)} \circ \varphi$ and $\theta_{\varphi(1S)} = \varphi \circ \theta_{\varphi(1S)}$ so $\varphi \circ T = \theta_{\varphi(1S)} \circ T \in \mathscr{R}(T)$.

To show that a range-closed idempotent need not have the property that $eS \in \mathscr{R}_k(S)$, we consider a three-element chain $S = \{0, e, \pi\}$ made into a Baer semigroup as in Example 12.3. In this case, every element is idempotent. Moreover, $\mathscr{R}(S) = \{0S, \pi S\}$ and $\varphi_e = \varphi_\pi$ is range-closed. However, $eS \notin \mathscr{R}(S)$.

We can now combine all of the above results to provide as follows a representation theorem for complemented modular lattices.

THEOREM 13.9. *For a bounded lattice L the following conditions are equivalent:*

(1) *L is a complemented modular lattice;*
(2) *L can be coordinatized by a weakly regular Baer semigroup;*
(3) *L can be coordinatized by a range-closed Baer semigroup;*
(4) *L can be coordinatized by a dually range-closed Baer semigroup.*

Proof. (1) $\Rightarrow$ (2): If L is a complemented modular lattice then the strongly range-closed residuated mappings on L form a Baer semigroup which coordinatizes L and which is clearly weakly regular. We leave the proof of this fact as an exercise for the reader (see Exercise 13.6, together with the hint provided).

(2) $\Rightarrow$ (3): clear.

(3) $\Rightarrow$ (1): Let $\langle S; k\rangle$ be a range-closed Baer semigroup which coordinatizes L. If $eS, fS \in \mathscr{R}_k$ and $Se^{\#} = L_k(e)$, then by the dual of Theorem 13.8 we see that $e^{\#}$ is dually range-closed. By hypothesis, $e^{\#}f$ is range-closed, so by Theorem 13.7 we have $M^*(\varphi_f(1S), \varphi_{e^{\#}}^{+}(0S))$. Noting that $fS = \varphi_f(1S)$ and $eS = R_k(e^{\#}) = \varphi_{e^{\#}}^{+}(0S)$ we conclude that $\mathscr{R}_k(S)$ is modular. The fact that it is also complemented comes from the observation that $e^{\#}$ is weakly regular. By Theorem 13.4, $Se^{\#}$ has a complement in $\mathscr{L}_k$. Since $eS = R_k(e^{\#})$, it follows that eS has a complement in $\mathscr{R}_k$.

(2) $\Rightarrow$ (4): clear.

(4) $\Rightarrow$ (1): Note that the argument used in the proof of (3) $\Rightarrow$ (1) can be dualized to show that if $\langle S; k\rangle$ is a dually range-closed Baer semigroup then $\mathscr{L}_k$ is a complemented modular lattice. Now use the fact that $\mathscr{R}_k$, $\mathscr{L}_k$ are dually isomorphic to show that $\mathscr{R}_k$ is also a complemented modular lattice.

To conclude the present section, we shall have a close look at mappings f with the property that, for $n = 1, 2, 3, \ldots$, f^n is weakly regular (where as usual $f^n = f \circ f \circ \cdots \circ f$ denotes the composition of f with itself n times). Our goal will be to generalize results about the *ascent* and *descent* of a linear transformation on a vector space. We refer the interested reader to [28], pp. 271–285, for a discussion of these concepts and their application to the solution of Fredholm integral equations.

Let f be a residuated mapping on a bounded lattice L. If we define $f^0 = \mathrm{id}$ and, for $n = 0, 1, 2, \ldots$, let $k^n = f^n(\pi)$ then we obtain the chain

$$\pi = k^0 \geq k^1 \geq k^2 \geq \cdots \geq k^n \geq k^{n+1} \geq \cdots.$$

Similarly, letting $(f^+)^0 = \mathrm{id}$ and $k_n = (f^+)^n(0)$, we obtain the dual chain

$$0 = k_0 \leq k_1 \leq k_2 \leq \cdots \leq k_n \leq k_{n+1} \leq \cdots.$$

If, for some non-negative integer n, we have $k^n = k^{n+1}$, then we have necessarily $k^n = k^{n+1} = k^{n+2} = \cdots$. If such an n exists, we can define an integer μ by

$$\mu = \min\{n;\, k^n = k^{n+1}\}.$$

This integer μ is clearly such that $(\forall n < \mu)\, k^n > k^{n+1}$ and $(\forall n \geq \mu)$ $k^n = k^{n+1}$. If such an integer μ exists, we shall call $\{k^n; n \geq 0\}$ a *Riesz tower* with associated *Riesz index* μ. The absence of such an integer will be denoted symbolically by writing $\mu = \infty$. In the dual situation, we consider the existence of an integer

$$\nu = \min\{n;\, k_n = k_{n+1}\}$$

which we call the *Riesz index* associated with the *dual Riesz tower* $\{k_n; n \geq 0\}$. The absence of such an integer will be denoted symbolically by writing $\nu = \infty$.

If we now suppose that each power of f is weakly regular we have the following information concerning the associated Riesz indices:

THEOREM 13.10. *Let L be a bounded lattice and let* $f \in \mathrm{Res}\,(L)$ *be such that, for* $n = 1, 2, 3, \ldots,$ f^n *is weakly regular. Then*

(1) $k^1 \cup k_1 = \pi \Leftrightarrow \mu \in \{0, 1\}$;
(2) $k^1 \cap k_1 = 0 \Leftrightarrow \nu \in \{0, 1\}$;
(3) $\mu = 0 \Rightarrow \nu \in \{0, \infty\}$;
(4) $\nu = 0 \Rightarrow \mu \in \{0, \infty\}$;
(5) $\mu \in \{0, 1\} \Rightarrow \nu \in \{0, 1, \infty\}$;
(6) $\nu \in \{0, 1\} \Rightarrow \mu \in \{0, 1, \infty\}$.

Proof. By virtue of the duality present it suffices to prove assertions (1), (3) and (5).

(1) Let $k^1 \cup k_1 = \pi$. Then $k^1 = f(\pi) = f(k^1 \cup k_1) = f(k^1) \cup f(k_1) = f(k^1) \cup 0 = f(k^1) = k^2$ and consequently $\mu \in \{0, 1\}$. Conversely, if $\mu \in \{0, 1\}$ then $k^1 = k^2$ and so $\pi = \pi \cup k_1 = (f^+ \circ f)(\pi) = f^+(k^1) = f^+(k^2) = (f^+ \circ f)(k^1) = k^1 \cup k_1$.

(3) We shall show that if $\mu = 0$ and $\nu \neq \infty$, then $\nu = 0$. Now if $\nu \neq \infty$ then ν is finite and $k_\nu = k_{\nu+1}$. If $\nu > 0$ this may be written $f^+(k_{\nu-1}) = f^+(k_\nu)$ and gives $k_{\nu-1} = \pi \cap k_{\nu-1} = f(\pi) \cap k_{\nu-1} = (f \circ f^+)(k_{\nu-1}) = (f \circ f^+)(k_\nu) = f(\pi) \cap k_\nu = k_\nu$. It follows that $\nu = 0$.

(5) Let us note first that for $i \geq 0$ and $j > 1$ we have

$$f(k^i \cap k_j) = k^{i+1} \cap k_{j-1}. \tag{*}$$

In fact, since each power of f is weakly regular,

$$\begin{aligned} f(k^i \cap k_j) &= [f \circ (f^i) \circ (f^i)^+](k_j) = [f^{i+1} \circ (f^{i+1})^+](k_{j-1}) \\ &= k^{i+1} \cap k_{j-1} \end{aligned}$$

To establish (5), we have to show that if $\mu \in \{0, 1\}$ and $\nu \neq \infty$ then $k_1 = k_2$. Now if $n > 1$ and $k_n = k_{n+1}$ then $f^+(k_{n-1}) = f^+(k_n)$ and so

$$k^1 \cap k_{n-1} = (f \circ f^+)(k_{n-1}) = (f \circ f^+)(k_n) = k^1 \cap k_n. \tag{**}$$

Consequently, for $n > 1$,

$$\begin{aligned} k_{n-1} &= k_{n-1} \cup (k^1 \cap k_{n-1}) & \\ &= k_{n-1} \cup (k^1 \cap k_n) & \text{[by (**)]} \\ &= k_{n-1} \cup k_1 \cup (k^1 \cap k_n) & \\ &= k_{n-1} \cup (f^+ \circ f)(k^1 \cap k_n) & \\ &= k_{n-1} \cup f^+(k^2 \cap k_{n-1}) & \text{[by (*)]} \\ &= k_{n-1} \cup f^+(k^1 \cap k_{n-1}) & \\ &= k_{n-1} \cup (f^+ \circ f)(k^0 \cap k_n) & \text{[by (*)]} \\ &= k_{n-1} \cup k_1 \cup (k^0 \cap k_n) & \\ &= k_{n-1} \cup k_n & [k^0 = \pi] \\ &= k_n. & \end{aligned}$$

A repeated application of this argument produces $k_1 = k_2$ and so $\nu \in \{0, 1\}$.

COROLLARY 1. *For each positive integer n,*

(1^n) $k^n \cup k_n = \pi \Leftrightarrow \mu \in [0, n]$;
(2^n) $k^n \cap k_n = 0 \Leftrightarrow \nu \in [0, n]$;
(5^n) $\mu \in [0, n] \Rightarrow \nu \in [0, n] \cup \{\infty\}$;
(6^n) $\nu \in [0, n] \Rightarrow \mu \in [0, n] \cup \{\infty\}$.

Proof. Consider the mapping $F = f^n$. By hypothesis, F^m is weakly regular for $m = 1, 2, 3, \ldots$ Define $K^m = F^m(\pi)$ and $K_m = (F^m)^+(0)$ for $m = 1, 2, 3, \ldots$, and as usual set $K^0 = \pi$ and $K_0 = 0$. Note now that $K^1 = K^2$ if and only if $k^n = k^{2n}$ which is in turn equivalent to $k^n = k^{n+1}$. The corollary then follows by applying the theorem to the mapping F.

COROLLARY 2. *If both μ and ν are finite then for $n > 0$ the following four conditions are equivalent:*

$$\text{(a) } k^n = k^{n+1}; \quad \text{(b) } k_n = k_{n+1}; \quad \text{(c) } k^n \cup k_n = \pi; \quad \text{(d) } k^n \cap k_n = 0.$$

Proof. This follows immediately from Corollary 1.

THEOREM 13.11. *Let L be a bounded lattice and let $f \in \text{Res}(L)$ be such that each power of f is weakly regular. If the Riesz indices μ, ν associated with f are both finite, then $\mu = \nu$; moreover, writing $\mu = \nu = [f]$ we then have $k^{[f]} \cap k_{[f]} = 0$ and $k^{[f]} \cup k_{[f]} = \pi$.*

Proof. If both μ and ν are finite, then by Corollary 2 of Theorem 13.10 we have $\mu \leq \max\{1, \nu\}$ and $\nu \leq \max\{1, \mu\}$. By virtue of Theorem 13.10 the conditions $\mu = 0$ and $\nu = 0$ are equivalent. We conclude that $\mu = \nu$. Writing $[f]$ for their common value and applying Corollary 2(c), (d) we deduce that $k^{[f]}$ and $k_{[f]}$ are complements.

EXAMPLE 13.6. The following particular case of the above results is often given under the name of Fitting's lemma: if M is an Artinian and Noetherian left Λ-module and if f is an endomorphism on M, then for some positive integer n we have the decomposition $M = \text{Im} f^n \oplus \text{Ker} f^n$.

EXERCISES

13.1. Let P, Q be ordered sets which are not necessarily bounded and let $f \in \text{Res}(P, Q)$. Let I be the ideal in Q generated by $\text{Im} f$ [i.e. the smallest ideal of Q containing $\text{Im} f$]. Show that f is range-closed if and only if the restriction of f^+ to I is injective.

13.2. Let L be a lattice which is not necessarily bounded and let $f \in \text{Res}(L)$. Show that f is totally range-closed if and only if $(\forall x, y \in L)\ f[f^+(x) \cap y] = x \cap f(y)$. [*Hint*. Use the fact that if $x \cap f(y) = f(a)$ with $a \leq y$, then $f(a) \leq f[f^+(x) \cap y] \leq f[f^+(x) \cap (f^+ \circ f)(y)] = f(a)$ to deduce that $f[f^+(x) \cap y] = x \cap f(y)$.]

13.3. In Example 13.4 show that if $s = (s', s'')$ is a continuous semilinear transformation, then ξ_s is totally range-closed if and only if $(\forall M \in L)$ M closed $\Rightarrow s''^{\rightarrow}(M)$ closed. [*Hint.* If the condition is satisfied then $s''^{\rightarrow}$ coincides with ξ_s on L. Use the fact that $s''^{\rightarrow}$ is totally range-closed.]

13.4. Let G be a group and let f be an endomorphism on G. If L denotes the lattice of subgroups of G, recall that the mapping $\xi_f : L \to L$ defined by $\xi_f(H) = f^{\rightarrow}(H)$ is residuated with $\xi_f^+ = f^{\leftarrow}$. Show that ξ_f is weakly regular.

13.5. Consider the Baer semigroup $(\mathrm{Rel}(X), \emptyset)$ of Example 12.4. For each $R \in \mathrm{Rel}(X)$ identify R with the subset $\{(x, y); xRy\}$. Show that in this way:

(1) R is range-closed if and only if there exist $R_1, R_2 \in \mathrm{Rel}(X)$ such that (a) $R = R_1 \cup R_2$; (b) R_1 is a function whose domain is a subset of X; (c) $\mathrm{Im}\, R = \mathrm{Im}\, R_1$; (d) $\mathrm{Dom}\, R_1 \cap \mathrm{Dom}\, R_2 = \emptyset$.

(2) R is dually range-closed if and only if R^t is range-closed.

(3) R is weakly regular if and only if R is a bijection whose domain and image are subsets of X.

(4) R is totally range-closed if and only if R is a function whose domain is a subset of X.

13.6. Prove that if L is a complemented modular lattice, then the strongly range-closed residuated maps on L form a Baer semigroup which coordinatizes L. [*Hint.* If a, b are complements in L, show that the mapping $f_{a,b} : L \to L$ described by setting $f_{a,b}(x) = (x \cup a) \cap b$ is a strongly range-closed idempotent. Show that in the semigroup T formed by the strongly range-closed residuated maps $R(g) = f_{a,b} \circ T$ and $L(g) = T \circ f_{c,d}$, where $b = g^+(0)$ and $c = g(\pi)$.]

13.7. Let L, M be bounded lattices.

(1) Prove that if $f, g \in \mathrm{Res}(L, M)$ are such that $f \curlyvee g$ is range-closed, then

$$(\forall x \in M) \quad x \cap [f(\pi) \cup g(\pi)] = [x \cap f(\pi)] \cup [x \cap g(\pi)].$$

(2) Let $f \in \mathrm{Res}(L, M)$ be weakly regular. Show that if L is distributive then f is a lattice homomorphism.

(3) Let $f \in \mathrm{Res}(L)$ be range-closed. Prove that if f is a lattice homomorphism then f is totally range-closed.

13.8. With notation as in Example 12.4, let $(X, \mathscr{T})$ be a T_1-topological space and let R be a continuous relation. Recall that the mapping η_R defined on the lattice of closed subsets of X by $\eta_R(A) = \mathrm{Cl}\,[\xi_R(A)]$ is residuated. Prove that the following are equivalent:

(1) R is totally range-closed;

(2) R is a "closed" function in that R is a function and $R(A)$ is closed for all closed subsets A.

13.9. Let V be the vector space formed by all infinite sequences $\{x_n\}$ of real numbers with respect to the laws $\{x_n\} + \{y_n\} = \{x_n + y_n\}$, $a\{x_n\} = \{ax_n\}$. Let f be the "shift operator" defined by

$$f(\{x_1, x_2, x_3, \ldots\}) = \{0, x_1, x_2, \ldots\}.$$

Observe that $f \in \text{Hom}(V, V)$ and let $f^{\rightarrow}$ be the induced residuated map on $L(V)$. Show that for $f^{\rightarrow}$ we have $\mu = \infty$ and $\nu = 0$.

13.10. Let L be a bounded modular lattice in which 0 and π are the only elements with complements. Suppose further that L has no infinite properly increasing or decreasing chains of elements. Show that if $f \in \text{Res}(L)$ is weakly regular then either f is an automorphism or f is nilpotent (in that $f^n = 0$ for some n).

13.11. Let S be a semigroup with 0 and let $P_0(S)$ denote the set of all subsets of S which contain 0, ordered by set inclusion. For each $x \in S$ let $X = \{0, x\}$. Define $\varrho_X : P_0(S) \to P_0(S)$ by setting $\varrho_X(A) = AX = \{ax; a \in A\}$ and recall that by Exercise 2.4 each mapping ϱ_X is residuated.

(1) Show that ϱ_X is range-closed.

(2) Show that ϱ_X is dually range-closed if and only if x satisfies the "generalized cancellation law"

$$yx = zx \Rightarrow yx = 0 \quad \text{or} \quad y = z.$$

13.12. Let S be a semigroup with 0 in which the cancellation laws

$$yx = zx \quad \text{with} \quad x \neq 0 \Rightarrow y = z$$

$$xy = xz \quad \text{with} \quad x \neq 0 \Rightarrow y = z$$

are both valid. Suppose further that S has no infinite properly decreasing chains of right or left ideals. Show that $S \setminus \{0\}$ is a group. [*Hint*. With notation as in Exercise 13.11 let $x \neq 0$ and consider ϱ_X. By the cancellation laws one can apply Exercise 13.11 to deduce that $(\varrho_X)^n$ is weakly regular for all n. The chain condition forces μ to be finite and the cancellation laws force $\nu = 0$. Hence, by Theorem 13.11, $\mu = 0$. It follows that $SX = X$ and similarly $XS = X$. These two facts can now be used to show that $S \setminus \{0\}$ is a group.]

13.13. Let A be a ring with an identity having no infinite properly decreasing chains of left ideals (left Artinian). Recall that an element $x \in A$ is said to be a right zero divisor if $yx = 0$ for some $y \neq 0$. Prove that if x is not a right zero divisor then x admits a left inverse. [*Hint*. If x is not a right zero divisor then the cancellation law $yx = zx \Rightarrow y = z$ is valid. Show from this that $(\varrho_X)^n$ is weakly regular for each n and proceed as in Exercise 13.12 to deduce that $AX = A$ whence $1 = yx$ for some $y \in A$.] If, furthermore, A has no infinite properly decreasing chains of right ideals (right Artinian), prove that the following conditions are equivalent: (a) x is not a left zero divisor; (b) x is not a right zero divisor; (c) x has a left inverse; (d) x has a right inverse; (e) x has a two-sided inverse.

13.14. Let A be a commutative Baer ring having no infinite properly decreasing chain of ideals. Prove that A is regular. [*Hint*. The chain condition is inherited by every subring of the form eA, where $e = e^2$. Let $x \in A$ and let $eA = RL(x)$. Then, working in eA, $R(ex) = \{0\}$. Hence, by Exercise 13.13, ex has an inverse ey in eA and so $(ey)(ex) = e$. It is immediate that $x = ex = (eyex)\,x = x\,(eye)\,x$.]

14. Strongly regular Baer semigroups

Although we do not propose to enter into a lengthy discourse on the subject, a few brief comments about *projective geometry* will serve to motivate the material in this section.

There are two basic approaches to projective geometry which we shall call the "combinatorial approach" and the "algebraic approach". In the combinatorial approach one deals with a set Ω of objects called *points* together with a collection of distinguished subsets of Ω called *lines* such that the following three axioms hold:

(PG 1) *If p, q are distinct points then there is a unique line $p \cup q$ containing both p and q.*

(PG 2) *If a line l intersects two sides of a triangle (other than at their intersection) then it also intersects the third side.*

(PG 3) *Every line contains at least three points.*

The properties of the geometry are then developed directly from the above axioms. In the algebraic approach one considers a (left) vector space V over a division ring D. The *points* of the geometry are taken to be the one-dimensional subspaces of V and the *lines* the two-dimensional subspaces. The properties of the resulting geometry are now developed by considering various algebraic equations in the underlying vector space.

The problem then arises as to the connection between the two approaches. The passage from the algebraic approach to the combinatorial one is trivial. One merely verifies that the algebraically defined points and lines satisfy the axioms (PG1), (PG2) and (PG3). However, the passage from the combinatorial approach to the algebraic approach is highly nontrivial. It involves the introduction of "coordinates" into the geometry so that the points and lines become defined by algebraic equations among the coordinates. Such a process is known as *coordinatization* (and hence our usage of this term in connection with Baer semigroups). Basically what one wants is a left vector space V over a division ring D which defines the given geometry algebraically.

Now just what has all this got to do with lattice theory? Let G be a projective geometry (defined combinatorially). A collection M of points of G is called a *variety* if $p, q \in M$ implies $p \cup q \in M$. If the varieties of G

are ordered by set inclusion, then there results an irreducible complemented modular lattice with chain conditions (*irreducible* in the sense that the only elements having unique complements are 0 and π, which by virtue of Theorems 8.3 and 9.3 is equivalent to saying that the centre of the lattice is $\{0, \pi\}$; *chain conditions* in the sense that there are no infinite properly ascending or descending chains of elements). Conversely, any such lattice L gives rise in a natural way to a projective geometry; one takes the points to be the atoms of L (which exist because of the descending chain condition) and the lines to be those sets of the form $\{r; r$ is a point and $r \leq p \cup q$, where p, q are distinct atoms of $L\}$. Hence the combinatorial approach to projective geometry may be regarded as equivalent to the study of irreducible complemented modular lattices satisfying the chain conditions. From the lattice-theoretic point of view, a coordinatization theorem for projective geometry becomes: *if L is an irreducible complemented modular lattice with chain conditions containing at least one chain of length 4 then there exists a division ring D (unique up to isomorphism) and a left vector space V over D such that L is isomorphic to the lattice of all subspaces of V.*

About 1935, John von Neumann (motivated in part by considerations involving the foundations of quantum mechanics) generalized the notion of projective geometry by removing the chain conditions and considering a complete irreducible complemented modular lattice with certain "continuity axioms". Such a lattice was called a *continuous geometry*. A precise definition of this type of geometry must be regarded as beyond the scope of this book and the interested reader is referred to [21]. At any rate, von Neumann sought a coordinatization theorem for continuous geometries. He began by reformulating the coordinatization theorem for projective geometries and considering, instead of the vector space V, its associated ring of linear transformations. Viewed in this context, the theorem becomes the following, in which a *regular ring* is a ring A in which $(\forall x \in A)\ (\exists y \in A)\ x = xyx$: *if L is an irreducible complemented modular lattice with chain conditions containing at least one chain of length 4 then there exists a regular ring A (unique up to isomorphism) such that L is isomorphic to the lattice of principal right ideals of A.* After literally hundreds of pages of inspired work, von Neumann was able to prove a coordinatization theorem for continuous geometries which (when it works) establishes an isomorphism between the given lattice and the lattice of principal right ideals of a (unique) regular ring.

Our goal in this section is to show that for an arbitrary complemented modular lattice we must be willing to sacrifice both the uniqueness part of von Neumann's theorem and the notion of a ring, but are nonetheless able to produce a Baer semigroup coordinatization which is regular in the above sense.

We begin by considering a regular ring A. Let $x \in A$ and choose $y \in A$ such that $x = xyx$. Setting $e = xy$ and $f = yx$ we observe that $e = e^2$, $f = f^2$, $xA = eA = R(1 - e)$ and $Ax = Af = L(1 - f)$. It follows that A is a Baer ring in which $(\forall x \in A)\ xA \in \mathscr{R}(A)$ and $Ax \in \mathscr{L}(A)$. This is the sort of thing which we wish to generalize to the case of a Baer semigroup.

Definition. Let $\langle S; k\rangle$ be a Baer semigroup. We shall say that $x \in S$ is *right regular* if $xS \in \mathscr{R}_k(S)$, *left regular* if $Sx \in \mathscr{L}_k(S)$ and *strongly regular* if it is both right and left regular. The Baer semigroup $\langle S; k\rangle$ will be called *right*, *left* or *strongly regular* if every element of S has the property in question.

Let us note that if x is right regular then there must exist an idempotent e such that $xS = eS$. Then $x = ex$ and $e = xy$ for some $y \in S$, so that $x = ex = xyx$. Thus right regularity implies regularity in the von Neumann sense. In the case of a Baer ring, these two notions of regularity coincide. However, if one computes Res (L) in the case where L is a three-element chain then the result is the following Baer semigroup which is regular in the sense of von Neumann but which is neither left nor right regular (see also Exercise 14.4):

	0	1	a	b	c	d
0	0	0	0	0	0	0
1	0	1	a	b	c	d
a	0	a	a	b	0	0
b	0	b	a	b	a	b
c	0	c	c	d	0	0
d	0	d	c	d	c	d

[For example, $aS = \{0, a, b\} \notin \mathscr{R}_0(S)$.]

Our goal will be to prove that *a bounded ordered set E is a complemented modular lattice if and only if it can be coordinatized by a strongly regular Baer semigroup*. Note first that Theorem 13.8 may now be restated as follows:

THEOREM 14.1. *Let $\langle S; k\rangle$ be a Baer semigroup. Every right regular element of S is range-closed. An idempotent e is range-closed if and only if the induced residuated map φ_e is right regular.*

It follows from this that every right regular Baer semigroup $\langle S; k\rangle$ is range-closed and so, by Theorem 13.9, $\mathcal{R}_k(S)$ is a complemented modular lattice. Thus, in order to prove our conjecture, it will suffice to prove that the strongly range-closed residuated maps on a complemented modular lattice form a strongly regular Baer semigroup (see Exercise 13.6).

For the moment, let us consider a more general question. Let E be an ordered set and let $f \in \text{Res}(E)$. When does there exist $g \in \text{Res}(E)$ such that $f = f \circ g \circ f$? First of all, the next theorem shows that we had best be able fo find g such that $f = f \circ g \circ f$ *and* $g = g \circ f \circ g$.

THEOREM 14.2. *Let x be an element of the semigroup S. The following conditions are then equivalent:*

(1) $(\exists y \in S)\ x = xyx;$

(2) $(\exists w \in S)\ x = xwx$ *and* $w = wxw;$

(3) *there exist idempotents* $e, f \in S$ *such that* $eS = xS$ *and* $Sf = Sx$.

Proof. (1) ⇒ (2): Suppose that $x = xyx$ and let $w = yxy$. Then we have $xwx = x(yxy)x = (xyx)yx = xyx = x$ while $wxw = (yxy)x(yxy) = y(xyx)(yxy) = yx(yxy) = y(xyx)y = yxy = w$.

(2) ⇒ (3): Let $x = xwx$ and $w = wxw$. Setting $e = xw$ and $f = wx$, we have $e = e^2$ and $f = f^2$. Also $x = xwx = ex$ puts x in eS while $e = xw$ puts e in xS. We conclude that $xS = eS$. A similar argument shows that $Sx = Sf$.

(3) ⇒ (1): If $e = e^2$ and $eS = xS$, then $x = ex$ and $e = xy$ for some $y \in S$ and so $x = ex = xyx$.

THEOREM 14.3. *Let E be an ordered set and let* $f \in \text{Res}(E)$. *If there exists* $g \in \text{Res}(E)$ *such that* $f = f \circ g \circ f$ *then there exist idempotents a,* $b \in \text{Res}(E)$ *such that* $\text{Im}\, a = \text{Im}\, f$ *and* $\text{Im}\, b^+ = \text{Im}\, f^+$.

Proof. Let $S = \text{Res}(E)$. If $f = f \circ g \circ f$, then by Theorem 14.2 there exist idempotents $a, b \in S$ such that $a \circ S = f \circ S$ and $S \circ b = S \circ f$. Then $f = a \circ f$ and, for some $h \in S$, $a = f \circ h$. It is immediate from this that $\text{Im}\, a = \text{Im}\, f$. To say that $S \circ b = S \circ f$ is equivalent to saying that $b^+ \circ S^+ = f^+ \circ S^+$ where $S^+ = \text{Res}^+(E)$. Thus a similar argument shows that $\text{Im}\, b^+ = \text{Im}\, f^+$.

THEOREM 14.4. *Let E be an ordered set and let $f \in \text{Res}(E)$. Suppose that a, b are idempotents of* Res (E) *such that* $\text{Im}\, a = \text{Im}\, f$ *and* $\text{Im}\, b^+ = \text{Im}\, f^+$. *Let $g = b \circ f^+ \circ a$ and $h = a^+ \circ f \circ b^+$. Then*

(1) *$g \in \text{Res}(E)$ with $g^+ = h$;*
(2) *$f = f \circ g \circ f$ and $g = g \circ f \circ g$;*
(3) *$f \circ g = a$ and $g \circ f = b$;*
(4) *$\text{Im}\, g = \text{Im}\, b$ and $\text{Im}\, h = \text{Im}\, a^+$ from which it follows that (i) g is range-closed if and only if b is range-closed, (ii) g is dually range-closed if and only if a is dually range-closed;*
(5) *f is right regular if and only if it is range-closed; and is left regular if and only if it is dually range-closed.*

Proof. (1) Note that since $\text{Im}\, f = \text{Im}\, a$ and $\text{Im}\, f^+ = \text{Im}\, b^+$ we must have $f = a \circ f$ and $f^+ = b^+ \circ f^+$, the latter giving $f = f \circ b$. It follows that

$$\begin{cases} f \circ b^+ \circ b = (f \circ b) \circ b^+ \circ b = f \circ (b \circ b^+ \circ b) = f \circ b = f; \\ a \circ a^+ \circ f = a \circ a^+ \circ (a \circ f) = (a \circ a^+ \circ a) \circ f = a \circ f = f. \end{cases}$$

We have thus established that

$$f = a \circ f = a \circ a^+ \circ f = f \circ b = f \circ b^+ \circ b. \qquad (\alpha)$$

Now $(\forall x \in E)\; a(x) \in \text{Im}\, f$ implies that $a(x) = f(y)$ for some y and so $(f \circ f^+ \circ a)(x) = (f \circ f^+ \circ f)(y) = f(y) = a(x)$ and we deduce that $a = f \circ f^+ \circ a$. A dual argument produces $b^+ = f^+ \circ f \circ b^+$. Thus

$$a = f \circ f^+ \circ a \quad \text{and} \quad b^+ = f^+ \circ f \circ b^+. \qquad (\beta)$$

We now apply (α) and (β) to write

$$\begin{aligned} h \circ g = (a^+ \circ f \circ b^+) \circ (b \circ f^+ \circ a) &= a^+ \circ (f \circ b^+ \circ b) \circ f^+ \circ a \\ &= a^+ \circ f \circ f^+ \circ a \\ &= a^+ \circ a \\ &\geq \mathrm{id}. \end{aligned}$$

Similarly, we can show that $g \circ h = b \circ b^+ \leq \mathrm{id}$, thus establishing (1).

(2) Making repeated use of (α), we have

$$f \circ g \circ f = f \circ (b \circ f^+ \circ a) \circ f = (f \circ b) \circ f^+ \circ (a \circ f) = f \circ f^+ \circ f = f$$

and likewise

$$\begin{aligned} g \circ f \circ g = (b \circ f^+ \circ a) \circ f \circ (b \circ f^+ \circ a) &= (b \circ f^+) \circ (a \circ f) \circ (b \circ f^+) \circ a \\ &= (b \circ f^+) \circ (f \circ f^+ \circ a) \\ &= b \circ f^+ \circ a \\ &= g. \end{aligned}$$

(3) By (α) and (β) we have

$$f \circ g = f \circ (b \circ f^+ \circ a) \circ f = (f \circ b) \circ f^+ \circ a = f \circ f^+ \circ a = a.$$

Similarly,

$$g \circ f = (b \circ f^+ \circ a) \circ f = (b \circ f^+) \circ (a \circ f) = b \circ f^+ \circ f = b.$$

(4) Since $g = b \circ f^+ \circ a$ it is clear that $\mathrm{Im}\, g \subseteq \mathrm{Im}\, b$; and the fact that $b = g \circ f$ produces the reverse inclusion. By a dual argument we see that $\mathrm{Im}\, h = \mathrm{Im}\, a^+$ and the remaining assertions in (4) are now obvious.

(5) We established in (α) and (β) that $f = a \circ f$ and $f \circ g = a$. It follows from this that $f \circ \mathrm{Res}\,(E) = a \circ \mathrm{Res}\,(E)$. Now if f is range-closed we must have a range-closed since $\mathrm{Im}\, f = \mathrm{Im}\, a$. By Theorem 14.1, a is right regular. It is immediate that f is right regular. If, on the other hand, f is right regular then by Theorem 14.1 it is range-closed. A similar argument shows that f is left regular if and only if it is dually range-closed.

COROLLARY. *Every weakly regular residuated mapping on a bounded lattice L is strongly regular.*

Proof. If $f \in \text{Res}(L)$ is weakly regular then $\text{Im} f = [0, f(\pi)]$ and $\text{Im} f^+ = [f^+(0), \pi]$. If we choose $a = \theta_{f(\pi)}$ and $b = \psi_{f^+(0)}$ (these maps being defined immediately preceding Theorem 12.4), we have $\text{Im}\, a = \text{Im} f$ and $\text{Im}\, b^+ = \text{Im} f^+$. It then follows by Theorem 14.4(5) that f is strongly regular.

Before stating the next theorem it will prove convenient to establish some additional notation. In a bounded lattice L we shall agree to write $x \oplus y = \pi$ to denote the fact that

$$x \cup y = \pi \quad \text{and} \quad x \cap y = 0 \quad \text{with} \quad M(x, y) \quad \text{and} \quad M^*(y, x).$$

THEOREM 14.5. *Let L be a bounded lattice and let* $f \in \text{Res}(L)$ *be weakly regular. Then the following conditions are equivalent:*

(1) *there exists a weakly regular element* $g \in \text{Res}(L)$ *such that* $f = f \circ g \circ f$ *and* $g = g \circ f \circ g$;

(2) $(\exists s, t \in L)\ s \oplus f(\pi) = \pi = f^+(0) \oplus t$.

Proof. Suppose first that such a mapping g can be found. Then $\text{Im}\, g \supseteq \text{Im}\, g \circ f$ and since $g(x) = (g \circ f)[g(x)]$ we have $\text{Im}\, g \subseteq \text{Im}\, g \circ f$. Thus $\text{Im}\, g = \text{Im}\, g \circ f$. Similar arguments show that $\text{Im} f = \text{Im} f \circ g$, $\text{Im} f^+ = \text{Im} f^+ \circ g^+$ and $\text{Im}\, g^+ = \text{Im}\, g^+ \circ f^+$. It is immediate that $f \circ g$ and $g \circ f$ are each weakly regular idempotents. By Theorem 13.4 there must then exist $s, t \in L$ such that $s \oplus f(\pi) = \pi = f^+(0) \oplus t$.

Suppose now that we are given elements $s, t \in L$ such that $s \oplus f(\pi) = \pi = f^+(0) \oplus t$. Then, as in the first part of the proof of Theorem 13.4, we can produce weakly regular idempotents $a, b \in \text{Res}(L)$ such that $\text{Im}\, a = \text{Im} f$ and $\text{Im}\, b^+ = \text{Im} f^+$. Taking g as in Theorem 14.4, we see that $\text{Im}\, g = \text{Im}\, b$ and $\text{Im}\, g^+ = \text{Im}\, a^+$ and so g is weakly regular.

We are now ready to relate this to the case where L is a complemented modular lattice. In view of the corollaries to Theorem 13.7*, we see that in Res (L) the concepts of strong regularity, weak regularity and strongly range-closed all coincide. It follows that the strongly range-closed maps form a strongly regular Baer semigroup which coordinatizes L. The next theorem summarizes the situation.

THEOREM 14.6. *A bounded ordered set E is a complemented modular lattice if and only if it can be coordinatized by one of the following types of Baer semigroup: strongly regular; left regular; right regular; strongly range-closed; range-closed; dually range-closed.*

EXAMPLE 14.1. Let L be a complemented modular lattice and let $f \in \text{Res}(L)$ be weakly regular. By Theorem 13.2 the restriction of f to the interval $[f^+(0), \pi]$ is an isomorphism of that interval onto $[0, f(\pi)]$. Let t be a complement of $f^+(0)$ and let $\hat{f}$ denote the restriction of f to $[0, t]$. Then defining g by the prescription $g(x) = f^+(x) \cap t$ for all $x \leq f(\pi)$, we see that, for $x \leq f(\pi)$,

$$(\hat{f} \circ g)(x) = f[f^+(x) \cap t] = x \cap f(t) = x$$

since $f(\pi) = f[f^+(0) \cup t] = f(t)$. Similarly, for $y \leq t$,

$$\begin{aligned}(g \circ \hat{f})(y) = g[f(y)] &= f^+[f(y)] \cap t \\ &= [y \cap f^+(0)] \cap t \\ &= y.\end{aligned}$$

Hence $\hat{f}$ is an isomorphism with g as its inverse.

Suppose now that in particular V is a vector space over a division ring D and let $L(V)$ be the lattice of subspaces of V. Let $f: L(V) \to L(V)$ be a weakly regular map and let $M = f(V)$ and $N = f^+\{0\}$. If T is a complement of N in $L(V)$, then $\hat{f} = f_{[\{0\}, T]}$ the restriction of f to $[\{0\}, T]$, is an isomorphism of $[\{0\}, T]$ onto $[\{0\}, M] = \text{Im} f$. If the dimension of M is at least three then by the "Fundamental Theorem of Projective Geometry" (see [2], p. 44) there exists a semilinear transformation $s = (s', s'')$ where $s'': T \to M$ such that $\hat{f} = s''^{\to}$. Let e be the projection of V onto T with kernel N and extend s to a semilinear transformation $\bar{s} = (s', s'' \circ e)$ on V. Then for each $X \in L(V)$ we have

$$(s'' \circ e)^{\to}(X) = s''^{\to}[e^{\to}(X)] = \hat{f}[e^{\to}(X)]. \tag{1}$$

Defining g as in the first paragraph we have

$$(\forall X \in L(V)) \quad (g \circ f)(X) = f^+[f(X)] \cap T = (X \cup N) \cap T. \tag{2}$$

But $e^{\rightarrow}$ is a weakly regular idempotent and so, by Theorem 13.4,

$$(\forall X \in L(V)) \quad e^{\rightarrow}(X) = [X \cup e^{\leftarrow}\{0\}] \cap e^{\rightarrow}(V) = (X \cup N) \cap T. \quad (3)$$

From (2) and (3) we deduce that $g \circ f = e^{\rightarrow}$ and so $(s'' \circ e)^{\rightarrow} = \hat{f} \circ e^{\rightarrow} = \hat{f} \circ g \circ f = f$. We conclude that, with the exception of certain low-dimensional cases, the weakly regular residuated mappings on $L(V)$ are precisely those induced by semilinear transformations.

EXERCISES

14.1. Prove that the focal ideal of a right regular Baer semigroup $\langle S; k \rangle$ is a group.

14.2. Prove that a binary relation on a set is range-closed if and only if it is right regular. [*Hint*. Use Exercise 13.5(1).]

14.3. Let E be an ordered set and let $f \in \text{Res}(E)$. Show that the following conditions are equivalent:

(1) there exists an idempotent $a \in \text{Res}(E)$ such that $\text{Im}\, a = \text{Im} f$ and $\text{Im}\, a^+ = \text{Im} f^+$;

(2) there exists $g \in \text{Res}(E)$ such that $f = f \circ g \circ f$, $g = g \circ f \circ g$ and $f \circ g = g \circ f$.

14.4. Let L be a finite chain. Prove that $\text{Res}(L)$ is regular in the von Neumann sense. [*Hint*. Let $f \in \text{Res}(L)$ and define g by

$$g(x) = \begin{cases} f^+(x) & \text{if } x \neq 0; \\ 0 & \text{if } x = 0. \end{cases}$$

Use Exercise 2.12 to show that $g \in \text{Res}(L)$ and then note that $f = f \circ g \circ f$.]

15. Decreasing Baer semigroups

By a *decreasing map* on an ordered set E we shall mean a map $f: E \to E$ which is such that $f \leq \text{id}_E$. In this section we shall first discuss decreasing residuated maps and then focus our attention on Baer semigroups in which every induced residuated map is decreasing. We shall see that this type of semigroup is intimately connected with a certain class of infinitely distributive lattices.

We begin with a study of residuated dual closure maps on a lattice L. Recall first that by Theorem 2.10 any such mapping f has the property that

$f = f \circ f^+$ and $f^+ = f^+ \circ f$. It is immediate from this that $f(x) = f(y)$ if and only if $f^+(x) = f^+(y)$. Let R_f be the equivalence relation associated with f and note that if $x \equiv y(R_f)$, then $(\forall t \in L)\ f(x \cup t) = f(x) \cup f(t) = f(y) \cup f(t) = f(y \cup t)$ and so $x \cup t \equiv y \cup t(R_f)$. In a similar way, since $f(x) = f(y) \Rightarrow f^+(x) = f^+(y)$, we can show that $f^+(x \cap t) = f^+(y \cap t)$ and hence deduce that $x \cap t \equiv y \cap t(R_f)$. This shows that R_f is a congruence relation on L. But even more can be said. For if $f(x) = f(y)$, then $f^+(x) = f^+(y)$ and $f(x) \leq y \leq f^+(x)$. On the other hand, if $f(x) \leq y \leq f^+(x)$, then $f(x) = (f \circ f)(x) \leq f(y) \leq (f \circ f^+)(x) = f(x)$ shows that $f(x) = f(y)$. We thus have

$$x \equiv y(R_f) \Leftrightarrow f(x) \leq y \leq f^+(x)$$

and so R_f has bounded congruence classes. Furthermore, f may be recaptured from R_f since

$$(\forall x \in L) \quad f(x) = \cap \{y \in L;\ y \equiv x(R_f)\}.$$

Suppose now that R is a congruence relation on L with bounded classes, say $(\forall x \in L)\ x/R = [x_R, x^R]$. Then, defining mappings $f, g : L \to L$ by the prescriptions $f(x) = x_R$ and $g(x) = x^R$, we see that

$$\begin{aligned} x \leq y \Rightarrow x = x \cap y \Rightarrow x_R &\equiv x_R \cap y \equiv x_R \cap y_R(R) \\ &\Rightarrow x_R \leq x \equiv x_R \cap y_R(R) \\ &\Rightarrow x_R = x_R \cap y_R \leq y_R, \end{aligned}$$

and in a similar way $x \leq y \Rightarrow x^R \leq y^R$. This shows that f, g are isotone. We now observe that $f \circ g = f \leq \mathrm{id}_L$ and $g \circ f = g \geq \mathrm{id}_L$ and so it follows that f is a residuated dual closure map with $f^+ = g$. The original congruence relation may be recaptured from f since $x \equiv y(R) \Leftrightarrow f(x) = f(y)$. We have therefore proved the following result:

THEOREM 15.1. *Let L be a lattice. If R is a congruence relation on L with bounded classes then the mapping described by $x \to \cap \{y \in L;\ y \in x/R\}$ is a residuated dual closure map. If, conversely, f is a residuated dual closure map and R_f is the associated equivalence then R_f is a congruence relation on L having bounded classes. Moreover, the mapping described by $f \to R_f$*

sets up a bijection between the residuated dual closure maps on L and the congruence relations on L which have bounded classes.

The reader may find it instructive to compare the above discussion with his solution of Exercises 6.7 and 6.8.

We next dispose of the question of when a residuated dual closure mapping is range-closed or dually range-closed.

THEOREM 15.2. *Let f be a residuated dual closure mapping on the bounded ordered set E. Then*

(1) *f is range-closed $\Leftrightarrow (\forall x \in E)\ x \cap f(\pi)$ exists and equals $f(x)$;*

(2) *f is dually range-closed $\Leftrightarrow (\forall x \in E)\ x \cup f^+(0)$ exists and equals $f^+(x)$.*

Proof. (1) By Theorem 13.1, f is range-closed if and only if $(\forall x \in E)$ $x \cap f(\pi)$ exists and equals $(f \circ f^+)(x)$. But by Theorem 2.10 we have $f = f \circ f^+$. (2) is established similarly.

We next show that in a fairly wide class of lattices *every* decreasing residuated mapping is of the form $x \to x \cap z$, where z is central and use this to generalize Theorem 9.4.

THEOREM 15.3. *Let L be a lattice which is both section and dual section semicomplemented. If f is a decreasing residuated mapping on L then $f(\pi)$ is central and $(\forall x \in L)\ f(x) = x \cap f(\pi)$.*

Proof. For arbitrary $x \in L$ we evidently have $x \geq [x \cap f(\pi)] \cup [x \cap f^+(0)]$. Let $y \leq x$ be chosen such that $y \cap \{[x \cap f(\pi)] \cup [x \cap f^+(0)]\} = 0$. Then

$$y \cap f(\pi) = y \cap x \cap f(\pi) \leq y \cap \{[x \cap f(\pi)] \cup [x \cup f^+(0)]\} = 0$$

and so $y \cap f(\pi) = 0$. Similarly, we can show that $y \cap f^+(0) = 0$. Since f is decreasing, we clearly have $f(y) \leq y \cap f(\pi) = 0$ and so $y \leq f^+(0)$ whence $y = y \cap f^+(0) = 0$. Since L is section semicomplemented we deduce that $x = [x \cap f(\pi)] \cup [x \cap f^+(0)]$. The same type of argument applied to the dual of L will yield $x = [x \cup f(\pi)] \cap [x \cup f^+(0)]$. It follows by Theorem 9.2 that $f(\pi)$ is central with $f^+(0)$ as its unique complement. The proof is completed by noting that $f(x) \leq x \cap f(\pi)$ and if $y \leq x \cap f(\pi)$ is such that $y \cap f(x) = 0$ then $f(y) \leq y \cap f(x)$ implies

$f(y) = 0$ and so $y \leq f^+(0)$. Since also $y \leq f(\pi)$ we deduce that $y = 0$ and consequently $f(x) = x \cap f(\pi)$.

THEOREM 15.4. *Let L be a complete lattice which is both section and dual section semicomplemented. Then the centre of L is a complete sublattice of L.*

Proof. Let $\{z_\alpha; \alpha \in A\}$ be a family of central elements. For each $\alpha \in A$ define f_α by the prescription $f_\alpha(x) = x \cap z_\alpha$. Note that each f_α is a decreasing residuated mapping on L. Now let $f: L \to L$ be described by $f(x) = \bigcup_{\alpha \in A} f_\alpha(x)$. We have f decreasing and so, by Theorem 15.3, $f(\pi)$ is central. But $f(\pi) = \bigcup_{\alpha \in A} f_\alpha(\pi) = \bigcup_{\alpha \in A} z_\alpha$. A dual argument produces the fact that $\bigcap_{\alpha \in A} z_\alpha$ is central.

We now turn to the consideration of *decreasing Baer semigroups*; i.e. Baer semigroups $\langle S; k \rangle$ in which each induced residuated mapping φ_x on $\mathscr{R}_k(S)$ is decreasing. The next result translates this condition into some interesting multiplicative properties of the semigroup $\langle S; k \rangle$. In this result, e and f denote idempotents as usual.

THEOREM 15.5. *For a Baer semigroup $\langle S; k \rangle$ the following conditions are equivalent:*

(1) *S is decreasing;*
(2) $(\forall x \in S)$ *$R_k(x)$ is a two-sided ideal;*
(3) $xy \in kS \Rightarrow xSy \subseteq kS$;
(4) $eS \in \mathscr{R}_k(S) \Rightarrow (\forall x \in S)\ xe = exe$;
(5) $eS \in \mathscr{R}_k(S) \Leftrightarrow Se = eSe$;
(6) $eS \in \mathscr{R}_k(S) \Rightarrow eSe$ *is a left ideal;*
(7) $Sf \in \mathscr{L}_k(S) \Rightarrow (\forall x \in S)\ fx = fxf$;
(8) $Sf \in \mathscr{L}_k(S) \Rightarrow fS = fSf$;
(9) $Sf \in \mathscr{L}_k(S) \Rightarrow fSf$ *is a right ideal.*

Proof. (1) $\Rightarrow$ (2): Let $eS = R_k(x)$. Then $(\forall y \in S)\ \varphi_y(eS) \subseteq eS$ gives $ye \in eS$ and so eS is a left as well as a right ideal of S.

(2) $\Rightarrow$ (4): Let eS be a two-sided ideal of S. Then $e = ee \in eS$ and so $(\forall x \in S)\ xe \in eS$ from which it follows that $xe = exe$.

(4) ⇒ (5): If $y \in Se$, then there exists $x \in S$ such that $y = xe$. By (4), $y = xe = exe \in eSe$ and so $Se \subseteq eSe$. The reverse inclusion is obvious.

(5) ⇒ (6): If $Se = eSe$, then eSe is a left ideal.

(6) ⇒ (3): Let $xy \in kS$ and let $eS = (R_k^{\rightarrow} \circ L_k)(y)$. Then $L_k(y) = L_k(e)$ and so $xe \in kS$. Since $e = eee \in eSe$ we have $(\forall w \in S)$ $we \in eSe$ and so $we = ewe$ and $xwe = xewe \in kS$. It follows that $xwy \in kS$ and hence that $xSy \subseteq kS$.

(3) ⇒ (1): Let $eS \in \mathscr{R}_k(S)$ and let $x \in S$. Then if $we \in kS$ we must have $wxe \in kS$. Thus $L_k(e) \subseteq L_k(xe)$ and $\varphi_x(eS) = (R_k^{\rightarrow} \circ L_k)(xe) \subseteq (R_k^{\rightarrow} \circ L_k)(e) = eS$ whence φ_x is decreasing.

The remaining equivalences follow from the symmetry of condition (3).

Corollary. *Every abelian Baer semigroup is decreasing.*

The question now arises as to which lattices may be coordinatized by a decreasing Baer semigroup. The answer is provided by:

Theorem 15.6. *A lattice L may be coordinatized by a decreasing Baer semigroup if and only if, for each $y \in L$, the translation $x \rightarrow x \cap y$ is residuated and the translation $x \rightarrow x \cup y$ is dually residuated.*

Proof. Let $\langle S; k \rangle$ be a decreasing Baer semigroup and let $eS, fS \in \mathscr{R}_k(S)$ with e, f idempotent. By Theorem 13.8, f is range-closed and so, by Theorem 15.2, $\varphi_f(eS) = eS \cap fS$. Thus the translation $eS \rightarrow eS \cap fS$ is residuated. Letting $Se^{\#} = L_k(e)$, $Sf^{\#} = L_k(f)$ and using the obvious right/left symmetry of Theorem 15.5, we also have the translation $Se^{\#} \rightarrow Se^{\#} \cap Sf^{\#}$ residuated on $\mathscr{L}_k(S)$. Taking right k-annihilators, this shows that $eS \rightarrow eS \cup fS$ is dually residuated on $\mathscr{R}_k(S)$.

Suppose, on the other hand, that L is a lattice in which, for all y, the translation $x \rightarrow x \cap y$ is residuated and the translation $x \rightarrow x \cup y$ is dually residuated. Evidently L is then bounded. For each $y \in L$ define $\mu_y(x) = x \cap y$ and let ν_y be the unique residuated map such that $\nu_y^+(x) = x \cup y$. Let S be the semigroup formed by the decreasing residuated maps on L and note that $(\forall y \in L)\, \mu_y, \nu_y \in S$. If $f, g \in S$ then by Theorem 12.4 we have $f \circ g = 0$ if and only if $g(\pi) \leq f^+(0)$. Let $y = f^+(0)$. If $g(\pi) \leq y$ then $g = \mu_y \circ g$ and if $g = \mu_y \circ g$ we have $g(\pi) = \mu_y[g(\pi)] = g(\pi) \cap y \leq y$. It follows that $R(f) = \mu_y \circ S$. Similarly, we have $L(f) = S \circ \nu_w$ where $w = f(\pi)$. Thus S is a Baer semigroup. Furthermore, as in the proof of Theorem 12.5, the mapping $\mu_y \circ S \to y$ is an isomorphism of $\mathscr{R}(S)$ onto L. It is immediate that S is a decreasing Baer semigroup which coordinatizes L.

Making use of the fact that a complete lattice is infinitely distributive if and only if it satisfies the conditions of the previous theorem, we have the following:

COROLLARY. *A complete lattice is infinitely distributive if and only if it can be coordinatized by a decreasing Baer semigroup. A finite lattice is distributive if and only if it can be so coordinatized.*

As a final item for this section, we present a semigroup characterization of the centre of the lattice of right k-annihilators of a decreasing Baer semigroup.

THEOREM 15.7. *Let $\langle S; k\rangle$ be a decreasing Baer semigroup and let $eS \in \mathscr{R}_k(S)$ with $e = e^2$. The following conditions are then equivalent:*

(1) *eS has a complement in $\mathscr{R}_k(S)$;*

(2) *$Se \in \mathscr{L}_k(S)$;*

(3) *e is in the centre of S.*

Proof. (1) $\Rightarrow$ (2): Let fS be a complement of eS in $\mathscr{R}_k(S)$ with $f = f^2$. Then, since

$$eS \cap fS = \varphi_e(fS) = (R_k^{\rightarrow} \circ L_k)(ef) = \varphi_f(eS) = (R_k^{\rightarrow} \circ L_k)(fe),$$

we must have $ef \in kS$ and $fe \in kS$. Letting $Se' = L_k(e)$ and $Sf' = L_k(f)$, we have $e = ef'$. Also, $eS \vee fS = 1S$ implies that $kS = L_k(1) = L_k^{\rightarrow}(eS \vee fS) = Se' \cap Sf'$. By an argument dual to the onc given above, we can show that $e'f' \in kS$ and $f'e' \in kS$. But $e'f' \in kS$ implies $f' \in R_k(e') = (R_k^{\rightarrow} \circ L_k)(e) = eS$ and so $f' = ef'$. It follows that $e = f'$ and so $Se \in \mathscr{L}_k(S)$.

(2) $\Rightarrow$ (3): This follows from Theorem 15.5.

(3) $\Rightarrow$ (1): Let e belong to the centre of S, let $Sf = L_k(e)$ and let $gS = R_k(e)$, where f, g are idempotent. Then $fe \in kS \Rightarrow ef \in kS \Rightarrow f = gf$. Similarly $eg \in kS \Rightarrow ge \in kS \Rightarrow g = gf$. It follows that $f = g$. Thus we have $Sf \in \mathscr{L}_k(S)$ and $fS \in \mathscr{R}_k(S)$, so by Theorem 15.5 we have $(\forall x \in S)$ $fx = fxf = xf$. The same argument applied to f in place of e now shows

that since $eS = R_k(f)$ we must have $Se = L_k(f)$. Clearly $eS \cap fS = kS$, and since $Se \cap Sf = kS$ we have that $1S = R_k^{\rightarrow}(kS) = R_k^{\rightarrow}(Se \cap Sf) = fS \curlyvee eS$ so fS is a complement of eS in $R_k(S)$.

EXERCISES

15.1. Let f be a decreasing residuated mapping on a bounded semicomplemented lattice. Show that $f(\pi) \cup f^+(0) = \pi$.

15.2. Let f be a decreasing residuated mapping on a bounded section semicomplemented lattice L. Show that

$$(\forall x \in L) \quad x = f(x) \cup [x \cap f^+(0)].$$

[*Hint*. Apply Exercise 15.1 to the interval $[0, x]$.] Deduce that f is idempotent and show finally that

$$f(\pi) \cap f^+(0) = 0 \Leftrightarrow (\forall x \in L)\ f(x) = x \cap f(\pi).$$

15.3. Prove that the multiplicative semigroup of a Baer ring A is decreasing if and only if every idempotent of A is central.

15.4. Let $(X, \mathscr{T})$ be a T_1-topological space and let R be a continuous relation on X. Show that the induced residuated mapping η_R on the lattice of closed subsets of X is decreasing if and only if there exists an open subset A of X such that $R = \{(x, x); x \in A\}$.

15.5. Let $\langle S; k\rangle$ be a Baer semigroup and let Z be its centre. Show that $\langle Z, k\rangle$ is a decreasing Baer semigroup such that $\mathscr{R}_k(Z)$ is a Boolean algebra.

15.6. Let $\langle S; k\rangle$ be a Baer semigroup with $eS \in \mathscr{R}_k(S)$. Show that eS is a two-sided ideal of S if and only if $L_k(e)$ is a two-sided ideal. Deduce that the set $\{eS \in \mathscr{R}_k(S);$ eS is an ideal$\}$ forms a sublattice of $\mathscr{R}_k(S)$. [*Hint*. The intersection operation in $\mathscr{R}_k(S)$ is set-theoretic while the union operation is given by

$$eS \curlyvee fS = R_k^{\rightarrow}[L_k(e) \cap L_k(f)].]$$

15.7. Let $\langle S; k\rangle$ be a decreasing strongly regular Baer semigroup and let $eS \in \mathscr{R}_k(S)$ with $e = e^2$. Define $G_e = \{x \in S; (R_k^{\rightarrow} \circ L_k)(x) = eS\}$. Prove that:

(1) e is in the centre of S;
(2) G_e is a subsemigroup of S which is in its own right a group;
(3) S is the disjoint union of the family of groups

$$\{G_e; eS \in \mathscr{R}_k(S)\}.$$

[*Hint*. To show that $x, y \in G_e \Rightarrow xy \in G_e$ argue that $L_k(xy) = L_k(xe) = L_k(ex) = L_k(x)$ and deduce that $(R_k^{\rightarrow} \circ L_k)(xy) = eS$.]

16. Annihilator-preserving homomorphisms

In the study of any branch of algebra the "structure preserving" mappings are of great importance. In the theory of Baer semigroups we have to consider, in addition to the semigroup structure, the crucial annihilator properties. We are thus led to define some sort of "annihilator-preserving" homomorphism. We begin by establishing some notation which we shall use throughout this section.

$\langle S; k\rangle$ will always denote a Baer semigroup and e, g, h will always denote idempotents elements of S. If f is a homomorphism of S into the semigroup T we shall agree to write $f(x) = \bar{x}$ for each $x \in S$ and $\operatorname{Im} f = \bar{S}$. For each subset A of S we write as usual $f^{\rightarrow}(A) = \{f(a); a \in A\}$. It is clear that $\bar{k}$ is a central idempotent in $\bar{S}$. We wish to consider annihilators in $\bar{S}$ with respect to the ideal $\bar{k}\bar{S}$. Accordingly, we define

$$R_{\bar{k}}(\bar{x}) = \{\bar{y} \in \bar{S};\quad \bar{x}\bar{y} \in \bar{k}\bar{S}\};\qquad L_{\bar{k}}(\bar{x}) = \{\bar{y} \in \bar{S};\quad \bar{y}\bar{x} \in \bar{k}\bar{S}\}.$$

Now if $xy \in kS$, then clearly $\bar{x}\bar{y} \in \bar{k}\bar{S}$ and so $(f^{\rightarrow} \circ R_k)(x) \subseteq R_{\bar{k}}(\bar{x}) = (R_{\bar{k}} \circ f)(x)$. Similarly, $(f^{\rightarrow} \circ L_k)(x) \subseteq (L_{\bar{k}} \circ f)(x)$. To see that equality does not hold in general, we present the following example:

Now S and T are pseudo-complemented lattices which may be regarded as Baer semigroups with respect to intersection, the foci being $0, \bar{0}$. If we define $f: S \to T$ by setting $f(x) = \bar{x}$ if $x \neq z$ and $f(z) = \bar{0}$, then f is a semigroup homomorphism of S onto T. Note that in T we have $R_{\{\bar{0}\}}(\bar{a}) = \{0, \bar{b}\}$ but $f^{\rightarrow}[R_{\{0\}}(a)] = \{f(0)\} = \{\bar{0}\}$. Now this is precisely the sort of thing we wish to avoid, and leads us to the following definition:

Definition. Let f be a homomorphism of S into the semigroup T. We shall call f *annihilator-preserving* or an *AP-homomorphism* if and only if

$$(1)\quad f^{\rightarrow} \circ R_k = R_{\bar{k}} \circ f \quad\text{and}\quad (2)\quad f^{\rightarrow} \circ L_k = L_{\bar{k}} \circ f.$$

We shall speak of f as being an AP-homomorphism of $\langle S; k\rangle$ into the Baer semigroup $\langle T; j\rangle$ if in addition to (1) and (2) we have

$$(3)\quad f(k) = j.$$

THEOREM 16.1. *Let f be an AP-homomorphism of $\langle S; k\rangle$ into the semigroup T. Then $\langle \bar{S}; \bar{k}\rangle$ is a Baer semigroup.*

Proof. Let $x \in S$ with $R_k(x) = eS$. Then if $\bar{y} = \bar{e}\bar{y}$ we have

$$f(xy) = f(x)f(y) = f(x)f(ey) = f(xe)f(y) = f(xek)f(y) = \bar{x}\bar{e}\bar{k}\bar{y} \in \bar{k}\bar{S}.$$

If $\bar{x}\bar{y} \in \bar{k}\bar{S}$, then $\bar{y} \in (R_{\bar{k}} \circ f)(x) = (f^{\to} \circ R_k)(x)$ implies that $\bar{y} = f(w)$ for some $w \in R_k(x)$. But then $w = ew$ forces $\bar{y} = \bar{e}\bar{y}$ and so $R_{\bar{k}}(\bar{x}) = \bar{e}\bar{S}$. Similarly, if $L_k(x) = Sg$, then $L_{\bar{k}}(\bar{x}) = \bar{S}\bar{g}$.

Remark. It is important to note from the above proof that if $eS = R_k(x)$, then $f^{\to}(eS) = (f^{\to} \circ R_k)(x) = (R_{\bar{k}} \circ f)(x) = \bar{e}\bar{S} \in \mathcal{R}_{\bar{k}}(\bar{S})$. Similarly, if $Sg \in \mathcal{L}_k(S)$, then $f^{\to}(Sg) = \bar{S}\bar{g} \in \mathcal{L}_{\bar{k}}(\bar{S})$. We shall find it convenient to let $\varphi_{\bar{x}}, \eta_{\bar{x}}$ denote the residuated maps induced by $\bar{x}$ on $\mathcal{R}_{\bar{k}}(\bar{S})$, $\mathcal{L}_{\bar{k}}(\bar{S})$. Although this notation is in a sense ambiguous, the reader should have little trouble in remembering that if $x \in S$, then $\varphi_x \in \text{Res}\,[\mathcal{R}_k(S)]$ while for $\bar{x} \in \bar{S}$ we have $\varphi_{\bar{x}} \in \text{Res}\,[\mathcal{R}_{\bar{k}}(\bar{S})]$. It is also worth mentioning at this stage that, in view of the previous theorem, we may restrict our attention without loss of generality to AP-homomorphisms of $\langle S; k\rangle$ onto a Baer semigroup $\langle \bar{S}; \bar{k}\rangle$.

THEOREM 16.2. *Let f be an AP-homomorphism of $\langle S; k\rangle$ onto the Baer semigroup $\langle \bar{S}; \bar{k}\rangle$. Then, for each $x \in S$, $f^{\to} \circ \varphi_x = \varphi_{\bar{x}} \circ f^{\to}$ with $f^{\to} \circ \varphi_x^+ = \varphi_{\bar{x}}^+ \circ f^{\to}$ and $f^{\to} \circ \eta_x = \eta_{\bar{x}} \circ f^{\to}$ with $f^{\to} \circ \eta_x^+ = \eta_{\bar{x}}^+ \circ f^{\to}$. It follows that the restriction of $f^{\to}$ to $\mathcal{R}_k(S)$ is a lattice epimorphism of $\mathcal{R}_k(S)$ onto $\mathcal{R}_{\bar{k}}(\bar{S})$.*

Proof. In the interest of notational convenience, let us identify the mappings L_k, $\hat{L}_k$ and $L_k^{\to}$ as well as the mappings R_k, $\hat{R}_k$ and $R_k^{\to}$ of Theorem 12.1. With this done, we have

$$\begin{aligned}(f^{\to} \circ \varphi_x)(eS) = (f^{\to} \circ R_k \circ L_k)(xe) &= (R_{\bar{k}} \circ f^{\to} \circ L_k)(xe)\\ &= (R_{\bar{k}} \circ L_{\bar{k}} \circ f)(xe)\\ &= \varphi_{\bar{x}}(\bar{e}\bar{S})\\ &= (\varphi_{\bar{x}} \circ f^{\to})(eS).\end{aligned}$$

Similarly, we can show that $f^{\rightarrow} \circ \eta_x = \eta_{\bar{x}} \circ f^{\rightarrow}$. We may now write

$$
\begin{aligned}
f^{\rightarrow} \circ \varphi_x^+ = f^{\rightarrow} \circ R_k \circ \eta_x \circ L_k = R_{\bar{k}} \circ f^{\rightarrow} \circ \eta_x \circ L_k &= R_{\bar{k}} \circ \eta_{\bar{x}} \circ f^{\rightarrow} \circ L_k \\
&= R_{\bar{k}} \circ \eta_{\bar{x}} \circ L_{\bar{k}} \circ f^{\rightarrow} \\
&= \varphi_{\bar{x}}^+ \circ f.
\end{aligned}
$$

A dual argument shows that $f^{\rightarrow} \circ \eta_x^+ = \eta_{\bar{x}}^+ \circ f^{\rightarrow}$. To see that the restriction of $f^{\rightarrow}$ to $\mathscr{R}_k(S)$ is a lattice homomorphism we now recall that, by Theorem 13.1, $eS \cap gS = (\varphi_g \circ \varphi_g^+)(eS)$ for all $eS, gS \in \mathscr{R}_k(S)$. Hence

$$
\begin{aligned}
f^{\rightarrow}(eS \cap gS) = (f^{\rightarrow} \circ \varphi_g \circ \varphi_g^+)(eS) &= (\varphi_{\bar{g}} \circ \varphi_{\bar{g}}^+ \circ f^{\rightarrow})(eS) \\
&= (\varphi_{\bar{g}} \circ \varphi_{\bar{g}}^+)(\bar{e}\bar{S}) \\
&= \bar{e}\bar{S} \cap \bar{g}\bar{S}.
\end{aligned}
$$

Similarly, $f^{\rightarrow}(eS \curlyvee gS) = \bar{e}\bar{S} \curlyvee \bar{g}\bar{S}$. That $f^{\rightarrow}$ maps $\mathscr{R}_k(S)$ onto $\mathscr{R}_{\bar{k}}(\bar{S})$ follows from the fact that f maps S onto $\bar{S}$.

The identification of L_k, $\hat{L}_k$ and $L_k^{\rightarrow}$ [resp. R_k, $\hat{R}_k$ and $R_k^{\rightarrow}$] will remain in force for the rest of this section.

We now switch our viewpoint from the external consideration of AP-homomorphisms to the internal consideration of the induced congruence relations. An equivalence relation E on a semigroup S will be called a *congruence* on S if and only if it is compatible on both the left and the right with the law of composition of S. Thus E is a congruence relation if and only if it is an equivalence relation such that $x \equiv y(E) \Rightarrow (\forall s \in S)\, xs \equiv ys(E)$ and $sx \equiv sy\,(E)$. As usual, we write $x/E = \{y \in S;\ y \equiv x(E)\}$ and $S/E = \{x/E;\ x \in S\}$. The quotient S/E can, whenever E is a congruence, be made into a semigroup by defining $(x/E) \odot (y/E) = (xy)/E$. Once this occurs, the canonical surjection $\natural_E : S \rightarrow S/E$ is a semigroup epimorphism of S onto S/E. Now if E is a congruence relation on the Baer semigroup $\langle S; k \rangle$ we shall agree to call E an AP-congruence whenever $\natural_E$ is annihilator-preserving. By Theorems 16.1 and 16.2, if E is an AP-congruence, then $\langle S/E; k/E \rangle$ is a Baer semigroup with $\mathscr{R}_{k/E}(S/E)$ a homomorphic image of $\mathscr{R}_k(S)$. We also have the following version of the "Fundamental Theorem of Homomorphisms":

THEOREM 16.3. *Let f be an AP-homomorphism of $\langle S; k \rangle$ onto the Baer semigroup $\langle \bar{S}; \bar{k} \rangle$. If E is the equivalence defined by $x \equiv y(E) \Leftrightarrow f(x)$*

$= f(y)$ then E is an AP-congruence and there is a unique isomorphism $\bar{f}$ which makes the following diagram commutative:

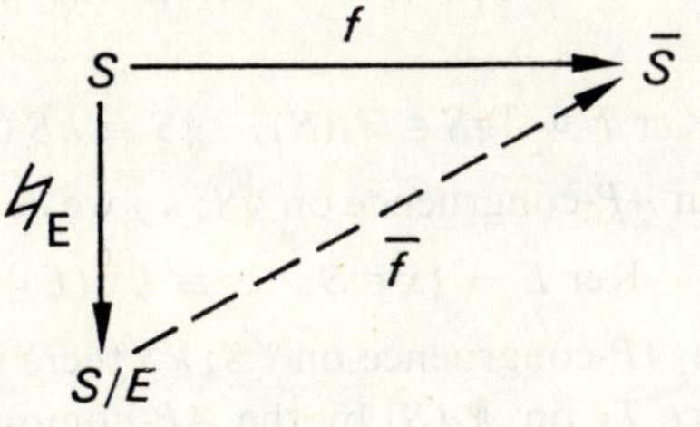

Furthermore, there is a unique lattice isomorphism $\bar{f}^{\to}$ which makes the following diagram commutative:

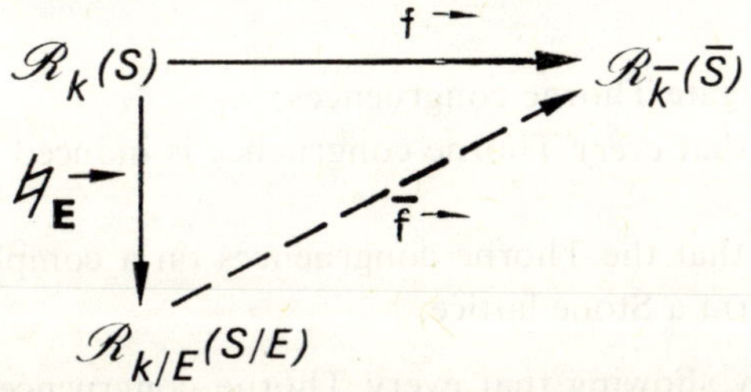

Proof. That E is an *AP*-congruence follows quickly from the fact that f is an *AP*-homomorphism. The mapping $\bar{f}$ is defined by $\bar{f}(x/E) = f(x)$ and the mapping $\bar{f}^{\to}$ by $\bar{f}^{\to}(g/E \odot S/E) = f^{\to}(gS)$. The routine proof of this theorem will be left as an exercise.

Suppose now that f is an *AP*-homomorphism of $\langle S; k\rangle$ onto the Baer semigroup $\langle \bar{S}; \bar{k}\rangle$. We have already seen that f induces a lattice epimorphism of $\mathscr{R}_k(S)$ onto $\mathscr{R}_{\bar{k}}(\bar{S})$. The resulting congruence relation T on $\mathscr{R}_k(S)$ which is given by

$$gS \equiv hS\,(T) \Leftrightarrow f^{\to}(gS) = f^{\to}(hS)$$

then satisfies (see Theorem 16.2)

$$gS \equiv hS\,(T) \Rightarrow (\forall x \in S)\begin{cases} \varphi_x(gS) \equiv \varphi_x(hS)\,(T) \\ \varphi_x^{+}(gS) \equiv \varphi_x^{+}(hS)\,(T). \end{cases}$$

An equivalence relation on $\mathscr{R}_k(S)$ which satisfies the above condition is evidently a lattice congruence; such a congruence relation will hereafter be called a *Thorne congruence*. We define the *kernel* of the Thorne congruence T by

$$\operatorname{Ker} T = \{gS \in \mathscr{R}_k(S);\quad gS \equiv kS\,(T)\}.$$

Similarly, if E is an AP-congruence on $\langle S; k\rangle$ we define the *kernel* of E by

$$\operatorname{Ker} E = \{x \in S;\quad x \equiv kx\,(E)\}.$$

Now if E is an AP-congruence on $\langle S; k\rangle$ there is induced naturally a Thorne congruence T_E on $\mathscr{R}_k(S)$ by the AP-homomorphism $\natural_E$. This is defined by

$$gS \equiv hS\,(T_E) \Leftrightarrow \natural_E^{\rightarrow}(gS) = \natural_E^{\rightarrow}(hS).$$

Thus $gS \equiv hS(T_E)$ if and only if $g \equiv hg\,(E)$ and $h \equiv gh\,(E)$. Our goal is now threefold:

(1) to investigate Thorne congruences;

(2) to show that *every* Thorne congruence is induced by an AP-congruence;

(3) to show that the Thorne congruences on a complete Baer semigroup form a Stone lattice.

We begin by showing that every Thorne congruence is determined naturally by its kernel in a manner analogous to that of section complemented lattices as shown in Theorem 10.11. In connection with this, it will prove convenient to denote by $x^{\#}$ an idempotent generator of $L_k(x)$.

THEOREM 16.4. *Let T be a Thorne congruence on $\mathscr{R}_k(S)$. The following conditions are then equivalent:*

(1) $gS \equiv hS\,(T)$;

(2) $\varphi_h^{\#}(gS) \curlyvee \varphi_g^{\#}(hS) \in \operatorname{Ker} T$;

(3) $(\exists eS \in \mathscr{R}_k(S))\; gS \curlyvee eS = hS \curlyvee eS\; [= gS \curlyvee hS]$;

(4) $(\exists eS \in \mathscr{R}_k(S))\; gS \curlyvee hS = (gS \cap hS) \curlyvee eS$.

Proof. (1) $\Rightarrow$ (2): Since $gS \equiv hS\,(T)$ and T is a Thorne congruence we must have $\varphi_h^{\#}(gS) \equiv \varphi_h^{\#}(hS)\,(T)$. But $\varphi_h^{\#}(hS) = R_kL_k(h^{\#}h) = kS$ whence $\varphi_h^{\#}(gS) \in \operatorname{Ker} T$. Similarly, $\varphi_g^{\#}(hS) \in \operatorname{Ker} T$, and since T is a lattice congruence the union of these two elements must also be in $\operatorname{Ker} T$.

(2) ⇒ (3): Let $eS = \varphi_g^{\#}(hS) \curlyvee \varphi_h^{\#}(gS)$. We wish to show that $gS \curlyvee eS = hS \curlyvee eS$, i.e. that

$$gS \curlyvee R_kL_k(g^{\#}h) \curlyvee R_kL_k(h^{\#}g) = hS \curlyvee R_kL_k(g^{\#}h) \curlyvee R_kL_k(h^{\#}g).$$

This is clearly equivalent to showing that

$$Sg^{\#} \cap L_k(g^{\#}h) \cap L_k(h^{\#}g) = Sh^{\#} \cap L_k(g^{\#}h) \cap L_k(h^{\#}g).$$

If x is an element of the right-hand side of this equality then $x = xh^{\#}$ and $xg = xh^{\#}g \in kS$ imply that $x \in L_k(g) = Sg^{\#}$. This evidently puts x in the left-hand side. A symmetric argument produces the reverse inclusion.

In order to show that $gS \curlyvee eS = hS \curlyvee eS = gS \curlyvee hS$ we need only show that $eS \subseteq gS \curlyvee hS$. This is equivalent to showing that

$$Sg^{\#} \cap Sh^{\#} \subseteq L_k(eS) = L_k(g^{\#}h) \cap L_k(h^{\#}g).$$

But if $x \in Sg^{\#} \cap Sh^{\#}$ then $x = xg^{\#}$ and $x = xh^{\#}$ and so $xg^{\#}h = xh = xh^{\#}h \in kS$ and similarly $xh^{\#}g \in kS$.

(3) ⇒ (1): This is clear, as is (4) ⇒ (1).

(1) ⇒ (4): Let $gS \equiv hS\,(T)$; then $gS \curlyvee hS \equiv gS \cap hS\,(T)$ and so by (3) we have $gS \curlyvee hS = (gS \cap hS) \curlyvee eS$ for some $eS \in \operatorname{Ker} T$.

The next result, when combined with the previous theorem, shows that if E is an AP-congruence on $\langle S; k\rangle$, then T_E is determined by the kernel of E.

THEOREM 16.5. *Let E be an AP-congruence on $\langle S; k\rangle$. Then*

$$x \in \operatorname{Ker} E \Leftrightarrow R_kL_k(x) \in \operatorname{Ker} T_E.$$

Proof. If $x \in \operatorname{Ker} E$ then $\natural_E(x) \in k/E \odot S/E$ and so

$$(\natural_E^{\rightarrow} \circ R_k \circ L_k)(x) = (R_{k/E} \circ L_{k/E} \circ \natural_E)(x) = k/E \odot S/E.$$

Thus if $gS = R_kL_k(x)$ we must have $\natural_E^{\rightarrow}(gS) = \natural_E^{\rightarrow}(kS)$ and so $gS \in \operatorname{Ker} T_E$. If, on the other hand, $gS \in \operatorname{Ker} T_E$, then $\natural_E^{\rightarrow}(gS) = \natural_E^{\rightarrow}(kS)$ implies $g \equiv kg\,(E)$ and so $x = gx \equiv kgx\,(E)$ and $x \in \operatorname{Ker} E$.

It is a little startling that T_E should be determined by Ker E since E is not itself so determined. We present an example to illustrate the point. The congruence defined by equality on S is clearly an AP-congruence, as is the congruence E defined by $x \equiv y(E) \Leftrightarrow \varphi_x = \varphi_y$ (see the proof of

Theorem 12.8). These two congruences are in general distinct yet they have the same kernel!

We now wish to show that every Thorne congruence is induced by an AP-congruence. It turns out to be easier notationally to phrase the results in terms of homomorphisms rather than congruence relations. Accordingly, let $\langle S; k\rangle$ and $\langle \bar{S}; \bar{k}\rangle$ be two Baer semigroups. Let $f: \mathscr{R}_k(S) \to \mathscr{R}_{\bar{k}}(\bar{S})$ be a surjective mapping such that $(\forall x \in S)\, f(gS) = f(hS) \Rightarrow (f \circ \varphi_x)(gS) = (f \circ \varphi_x)(hS)$ and $(f \circ \varphi_x^+)(gS) = (f \circ \varphi_x^+)(hS)$. Our motivation for this definition comes from the fact that for any Thorne congruence T on $\mathscr{R}_k(S)$ the canonical lattice epimorphism of $\mathscr{R}_k(S)$ onto $\mathscr{R}_k(S)/T$ satisfies this property. It should be noted that f is of necessity a lattice epimorphism. Given $x \in S$ we can define mappings $\bar{\varphi}_x, \bar{\varphi}_x^+ : \mathscr{R}_{\bar{k}}(\bar{S}) \to \mathscr{R}_{\bar{k}}(\bar{S})$ by the prescriptions

$$\bar{\varphi}_x(\bar{g}\bar{S}) = (f \circ \varphi_x)(gS); \quad \bar{\varphi}_x^+(\bar{g}\bar{S}) = (f \circ \varphi_x^+)(gS)$$

where $gS \in \mathscr{R}_k(S)$ and $f(gS) = \bar{g}\bar{S}$. These mappings are evidently well-defined, isotone and make each of the following diagrams commutative:

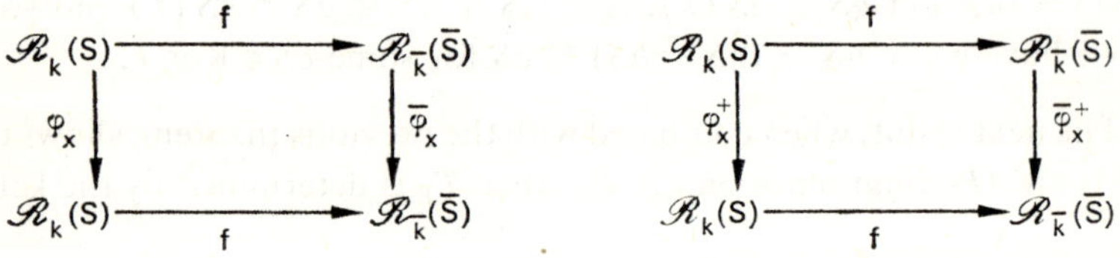

We claim that $\bar{\varphi}_x$ is residuated with $\bar{\varphi}_x^+$ as its associated residual map, thus justifying our notation. We have

$$\bar{\varphi}_x^+ \circ \bar{\varphi}_x \circ f = \bar{\varphi}_x^+ \circ f \circ \varphi_x = f \circ \varphi_x^+ \circ \varphi_x \geq f;$$
$$\bar{\varphi}_x \circ \bar{\varphi}_x^+ \circ f = \bar{\varphi}_x \circ f \circ \varphi_x^+ = f \circ \varphi_x \circ \varphi_x^+ \leq f,$$

from which it follows that

$$\bar{\varphi}_x^+ \circ \bar{\varphi}_x \geq \mathrm{id}_{\mathscr{R}_{\bar{k}}(\bar{S})} \geq \bar{\varphi}_x \circ \bar{\varphi}_x^+,$$

thereby establishing our claim.

Our next assertion is that the mapping $\bar{\varphi}: S \to \mathrm{Res}\,[\mathscr{R}_{\bar{k}}(\bar{S})]$ defined by $\bar{\varphi}(x) = \bar{\varphi}_x$ is an AP-homomorphism. The proof of this will be broken up into a number of parts:

(1) $\bar{\varphi}$ *is a semigroup homomorphism.*

Proof. Given $x, y \in S$ we have

$$\bar{\varphi}_x \circ \bar{\varphi}_y \circ f = \bar{\varphi}_x \circ f \circ \varphi_y = f \circ \varphi_x \circ \varphi_y = f \circ \varphi_{xy} = \bar{\varphi}_{xy} \circ f$$

and so $\bar{\varphi}_x \circ \bar{\varphi}_y = \bar{\varphi}_{xy}$.

(2) *If* $eS = R_k(x)$ *and* $\bar{h}\bar{S} \subseteq \bar{e}\bar{S}$ *then* $\bar{\varphi}_e(\bar{h}\bar{S}) = \bar{h}\bar{S}$.

Proof. If $f(hS) = \bar{h}\bar{S}$, then $f(hS \cap eS) = \bar{h}\bar{S} \cap \bar{e}\bar{S} = \bar{h}\bar{S}$. Hence $\bar{\varphi}_e(\bar{h}\bar{S}) = (\bar{\varphi}_e \circ f)(hS \cap eS) = (f \circ \varphi_e)(hS \cap eS) = f(hS \cap eS) = \bar{h}\bar{S}$. Here, of course, we have made use of the fact that e is a range-closed element of S.

(3) *If* $eS = R_k(x)$ *then* $\bar{\varphi}_x \circ \bar{\varphi}_y = 0 \Leftrightarrow \bar{\varphi}_y = \bar{\varphi}_e \circ \bar{\varphi}_y$.

Proof. If $\bar{\varphi}_y = \bar{\varphi}_e \circ \bar{\varphi}_y$, then by (1) we have

$$\bar{\varphi}_x \circ \bar{\varphi}_y \circ f = \bar{\varphi}_x \circ \bar{\varphi}_e \circ \bar{\varphi}_y \circ f = \bar{\varphi}_{xey} \circ f = f \circ \varphi_{xey} = f \circ \varphi_k$$

from which it follows that $\bar{\varphi}_x \circ \bar{\varphi}_y = 0$. If, on the other hand, $\bar{\varphi}_x \circ \bar{\varphi}_y = 0$, then for each $gS \in \mathscr{R}_k(S)$ we have

$$\begin{aligned}\bar{\varphi}_y(\bar{g}\bar{S}) \subseteq (\bar{\varphi}_x^+ \circ \bar{\varphi}_x \circ \bar{\varphi}_y)(\bar{g}\bar{S}) = \bar{\varphi}_x^+(\bar{k}\bar{S}) &= (f \circ \varphi_x^+)(kS)\\ &= (f \circ R_k)(x)\\ &= f(eS)\\ &= \bar{e}\bar{S}.\end{aligned}$$

Applying (2), we see that $\bar{\varphi}_e[\bar{\varphi}_y(\bar{g}\bar{S})] = \bar{\varphi}_y(\bar{g}\bar{S})$, and since gS is arbitrary we deduce that $\bar{\varphi}_y = \bar{\varphi}_e \circ \bar{\varphi}_y$.

The remainder of the proof is dual to the above but for sake of completeness we shall give a brief sketch of it.

(4) *If* $Sh = L_k(x)$, $h'S = R_k(h)$ *and* $gS \supseteq h'S$ *then* $\bar{\varphi}_h^+(\bar{g}\bar{S}) = \bar{g}\bar{S}$.

Proof. This is dual to (2).

(5) *If* $L_k(x) = Sh$ *then* $\bar{\varphi}_y \circ \bar{\varphi}_x = 0 \Leftrightarrow \bar{\varphi}_y = \bar{\varphi}_y \circ \bar{\varphi}_h$.

Proof. If $\bar{\varphi}_y = \bar{\varphi}_y \circ \bar{\varphi}_h$ we proceed as in (3). If $\bar{\varphi}_y \circ \bar{\varphi}_x = 0$, then for each $gS \in \mathscr{R}_k(S)$ we have

$$\begin{aligned}\bar{\varphi}_y^+(\bar{g}\bar{S}) \supseteq (\bar{\varphi}_x \circ \bar{\varphi}_x^+ \circ \bar{\varphi}_y^+)(\bar{g}\bar{S}) = \bar{\varphi}_x(\bar{1}\bar{S}) &= (f \circ \varphi_x)(1S)\\ &= f[R_k L_k(x)]\\ &= (f \circ R_k)(h).\end{aligned}$$

Making use of (4), we have $(\bar{\varphi}_h^+ \circ \bar{\varphi}_y^+)(\bar{g}\bar{S}) = \bar{\varphi}_y^+(\bar{g}\bar{S})$ so $\bar{\varphi}_y^+ = \bar{\varphi}_h^+ \circ \bar{\varphi}_y^+$. It follows that $\bar{\varphi}_y = \bar{\varphi}_y \circ \bar{\varphi}_h$.

The fact that $\bar{\varphi}$ is an AP-homomorphism is an immediate consequence of (3) and (5). The only thing remaining is to show that if E is the AP-congruence induced on S by $\bar{\varphi}$ and if T is the Thorne congruence induced on $\mathscr{R}_k(S)$ by f then $T = T_E$. Now we observe that

$$x \equiv y(E) \Leftrightarrow \bar{\varphi}(x) = \bar{\varphi}(y); \quad gS \equiv hS\,(T) \Leftrightarrow f(gS) = f(hS).$$

Thus we must establish

(6) $f(gS) = f(hS) \Leftrightarrow \bar{\varphi}^{\rightarrow}(gS) = \bar{\varphi}^{\rightarrow}(hS)$.

By Theorem 16.2 we have $\bar{\varphi}^{\rightarrow}(gS) = \bar{\varphi}_g \circ \text{Res}\,[\mathscr{R}_{\bar{k}}(\bar{S})] \in \mathscr{R}\,[\text{Res}\,[\mathscr{R}_{\bar{k}}(\bar{S})]]$. Also, it was shown in the course of proving Theorem 12.5 that for any bounded lattice L the mapping $\xi \circ \text{Res}\,(L) \to \xi(\pi)$ of $\mathscr{R}\,[\text{Res}\,(L)] \to L$ is an isomorphism. Since the greatest element of $\mathscr{R}_{\bar{k}}(\bar{S})$ is $\bar{1}\bar{S}$ and since

$$\bar{\varphi}_g(\bar{1}\bar{S}) = (\bar{\varphi}_g \circ f)(1S) = (f \circ \varphi_g)(1S) = f(gS),$$

we see that (6) is indeed true, thus completing the proof.

In summary, we have proved:

THEOREM 16.6. *Let T be a Thorne congruence on $\mathscr{R}_k(S)$. Then there exists an AP-congruence E on $\langle S; k\rangle$ such that $T = T_E$.*

Our final goal in this section is to show that if $\langle S; k\rangle$ is a complete Baer semigroup (see Exercise 12.3) then the Thorne congruences on $\langle S; k\rangle$ form a Stone lattice. We shall require a number of preliminary results which are in their own right of some interest.

THEOREM 16.7. *Let E be an AP-congruence on $\langle S; k\rangle$ and let $J = \text{Ker}\,E$. Then $L_k(J) = R_k(J)$.*

Proof. Let T_E be the Thorne congruence induced by E on $\mathscr{R}_k(S)$. Recall from Theorem 16.5 the fact that $w \in J \Leftrightarrow R_k L_k(w) \in \text{Ker}\,T_E$. Now let $x \in J$ and $y \in R_k(J)$. Since $R_k(J)$ is a right ideal we have $yx \in R_k(J)$ and since J is an ideal we have $yx \in J$. If $eS = R_k L_k(yx)$ we may apply Theorem 16.5 twice to see that $yx \in J \Rightarrow eS \in \text{Ker}\,T_E \Rightarrow e \in J$. Hence $yx = eyx \in kS$ puts y in $L_k(J)$. This shows that $R_k(J) \subseteq L_k(J)$ and a dual argument produces the reverse inclusion.

THEOREM 16.8. *Let E be an AP-congruence on the complete Baer semigroup* $\langle S; k\rangle$ *and let* $J = \operatorname{Ker} E$. *If* $R_k L_k(J) = eS$ *with* $e = e^2$ *then e belongs to the centre of S.*

Proof. Let $gS = R_k(J)$ and $Sh = L_k(J)$. By Theorem 16.7 we have $gS = Sh$ and so $g = gh = h$. Then $gS = Sg$ and, for each $x \in S$,

$$gx \in Sg \Rightarrow gx = gxg \quad \text{and} \quad xg \in gS \Rightarrow xg = gxg.$$

It follows from this that $(\forall x \in S)\, gx = xg$. If now $eS = R_k L_k(J) = R_k(g)$, the same sort of argument will show that $(\forall x \in S)\, ex = xe$.

THEOREM 16.9. *Let e be an idempotent element of the Baer semigroup* $\langle S; k\rangle$ *such that e belongs to the centre of S. Define* $x \equiv y(E) \Leftrightarrow ex = ey$. *Then E is an AP-congruence such that* $\operatorname{Ker} E = R_k(e)$.

Proof. That E is a congruence relation is clear. If $xy \equiv kxy\,(E)$ then $xye = kxye$ and so $ye \in R_k(x)$ with $y \equiv ye\,(E)$. A similar argument for left k-annihilators shows that E is an AP-congruence. Finally,

$$x \in \operatorname{Ker} E \Leftrightarrow xe = xke \Leftrightarrow x \in R_k(e).$$

THEOREM 16.10. *Let* $\langle S; k\rangle$ *be a complete Baer semigroup with* $L = \mathcal{R}_k(S)$. *Order the set of Thorne congruences on L by*

$$T_1 \leq T_2 \Leftrightarrow (gS \equiv hS\,(T_1) \Rightarrow gS \equiv hS\,(T_2)).$$

With this ordering the Thorne congruences on L form a Stone lattice which is in fact a complete sublattice of Con (L).

Proof. By the nature of the lattice operations in Con (L) as given in Theorem 10.4, it is clear that for any family $\{T_\alpha;\, \alpha \in A\}$ of Thorne congruences both their union and their intersection (as computed in Con (L)) must be Thorne congruences. It follows that they form a complete sublattice of Con (L) and hence a distributive lattice. We leave the reader the routine verification that both the smallest and the greatest elements of Con (L) are in fact Thorne congruences.

Now let T be a Thorne congruence on L. By Theorem 16.6 there exists an AP-congruence E on $\langle S; k\rangle$ such that $T = T_E$. Let $J = \operatorname{Ker} E$ and $eS = R_k L_k(J)$. By Theorem 16.8, e is in the centre of S and by Theorem 16.9 we can define an AP-congruence E^* by $x \equiv y(E^*) \Leftrightarrow ex = ey$. It is important to note that $\operatorname{Ker} E^* = R_k(e) = R_k(J)$. Let $T^* = T_{E^*}$. If

$gS \in \text{Ker } T \cap \text{Ker } T^*$, then by Theorem 16.5 we have $g \in \text{Ker } E \cap \text{Ker } E^* = J \cap R_k(J)$. Since $g = g^2$ it follows that $g \in kS$. Since by Theorem 16.4 every Thorne congruence is determined by its kernel, we deduce that $T \cap T^* = \omega$, the zero element of Con (L). Suppose now that T' is a Thorne congruence such that $T \cap T' = \omega$. We claim that $T' \leq T^*$. If E' is an AP-congruence such that $T' = T_{E'}$ and if $x \in J \cap \text{Ker } E'$, then by Theorem 16.5 we have $R_k L_k(x) \in \text{Ker } T \cap \text{Ker } T' = kS$. It follows that $x \in kS$ and so $J \cap \text{Ker } E' = kS$. If $x \in J$ and $y \in \text{Ker } E'$, then we see that $xy \in J \cap \text{Ker } E' = kS$ and so $\text{Ker } E' \subseteq R_k(J) = \text{Ker } E^*$. It follows from this that $\text{Ker } T' \subseteq \text{Ker } T^*$ whence $T' \leq T^*$. This shows that T^* is the pseudo-complement of T in the lattice of Thorne congruences.

We must still show that T^* has a complement. Let $e'S = R_k(e)$ and note that e' is in the centre of S. Define E^{**} by

$$x \equiv y(E^{**}) \Leftrightarrow e'x = e'y$$

and note that E^{**} is an AP-congruence with kernel eS. If $T^{**} = T_{E^{**}}$ we clearly have $T^* \cap T^{**} = \omega$. We shall require to know that $eS \curlyvee e'S = 1S$. To see this, it suffices to show that $L_k(e) \cap L_k(e') = kS$. Now if $x \in L_k(e) \cap L_k(e')$ then $xe \in kS \Rightarrow ex \in kS \Rightarrow x = e'x \Rightarrow x = e'x = xe' \in kS$ as desired. We may now complete the proof by noting that $0S \equiv eS\,(T^{**})$ and $0S \equiv e'S\,(T^*)$ and so $eS = eS \curlyvee 0S \equiv eS \curlyvee e'S\,(T^*)$. Thus $0S \equiv 1S\,(T^{**} \curlyvee T^*)$ and we conclude that T^{**} is a complement of T^*.

In retrospect, we have shown that Thorne congruences interact in much the same way as do ordinary lattice congruences on a bounded relatively complemented lattice! To see this, the reader need only compare the above results with those of Theorems 10.10 and 10.11.

EXERCISES

16.1. Prove Theorem 16.3.

16.2. Let us call a mapping f on a lattice L *algebraic* if f can be represented by the composition of a finite number of mappings, each of which is either a $\cup$-translation or an $\cap$-translation. We then call a Baer semigroup $\langle S; k\rangle$ *algebraic* whenever, for each $x \in S$, φ_x and φ_x^+ are algebraic.

(1) Show that every complemented modular lattice can be coordinatized by an algebraic Baer semigroup. [*Hint*. If g', g are complements in such a lattice then the mapping $\varphi_{g',g}$ defined by $\varphi_{g',g}(x) = (x \cup g') \cap g$ is residuated. Consider the semigroup generated by all mappings of this type.]

(2) Show that if $\langle S; k \rangle$ is algebraic then *every* congruence relation on $\mathscr{R}_k(S)$ is a Thorne congruence.

16.3. Let T be a Thorne congruence on $\mathscr{R}_k(S)$. Given $eS \in \mathscr{R}_k(S)$, let $Se^{\#} = L_k(e)$. Show that $eS \equiv 1S\,(T) \Leftrightarrow R_k L_k\,(e^{\#}) \equiv kS\,(T)$.

16.4. Let T be a Thorne congruence on $\mathscr{R}_k(S)$. Define a relation T^d on $\mathscr{L}_k(S)$ by

$$Sg \equiv Sh\,(T^d) \Leftrightarrow R_k(g) \equiv R_k(h)\,(T).$$

Show that T^d is an equivalence relation such that

$$Sg \equiv Sh\,(T^d) \Rightarrow (\forall x \in S) \begin{cases} \eta_x\,(Sg) \equiv \eta_x\,(Sh)\,(T^d), \\ \eta_x^+\,(Sg) \equiv \eta_x^+\,(Sh)\,(T^d). \end{cases}$$

17. The notion of involution

As a prelude to our consideration of orthomodular lattices and Foulis semigroups in the next two sections, we shall consider here the theory of ordered sets equipped with some sort of involution.

By an *involution ordered set* we shall mean a pair (E, i) where E is an ordered set and $i: E \to E$ is an antitone mapping such that $i \circ i = \mathrm{id}_E$. The mapping i will be called the *involution* on E. In case E also happens to be a lattice, we shall speak of the pair (E, i) as being an *involution lattice*. An *involution semigroup* is defined to be a pair $(S, *)$, where S is a semigroup and $*: S \to S$ is a mapping such that $(\forall a, b \in S)\ *(ab) = *(b)\,*(a)$ and $* \circ * = \mathrm{id}_S$. The mapping $*$ will be called the *involution* or the *adjoint mapping* and the element $*(a)$ the *adjoint* of the element a. We shall often write a^* instead of $*(a)$. An idempotent $e \in S$ such that $e = e^*$ will be called a *projection*.

Note that if X is any set then $\mathbf{P}(X)$ becomes an involution lattice with respect to the involution which sends every subset M of X to its complement. More generally, if L is any Boolean algebra then the mapping which sends each element to its unique complement is an involution. Also, if H is a Hilbert space then the lattice of closed subspaces of H becomes an involution lattice with respect to the mapping which sends the closed subspace M to $M^{\perp}$, the orthogonal complement of M. When either of these types of lattice is referred to in the text as an involution lattice, it will be with respect to the above-mentioned involutions, unless otherwise specified.

Let us note also that for any set X the semigroup Rel (X) of relations on X forms an involution semigroup with respect to the involution t given by $t(R) = R^t$. In the case of a Hilbert space H, the bounded operators on H form an involution semigroup with respect to the usual notion of adjoint. Whenever we speak of these semigroups as involution semigroups, it will be with respect to these involutions unless otherwise stated.

Although our main concern here will be with the coordinatization problem for involution lattices, we first state an easily proved but nonetheless useful result which provides a sort of "de Morgan law" for involution ordered sets. The proof of the theorem will be omitted on the grounds that it is an immediate consequence of the fact that any involution on E is amongst other things a dual automorphism on E.

THEOREM 17.1. *Let (E, i) be an involution ordered set. Then*

(1) *if E has a minimum element 0 the element $i(0)$ is the maximum element of E;*

(2) *if E has a maximum element π the element $i(\pi)$ is the minimum element of E;*

(3) *if $x = \bigcup \{e_\alpha; \alpha \in A\}$ exists then so does $\bigcap \{i(e_\alpha); \alpha \in A\}$ and this coincides with $i(x)$;*

(4) *if $y = \bigcap \{e_\alpha; \alpha \in A\}$ exists then so does $\bigcup \{i(e_\alpha); \alpha \in A\}$ and this coincides with $i(y)$.*

COROLLARY. *Let (L, i) be an involution lattice. Then*

$$(\forall x, y \in L) \quad i(x \cap y) = i(x) \cup i(y); \quad i(x \cup y) = i(x) \cap i(y).$$

To begin our programme of relating involution lattices with involution semigroups, we show that if (E, i) is an involution ordered set then there is induced a "natural" involution on Res (E).

THEOREM 17.2. *Let (E, i) be an involution ordered set and let $f \in$ Res (E). Define $f^* : E \to E$ by $f^* = i \circ f^+ \circ i$. Then $f^* \in$ Res (E) with $(f^*)^+ = i \circ f \circ i$. The mapping * : Res $(E) \to$ Res (E) thus defined is an involution.*

Proof. Clearly f^* and $i \circ f \circ i$ are isotone. We also have

$$(i \circ f^+ \circ i) \circ (i \circ f \circ i) = i \circ f^+ \circ f \circ i \leq \mathrm{id}_E;$$

$$(i \circ f \circ i) \circ (i \circ f^+ \circ i) = i \circ f \circ f^+ \circ i \geq \mathrm{id}_E,$$

thus showing that f^* is residuated with $(f^*)^+ = i \circ f \circ i$. Furthermore,

$$\begin{aligned}(f \circ g)^* &= i \circ (f \circ g)^+ \circ i = i \circ g^+ \circ f^+ \circ i = (i \circ g^+ \circ i) \circ (i \circ f^+ \circ i) \\ &= g^* \circ f^*\end{aligned}$$

and $f^{**} = i \circ (f^*)^+ \circ i = i \circ (i \circ f \circ i) \circ i = f$.

If (E, i) is an involution ordered set, the mapping $* : \mathrm{Res}(E) \to \mathrm{Res}(E)$ defined in the above theorem will be called the *natural involution* on $\mathrm{Res}(E)$. Unless otherwise specified, we shall always be working with this particular involution on $\mathrm{Res}(E)$. Given $x, y \in E$ we say that x is *orthogonal* to y, and write $x \perp y$, whenever $x \leq i(y)$. Note that orthogonality satisfies the following axioms:

($^\perp$1) $x \perp y \Rightarrow y \perp x$;

($^\perp$2) $x \perp y,\ x_1 \leq x \Rightarrow x_1 \perp y$;

($^\perp$3) $x \perp y,\ x \perp z \Rightarrow x \perp (y \cup z)$.

For involution ordered sets, we have the following characterization of residuated mappings:

THEOREM 17.3. *Let (E, i) be an involution ordered set. An isotone mapping $f: E \to E$ is residuated if and only if there is an isotone mapping $g: E \to E$ such that $g \circ i \circ f \leq i$ and $f \circ i \circ g \leq i$. At most one such g exists and when it does it is necessarily equal to f^*.*

Proof. Assume first that $f \in \mathrm{Res}(E)$. Then

$$f^* \circ i \circ f = (i \circ f^+ \circ i) \circ i \circ f = i \circ f^+ \circ f \leq i;$$

$$f \circ i \circ f^* = f \circ i \circ (i \circ f^+ \circ i) = f \circ f^+ \circ i \leq i.$$

Suppose next that g can be found such that $g \circ i \circ f \leq i$ and $f \circ i \circ g \leq i$. Then

$$g \circ i \circ f \leq i \Rightarrow (i \circ g \circ i) \circ f \geq \mathrm{id}_E$$

and

$$f \circ i \circ g \leq i \Rightarrow f \circ (i \circ g \circ i) \leq i \circ i = \mathrm{id}_E.$$

This shows that $f \in \mathrm{Res}\,(E)$ with $f^+ = i \circ g \circ i$. It follows that $f^* = i \circ f^+ \circ i = i \circ (i \circ g \circ i) \circ i = g$.

In view of the previous result, all of the structure of $\mathrm{Res}^+(E)$ can be recaptured directly from that of $\mathrm{Res}(E)$ and any theorem involving both residuated and residual maps can be rephrased as one involving only residuated maps. Although we shall not in general bother to do this, there are one or two cases of sufficient interest to warrant their explicit enunciation. At any rate, it is good practice! For example, the analogue of Theorem 12.4 is:

THEOREM 17.4. *Let (E, i) be an involution ordered set which is bounded. Then in $S = \mathrm{Res}(E)$,*

(1) $\theta \circ \psi = 0$ *if and only if* $\psi(\pi) \perp \theta^*(\pi)$;

(2) *if* $R(\theta) = \psi \circ S$ *with* $\psi = \psi^2$ *then* $\psi(\pi) = (i \circ \theta^*)(\pi)$.

If (L, i) is a bounded involution lattice and $f \in \mathrm{Res}(L)$ then by Theorem 17.3 we have

$$(\forall x \in L) \quad (f \circ i \circ f^* \circ i)(x) \leq x \cap f(\pi).$$

It is natural to ask when equality holds. The answer is provided by Theorem 13.1: the necessary and sufficient condition that

$$(\forall x \in L) \quad (f \circ i \circ f^* \circ i)(x) = x \cap f(\pi)$$

is that f be range-closed. Interestingly enough, the concept of dually range-closed is no longer required. For to say that f is dually range-closed is equivalent to saying that

$$(\forall x \in L) \quad (f^+ \circ f)(x) = x \cup f^+(0)$$

and this says that

$$(\forall x \in L) \quad (i \circ f^* \circ i \circ f)(x) = x \cup (i \circ f^* \circ i)(0).$$

Applying i to this identity we obtain $(f^* \circ i \circ f)(x) = i(x) \cap f^*(\pi)$. Replacing x by $i(x)$ we obtain $(f^* \circ i \circ f \circ i)(x) = x \cap f^*(\pi)$. It follows that f is dually range-closed if and only if f^* is range-closed, and hence that f is weakly regular if and only if both f and f^* are range-closed. Thus in an involution ordered set, rather than working with a pair of dually isomorphic semigroups of mappings, we are faced with a single semigroup equipped with a dual automorphism.

We turn next to the question of defining an involution Baer semigroup. We are motivated by the fact that for our chosen definition we would like to be able to prove that $\mathscr{R}_k(S)$ is in some natural way an involution lattice. For there to be any hope of this, the involution must be related to the annihilator properties of $\langle S; k\rangle$. A reasonable requirement is

$$x \in kS \Rightarrow x^* \in kS.$$

In particular, we must then have $k^* \in kS$ and so $k^* = kk^* = k$. We are thus led to call a triple $\langle S; k; {}^*\rangle$ an *involution Baer semigroup* whenever

(1) $\langle S; k\rangle$ is a Baer semigroup;
(2) $(S, {}^*)$ is an involution semigroup;
(3) $k^* = k$.

We then have:

THEOREM 17.5. *Let* $\langle S; k; {}^*\rangle$ *be an involution Baer semigroup with* $L = \mathscr{R}_k(S)$. *If* $i: L \to L$ *is defined by* $i(eS) = R_k(e^*)$ *then* (L, i) *is an involution lattice. Moreover, every bounded involution lattice arises in this manner.*

Proof. Note that if $eS \subseteq gS$ then $e = ge$ and so $e^* = e^*g^*$ whence $R_k(g^*) \subseteq R_k(e^*)$. This shows that i is both well-defined and antitone. Let $i(eS) = R_k(e^*) = fS$. Since $xy \in kS \Leftrightarrow y^*x^* \in kS$ we see that $Sf^* = L_k(e)$. Hence $(i \circ i)(eS) = i(fS) = R_k(f^*) = (R_k^{\rightarrow} \circ L_k)(e) = eS$, thus completing the proof that i is an involution on L. Suppose now that (M, j) is a bounded involution lattice with $S = \text{Res}(M)$ equipped with the natural involution * as defined in Theorem 17.2. We know that $\langle S; 0\rangle$ is a Baer semigroup and that $(S, {}^*)$ is an involution semigroup. We also have $0 = 00^*$ so that

$$0^* = (00^*)^* = 0^{**}0^* = 00^* = 0.$$

Hence $\langle S; 0; {}^*\rangle$ is an involution Baer semigroup. Recall from the proof of Theorem 12.5 that the mapping $f: \mathscr{R}(S) \to M$ defined by $f(\theta_x \circ S) = x$ is an isomorphism. We know that $\mathscr{R}(S)$ can be equipped with an involution i by the formula $i(\theta_x \circ S) = R(\theta_x^*) = \theta_y \circ S$ where $y = (\theta_x^*)^+(0) = (j \circ \theta_x \circ j)(0) = (j \circ \theta_x)(\pi) = j(x)$. Thus $f \circ i = j \circ f$ and so the isomorphism f induces both the lattice structure and the involution on M.

Now if (L, i) and (M, j) are involution lattices we agree to call a homomorphism $f: L \to M$ *involution-preserving* in case $f \circ i = j \circ f$. We agree to say that the involution lattice (L, i) is *coordinatized by the involution Baer semigroup* $\langle S; k; * \rangle$ in case there is an involution-preserving lattice isomorphism of $\mathscr{R}_k(S)$ (equipped with the natural involution) onto L. It should be noted that, as was shown in Theorem 17.5, *every* bounded involution lattice can be coordinatized by an involution Baer semigroup. The coordinatization problem for bounded involution lattices is solved in the following two theorems.

THEOREM 17.6. *For a bounded involution ordered set (E, i) the following conditions are equivalent:*

(1) *E is a lattice;*
(2) $\langle \mathrm{Res}\,(E); 0; * \rangle$ *is an involution Baer semigroup;*
(3) (E, i) *may be coordinatized by an involution Baer semigroup.*

Proof. This is immediate from Theorems 12.6 and 17.5.

THEOREM 17.7. *Let $\langle S; k; * \rangle$ be an involution Baer semigroup with $L = \mathscr{R}_k(S)$. If L is equipped with the natural involution induced from S and* $\mathrm{Res}\,(L)$ *the natural involution induced from L, then the homomorphism $x \to \varphi_x$ described in Theorem 12.8 is involution-preserving.*

Proof. Recall that for $eS \in L$ we have $i\,(eS) = R_k(e^*)$ and for $\varphi \in \mathrm{Res}\,(L)$ we have $\varphi^* = i \circ \varphi^+ \circ i$. Given $eS \in L$ and $x \in S$ let $gS = (R_k^{\rightarrow} \circ L_k)\,(xe)$ and $hS = i\,(gS) = R_k(g^*)$. Then

$$(\varphi_{x^*} \circ i \circ \varphi_x)\,(eS) = (\varphi_{x^*} \circ i)\,(gS) = \varphi_{x^*}\,(hS) = (R_k^{\rightarrow} \circ L_k)\,(x^*h).$$

Now

$$\begin{aligned} h \in R_k(g^*) \Rightarrow g^*h \in kS \Rightarrow h^*g \in kS \Rightarrow h^* \in L_k(g) &= L_k\,(xe) \\ &\Rightarrow h^*xe \in kS \\ &\Rightarrow e^*x^*h \in kS \\ &\Rightarrow x^*h \in R_k(e^*) = i\,(eS). \end{aligned}$$

It follows that $\varphi_{x^*} \circ i \circ \varphi_x \leq i$ and a similar argument produces $\varphi_x \circ i \circ \varphi_{x^*} \leq i$. Applying Theorem 17.3, we conclude that $\varphi_{x^*} = (\varphi_x)^*$.

EXERCISES

17.1. Let (L, i) be an involution lattice. Show that, for all $x \in L$,

$$(\alpha_x)^* = \beta_{i(x)}, \quad (\beta_x)^* = \alpha_{i(x)}, \quad (\theta_x)^* = \psi_{i(x)}, \quad (\psi_x)^* = \theta_{i(x)}.$$

17.2. Let (L, i) be a bounded involution lattice. Suppose that $a, b \in L$ are such that $a \cup b = \pi$, $a \cap b = 0$, $M(a, b)$ and $M^*(b, a)$. Let $\varphi_{a,b} : L \to L$ be given by $\varphi_{a,b}(x) = (x \cup a) \cap b$. Use Theorem 17.3 to show that $\varphi_{a,b} \in \text{Res}(L)$ with $(\varphi_{a,b})^* = \varphi_{i(b),i(a)}$.

17.3. Let L be a three-element chain. Show that there is precisely one involution on Res (L) and describe it explicitly. [*Hint.* There is a Cayley table for Res (L) on page 17.]

17.4. Show that every abelian Baer semigroup may be regarded as an involution Baer semigroup.

17.5. Let $\langle S; k; * \rangle$ be an involution Baer semigroup and let i be the natural involution on $\mathscr{R}_k(S)$. Show that if $R_k(x) = eS$ where e is a projection then eS and $i(eS)$ are complements such that $M(i(eS), eS)$ and $M^*(eS, i(eS))$ both hold. [*Hint.* Use Theorem 12.9.]

18. Orthomodular lattices

In this section we shall consider a seemingly modest strengthening of the notion of involution and show that the resulting class of lattices has new and somewhat amazing properties. However, we must warn the reader that there is a vast literature on this subject and one could very well devote an entire volume to the theory of orthomodular lattices alone. For this reason we must be content with a very brief glimpse into their most elementary properties.

An involution lattice (L, i) is called an *ortholattice* and the involution i an *orthocomplementation* whenever

(1) L is bounded;
(2) $(\forall x \in L)\ x \cap i(x) = 0$ [and hence $x \cup i(x) = \pi$].

If, in addition, the *orthomodular identity*

$$e \leq f \Rightarrow f = e \cup [f \cap i(e)]$$

holds in L, then L is called an *orthomodular lattice*. We point out that we shall often write x' instead of $i(x)$ in an ortholattice and call x' the *orthocomplement* of x.

At this juncture it seems appropriate to say a word or two about how orthomodular lattices arise. First of all, any distributive orthomodular lattice is a Boolean algebra and it is easy to show that, conversely, every Boolean algebra is a distributive orthomodular lattice.

A second important class of orthomodular lattice arises in connection with Hilbert spaces. The lattice of closed subspaces of any Hilbert space is easily seen to be orthomodular. In fact, Araki and Amemiya [1] have recently proved that the lattice of closed subspaces of a pre-Hilbert space is orthomodular if and only if the pre-Hilbert space is complete (i.e. is a Hilbert space). More generally, suitable sublattices of the lattice of closed subspaces of a Hilbert space are themselves orthomodular. Here we have in mind the projection lattice of a von Neumann algebra.

It is well known that in classical logic propositions tend to band together so as to form a Boolean algebra. On the other hand, the lattice of closed subspaces of a suitable Hilbert space is regarded by many physicists as being an appropriate model for the underlying "logic" of quantum physics. This suggests (see [25]) that some sort of orthomodular lattice might serve as a "logic" of empirical science.

As another indication of the possible importance of orthomodular lattices, we mention the fact that L. H. Loomis [19] has found them to be a suitable vehicle for an abstract lattice-theoretic version of the Murray–von Neumann dimension theory of operator algebras.

Aside from all this, the theory of these lattices is sufficiently interesting to warrant its study on its own merits. The remainder of this section will be devoted to illustrating this point.

Recall first that an ortholattice (L, i) is orthomodular if and only if the following identity holds:

$$e \leq f \Rightarrow f = e \cup (f \cap e').$$

To say that the dual of L is orthomodular is equivalent to saying that L satisfies the *dual orthomodular identity*

$$e \leq f \Rightarrow e = (e \cup f') \cap f.$$

THEOREM 18.1. *For an ortholattice (L, i) the following conditions are equivalent:*

(1) *the orthomodular identity holds;*
(2) *the dual orthomodular identity holds;*
(3) $e \leq f$ *and* $f \cap e' = 0 \Rightarrow e = f$.

Proof. (1) ⇒ (3): Let $e \leq f$ and $f \cap e' = 0$. Then by (1) we have $f = e \cup (f \cap e') = e \cup 0 = e$.

(3) ⇒ (2): If (2) failed, we could find $e, f \in L$ such that $e \leq f$ and $e \neq (e \cup f') \cap f$. Then $e < (e \cup f') \cap f$ and

$$[(e \cup f') \cap f] \cap e' = (e \cup f') \cap (e \cup f')' = 0,$$

a contradiction.

(2) ⇒ (1): If $e \leq f$, then $f' \leq e'$ and by (2) we have $f' = (f' \cup e) \cap e'$. Taking orthocomplements, this produces $f = (f \cap e') \cup e$.

COROLLARY. *An ortholattice (L, i) is orthomodular if and only if its dual is orthomodular.*

EXAMPLE 18.1. When trying to prove that an ortholattice is orthomodular, Theorem 18.1(3) is often helpful. As an illustration of this point we shall consider in some detail the lattice of closed subspaces of a Hilbert space H. Basically, a *pre-Hilbert space* is a pair consisting of a vector space H over the field $\mathbf{C}$ of complex numbers together with a mapping $(\, , \,): H \times H \to \mathbf{C}$ such that, for all $x, y, z \in H$ and all $\lambda \in \mathbf{C}$,

(SP1) $(x, y) = (y, x)^*$ [the complex conjugate of (y, x)];
(SP2) $(x + y, z) = (x, z) + (y, z)$;
(SP3) $(\lambda x, y) = \lambda (x, y)$;
(SP4) $(x, x) > 0$ for all $x \neq 0$.

We now define the *norm* of the vector x by $\|x\| = \sqrt{(x, x)}$. We leave to the reader the routine verification that $(x, y) = 0$ in case either x or y is the zero vector.

(A) [*Cauchy–Schwartz inequality*] *For all vectors x, y in the pre-Hilbert space H, $|(x, y)| \leq \|x\| \cdot \|y\|$.*

Proof. Assume first that $\|y\| = 1$ and note that with $\lambda = (x, y)$ we have

$$\begin{aligned}\|x - \lambda y\|^2 &= (x - \lambda y, x - \lambda y) \\ &= (x, x - \lambda y) + (-\lambda y, x - \lambda y) \\ &= (x, x) + (x, -\lambda y) + (-\lambda y, x) + (-\lambda y, -\lambda y) \\ &= \|x\|^2 - \lambda^* (x, y) - \lambda (y, x) + \lambda\lambda^* (y, y) \\ &= \|x\|^2 - \lambda^*\lambda - \lambda\lambda^* + \lambda\lambda^* \\ &= \|x\|^2 - |(x, y)|^2.\end{aligned}$$

It follows from this that $|(x, y)| \leq \|x\|$. If $y = 0$, there is nothing more to prove; and if $y \neq 0$ then $y_1 = y/\|y\|$ has norm 1 and so $|(x, y_1)| \leq \|x\|$ and consequently $|(x, y)| \leq \|x\| \cdot \|y\|$.

(B) [*Triangle inequality*] *For all vectors x, y in the pre-Hilbert space H,* $\|x + y\| \leq \|x\| + \|y\|$.

Proof. We begin by observing that if we denote by $\text{Re}(\lambda)$ the real part of each $\lambda \in \mathbf{C}$, then $\lambda + \lambda^* = 2\,\text{Re}(\lambda) \leq 2|\lambda|$. Making use of (A), we may now write

$$\begin{aligned}\|x + y\|^2 &= \|x\|^2 + \|y\|^2 + (x, y) + (x, y)^* \\ &\leq \|x\|^2 + \|y\|^2 + 2\,|(x, y)| \\ &\leq \|x\|^2 + \|y\|^2 + 2\,\|x\| \cdot \|y\| \\ &= (\|x\| + \|y\|)^2,\end{aligned}$$

from which the result follows.

(C) [*Parallelogram law*] *For all vectors x, y in the pre-Hilbert space H,* $\|x + y\|^2 + \|x - y\|^2 = 2\,\|x\|^2 + 2\,\|y\|^2$.

Proof. Simply add together the equations

$$\|x + y\|^2 = \|x\|^2 + \|y\|^2 + (x, y) + (y, x),$$

$$\|x - y\|^2 = \|x\|^2 + \|y\|^2 - (x, y) - (y, x).$$

(D) *For all* $x, y \in H$ *define* $d(x, y) = \|x - y\|$. *Then* d *becomes a metric on* H *in the sense that it satisfies*

(1) $d(x, y) \geq 0$ *and* $d(x, y) = 0$ *holds only when* $x = y$;
(2) $d(x, y) = d(y, x)$;
(3) $d(x, y) \leq d(x, z) + d(z, y)$.

Proof. The first two assertions are clear while the third follows from (B) and the observation that $x - y = (x - z) + (z - y)$.

If the pre-Hilbert space H forms a complete metric space with respect to the above metric, then H is called a *Hilbert space.* For the remainder of this example it will be assumed that we are working in a Hilbert space H.

We agree to call two vectors x, y *orthogonal,* and write $x \perp y$, whenever $(x, y) = 0$. We leave to the reader the routine verification that, for any subspace M of H, $M^{\perp} = \{x \in H; (\forall m \in M)\, x \perp m\}$ is a subspace of H. It follows that the mapping $M \to M^{\perp}$ sets up a Galois connection on the lattice of all subspaces of H. We let L denote the complete lattice formed by the Galois closed subspaces of H; i.e. L consists of those subspaces M such that $M = M^{\perp\perp}$. Since we have $M \cap M^{\perp} = (0)$ for each $M \in L$, it is clear that L is an ortholattice. Our goal is to prove that it is in fact orthomodular.

(E) *Every Galois closed subspace of H is closed in the metric topology.* [*Note: the converse is also true, but we shall not need this fact*].

Proof. Let $M \in L$ and let x be any vector in the closure of M. Then there is a sequence (x_n) of vectors in M such that $\lim_n x_n = x$. Now if $y \in M^{\perp}$ we have $x_n \perp y$ for all n and hence

$|(x, y)| = |(x - x_n + x_n, y)| \leq |(x - x_n, y)| + |(x_n, y)| \leq \|x - x_n\| \cdot \|y\|$.

Since $\lim_n x_n = x$, this forces $x \perp y$. It is immediate that $x \in M^{\perp\perp} = M$.

(F) *Let* $M \in L$ *and let* x *be any vector in* H. *If* $\delta = \inf\{\|y - x\|; y \in M\}$ *then there exists a vector* $y_0 \in M$ *such that* $\|y_0 - x\| = \delta$.

Proof. Let (y_n) be a sequence of vectors in M such that $\lim_n (\|y_n - x\|) = \delta$. By (C),

$$\|(y_n - x) + (y_m - x)\|^2 + \|(y_n - x) - (y_m - x)\|^2$$
$$= 2\,\|y_n - x\|^2 + 2\,\|y_m - x\|^2.$$

Rephrasing this, we have

$$\|y_n - y_m\|^2 = 2\,\|y_n - x\|^2 + 2\,\|y_m - x\|^2 - \|y_n + y_m - 2x\|^2.$$

Now $y_n, y_m \in M \Rightarrow \frac{1}{2}(y_n + y_m) \in M$ and so $\|\frac{1}{2}(y_n + y_m) - x\| \geq \delta$. It follows that $\|y_n + y_m - 2x\| \geq 2\delta$, so

$$0 \leq \|y_n - y_m\|^2 \leq 2\,\|y_n - x\|^2 + 2\,\|y_m - x\|^2 - 4\delta^2.$$

As $n, m \to \infty$ the right side of this inequality tends to zero. It follows from this that the sequence (y_n) is a Cauchy sequence and so, by the completeness of H as a metric space, $\lim_n y_n = y_0$ for some $y_0 \in H$. It follows from (E) that $y_0 \in M$ and from (B) that

$$\|y_0 - x\| = \lim_n (\|y_n - x\|) = \delta.$$

(G) *Given $M, N \in L$ with $M \subset N$, it follows that $N \cap M^{\perp} \neq 0$.*

Proof. Let x be any vector in N but not in M. Define

$$\delta = \inf\{\|y - x\|;\ y \in M\}$$

and use (F) to find a vector y_0 in M such that $\|y_0 - x\| = \delta$. Now let $w = y_0 - x$ and note that $w \in N$. Consider a vector z in M with norm 1. We have from the proof of (A) that, with $\lambda = (w, z)$, $\|w - \lambda z\|^2 = \|w\|^2 - |(w, z)|^2$ and so $\|w - \lambda z\|^2 \leq \|w\|^2$. On the other hand, $w - \lambda z = (y_0 - x) - \lambda z = (y_0 - \lambda z) - x$, and by our choice of w this forces $\|w\| \leq \|w - \lambda z\|$. It follows that

$$\|w\|^2 = \|w - \lambda z\|^2 = \|w\|^2 - |(w, z)|^2$$

and so $w \perp z$. This puts $w \in N \cap M^{\perp}$ as desired.

(H) We may now apply Theorem 18.1(3) to deduce that L is indeed orthomodular.

[*Note*: The reader who was not able to fill in complete details of the above proofs should refer to [6] or to [14] for an introduction to the theory of Hilbert spaces.]

Definition. Let (L, i) be an involution lattice. For each $b \in L$ we define the *Sasaki projection* $\varphi_b : L \to L$ by the prescription

$$(\forall x \in L) \quad \varphi_b(x) = [x \cup i(b)] \cap b.$$

THEOREM 18.2. *An involution lattice (L, i) is an ortholattice if and only if L has a minimum element 0 and $(\forall b \in L)\ \varphi_b(0) = 0$; it is orthomodular if and only if it has a minimum element and*

$$(\forall b \in L)\ (\forall x \leq b) \quad \varphi_b(x) = x.$$

Proof. If L is an ortholattice it must have a minimum element 0 and

$$(\forall b \in L) \quad \varphi_b(0) = [0 \cup i(b)] \cap b = i(b) \cap b = 0.$$

Conversely, if $0 \in L$ and $(\forall b \in L)\ \varphi_b(0) = 0$ then $0 = \varphi_b(0) = [0 \cup i(b)] \cap b = i(b) \cap b$ and so L is an ortholattice. For an ortholattice (L, i) the assertion that $(\forall b \in L)\ (\forall x \leq b)\ \varphi_b(x) = x$ is none other than the dual of the orthomodular identity. The result follows by Theorem 18.1.

In a Boolean algebra we have $(\forall a, b \in L)\ \varphi_b(a) = a \cap b$. This suggests the following definition. Let (L, i) be an involution lattice. Given $a, b \in L$ we say that *a commutes* with b, and write aCb, whenever $\varphi_b(a) = a \cap b$. For each subset N of L we let $C(N) = \{x \in L; (\forall n \in N)\ xCn\}$ and if $N = \{n\}$ we write $C(n)$ in place of $C(\{n\})$. In the next theorem we gather up a few important facts about commutativity in an orthomodular lattice.

THEOREM 18.3. *In an orthomodular lattice (L, i) the following conditions are equivalent:*

(1) eCf;
(2) $f = (f \cap e) \cup (f \cap e')$;
(3) fCe;
(4) $e = (e \cap f) \cup (e \cap f')$;
(5) eCf';
(6) *there exist pairwise orthogonal elements* e_1, f_1, g *such that* $e = e_1 \cup g$ *and* $f = f_1 \cup g$;
(7) $f = (f \cup e) \cap (f \cup e')$;
(8) $e = (e \cup f) \cap (e \cup f')$;
(9) $e \cap (e' \cup f') \perp f \cap (e' \cup f')$.

Proof. (1) ⇒ (2): If eCf, then $\varphi_f(e) = (e \cup f') \cap f = e \cap f$ and so $[(e \cup f') \cap f] \cap (e' \cup f') = (e \cap f) \cap (e' \cup f') = 0$. Since $f' \leq (e \cup f') \cap (e' \cup f')$ and $f \cap [(e \cup f') \cap (e' \cup f')] = 0$ we see by Theorem 18.1

that $f' = (e \cup f') \cap (e' \cup f')$. The proof is completed by taking orthocomplements.

(2) $\Rightarrow$ (3): If $f = (f \cap e) \cup (f \cap e')$, then $f \cup e' = (f \cap e) \cup (f \cap e') \cup e' = (f \cap e) \cup e'$. By the orthomodular identity we deduce that $(f \cup e') \cap e = [(f \cap e) \cup e'] \cap e = f \cap e$ and so fCe.

(3) $\Rightarrow$ (4): Interchange the rôles of e and f in the proof of (1) $\Rightarrow$ (2).

(4) $\Rightarrow$ (1): Interchange the rôles of e and f in the proof of (2) $\Rightarrow$ (3). We have at this point established the equivalence of (1), (2), (3), (4).

(1) $\Leftrightarrow$ (5): Use the symmetry of f, f' in (4).

(1) $\Rightarrow$ (6): Let eCf. Then $e = (e \cap f) \cup (e \cap f')$ and $f = (f \cap e) \cup (f \cap e')$. Take $e_1 = e \cap f'$, $f_1 = f \cap e'$ and $g = e \cap f$. Then e_1, f_1, g are pairwise orthogonal with $e = e_1 \cup g$ and $f = f_1 \cup g$.

(6) $\Rightarrow$ (1): Let e_1, f_1, g be as in (6). Then $e_1 \le f_1' \cap g' = (f_1 \cup g)' = f'$ and $g \le f$ so $g = (g \cup f') \cap f$. We may now write

$$e \cap f \le (e \cup f') \cap f = (e_1 \cup g \cup f') \cap f = (g \cup f') \cap f = g \le f \cap e$$

and so eCf.

(4) $\Leftrightarrow$ (8) and (2) $\Leftrightarrow$ (7) are clear in view of the equivalence of the first five conditions.

(1) $\Rightarrow$ (9): If eCf then $e'Cf$ and $f'Ce$ so $e \cap (e' \cup f') = e \cap f'$ and $f \cap (e' \cup f') = f \cap e'$. Note now that $e \cap f' \perp f \cap e'$.

(9) $\Rightarrow$ (1): If $e \cap (e' \cup f') \le [f \cap (e' \cup f')]' = f' \cup (e \cap f)$ then we have $e \cap (e' \cup f') \le [f' \cup (e \cap f)] \cap (e' \cup f') = f'$ so $e \cap (e' \cup f') = e \cap (e' \cup f') \cap f' = e \cap f'$. This shows that $f'Ce$, and in view of the equivalence of conditions (1), (3), (5) it follows that eCf.

COROLLARY. *If $e \le f$ or $e \perp f$ then eCf.*

Proof. $e \le f \Rightarrow (e \cup f') \cap f = e = e \cap f$; $e \perp f \Rightarrow (e \cup f') \cap f = f' \cap f = 0 = e \cap f$.

THEOREM 18.4. *A necessary and sufficient condition that the ortholattice (L, i) be orthomodular is that the relation C be symmetric.*

Proof. If L is orthomodular we may apply Theorem 18.3 to deduce that C is symmetric. Suppose now that C is symmetric on L. Let $e \le f$. Then $f \cup e' = \pi \Rightarrow (f \cup e') \cap e = \pi \cap e = e = f \cap e$ and so fCe. It follows that eCf and so $(e \cup f') \cap f = e \cap f$. This establishes the dual orthomodular identity on L. We now appeal to Theorem 18.1.

The next theorem is of great interest in that it says that every interval sublattice of an orthomodular lattice is itself orthomodular. It follows from this, of course, that every orthomodular lattice is relatively complemented.

THEOREM 18.5. *Let (L, i) be an ortholattice. For each interval $[a, b]$ define a mapping $i_{ab} : [a, b] \to [a, b]$ by setting*

$$(\forall x \in [a, b]) \quad i_{ab}(x) = (x' \cup a) \cap b.$$

Then a necessary and sufficient condition for (L, i) to be orthomodular is that for every interval $[a, b]$ the pair $([a, b], i_{ab})$ be an involution lattice. If (L, i) is orthomodular then so is every lattice $([a, b], i_{ab})$.

Proof. Suppose first that (L, i) is orthomodular and let $a, b \in L$ be such that $a < b$. For $a \leq x \leq b$ write $i_{ab}(x) = x^{\perp}$. If $a \leq x \leq y \leq b$, then $y' \leq x' \Rightarrow y^{\perp} \leq x^{\perp}$ and we also have

$$\begin{aligned} x^{\perp\perp} = (x^{\perp\prime} \cup a) \cap b &= \{[(x' \cup a) \cap b]' \cup a\} \cap b \\ &= [(x \cap a') \cup b' \cup a] \cap b. \end{aligned}$$

By the orthomodular identity, $a \leq x \Rightarrow x = a \cup (x \cap a')$. Hence

$$x^{\perp\perp} = [(x \cap a') \cup a \cup b'] \cap b = (x \cup b') \cap b = x$$

and so i_{ab} is an involution. Since

$$x^{\perp} \cap x = (x' \cup a) \cap b \cap x = (x' \cup a) \cap x = a,$$

we see that i_{ab} is in fact an orthocomplementation. To show that $[a, b]$ is orthomodular, we shall apply Theorem 18.1. Accordingly, let $a \leq x \leq y \leq b$ with $y \cap x^{\perp} = a$. Then $a = y \cap x^{\perp} = y \cap (x' \cup a) \cap b = y \cap (x' \cup a)$ and so

$$y \cap x' = y \cap x' \cap a' \leq y \cap (x' \cup a) \cap a' = a \cap a' = 0.$$

By Theorem 18.1, $x \leq y$ with $y \cap x' = 0 \Rightarrow x = y$. Applying Theorem 18.1 to the interval $[a, b]$ we conclude that it is in fact orthomodular.

Suppose now that for every interval $[a, b]$ the mapping i_{ab} is an involution. Then if $e \leq f$ with $f \cap e' = 0$ we see that $i_{0f}(e) = (e' \cup 0) \cap f = e' \cap f = 0$ and so $e = (i_{0f} \circ i_{0f})(e) = i_{0f}(0) = f$. It follows that L is orthomodular.

If we were asked to pick the one theorem which is the most useful tool for handling orthomodular lattices, it would be the next one. This extremely important theorem is often referred to as the *Foulis–Holland Theorem* and says, roughly speaking, that whenever one really needs it an orthomodular lattice behaves as though it were a Boolean algebra.

THEOREM 18.6. *Let e, f, g be any three elements of an orthomodular lattice (L, i). If any two of the relations eCf, eCg or fCg hold, then for any permutation (x, y, z) of the triple (e, f, g) we have both $D(x, y, z)$ and $D^*(x, y, z)$.*

Proof. We begin by proving that

(1) $eCg, fCg \Rightarrow D(e, f, g)$.

To see this, note that $(e \cup f) \cap g \geq (e \cap g) \cup (f \cap g)$ and

$$(e \cup f) \cap g \cap [(e \cap g) \cup (f \cap g)]' = (e \cup f) \cap g \cap (e' \cup g') \cap (f' \cup g').$$

Now $eCg \Rightarrow e'Cg \Rightarrow (e' \cup g') \cap g = e' \cap g$; and $fCg \Rightarrow f'Cg \Rightarrow (f' \cup g') \cap g = f' \cap g$. It follows that

$$\begin{aligned}(e \cup f) \cap g \cap (e' \cup g') \cap (f' \cup g') &= (e \cup f) \cap g \cap e' \cap (f' \cup g') \\ &= (e \cup f) \cap g \cap e' \cap f' \\ &= 0.\end{aligned}$$

By Theorem 18.1 we have $(e \cup f) \cap g = (e \cap g) \cup (f \cap g)$.

We next establish

(2) $eCf, fCg \Rightarrow D(e, f, g)$.

For this, it will prove convenient to let $h = (e \cup f) \cap g$ and $k = (e \cap g) \cup (f \cap g)$. As in the proof of (1) we have $k \leq h$ and $h \cap k' = (e \cup f) \cap g \cap (e' \cup g') \cap (f' \cup g')$. Then $fCg \Rightarrow f'Cg \Rightarrow (f' \cup g') \cap g = f' \cap g$ and so there results $h \cap k' = (e \cup f) \cap g \cap f' \cap (e' \cup g')$. Since eCf we have

$(e \cup f) \cap f' = e \cap f'$ and so $h \cap k' = e \cap f' \cap g \cap (e' \cup g') = 0$. Thus $h = k$ and $D(e, f, g)$ follows.

Now let (x, y, z) be any permutation of the triple (e, f, g). Then two of the three relations xCy, xCz, yCz must hold. Now

(a) $xCy, yCz \Rightarrow D(x, y, z)$ by (2);
(b) $xCy, xCz \Rightarrow yCx, xCz \Rightarrow D(y, x, z)$ by (2) and so $D(x, y, z)$;
(c) $xCz, yCz \Rightarrow D(x, y, z)$ by (1).

Finally, to obtain $D^*(x, y, z)$ we apply the above arguments to the triple (x', y', z'), noting of course that $xCy \Rightarrow x'Cy'$, etc. This establishes $D(x', y', z')$ and we now merely take orthocomplements.

COROLLARY *$eCf \Rightarrow M(e, f)$ and $M^*(e, f)$.*

Proof. Let $a \leq f$. Then aCf and eCf so

$$(a \cup e) \cap f = (a \cap f) \cup (e \cap f) = a \cup (e \cap f).$$

A similar argument establishes $M^*(e, f)$.

In the next theorem we gather up a number of conditions, each of which is equivalent to the ortholattice (L, i) being orthomodular.

THEOREM 18.7. *Let (L, i) be an ortholattice. The following conditions are equivalent:*

(1) *(L, i) is orthomodular;*
(2) *the dual of (L, i) is orthomodular;*
(3) *$a \leq b$ and $b \cap a' = 0 \Rightarrow a = b$;*
(4) *$a \perp b \Rightarrow M(a, b)$;*
(5) *$(\forall e \in L)\ M(e, e')$;*
(6) *if $a = b \cup c$ with $b \perp c$ then $b = c' \cap a$;*
(7) *$b \perp c \Rightarrow b = (b \cup c) \cap c'$;*
(8) *if $a = b \cup c$ with $b \leq k$ and $c \leq k'$ then $b = k \cap a$;*
(9) *$b \leq k \leq c' \Rightarrow b = k \cap (b \cup c)$;*
(10) *$c \perp (d \cup b) \Rightarrow d \cap b = d \cap (b \cup c)$.*

Proof. The equivalence of the first three conditions was established in Theorem 18.1.

(1) $\Rightarrow$ (4): If $a \perp b$ then aCb and so $M(a, b)$ follows by the corollary to Theorem 18.6.

(4) $\Rightarrow$ (5): This is clear.

(5) $\Rightarrow$ (6): If $a = b \cup c$ with $b \perp c$, then $b \leq c'$ and by hypothesis $M(c, c')$. It follows that $b = b \cup (c \cap c') = (b \cup c) \cap c' = a \cap c'$.

(6) $\Rightarrow$ (7): Let $b \perp c$ and take $a = b \cup c$.

(7) $\Rightarrow$ (8): Let $a = b \cup c$ with $b \leq k$ and $c \leq k'$. Then $b \leq k \leq c'$ and so $b \perp c$. By (7) we have $b = (b \cup c) \cap c' = a \cap c'$. Now $c \leq k'$ $\Rightarrow k \leq c'$ and so $b = a \cap c' \geq a \cap k \geq b$ whence $b = a \cap k$.

(8) $\Rightarrow$ (9): Let $b \leq k \leq c'$. By (8), $b \leq k$ and $c \leq k' \Rightarrow b = k \cap (b \cup c)$.

(9) $\Rightarrow$ (10): If $c \perp (d \cup b)$ then $b \leq d \cup b \leq c' \Rightarrow b = (d \cup b) \cap (b \cup c)$ and so $d \cap b = (d \cup b) \cap (b \cup c) \cap d = (b \cup c) \cap d$.

(10) $\Rightarrow$ (1): Let $e \leq f$. Then $f' \perp (e \cup f) = f$ and so $e = e \cap f$ $= f \cap (e \cup f')$.

In the course of developing a coordinatization theory for orthomodular lattices, we shall find the Sasaki projections to be extremely useful. For this reason we pause to consider their properties.

THEOREM 18.8. *Let (L, i) be an orthomodular lattice with $a, b \in L$. Then*

(1) $a \cap b \leq \varphi_b(a) \leq b$;

(2) $a = \varphi_b(a) \Leftrightarrow a \leq b$;

(3) $aCb \Leftrightarrow \varphi_b(a) \leq a$;

(4) $(\varphi_b \circ i \circ \varphi_b \circ i)(a) = a \cap b$;

(5) φ_b *is a projection in* Res(L) *such that* $\varphi_b(\pi) = b$ *and* $\varphi_b^+(0) = b'$;

(6) φ_b *is weakly regular*;

(7) $\varphi_b(a) = 0 \Leftrightarrow a \perp b$;

(8) $\varphi_b(a) = b \Leftrightarrow a' \cap b = 0$;

(9) $aCb \Leftrightarrow \varphi_a \circ \varphi_b = \varphi_b \circ \varphi_a$;

(10) $a \leq b \Leftrightarrow \varphi_a = \varphi_b \circ \varphi_a$.

Proof. (1) is clear from the definition of φ_b.

(2) This follows from Theorem 18.2.

(3) If aCb, then $\varphi_b(a) = a \cap b \leq a$. If, conversely, $\varphi_b(a) \leq a$, then $a \cap b \leq \varphi_b(a) \leq a \cap b$ forces $\varphi_b(a) = a \cap b$.

(4) $(\varphi_b \circ i \circ \varphi_b \circ i)(a) = (\varphi_b \circ i \circ \varphi_b)(a') = (\varphi_b \circ i)[(a' \cup b') \cap b]$
$= \varphi_b[(a \cap b) \cup b']$
$= [(a \cap b) \cup b'] \cap b$
$= a \cap b.$

(5) In view of (4) we may apply Theorem 17.3 to see that $\varphi_b \in \text{Res}(L)$ with $\varphi_b = (\varphi_b)^*$. Since $(\forall x \in L)\ \varphi_b(x) \leq b$ it follows from (2) that $(\varphi_b \circ \varphi_b)(x) = \varphi_b(x)$ and so φ_b is a projection. Clearly $\varphi_b(\pi) = b$ and $\varphi_b^+(0) = (i \circ \varphi_b \circ i)(0) = (i \circ \varphi_b)(\pi) = i(b) = b'$.

(6) By (4) we have $(\varphi_b \circ \varphi_b^+)(a) = a \cap b = a \cap \varphi_b(\pi)$ and so φ_b is range-closed. Since $\varphi_b = (\varphi_b)^*$ we see that it is in fact weakly regular.

(7) This follows from the fact that $\varphi_b^+(0) = b'$.

(8) If $\varphi_b(a) = b$, then $(a \cup b') \cap b = b$ implies that $b \leq a \cup b'$ whence $a \cup b' = \pi$ and $a' \cap b = 0$. The converse is clear.

(9) Let $a\,C\,b$. Then $(\forall x \in L)\ a\,C\,b$ and $a\,C\,(x \cup a')$ so, by Theorem 18.6, $D^*(x \cup a', a, b')$. Then

$$(\varphi_b \circ \varphi_a)(x) = \varphi_b[(x \cup a') \cap a] = \{[(x \cup a') \cap a] \cup b'\} \cap b$$
$$= (x \cup a' \cup b') \cap (a \cup b') \cap b$$
$$= (x \cup a' \cup b') \cap a \cap b$$
$$= \varphi_{a \cap b}(x).$$

Similarly, $(\varphi_a \circ \varphi_b)(x) = \varphi_{a \cap b}(x)$ and so $\varphi_a \circ \varphi_b = \varphi_b \circ \varphi_a$. If, on the other hand, $\varphi_a \circ \varphi_b = \varphi_b \circ \varphi_a$, then

$$\varphi_b(a) = (\varphi_b \circ \varphi_a)(\pi) = (\varphi_a \circ \varphi_b)(\pi) = \varphi_a(b) \leq a,$$

and so, by (3), aCb.

(10) If $\varphi_a = \varphi_b \circ \varphi_a$ then $a = \varphi_a(a) = (\varphi_b \circ \varphi_a)(a) \leq b$. Conversely, if $a \leq b$, then $(\forall x \in L)\ \varphi_a(x) \leq b \Rightarrow \varphi_a(x) = (\varphi_b \circ \varphi_a)(x)$.

COROLLARY. *If* $(\forall \alpha \in A)\ x_\alpha\, Cb$ *and if* $x = \bigcup_{\alpha \in A} x_\alpha$ *exists then* xCb.

Proof. $\varphi_b(x) = \varphi_b\left(\bigcup_{\alpha \in A} x_\alpha\right) = \bigcup_{\alpha \in A} \varphi_b(x_\alpha) = \bigcup_{\alpha \in A} (x_\alpha \cap b) \leq x$, and so, by (3) of the theorem, we have xCb.

In connection with the next theorem we shall require one additional item of terminology. A sublattice M of an ortholattice (L, i) will be called an *orthosublattice* if it satisfies the property $m \in M \Rightarrow m' \in M$. We leave to the reader the routine verification that every orthosublattice of an orthomodular lattice is itself an orthomodular lattice.

THEOREM 18.9. *Let M be a non-empty subset of the orthomodular lattice (L, i). Then*

(1) *$C(M)$ is a complete orthosublattice of L;*

(2) *a necessary and sufficient condition that $CC(M)$ be a Boolean sublattice of (L, i) is that $M \subseteq C(M)$. In particular, this is true if $M = C(L)$ or $M = \{m\}$.*

Proof. By the corollary to Theorem 18.8, $C(M)$ is stable under the formation of existing unions; and by Theorem 18.3, $x \in C(M) \Rightarrow x' \in C(M)$. It is immediate that $C(M)$ is a complete orthosublattice of L.

To prove (2), we note that if $CC(M)$ is Boolean then $M \subseteq CC(M)$. Now if $x, y \in M$ then x, y, y' are all in $CC(M)$ which is distributive. It follows that

$$\varphi_y(x) = (x \cup y') \cap y = (x \cap y) \cup (y' \cap y) = x \cap y$$

and so $x\,C\,y$. But this shows that $M \subseteq C(M)$. We now assume that $M \subseteq C(M)$. This clearly implies $CC(M) \subseteq C(M)$, so if $x, y \in CC(M)$ then $x \in CC(M)$ with $y \in C(M)$ implies xCy. It follows from Theorem 18.6 that $CC(M)$ is distributive and hence a Boolean sublattice of L. The remaining assertions are clear.

THEOREM 18.10. *Let (L, i) be an orthomodular lattice. Then, for each $a \in L$, we have*

$$C(a) = \{(b \cup a) \cap (b \cup a');\ b \in L\} = \{(b \cap a) \cup (b \cap a');\ b \in L\}$$
$$= \operatorname{Im}(\varphi_a \curlyvee \varphi_{a'}).$$

Proof. If bCa then by Theorem 18.3 we have

$$b = (b \cup a) \cap (b \cup a') = (b \cap a) \cup (b \cap a') = (\varphi_a \curlyvee \varphi_{a'})(b).$$

On the other hand, by Theorem 18.9, any element of the form $(b \cup a) \cap (b \cup a')$, $(b \cap a) \cup (b \cap a')$ or $\varphi_a(b) \cup \varphi_{a'}(b)$ must commute with a.

THEOREM 18.11. *Let a be an element of the orthomodular lattice (L, i). Then the set of complements of a is given by*

$$\{[(a' \cup f') \cap f] \cup (a' \cap f');\ f \in L\}.$$

Moreover, given $f \in L$, $aCf \Leftrightarrow [(a' \cup f') \cap f] \cup (a' \cap f') = a'$.

Proof. Note first that since $(a' \cup f')\, Cf$ and $(a' \cup f')\, Ca$ we have by Theorem 18.6 that

$$a \cup [(a' \cup f') \cap f] = (a \cup a' \cup f') \cap (a \cup f) = a \cup f.$$

Hence

$$a \cup \{[(a' \cup f') \cap f\} \cup (a' \cap f')] = (a \cup f) \cup (a' \cap f') = \pi.$$

We next observe that $(a' \cup f') \cap f \leq a \cup f = (a' \cap f')'$ and so we have $[(a' \cup f') \cap f]\, C\, (a' \cap f')$. Since also $(a' \cap f')\, Ca$ we have

$$a \cap \{[(a' \cup f') \cap f] \cup (a' \cap f')\} = [a \cap (a' \cup f') \cap f] \cup (a \cap a' \cap f') = 0.$$

On the other hand, if x is a complement of a, then $[(a' \cup x') \cap x] \cup (a' \cap x') = x$.

If aCf, then by Theorem 18.3

$$[(a' \cup f') \cap f] \cup (a' \cap f') = (a' \cap f) \cup (a' \cap f') = a'.$$

Conversely, if $[(a' \cup f') \cap f] \cup (a' \cap f') = a'$, then $(a' \cup f') \cap f \leq a'$ forces $a'Cf$ and consequently aCf.

COROLLARY. *$C(L)$ is the centre of L.*

Proof. If $z \in C(L)$ then, by the theorem, z has a unique complement in L. By Theorem 9.3, z is central. The proof is completed by noting that every central element z must commute with all elements of L.

Since an orthomodular lattice is relatively complemented, it follows from Theorem 9.3 that it is Boolean if and only if it is uniquely complemented. We close this section by extending this result to an arbitrary ortholattice.

THEOREM 18.12. *An ortholattice (L, i) is a Boolean algebra if and only if it is uniquely complemented.*

Proof. Every Boolean lattice is uniquely complemented, so it suffices to start with a uniquely complemented ortholattice (L, i) and show that it is Boolean. In view of the remarks preceding the theorem, it is enough to show that (L, i) is orthomodular. This we now proceed to do. Accordingly, let $a, b \in L$ be such that $a \leq b$ and set $c = b \cap a'$. Then

$$c' \cap a' \cap b = (b' \cup a) \cap a' \cap b = 0,$$

and since $c \cup a \leq b$ we must have $c' \cap a' \geq b'$, so $(c' \cap a') \cup b = \pi$. It follows that $c' \cap a' = b'$ and $b = a \cup c = a \cup (b \cap a')$. But this is none other than the orthomodular identity, thus completing the proof.

COROLLARY. *A uniquely complemented lattice is Boolean if and only if the mapping which sends each element to its complement is an involution.*

EXERCISES

Note. In each of the following exercises we shall be working in an orthomodular lattice (L, i) unless otherwise specified.

18.1. Show that $(\forall a, b \in L)\ \varphi_a(b)$ and $(i \circ \varphi_b)(a)$ are complements.

18.2. Show that $aCb \Leftrightarrow \varphi_a(b)\, C\varphi_b(a)$.

18.3. Given $a \in L$, define $\sigma_a : L \to L$ by setting

$$(\forall x \in L) \quad \sigma_a(x) = (x \cup a) \cap (x \cup a').$$

Prove that:

(1) $C(a) = \operatorname{Im} \sigma_a$;
(2) σ_a is an increasing projection in Res (L);
(3) $\sigma_a = \sigma_b \circ \sigma_a \Leftrightarrow b \in CC(a)$;
(4) $\varphi_a = \sigma_a \circ \varphi_a$.

18.4. Show that if $e, f \in [a, b]$ then $\varphi_f(e) = [e \cup i_{ab}(f)] \cap f$. Deduce that $\varphi_f(e) \sim \varphi_e(f)$ in every interval containing e and f. Then prove that $\varphi_f(e) \sim \varphi_e(f)$ in every interval which contains them.

18.5. Given $a, b \in L$ let $x = a \cap b$ and $y = a \cup b$. With notation as in Theorem 18.5, show that $aCb \Leftrightarrow b = i_{xy}(a)$. Deduce that if aCb, then a commutes with all elements in $[x, b]$ as well as with all elements in $[b, y]$.

18.6. Prove that an ortholattice is orthomodular if and only if it contains no sublattice of the form

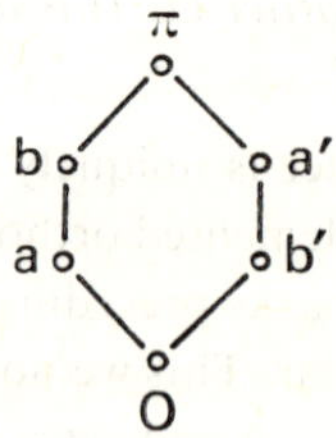

[*Hint*. Use Theorem 18.1(3).]

19. Foulis semigroups

Our goal in this section will be to solve the coordinatization problem for orthomodular lattices. We begin with some general observations about an involution semigroup $(S, *)$. We agree to let $P(S)$, or if there is no danger of confusion, simply P denote the set of projections of S. Thus

$$P(S) = \{e \in S;\ e = e^2 = e^*\}.$$

THEOREM 19.1. *Let $(S, *)$ be an involution semigroup. Then for elements $e, f \in P(S)$ the following conditions are equivalent:*

(1) $e = ef$; (2) $e = fe$; (3) $eS \subseteq fS$; (4) $Se \subseteq Sf$.

Proof. The equivalence of the first two conditions is established by taking adjoints.

(1) $\Rightarrow$ (4): If $e = ef$, then $xe \in Se \Rightarrow xe = xef \in Sf$.

(4) $\Rightarrow$ (1): If $Se \subseteq Sf$, then $e = ee \Rightarrow e \in Se \subseteq Sf$ and so there exists $x \in S$ such that $e = xf$ whence $ef = (xf)f = xf = e$.

(2) $\Leftrightarrow$ (3): This is the dual of (1) $\Leftrightarrow$ (4).

COROLLARY 1. *The relation $e \leq f \Leftrightarrow e = ef$ is an ordering on $P(S)$.*

COROLLARY 2. *If $e, f \in P(S)$ and $eS = fS$, then $e = f$.*

In view of the above result we shall on occasion identify the projection e with the principal right ideal eS which it generates.

THEOREM 19.2. *Let $(S, *)$ be an involution semigroup.*

(1) *If 0 is an element of S such that $(\forall x \in S)\ x0 = 0$ then $0 \in P(S)$ and $(\forall x \in S)\ 0x = 0$. Such an element (when it exists) is unique and is effective as a multiplicative zero element for S;*

(2) *If 1 is an element of S such that $(\forall x \in S)\ x1 = x$ then $1 \in P(S)$ and $(\forall x \in S)\ 1x = x$. Such an element (when it exists) is unique and is effective as a multiplicative identity for S.*

Proof. (1) We evidently have $00 = 0$ and $0^*0 = 0$. Taking adjoints this produces $0^* = (0^*0)^* = 0^*0^{**} = 0^*0 = 0$ and so $0 \in P(S)$. But then $(\forall x \in S)\ \ x^*0 = 0 \Rightarrow 0 = 0^* = (x^*0)^* = 0x^{**} = 0x$. If $\underline{0} \in S$ had the same property then we would clearly have $0 = 0\underline{0} = \underline{0}$.

(2) Note that $11 = 1$ and $1^*1 = 1^*$. Hence $1 = 1^{**} = (1^*1)^* = 1^*1^{**} = 1^*1 = 1^*$ and $1 \in P(S)$. It follows from this that $(\forall x \in S)\ 1x = (x^*1)^* = x^{**} = x$. The uniqueness is clear.

We are now ready to define a Foulis semigroup. The definition is motivated by our desire to have a Foulis semigroup as an involution Baer semigroup such that $\mathscr{R}_k(S)$ forms an orthomodular lattice. In view of Exercise 17.5, there is only one reasonable type of definition. Right and left k-annihilators must be generated by projections. A triple $\langle S; k; ^*\rangle$ will be called a *Foulis semigroup* (or a *Baer *-semigroup*) if and only if

(1) $(S, ^*)$ is an involution semigroup;

(2) k is a central projection of S;

(3) $(\forall x \in S)\ (\exists e_x \in P(S))\ R_k(x) = e_x S$.

We note that since $xy \in kS \Leftrightarrow y^*x^* \in kS$ we have

$$L_k(x) = \{y \in S; y^* \in R_k(x^*)\} = \{y \in S; y^* = e_{x^*}y^*\}$$
$$= \{y \in S; y = ye_{x^*}\} = Se_{x^*}.$$

It follows that $\langle S; k; ^*\rangle$ is an involution Baer semigroup and so $\mathscr{R}_k(S)$ is an involution lattice. By Theorem 19.1, both $R_k(x)$ and $L_k(x)$ have *unique* projection generators. It will prove convenient in what follows to let x' denote the projection which generates $L_k(x)$ and $x'' = (x')'$. It is then clear that $L_k(x) = Sx'$, $R_k(x) = (x^*)'\, S$, $(R_k^{\rightarrow} \circ L_k)(x) = x''S$ and $(L_k^{\rightarrow} \circ R_k)(x) = S(x^*)''$. Almost all of our knowledge of this class of semigroup stems from the work of D. J. Foulis (hence our terminology) who established their basic connection with orthomodular lattices. It was in fact the work of Foulis which provided much of the inspiration and impetus for the later development of the theory of Baer semigroups. Before doing anything else, we consider a few examples.

EXAMPLE 19.1. Any abelian Baer semigroup $\langle S; k\rangle$ may be converted into a Foulis semigroup by taking $(\forall x \in S)\ x^* = x$.

EXAMPLE 19.2. We noted in § 17 that for any set X, $\langle \mathrm{Rel}(X), \emptyset, t\rangle$ is an involution Baer semigroup. However, if we refer back to Example 12.4, we see that, for any binary relation S, $R_\emptyset(S) = I_A \circ \mathrm{Rel}(X)$ where $A = [\mathrm{Dom}\, S]'$ and $x\, I_A\, y \Leftrightarrow x = y \in A$. Noting that I_A is a projection, we see that we have an example of a Foulis semigroup.

EXAMPLE 19.3. An *involution ring* is a pair $(A, *)$ where

(1) A is a ring;
(2) $*$ is an involution on the multiplicative semigroup of A;
(3) $(\forall x, y \in A)\ (x + y)^* = x^* + y^*$.

A *Baer *-ring* is an involution ring whose multiplicative semigroup is a Foulis semigroup with focus 0. A specific example is provided by the ring $B(H)$ of bounded operators on the Hilbert space H. With respect to the usual notion of adjoint, it is well known that $B(H)$ becomes an involution ring. As was noted in Example 11.3, if $t \in B(H)$ then $R(t) = e \circ B(H)$ where e is the orthogonal projection on the null space of t. Since $e = e^2 = e^*$ we see that $B(H)$ is in fact a Baer *-ring. Other examples of Foulis semigroups may now be concocted by taking suitable subsemigroups of a Baer *-ring. For example, we can consider the semigroup formed by those bounded operators whose norm does not exceed 1.

EXAMPLE 19.4. Let $(X, \mathscr{T})$ be a topological space which is *completely regular*; i.e. it is a Hausdorff space such that for every closed set F and every $x \notin F$ there exists a continuous real-valued function g on X such that $g(x) = 1$ and $(\forall y \in F)\ g(y) = 0$. Let $C(X)$ denote the set of all continuous real-valued functions on X and make $C(X)$ into a ring by means of the "point-wise" operations

$$(\forall x \in X)\ (f + g)\,(x) = f(x) + g(x);\ (f \cdot g)\,(x) = f(x)\,g(x).$$

The constant function $\hat{0}$ defined by $(\forall x \in X)\ \hat{0}(x) = 0$ is the zero element of $C(X)$ and the function $\hat{1}$ defined by $(\forall x \in X)\ \hat{1}(x) = 1$ acts as an identity element. Thus $C(X)$ is a commutative ring with an identity. It seems reasonable to ask when (if ever) it forms a Baer *-ring. A subset G of X is called a *cozero set* if and only if $G = \{x \in X;\ g(x) \neq 0\}$ for some $g \in C(X)$. We claim that $C(X)$ *is a Baer *-ring if and only if the closure of every cozero set is open*. To see this, let $g \in C(X)$ with $G = \{x \in X;\ g(x) \neq 0\}$. Suppose also that $R(g) = e \cdot C(X)$ with $e = e^2$. Then $\operatorname{Im} e \subseteq \{0, 1\}$, from which it follows that $e^{\leftarrow}(0)$ and $e^{\leftarrow}(1)$ are complementary subsets of X. Thus $e^{\leftarrow}(0)$ is both open and closed. Since $g \cdot e = 0$ we have $x \in G \Rightarrow e(x) = 0$ and so $G \subseteq e^{\leftarrow}(0)$. Since $e^{\leftarrow}(0)$ is closed, $G^- \subseteq e^{\leftarrow}(0)$. If $G^- \neq e^{\leftarrow}(0)$ choose

$w \in e^{\leftarrow}(0) \backslash G^{-}$. Using complete regularity, we may now find an $h \in C(X)$ such that $h(w) = 1$ and $h(x) = 0$ for all $x \in G^{-}$. But then $g \cdot h = 0$ implies $h = e \cdot h$ and so $1 = h(w) = e(w)\, h(w) = 01 = 0$, a contradiction. We conclude that $G^{-} = e^{\leftarrow}(0)$ and so G^{-} is both open and closed. It follows from this that if $C(X)$ is a Baer *-ring the closure of every cozero set must be open. To establish the converse implication, we note that if H is both open and closed we can define $e \in C(X)$ by setting $e(x) = 0$ for $x \in H$ and $e(x) = 1$ for $x \notin H$ and obtain $e = e^2$. The details are left to the reader.

EXAMPLE 19.5. Let $G = \{g_1, g_2, \ldots, g_n\}$ be a finite group of order n. Let $(F, *)$ be an involution ring such that

(1) F is a field;

(2) $\sum_{i=1}^{n} \lambda_i^* \lambda_i = 0$ in $F \Rightarrow$ each $\lambda_i = 0$.

Consider the set A of all formal linear combinations of the form $\sum_{i=1}^{n} \lambda_i g_i$ where each $\lambda_i \in F$. With respect to the operations

$$\sum_{i=1}^{n} \lambda_i g_i + \sum_{i=1}^{n} \mu_i g_i = \sum_{i=1}^{n} (\lambda_i + \mu_i)\, g_i$$

$$\left\{\sum_{i=1}^{n} (\lambda_i g_i)\right\} \cdot \left\{\sum_{i=1}^{n} (\mu_i g_i)\right\} = \sum_{i,j=1}^{n} (\lambda_i \mu_j)\, g_i g_j$$

we see that A forms a ring. If we define $\left(\sum_{i=1}^{n} \lambda_i g_i\right)^* = \sum_{i=1}^{n} \lambda_i^* g_i^{-1}$ it turns out that A becomes a Baer *-ring.

The above examples were chosen to illustrate the fact that Foulis semigroups and Baer *-rings crop up in a variety of situations and, apart from their possible connection with orthomodular lattices, are in their own right of considerable interest.

We are now ready to proceed with our discussion of the coordinatization of an orthomodular lattice. Although some of the material is merely a restatement of previously proven results for Baer semigroups, we state it in the present context for sake of completeness. In connection with this, it will be convenient to work with the projection generators of right k-annihilators rather than with the right k-annihilators themselves. For this reason, if $\langle S; k; * \rangle$ is a Foulis semigroup we agree to let

$$P_k'(S) = \{e \in P(S); \quad (\exists x \in S)\ eS = R_k(x)\},$$

and order $P_k'(S)$ by the prescription $e \leq f \Leftrightarrow e = ef$. By Theorem 19.1, $P_k'(S)$ is a bounded involution lattice. Unless there is some danger of confusion, we shall use the symbol $P'(S)$ or even simply P' in place of $P_k'(S)$. It will also be convenient to call a projection e *closed* in case $e \in P'$.

THEOREM 19.3. *Let $\langle S; k; * \rangle$ be a Foulis semigroup. Then*

(1) $P'(S) = \{e \in S; (\exists x \in S)\ e = x'\} = \{e \in S; e = e''\}$;
(2) *the mapping given by* $i(e) = e'$ *is an involution on* $P'(S)$;
(3) $(\forall a \in S)\ (\forall e \in P')\ a = ea \Leftrightarrow a'' \leq e$;
(4) *if* $a = a^*$ *and* $ab = ba$ *then* $ab' = b'a$;
(5) $(ab)'' = (ab'')'' \leq a''$.

Proof. The fact that $P'(S) = \{e \in S; (\exists x \in S)\ e = x'\}$ follows from the fact that for $e \in P(S)$ we have $eS = R_k(x) \Leftrightarrow Se = L_k(x^*)$. For any projection g, we have $g'g \in kS \Rightarrow gg' \in kS \Rightarrow g = gg''$ so $g \leq g''$. If $e = x'$ then $ex \in kS \Rightarrow x^*e \in kS \Rightarrow x^* = x^*e' \Rightarrow x = e'x$ and so $e''x = e''e'x \in kS$ and $e'' = e''e$. Thus $e'' \leq e$ and by Corollary 1 to Theorem 19.1 we deduce that $e = e''$. If $e = e''$ then $e = (e')'$ shows e to be closed, thus completing the proof of (1).

(2) This can be deduced from the material in § 17, but it is just as easy to give a direct proof. If $e, f \in P'$ with $e \leq f$, then $e = fe$ and $f'e = f'fe \in kS$. It follows that $f' = f'e'$ and hence that $f' \leq e'$. By (1) we have $(\forall e \in P')\ e = e''$.

(3) If $a = ea$, then $e'a = e'ea \in kS$ gives $e' = e'a'$ and so $e' \leq a'$. By (2) we have $a'' \leq e$. If conversely $a'' \leq e$, then $e' \leq a'$ and so $e'a = e'a'a \in kS$, $a^*e' \in kS$, $a^* = a^*e$ and, finally, $a = ea$.

(4) If $ab = ba$, then $b'ab = b'ba \in kS$ gives $b'a = b'ab'$. Since $a = a^*$ it follows that $b'a = b'ab' = (b'ab')^* = (b'a)^* = ab'$.

(5) $xab'' \in kS \Rightarrow xab = xab''b \in kS$ and $xab \in kS \Rightarrow xa = xab' \Rightarrow xab'' = xab'b'' \in kS$. Thus $L_k(ab) = L_k(ab'')$. It follows that $(ab)'' = (ab'')''$. By (3) we have $a = a''a$, so $ab = a''ab$ and consequently $(ab)'' \leq a''$.

THEOREM 19.4. *For every Foulis semigroup* $\langle S; k; * \rangle$, $P'(S)$ *is an orthomodular lattice.*

Proof. For each $e \in P'$ we have $R_k(e) = e'S$, $eS \in \mathscr{R}_k(S)$ and $Se \in \mathscr{L}_k(S)$. By Theorem 12.9, eS and $e'S$ are complements in $\mathscr{R}_k(S)$ such that $M(e'S, eS)$ holds. The obvious isomorphism $eS \to e$ of $\mathscr{R}_k(S)$ onto P' then shows that e and e' are complements such that $M(e', e)$. By Theorems 19.3(2) and 18.7 it follows that (P', i) is orthomodular.

In line with our previous definition of the coordinatization of an involution lattice, we agree that the Foulis semigroup $\langle S; k; * \rangle$ shall *coordinatize* the orthomodular lattice L in case there is an orthocomplement-preserving lattice isomorphism of $P_k'(S)$ onto L. We then have:

THEOREM 19.5. *If* (L, i) *is an orthomodular lattice then* $\langle \text{Res}(L); 0; * \rangle$ *is a Foulis semigroup which coordinatizes L.*

Proof. By Theorem 17.2, $\langle \text{Res}(L); 0; * \rangle$ is an involution Baer semigroup which coordinatizes L. By Theorem 18.8, φ_e is a projection in Res (L) for each $e \in L$; and by Theorem 17.4, we have

$$\theta \circ \varphi = 0 \Leftrightarrow \varphi(\pi) \perp \theta^*(\pi) \Leftrightarrow \varphi(\pi) \leq [\theta^*(\pi)]'.$$

Now if $e = (i \circ \theta^*)(\pi)$ we see that $\theta \circ \varphi_e = 0$; and if $\theta \circ \varphi = 0$ then $\varphi(\pi) \leq e$ gives $\varphi = \varphi_e \circ \varphi$. It follows that $R(\theta) = \varphi_e \circ \text{Res}(L)$ and so Res (L) is in fact a Foulis semigroup. The proof is now completed by making use of the fact that the mapping $eS \to e$ is an orthocomplement-preserving lattice isomorphism of $\mathscr{R}_k(S)$ onto $P'(S)$ for *any* Foulis semigroup $\langle S; k; * \rangle$ and in particular for the one presently being considered.

Combining the above results with Theorem 17.6, we have established

THEOREM 19.6. *For a bounded involution ordered set* (E, i) *the following conditions are equivalent:*

(1) (E, i) *is an orthomodular lattice;*
(2) $\langle \text{Res}(E); 0; * \rangle$ *is a Foulis semigroup;*
(3) (E, i) *may be coordinatized by a Foulis semigroup.*

Let $\langle S; k; * \rangle$ be a Foulis semigroup with $L = P'(S)$. Then for each $\in S$ we can define $\varphi_a : L \to L$ by setting $\varphi_a(e) = (ae)''$. Since we have

$(R_k^{\rightarrow} \circ L_k)(ae) = (ae)'' S$ we see from Theorem 17.7 that $\varphi_a \in \text{Res}(L)$ with $(\varphi_a)^* = \varphi_{a^*}$. There is no conflict here with the notation for Sasaki projections in that the Sasaki projections are precisely the closed projections in Res (L), so if g is a closed projection in S the induced residuated map φ_g is none other than the Sasaki projection determined by g. Combining these observations with Theorem 17.7, we obtain:

THEOREM 19.7. *Let $\langle S; k; * \rangle$ be a Foulis semigroup and let $L = P'(S)$. The mapping $x \rightarrow \varphi_x$ is an involution-preserving semigroup homomorphism of S into* Res (L) *which maps the closed projections of S onto the Sasaki projections of* Res (L). *Moreover, $\{\varphi_x; x \in S\}$ forms a Foulis semigroup (with the same focus and involution as* Res (L)*) which coordinatizes L.*

In closing, we mention that the above results constitute only a very brief introduction to the theory of Foulis semigroups.

EXERCISES

Note. In each of the following exercises $\langle S; k; * \rangle$ denotes a Foulis semigroup with $L = P'(S)$.

19.1. Let $\{e_\alpha; \alpha \in A\} \subseteq L$ and suppose that $e = \bigcup_{\alpha \in A} e_\alpha$ exists in L. Prove that if $(\forall \alpha \in A)\ e_\alpha x = x e_\alpha$ then $ex = xe$.

19.2. Prove that if $e, f \in L$ and $ef = fe$ then $ef \in L$ and $ef = e \cap f$. Prove in general that for $e, f \in L$ we have $e \cap f = (fe')' f$.

19.3. Prove that e, f commute (in the lattice theoretic sense) in L if and only if e, f commute (in the semigroup sense) in S.

19.4. Let $a \in S$ and $e \in L$. Prove that $ea = ae \Leftrightarrow (ae)'' \cup (a^*e)'' \leq e$.

19.5. Let $e \in L$ and suppose that $g = \bigcup_{x \in S} (xe)''$ exists in L. Prove that $(\forall y \in S)$ $gy = yg$. Prove further that $g \geq e$ and if $h \geq e$ has the property that $(\forall y \in S)\ hy = yh$ then $h \geq g$.

20. Idempotent residuated mappings

It should have become apparent by now to the reader that idempotent residuated maps are extremely important. The very notion of Baer semigroup rests heavily on their existence and, as we saw in § 14, they are intimately connected with notions of regularity. As an added indication of their importance, we list a number of facts about a bounded ordered set E. The reader should have no trouble verifying each of the following items from the material already at hand:

(1) *E is an $\cap$-semilattice if and only if, for each $x \in E$, there exists an idempotent range-closed residuated map e_x on E such that $e_x(\pi) = x$;*
(2) *E is a $\cup$-semilattice if and only if, for each $x \in E$, there exists an idempotent dually range-closed residuated map f_x such that $f_x^+(0) = x$;*
(3) *E is a lattice if and only if, for each $x \in E$, there exist idempotents $e_x, f_x \in$ Res (E) such that e_x is range-closed, f_x is dually range-closed, $e_x(\pi) = x$ and $f_x^+(0) = x$;*
(4) *E is a complemented modular lattice if and only if, for each $x \in E$, there exist strongly range-closed idempotents $e_x, f_x \in$ Res (E) such that $e_x(\pi) = x = f_x^+(0)$.*

This list could be enlarged, but we hope that we have made our point: *idempotent residuated mappings are important.* Our purpose here is to consider this class of mappings in some detail and to prove a number of results which will be required in the next section.

Definition. Let E be an ordered set. Then

(1) a mapping $f: E \to E$ will be called a *residuated closure map* in case it is both residuated and a closure map;
(2) a subset M of E will be called *bicomplete* if and only if, for each $x \in E$, $[\leftarrow, x] \cap M$ has a greatest element and $[x, \to] \cap M$ has a smallest element. In other words, to say that M is bicomplete is equivalent to saying that M is a closure subset of both E and its dual.

Let f be a residuated closure map on the ordered set E. By Theorem 2.10, $f = f^+ \circ f$ and $f^+ = f \circ f^+$. If $x = f(x)$, then $f^+(x) = (f^+ \circ f)(x) = f(x) = x$ and, dually, $x = f^+(x)$ gives $x = f(x)$. Thus $\operatorname{Im} f = \operatorname{Im} f^+$, and so by Theorem 4.3 and its dual $\operatorname{Im} f$ is bicomplete. Suppose now that M is a bicomplete subset of E. For each $x \in E$ define

$$f(x) = \text{the smallest element of } [x, \to] \cap M;$$

$$g(x) = \text{the greatest element of } [\leftarrow, x] \cap M.$$

Then $f, g: E \to E$ are both isotone, $f \circ g = g \leq \mathrm{id}_E$ and $g \circ f = f \geq \mathrm{id}_E$. It follows that f is a residuated closure map with $g = f^+$. Clearly $\mathrm{Im}\, f = M$. Since by Theorem 4.5 any closure map is completely determined by its image, we have established:

THEOREM 20.1. *Let E be an ordered set. There is a bijection between the set of residuated closure maps on E and the set of bicomplete subsets of E, namely that given by* $f \to \mathrm{Im}\, f$.

We now ask the reader to recall our consideration in § 15 of residuated dual closure maps on a lattice L. By Theorem 15.1 they are in one–one correspondence with congruence relations having bounded congruence classes. One may very well ask just what all this has to do with the nature of an arbitrary idempotent residuated map. The answer is provided in the next theorem.

THEOREM 20.2. *Given a lattice L, let f be a residuated closure map on L and let g be a residuated dual closure map on* $\mathrm{Im}\, f$. *Then* $g \circ f$ *is an idempotent element of* Res (L). *Moreover, every idempotent element of* Res (L) *arises in this manner.*

Proof. (1) Let f, g be as in the enunciation of the theorem. With some abuse of notation, let g^+ represent the residual of g in Res $(\mathrm{Im}\, f)$. Since $\mathrm{Im}\,(g \circ f) \subseteq \mathrm{Im}\, f = \mathrm{Im}\, f^+$ we have $f^+ \circ g \circ f = g \circ f$. Similarly, $f \circ g^+ \circ f^+ = g^+ \circ f^+$. Hence

$$(g^+ \circ f^+) \circ (g \circ f) = g^+ \circ g \circ f \geq \mathrm{id}_L$$

and

$$(g \circ f) \circ (g^+ \circ f^+) = g \circ g^+ \circ f^+ \leq \mathrm{id}_L.$$

This shows that $g \circ f \in \mathrm{Res}\,(L)$ with $(g \circ f)^+ = g^+ \circ f^+$. Also, $(g \circ f) \circ (g \circ f) = g \circ g \circ f = g \circ f$. [*Note.* This much of the theorem is true for any ordered set!]

(2) Let $h = h \circ h \in \mathrm{Res}\,(L)$. Set $f = h \curlyvee \mathrm{id}_L$ and note that f is a residuated closure map whose image is $\{x \in L;\, h(x) \leq x\}$. Let g denote the restriction of h to $\mathrm{Im}\, f$ and let g^+ denote the restriction of h^+ to $\mathrm{Im}\, f$. Then on $\mathrm{Im}\, f$ we have $g^+ \circ g = h^+ \circ h \leq \mathrm{id}_{\mathrm{Im}\, f}$ and $g \circ g^+ = h \circ h^+ \geq \mathrm{id}_{\mathrm{Im}\, f}$. This shows that $g \in \mathrm{Res}\,(\mathrm{Im}\, f)$ with g^+ its associated residual map. Clearly g is a residuated dual closure map on $\mathrm{Im}\, f$. The proof is

completed by noting that for each $x \in L$

$$(g \circ f)(x) = g[x \cup h(x)] = h[x \cup h(x)] = h(x) \cup (h \circ h)(x) = h(x)$$

and so $h = g \circ f$.

Our next goal will be to develop an explicit characterization of the projections in Res (L) for an arbitrary orthomodular lattice L. It turns out that much of the needed machinery can be developed in a much more general setting. This we now proceed to do. It will prove useful to call a residuated map f on the ordered set E *weakly increasing* if the restriction of f to the order ideal generated by its image is increasing. We then have:

THEOREM 20.3. *Let L be a bounded lattice and let* $f = f^2 \in$ Res (L). *The following conditions are then equivalent:*

(1) *f is weakly increasing;*
(2) $(\forall x \in L) \quad f(x) = [x \cup f(x)] \cap f(\pi)$;
(3) $f(x) \leq x \Rightarrow f(x) = x \cap f(\pi)$;
(4) $x \in \text{Im} f^+ \Rightarrow f(x) = x \cap f(\pi)$;
(5) $(\forall x \in L) \quad f(x) \geq x \cap f(\pi)$.

Proof. (1) ⇒ (2): We clearly have $[x \cup f(x)] \cap f(\pi) \leq x \cup f(x)$ and so $\{f[x \cup f(x)] \cap f(\pi)\} \leq f[x \cup f(x)] = f(x)$. Since f is weakly increasing, we have $[x \cup f(x)] \cap f(\pi) \leq f\{[x \cup f(x)] \cap f(\pi)\}$. Hence

$$f(x) \leq [x \cup f(x)] \cap f(\pi) \leq f\{[x \cup f(x)] \cap f(\pi)\} \leq f(x)$$

from which it follows that $f(x) = [x \cup f(x)] \cap f(\pi)$.

(2) ⇒ (3): If $x \geq f(x)$, then $f(x) = [x \cup f(x)] \cap f(\pi) = x \cap f(\pi)$.

(3) ⇒ (4): This follows from the fact that if $x = f^+(y)$, then $f(x) = (f \circ f^+)(y) = (f \circ f^+)[f^+(y)] \leq f^+(y) = x$.

(4) ⇒ (5): Note that $f(x) = (f \circ f^+ \circ f)(x)$ with $(f^+ \circ f)(x) \in \text{Im} f^+$. It thus follows by (4) that $f(x) = f[(f^+ \circ f)(x)] = (f^+ \circ f)(x) \cap f(\pi) \geq x \cap f(\pi)$.

(5) ⇒ (1): This is clear.

COROLLARY. *If* $f \in$ Res (L) *is a weakly increasing idempotent then*

$$f^+(0) \cap f(\pi) = 0.$$

The only explicit formula which we have thus far obtained for an idempotent residuated map was that given in Theorem 13.4: every weakly regular idempotent residuated map on a bounded lattice L is of the form

$$(\forall x \in L) \quad f(x) = [x \cup f^+(0)] \cap f(\pi).$$

We now see what this means in the weakly increasing case.

THEOREM 20.4. *Let f be a weakly increasing idempotent residuated map on the bounded lattice L. The following conditions are then equivalent:*

(1) $(\forall x \in L) \quad f(x) = [x \cup f^+(0)] \cap f(\pi)$;
(2) $x \geq f^+(0) \Rightarrow x \leq f^+(x)$;
(3) $x \geq f^+(0) \Rightarrow x \geq f(x)$.

Proof. (2) $\Leftrightarrow$ (3): If $x \leq f^+(x)$, then $f(x) \leq (f \circ f^+)(x) \leq x$. Dually, $f(x) \leq x$ gives $x \leq (f^+ \circ f)(x) \leq f^+(x)$.

(1) $\Rightarrow$ (3): If $x \geq f^+(0)$, then $f(x) = [x \cup f^+(0)] \cap f(\pi) = x \cap f(\pi) \leq x$.

(3) $\Rightarrow$ (1): $(\forall x \in L)$ $x \cup f^+(0) \geq f^+(0)$. By (3) and the fact that f is weakly increasing, we deduce $f(x) = f[x \cup f^+(0)] = [x \cup f^+(0)] \cap f(\pi)$.

COROLLARY. *If f is dually range-closed then*

$$(\forall x \in L) \quad f(x) = [x \cup f^+(0)] \cap f(\pi).$$

THEOREM 20.5. *Suppose that f is a weakly increasing idempotent residuated map on the bounded lattice L and that f^+ is weakly increasing on the dual of L. Then a necessary and sufficient condition that f be dually range-closed is*

$$(\forall x \in L) \quad f(x) = [x \cup f^+(0)] \cap f(\pi).$$

Proof. Suppose that $(\forall x \in L)$ $f(x) = [x \cup f^+(0)] \cap f(\pi)$. By Theorem 20.4, $x \geq f^+(0) \Rightarrow x \leq f^+(x)$. But by hypothesis we have $x \geq f^+(x)$ for each $x \geq f^+(0)$ and so f is dually range-closed. The converse implication is contained in the corollary to Theorem 20.4.

We are now ready to apply all of this to the case of an orthomodular lattice. Accordingly, *until further notice we shall be working in an orthomodular lattice (L, i) with* Res (L) *equipped with the natural involution*. We agree to call an element f of Res (L) a *symmetric closure map* whenever f is an increasing projection. Evidently, every symmetric closure map is among other things a residuated closure map. The analogue of Theorem 20.1 is:

THEOREM 20.6. *There is a bijection between the set of symmetric closure maps on L and the set of closure subsets of L which are stable under the formation of orthocomplements, namely that given by* $f \to \operatorname{Im} f$.

Proof. Every closure subset which is stable under the formation of orthocomplements is evidently bicomplete. Thus, in view of Theorem 20.1, it suffices to show that a residuated closure map is symmetric if and only if its image is stable under the formation of orthocomplements. This we now proceed to do.

First let f be a symmetric closure map on L. Using the fact that $f = f^*$ we see that if $x = f(x)$, then $(f \circ i)(x) = (f \circ i \circ f)(x) \leq i(x)$. But since f is increasing we must have $i(x) \leq (f \circ i)(x)$. We deduce that $i(x) = (f \circ i)(x)$ and so $\operatorname{Im} f$ is stable under i. Suppose now that f is a residuated closure map and that $x \in \operatorname{Im} f \Rightarrow i(x) \in \operatorname{Im} f$. Then for each $x \in L$ we have

$$f(x) \in \operatorname{Im} f \Rightarrow (i \circ f)(x) \in \operatorname{Im} f \Rightarrow (f \circ i \circ f)(x) = (i \circ f)(x).$$

Now $x \leq f(x) \Rightarrow (i \circ f)(x) \leq i(x)$ and so $(f \circ i \circ f)(x) \leq i(x)$. It follows that $f = f^*$.

COROLLARY. *For any symmetric closure map f on L,* $\operatorname{Im} f$ *is an orthomodular lattice.*

We are now able to produce our long-sought characterization of the projections in $\operatorname{Res}(L)$.

THEOREM 20.7. *Let f be a symmetric closure map on L and let z be a central element of* $\operatorname{Im} f$. *Define* $g : \operatorname{Im} f \to \operatorname{Im} f$ *by the prescription* $g(x) = x \cap z$. *Then* $g \circ f$ *is a projection in* $\operatorname{Res}(L)$. *Moreover, every projection in* $\operatorname{Res}(L)$ *arises in this manner.*

Proof. (1) Note first that f is a projection in $\operatorname{Res}(L)$ and that g is a projection in $\operatorname{Res}(\operatorname{Im} f)$. Letting j denote the restriction of i to $\operatorname{Im} f$ and using the arguments given in the proof of Theorem 20.2, we see that

$$\begin{aligned}(g \circ f)^* &= i \circ (g \circ f)^+ \circ i = i \circ (g^+ \circ f^+) \circ i = (j \circ g^+ \circ j) \circ (i \circ f^+ \circ i) \\ &= g \circ f.\end{aligned}$$

Hence $g \circ f$ is a projection in $\operatorname{Res}(L)$.

(2) Now let h be a projection in Res (L). Setting $f = h \curlyvee \mathrm{id}_L$ it is clear that f is a symmetric closure map on L. Then if g is the restriction of h to Im f we have $h = g \circ f$ by Theorem 20.2. But by the corollary to Theorem 20.6, Im f is orthomodular and hence relatively complemented. Since g is a decreasing residuated map on Im f, we may apply Theorem 15.3 to deduce that $g(\pi) = h(\pi)$ is central in Im f with $g(x) = x \cap g(\pi)$ for all $x \in \mathrm{Im}\, f$.

COROLLARY. *Every projection in* Res (L) *is weakly increasing.*

The above theorem can be used to provide an even more useful characterization of the projections in Res (L).

THEOREM 20.8. *Let $x \in L$ and let f be a symmetric closure map on the interval* $[0, x]$. *Then $f \circ \varphi_x$ is a projection in* Res (L). *Moreover, every projection h arises in this manner. The projection h uniquely determines both f and x by the requirement that $x = h(\pi)$ and $f =$ the restriction of h to* $[0, x]$.

Proof. (1) It is implicit in the statement of the theorem that the interval $[0, x]$ is equipped with the natural orthocomplementation given by $j(y) = x \cap i(y)$ so that, by Theorem 18.5, $([0, x], j)$ is an orthomodular lattice. Thus it is meaningful to speak of a symmetric closure map on $[0, x]$. With notation as given above, we have

$$(\forall y \in L) \quad (i \circ f \circ \varphi_x)(y) \geq i(x) \Rightarrow (\varphi_x \circ i \circ f \circ \varphi_x)(y) = x \cap (i \circ f \circ \varphi_x)(y)$$
$$= (j \circ f \circ \varphi_x)(y).$$

Hence

$$\begin{aligned}(f \circ \varphi_x \circ i \circ f \circ \varphi_x)(y) = (f \circ j \circ f \circ \varphi_x)(y) &\leq (j \circ \varphi_x)(y)\\ &= [(y \cup x') \cap x]' \cap x\\ &= [(y' \cap x) \cup x'] \cap x\\ &= y' \cap x\\ &\leq y'\\ &= i(y).\end{aligned}$$

Thus $f \circ \varphi_x = (f \circ \varphi_x)^* \in$ Res (L). Clearly, $f \circ \varphi_x$ is idempotent.

(2) Now let h be a projection in Res (L). Taking $x = h(\pi)$ we have $h = \varphi_x \circ h$. Applying the adjoint operation, this implies $h = h \circ \varphi_x$. We must now show that f, the restriction of h to $[0, x]$, is a symmetric closure map on this interval. Letting j denote the orthocomplementation on $[0, x]$ we have that $f \circ j \circ f \leq h \circ i \circ h \leq i$ from which it follows that $f \circ j \circ f \leq j$ and so $f = f^* \in$ Res $([0, x])$. Clearly f is idempotent and, by the corollary to Theorem 20.7, it is increasing.

(3) We must still show that if $h \in P$ [Res (L)] and if $h = f \circ \varphi_x$ with f a symmetric closure map on $[0, x]$ then $x = h(\pi)$ and f coincides with the restriction of h to $[0, x]$. Both of these facts are indeed immediate! Note first that $h(\pi) = (f \circ \varphi_x)(\pi) = f(x) = x$. Also, for $y \leq x$, $h(y) = (f \circ \varphi_x)(y) = f(y)$, thus completing the proof.

COROLLARY 1. *If $h \in P$ [Res (L)] then the restriction of h to $[0, h(\pi)]$ is a symmetric closure map on that interval.*

COROLLARY 2. *The projections on* Res (L) *can be put in one–one correspondence with the symmetric closure maps on intervals of the form* $[0, x]$.

Our next and last item of business in this section will be to provide a characterization of bicomplete subsets in terms of *extensions* of residuated maps. *We therefore now drop the assumption that* (L, i) *is an orthomodular lattice and work instead in a bounded ordered set* E. Suppose that we have $\{0, \pi\} \subseteq M \subseteq E$. Then with the inherited ordering M itself forms a bounded ordered set, so we may consider Res (M). We may also consider the set

$$\text{Res}\,(E|M) = \{f \in \text{Res}\,(E);\ \text{Im}\, f \subseteq M,\ \text{Im}\, f^+ \subseteq M\}.$$

Evidently Res $(E|M)$ is a subsemigroup of Res (E). To say that an element g of Res (M) can be *extended* to f in Res $(E|M)$ will be to say that g is the restriction of f to M. Note that if g can be extended to f in Res $(E|M)$ then for all $x, y \in M$ we have

$$g(x) \leq y \Leftrightarrow f(x) \leq y \Leftrightarrow x \leq f^+(y).$$

Since $f^+(y) \in M$ it follows that g^+ is the restriction of f^+ to M. Note further that at least two elements of Res (M) can be extended to Res $(E|M)$, namely the zero map on M and the residuated closure map whose image is $\{0, \pi\}$. To say that M is bicomplete turns out to be equivalent to saying that *every* element of Res (M) can be so extended:

THEOREM 20.9. *Let E be a bounded ordered set and let $\{0, \pi\} \subseteq M \subseteq E$. The following conditions are then equivalent:*

(1) *M is bicomplete;*
(2) *there is a residuated closure map f on E such that* $\operatorname{Im} f = M$;
(3) *every element of* Res (M) *can be extended to* Res $(E|M)$;
(4) *the identity map on M can be extended to* Res $(E|M)$;
(5) *there is a semigroup isomorphism between* Res (E) *and* Res $(E|M)$;
(6) Res $(E|M)$ *has a multiplicative identity element.*

Proof. (1) $\Leftrightarrow$ (2): This was established in Theorem 20.1.

(2) $\Rightarrow$ (3): Let $g \in \operatorname{Res}(M)$. Then $g \circ f: E \to E$ and $g^+ \circ f^+ : E \to E$ are each isotone. Since $\operatorname{Im} f = \operatorname{Im} f^+ = M$ and $\operatorname{Im}(g \circ f) \subseteq M$, we see that $f^+ \circ (g \circ f) = g \circ f$. Hence $(g^+ \circ f^+) \circ (g \circ f) = g^+ \circ g \circ f \geq f \geq \mathrm{id}_E$. Dually, we have $(g \circ f) \circ (g^+ \circ f^+) \leq \mathrm{id}_E$ and so $g \circ f \in \operatorname{Res}(E)$ with $(g \circ f)^+ = g^+ \circ f^+$. Evidently, $g \circ f \in \operatorname{Res}(E|M)$ and g is the restriction of $g \circ f$ to M.

(3) $\Rightarrow$ (4): This is obvious.

(4) $\Rightarrow$ (5): Let f be the extension of id_M to Res $(E|M)$. Then id_M is evidently the restriction of f^+ to M. It follows from this that $f = f^+ \circ f$ and so f is a residuated closure map. As in the proof of (2) $\Rightarrow$ (3), for each $g \in \operatorname{Res}(M)$ we have $g \circ f \in \operatorname{Res}(E|M)$ with $(g \circ f)^+ = g^+ \circ f^+$. Define $F : \operatorname{Res}(M) \to \operatorname{Res}(E|M)$ by setting $F(g) = g \circ f$. Since f is the extension of id_M, we have $F(g \circ h) = g \circ h \circ f = (g \circ f) \circ (h \circ f) = F(g) \circ F(h)$ and so F is a semigroup homomorphism. If $F(g) = F(h)$, then

$$(\forall x \in M) \quad g(x) = (g \circ f)(x) = (h \circ f)(x) = h(x)$$

and so $g = h$. To show that F is surjective, let $g \in \operatorname{Res}(E|M)$ and let h be the restriction of g to M. Then $h \in \operatorname{Res}(M)$ with h^+ the restriction of g^+ to M. It follows that $g = F(h)$.

(5) $\Rightarrow$ (6): This is clear.

(6) $\Rightarrow$ (1): Let f be the multiplicative identity element of Res $(E|M)$.

Given $m \in M$ recall that $\alpha_m \in \text{Res}\,(E)$ was defined by

$$\alpha_m(x) = \begin{cases} m & \text{if} \quad x \neq 0; \\ 0 & \text{if} \quad x = 0. \end{cases}$$

Also, α_m^+ is given by

$$\alpha_m^+(x) = \begin{cases} \pi & \text{if} \quad x \geq m; \\ 0 & \text{otherwise.} \end{cases}$$

Clearly $\alpha_m \in \text{Res}\,(E|M)$ so that $f \circ \alpha_m = \alpha_m \circ f = \alpha_m$. But then $m = \alpha_m(m) = (f \circ \alpha_m)(m) = f(m)$. Thus $(\forall m \in M)\ f(m) = m$ and a dual argument shows that $f^+(m) = m$. Thus $f = f^+ \circ f$ is a residuated closure map whose image is M.

COROLLARY 1. *If E is a lattice then M is bicomplete if and only if* Res $(E|M)$ *is a Baer semigroup.*

Suppose now that f is a residuated closure map and that $M = \text{Im}\,f$. For $g \in \text{Res}\,(E)$ we have $\text{Im}\,g \subseteq M \Leftrightarrow g = f \circ g$ and $\text{Im}\,g^+ \subseteq M \Leftrightarrow g^+ = f^+ \circ g^+$, this latter condition being equivalent to $g = g \circ f$. It follows from this that $g \in \text{Res}\,(E|M) \Leftrightarrow g = f \circ g \circ f$ and so $\text{Res}\,(E|M) = f \circ \text{Res}\,(E) \circ f$. The next corollary is now immediate:

COROLLARY 2. *Let f be a residuated closure map on the bounded ordered set E and let $M =$* Im f. *Then* Res (M) *is isomorphic to* $f \circ \text{Res}\,(E) \circ f$, *the isomorphism being given by* $g \rightarrow g \circ f$.

We are now in a position to state a representation theorem for residuated mappings on a complete infinitely distributive lattice.

THEOREM 20.10. *Let L be a complete infinitely distributive lattice. There exists a Boolean algebra A and a residuated closure map f on A such that* Res (L) *is isomorphic to* $f \circ \text{Res}\,(A) \circ f$.

Proof. This follows immediately from Theorems 10.7 and 20.9.

EXERCISES

20.1. Let L be a complete lattice and let $T = \{t_\alpha;\ \alpha \in A\}$ be a semigroup of residuated maps on L such that at least one t_α is increasing. Let $t = \bigvee_{\alpha \in A} t_\alpha$. Prove that t is a residuated closure map on L whose image is $\{x \in L;\ (\forall \alpha \in A)\ t_\alpha(x) \leq x\}$. [*Hint.* The fact that T is a semigroup guarantees that $t \circ t \leq t$ and since some t_α is increasing so is t.] Show that if in fact T is a group of automorphisms on L then the image of t is $\{x \in L; (\forall \alpha \in A)\ t_\alpha(x) = x\}$.

20.2. Call a residuated map f on a bounded lattice L *weakly decreasing* if the restriction of f to $[0, f(\pi)]$ is decreasing. Show that if L is relatively complemented then an idempotent $f \in \mathrm{Res}\,(L)$ is weakly decreasing if and only if it is range-closed. [*Hint.* Apply Theorem 15.3.]

20.3. Let f be a weakly decreasing idempotent residuated map on a bounded relatively complemented lattice L. Prove that the following conditions are equivalent:

(1) f is dually range-closed;
(2) $(\forall x \in L)\ f(x) = [x \cup f^{+}(0)] \cap f(\pi)$.

21. Boolean algebras

There is a vast amount of research which has been done in this general area of mathematics. Our purpose in this section is definitely *not* to survey this literature. Rather, we wish to see how the notions of Baer semigroup and residuated map tie in with Boolean algebras and, while we are at it, to prove a few results which will be of use to us in the sequel. We begin with some remarks concerning the coordinatization problem for Boolean algebras. In what follows, we shall use the symbol x' to denote the unique complement of x in a Boolean algebra.

THEOREM 21.1. *Every Boolean algebra may be coordinatized by a decreasing Baer semigroup.*

Proof. We leave to the reader the routine verification that in any Boolean algebra L each translation $x \to x \cap a$ is residuated with $x \to x \cup a'$ its associated residual map. Now apply Theorem 15.6.

Thus the question of coordinatizing a Boolean algebra with a decreasing Baer semigroup amounts to deciding when such a semigroup has the property that its lattice of right k-annihilators is a Boolean algebra. This we now proceed to answer.

THEOREM 21.2. *Let $\langle S; k\rangle$ be a decreasing Baer semigroup. The following conditions are then equivalent:*

(1) *$\mathscr{R}_k(S)$ is a Boolean algebra;*
(2) *$eS \in \mathscr{R}_k(S) \Rightarrow Se \in \mathscr{L}_k(S)$;*

(3) *$eS \in \mathscr{R}_k(S) \Rightarrow e$ is in the centre of S;*
(4) *$(\forall x \in S)\ R_k(x) = R_k(x^2)$;*
(5) *kS is a radical ideal (in the sense that $x^n \in kS \Rightarrow x \in kS$);*
(6) *$(\forall x \in S)\ L_k(x) = R_k(x)$.*

Proof. The equivalence of the first three conditions follows from Theorem 15.7.

(3) $\Rightarrow$ (4): If $xy \in kS$ we must clearly have $x^2y \in kS$. Suppose now that $x^2y \in kS$ and let $eS = R_k(x)$. Then $xy \in R_k(x)$ implies $xy = exy$ so that, by (3), $xy = exy = xey$ and so $xy \in kS$.

(4) $\Rightarrow$ (5): If $x^n \in kS$ with $n > 1$, then $2(n-1) \geq n$ and so $(x^{n-1})^2 \in kS$. Thus $R_k(x^{2n-2}) = S$ and so, by (4), $R_k(x^{n-1}) = S$ thereby showing that $x^{n-1} \in kS$. Repeated applications of this argument will now show that $x \in kS$.

(5) $\Rightarrow$ (6): If $y \in R_k(x)$, then $(yx)^2 = yxyx = y(xy)x \in kS$ implies $yx \in kS$ and so $y \in L_k(x)$. A dual argument produces the reverse inclusion.

(6) $\Rightarrow$ (2): Let $eS = R_k(x)$ and $Sf = L_k(x)$. Then $eS = Sf$ and so $e = ef = f$ and $eS = Se \in \mathscr{L}_k(S)$.

COROLLARY. *If $\langle S; k\rangle$ is an abelian Baer semigroup then $\mathscr{R}_k(S)$ is a Boolean algebra.*

For a decreasing Baer semigroup, distributivity of the associated lattice is automatic and any condition producing complementation will consequently produce a Boolean algebra. In particular, one might conjecture that every Boolean algebra may be coordinatized by a range-closed decreasing Baer semigroup. The next result verifies this conjecture.

THEOREM 21.3. *Let $\langle S; k\rangle$ be a decreasing Baer semigroup. Then a necessary and sufficient condition that $\mathscr{R}_k(S)$ be a Boolean algebra is that $\langle S; k\rangle$ be range-closed.*

Proof. If $\langle S; k\rangle$ is range-closed then by Theorem 13.9 the lattice $\mathscr{R}_k(S)$ is complemented and by Theorem 15.6 it is distributive.

Suppose conversely that $\mathscr{R}_k(S)$ is a Boolean algebra. Then we have, by Theorem 21.2, $eS \in \mathscr{R}_k(S)$ implies that e is in the centre of S. Now let $x \in S$, $fS = (R_k^{\rightarrow} \circ L_k)(x)$ and $eS \in \mathscr{R}_k(S)$. Then since $L_k(x) = L_k(f)$

we have

$$a\,(xe) \in kS \Leftrightarrow aex \in kS \Leftrightarrow aef \in kS \Leftrightarrow a\,(fe) \in kS$$

so $L_k(xe) = L_k(fe)$. It follows that

$$\varphi_x\,(eS) = (R_k^{\rightarrow} \circ L_k)\,(xe) = (R_k^{\rightarrow} \circ L_k)\,(fe) = \varphi_f\,(eS).$$

Thus $\varphi_x = \varphi_e$ and so, by Theorem 13.8, x is range-closed.

By duality, one can also say that the decreasing Baer semigroup $\langle S; k\rangle$ coordinatizes a Boolean algebra if and only if $\langle S; k\rangle$ is dually range-closed.

A Boolean algebra is, amongst other things, an orthomodular lattice and so it seems reasonable to inquire about a Foulis coordinatization. The next result summarizes the situation.

THEOREM 21.4. *Let $\langle S; k; {}^*\rangle$ be a Foulis semigroup. Then*

(1) *$\langle S; k\rangle$ is a decreasing Baer semigroup if and only if every closed projection of S is in the centre of S;*

(2) *$P'(S)$ is a Boolean algebra if and only if, for all $e, f \in P'(S)$, $ef = fe$.*

Proof. (1) This follows from Theorem 21.2 and the fact that if e is a closed projection then $eS \in \mathscr{R}_k(S)$ and $Se \in \mathscr{L}_k(S)$.

(2) This follows from Exercise 19.3.

Our next major goal will be to give a topological interpretation to residuated mappings on a Boolean algebra and to give a coordinatization in terms of a semigroup of continuous relations. This task will occupy our attention for the remainder of this section, but will also provide some useful information about Boolean algebras and, in particular, about prime and maximal ideals of Boolean algebras. We begin with two important examples.

EXAMPLE 21.1. Let X be a topological space. We ask the reader to recall the notation introduced in Examples 12.4 and 12.6. In particular, we write $\mathrm{Cl}\,(A)$ for the closure of A, $\imath(A)$ for the complement of A and call a binary relation S on X *continuous if* A open $\Rightarrow S^t(A)$ open. Let us consider the set $\mathrm{CR}^*\,(X)$ of binary relations S on X such that both S and S^t are continuous. Clearly, $(\mathrm{CR}^*\,(X), t)$ is an involution semigroup.

Also, by Example 12.6, if $S, T \in \mathrm{CR}^*(X)$ then $S \circ T = \emptyset \Leftrightarrow \mathrm{Dom}\, S \subseteq (\imath \circ \mathrm{Cl})(\mathrm{Im}\, T)$ and so $L_\emptyset(T) = \mathrm{CR}^*(X) \circ I_A$ where $A = (\imath \circ \mathrm{Cl})(\mathrm{Im}\, T)$. Since I_A is a projection in $\mathrm{CR}^*(X)$, it follows that $\mathrm{CR}^*(X)$ is a Foulis semigroup. We now investigate the nature of $P'(\mathrm{CR}^*(X))$.

The mapping $A \to (\imath \circ \mathrm{Cl})(A)$ is easily seen to set up a Galois connection on the lattice of open subsets of X. It follows that

$$A = (\imath \circ \mathrm{Cl} \circ \imath \circ \mathrm{Cl})(A) \Leftrightarrow (\exists B \text{ open}) \quad A = (\imath \circ \mathrm{Cl})(B).$$

Such a set is called a *regular open set.* We have already seen that every closed projection is of the form I_A with A a regular open set. Suppose now that A is an arbitrary regular open set. Then if $B = (\imath \circ \mathrm{Cl})(A)$ we have $I_B \in \mathrm{CR}^*(X)$ and $L_\emptyset(I_B) = \mathrm{CR}^*(X) \circ I_D$ where $D = (\imath \circ \mathrm{Cl})(\mathrm{Im}\, I_B) = (\imath \circ \mathrm{Cl})(B) = (\imath \circ \mathrm{Cl} \circ \imath \circ \mathrm{Cl})(A) = A$. It is easily seen from this that $P'(\mathrm{CR}^*(X))$ is isomorphic to the Boolean algebra formed by the regular open subsets of X.

EXAMPLE 21.2. A subset K of a topological space X is called *clopen* if it is both open and closed. The space is called *totally disconnected* if every open set is the union of a family of clopen sets; and a *Boolean space* if it is a compact totally disconnected Hausdorff space. Let X be a Boolean space and let $\mathscr{A}$ denote the associated Boolean algebra formed by the clopen subsets of X. Finally, let $B^*(X)$ be the set of binary relations S on X such that

$$\begin{cases} A \text{ open} \Rightarrow S(A),\ S^t(A) \quad \text{open;} \\ B \text{ closed} \Rightarrow S(B),\ S^t(B) \text{ closed.} \end{cases}$$

If $S \in B^*(X)$ then the mapping $\xi_S : \mathscr{A} \to \mathscr{A}$ defined by $\xi_S(A) = S(A)$ is then evidently residuated with $\xi_S^+(A) = (\imath \circ S^t \circ \imath)(A)$. Our goal is to show that $B^*(X)$ is isomorphic to $\mathrm{Res}(\mathscr{A})$. We clearly have:

(1) $S \to \xi_S$ *is a homomorphism.*

We claim that this homomorphism is surjective. To see this, let $f \in \mathrm{Res}(\mathscr{A})$ and define S by

$$x\, S\, y \Leftrightarrow y \in \bigcap \{f(K);\ K \in \mathscr{A},\ x \in K\}.$$

We claim that

(2) $(\forall K \in \mathscr{A}) \quad f(K) = S(K)$.

To see this, note that if $h \in S(K)$ then there exists $x \in K$ such that xSy and by the definition of S we must have $y \in f(K)$. This shows that $S(K) \subseteq f(K)$. Suppose now that $y \notin S(K)$. Then for each $x \in K$ there exists $K_x \in \mathscr{A}$ such that $x \in K_x$ and $y \notin f(K_x)$. Now $K \subseteq \bigcup_{x \in K} K_x$ and since K is compact, $K \subseteq \bigcup_{x \in F} K_x$ for some finite subset F of K. Since $f \in \text{Res}\ \mathscr{A}$ we have $f(K) \subseteq \bigcup_{x \in F} f(K_x)$ with the union being set-theoretic. It follows that $y \notin f(K)$, so $f(K) = S(K)$ which completes the proof of (2).

Now let f^* be the adjoint of f and define S^* by

$$xS^*y \Leftrightarrow y \in \bigcap \{f^*(K);\ K \in \mathscr{A},\ x \in K\}.$$

We claim that

(3) $S^* = S^t$.

To see this, let xSy. If yS^*x failed then $(\exists K \in \mathscr{A})\ y \in K,\ x \notin f^*(K)$. This implies $x \in (\text{¡} \circ f^*)(K)$ which is clopen, so by the definition of S we must have $y \in (f \circ \text{¡} \circ f^*)(K)$. But, by the definition of the adjoint map, $f \circ \text{¡} \circ f^* \leq \text{¡}$ and so this puts $y \in K \cap \text{¡}(K)$, a contradiction. We conclude that $xSy \Rightarrow yS^*x$ and a similar argument shows that $xS^*y \Rightarrow ySx$. It follows that $S^* = S^t$.

Notice now that, by (2), S maps clopen sets to clopen sets. Since every open set is the union of a family of clopen sets, it follows that S maps open sets into open sets. A similar observation applies to S^*. This establishes

(4) *A open $\Rightarrow S(A), S^t(A)$ open.*

We now show that

(5) *B closed $\Rightarrow S(B), S^t(B)$ closed.*

It clearly suffices to prove that $S(B)$ is closed. For this purpose, suppose that $y \in (\text{Cl} \circ S)(B) \cap (\text{¡} \circ S)(B)$. Now $y \notin S(B) \Rightarrow (\forall x \in B)\ xSy$ fails. It follows that $(\forall x \in B)\ (\exists M_x \in \mathscr{A})\ x \in M_x,\ y \notin f(M_x)$. Now $B \subseteq \bigcup_{x \in B} M_x$ and by compactness there exist $x_1, x_2, \ldots, x_n \in B$ such that $B \subseteq \bigcup_{i=1}^{n} M_{x_i}$. Hence $S(B) \subseteq S\left(\bigcup_{i=1}^{n} M_{x_i}\right) = f\left(\bigcup_{i=1}^{n} M_{x_i}\right) = \bigcup_{i=1}^{n} f(M_{x_i})$ which is clopen and so

$(\mathrm{Cl} \circ S)(B) \subseteq \bigcup_{i=1} f(M_{x_i})$. Since this union is set-theoretic and $y \notin f(M_{x_i})$ for $i = 1, 2, \ldots, n$ we see that $y \notin (\mathrm{Cl} \circ S)(B)$, contrary to our initial choice of y. This then shows that $S(B)$ is closed.

In summary, we have established

(6) *Every* $f \in \mathrm{Res}(\mathscr{A})$ *is of the form* $\hat{\xi}_S$ *for some* $S \in B^*(X)$.

We must finally show that

(7) $S \to \hat{\xi}_S$ *is injective.*

Accordingly, let $S, T \in B^*(X)$ with $\hat{\xi}_S = \hat{\xi}_T$. Now S, T are each continuous so they induce residuated mappings ξ_S, ξ_T on the lattice of closed subsets of X according to the prescriptions

$$\xi_S(B) = (\mathrm{Cl} \circ S)(B) = S(B), \quad \xi_T(B) = T(B).$$

Evidently $\hat{\xi}_S$ is the restriction of ξ_S to $\mathscr{A}$ with $\hat{\xi}_S^+$ the restriction of ξ_S^+ to $\mathscr{A}$. Now every closed set is obviously the intersection of a family of clopen sets, so if B is closed with $B = \bigcap_\alpha K_\alpha$ where each $K_\alpha \in \mathscr{A}$, we have

$$\begin{aligned} \xi_S^+(B) = \xi_S^+\left(\bigcap_\alpha K_\alpha\right) &= \bigcap_\alpha \xi_S^+(K_\alpha) = \bigcap_\alpha \hat{\xi}_S^+(K_\alpha) \\ &= \bigcap_\alpha \hat{\xi}_T^+(K_\alpha) \\ &= \xi_T^+\left(\bigcap_\alpha K_\alpha\right) \\ &= \xi_T^+(B). \end{aligned}$$

This shows that $\xi_S^+ = \xi_T^+$ and so $\xi_S = \xi_T$. It follows from this that $(\forall x \in X)\ S(\{x\}) = T(\{x\})$ from which we obtain $S = T$.

We wish to show that *every* Boolean algebra may be regarded as the Boolean algebra of clopen subsets of a suitable Boolean space. This will be achieved by having a close look at the maximal ideals of a Boolean algebra. Since it will not cost us anything, we shall phrase our results wherever possible in a more general context. Recall first that an ideal J of a lattice L is called *maximal* if $J \neq L$ and the only ideal properly containing J is L. The ideal J is called *prime* if (1) $J \neq L$, (2) $x \cap y \in J \Rightarrow x \in J$ or $y \in J$. We begin with the following characterization of prime ideals in an arbitrary ortholattice.

THEOREM 21.5. *Let (L, i) be an ortholattice and let J be a $\cup$-subsemilattice of L such that $\pi \notin J$. A necessary and sufficient condition that J be a prime ideal of L is that $(\forall x \in L)$ either $x \in J$ or $i(x) \in J$.*

Proof. If J is a prime ideal then the properties $\pi \notin J$ and $(\forall x \in L)$ $x \cap i(x) = 0 \in J$ imply that either $x \in J$ or $i(x) \in J$. Conversely, suppose that this condition is satisfied by J. Then since $\pi \notin J$ we must have $0 \in J$. If $a \in J$ and $b \leq a$, then we must have $b \in J$ since otherwise $i(b) \in J$ would imply $a \cup i(b) = \pi \in J$, a contradiction. This shows that J is an ideal of L. Now if $a \cap b \in J$ with $a \notin J$ and $b \notin J$ then from $i(a), i(b) \in J$ we deduce that $\pi = (a \cap b) \cup i(a) \cup i(b) \in J$ which is once again a contradiction. We conclude that J is a prime ideal of L.

THEOREM 21.6. (1) *Every prime ideal of a complemented lattice is maximal.* (2) *An ideal of an ortholattice is prime if and only if it is maximal and is the kernel of a congruence relation.*

Proof. (1) It clearly suffices to show that if P is a prime ideal of L and $x \notin P$, then $[0, x] \curlyvee P = L$. Accordingly, let $x \notin P$ and $y \in L$. Then if x' is a complement of x we must have $x' \in P$. Since $y \leq x \cup x'$ we see that $y \in [0, x] \curlyvee P$ and so $[0, x] \curlyvee P = L$.

(2) Let P be a prime ideal of the ortholattice (L, i). Then, by (1), P is maximal and the mapping $\hat{p} : L \to \{0, \pi\}$ defined by

$$\hat{p}(x) = \begin{cases} 0 & \text{if} \quad x \in P; \\ \pi & \text{if} \quad x \notin P \end{cases}$$

is evidently a lattice homomorphism whose kernel is P. Now suppose that P is a maximal ideal of L and that P is the kernel of a congruence relation R on L. Then if $x \notin P$ we must have $P \curlyvee [0, x] = L$ and so there exists $p \in P$ such that $i(x) \leq p \cup x$. Then $i(x) = i(x) \cap (p \cup x) \equiv i(x) \cap (0 \cup x) = i(x) \cap x = 0(R)$ puts $i(x) \in P$. Thus for each $x \in L$ we have either $x \in P$ or $i(x) \in P$. It follows by Theorem 21.5 that P is a prime ideal of L.

COROLLARY. *An orthomodular lattice (L, i) is Boolean if and only if the prime and maximal ideals of L coincide.*

Proof. If L is Boolean then every ideal is the kernel of a congruence relation, so by part (2) of the Theorem an ideal is maximal if and only if it is prime. Suppose conversely that the prime and maximal ideals coincide. By the dual of Theorem 7.7, every principal ideal is the intersection of a family of maximal ideals, hence of a family of prime ideals. It follows that every principal ideal is the kernel of a congruence relation and a glance at the proof of Theorem 10.5 will show that L is therefore distributive.

Another interesting characterization of Boolean algebras is given in the next result.

THEOREM 21.7. *The following conditions on a lattice L are equivalent:*

(1) *L is distributive;*
(2) *every proper ideal of L is the intersection of a family of prime ideals;*
(3) *every proper principal ideal of L is the intersection of a family of prime ideals.*

Proof. (1) ⇒ (2): Let I be an ideal of L and let $x \notin I$. Consider the set X of all ideals J of L such that $x \notin J$ and $I \subseteq J$. Clearly $X \neq \emptyset$. Let us order X by set inclusion and consider a chain $\{J_\alpha\}$ of elements of X. Since the set-theoretic union of the family $\{J_\alpha\}$ also belongs to X, we may apply Zorn's axiom to deduce that X has a maximal member M. We claim that M is a prime ideal of L. Suppose that $v \notin M$, $w \notin M$ but $v \cap w \in M$. Then $[\leftarrow, v] \curlyvee M \notin X \Rightarrow x \in [\leftarrow, v] \curlyvee M$ and so there exists $m \in M$ such that $x \leq v \cup m$. Similarly there exists $n \in M$ such that $x \leq w \cup n$. Hence

$$x \leq (v \cup m) \cap (w \cup n) = [v \cap (w \cup n)] \cup [m \cap (w \cup n)]$$

$$= (v \cap w) \cup (v \cap n) \cup (m \cap w) \cup (m \cap n).$$

But this puts $x \in M$, a contradiction.

Now if I is a proper ideal of L the above argument shows that there is a prime ideal containing I. Consider the family $\{P_\alpha\}$ of all prime ideals containing I. Clearly $I \subseteq \bigcap_\alpha P_\alpha$ and if $x \notin I$ then $x \notin \bigcap_\alpha P_\alpha$. It follows that $I = \bigcap_\alpha P_\alpha$.

(2) $\Rightarrow$ (3): This is obvious.

(3) $\Rightarrow$ (1): If every proper principal ideal is the intersection of a family of prime ideals then every principal ideal of L is the kernel of a congruence relation. It follows from the proof of Theorem 10.5 that L is distributive.

COROLLARY. *A complemented lattice is a Boolean algebra if and only if every proper ideal of L is the intersection of a family of prime ideals.*

We are now ready to associate with an arbitrary Boolean algebra a Boolean space X whose algebra of clopen subsets forms a Boolean algebra isomorphic to the given one. This, of course, is a version of the well-known *Stone representation theorem* for Boolean algebras.

THEOREM 21.8. *For every Boolean algebra A there exists a Boolean space X such that A is isomorphic to the algebra of clopen subsets of X.*

Proof. Let A be a Boolean algebra and for each $x \in A$ let M_x be the set of maximal ideals of A that do *not* contain x. We begin by observing that

(1) $M_x \cap M_y = M_{x \cap y}$ *and* $M_x \cup M_y = M_{x \cup y}$.

To prove the first of these, we observe that if $x \cap y \notin M$ then we clearly cannot have $x \in M$ or $y \in M$; on the other hand, since every maximal ideal is prime, if $x \notin M$ and $y \notin M$ for a maximal ideal M, then $x \cap y \notin M$. The second equality comes from the observation that for any ideal M we have $x \cup y \notin M \Leftrightarrow x \notin M$ or $y \notin M$.

Let us now use $\{M_x; x \in A\}$ as a base for open sets of a topology on $\mathcal{M}$, the space of maximal ideals of A. Thus we agree to call a collection $\mathcal{O}$ of maximal ideals open if and only if $\mathcal{O}$ can be expressed as the union of a family of sets of the form M_x. Notice that, by (1), M_x and $M_{x'}$ are complementary subsets of $\mathcal{M}$, so each M_x is clopen. This shows that our space is totally disconnected.

(2) *$\mathcal{M}$ is a Hausdorff space.*

For, let M and N be distinct maximal ideals of A. With no loss of generality we may assume the existence of an element x such that $x \in M$ but

$x \notin N$. But then $N \in M_x$ and $M \notin M_x$ whence $M \in M_{x'}$. Thus M_x and $M_{x'}$ are disjoint open sets such that $N \in M_x$ and $M \in M_{x'}$.

(3) *$\mathscr{M}$ is compact.*

It clearly suffices to prove that if $\bigcup \{M_{x_\beta}; \beta \in B\} = \mathscr{M}$ then there exists a finite subset B_f of B such that $\mathscr{M} = \bigcup \{M_{x_\beta}; \beta \in B_f\}$. Let I be the ideal of A generated by $\{x_\beta; \beta \in B\}$. If $I \neq A$ then by Theorem 21.7 there exists a maximal ideal M containing I. But then $(\forall \beta \in B)\ x_\beta \in M$ which gives $M \notin \bigcup_{\beta \in B} M_{x_\beta}$, contrary to the fact that $\mathscr{M} = \bigcup \{M_{x_\beta}; \beta \in B\}$. We conclude that $I = A$ and so there exists a finite subset B_f of B such that $\bigcup_{\beta \in B_f} x_\beta = \pi$. It follows from (1) that $\bigcup_{\beta \in B_f} M_{x_\beta} = \mathscr{M}$.

At this point we have shown that $\mathscr{M}$ is indeed a Boolean space. The last step is provided by

(4) *the mapping $x \to M_x$ is an isomorphism of A onto the algebra of clopen subsets of $\mathscr{M}$.*

We have already seen in (1) that the mapping in question is a homomorphism. That it is injective follows from (2). Thus we need only show that if $\mathscr{K}$ is a clopen subset of $\mathscr{M}$ then $\mathscr{K} = M_x$ for some $x \in A$. Now if $\mathscr{K}$ is clopen we may write $\mathscr{K} = \bigcup_\alpha M_{x_\alpha}$ and note that there must exist indices $\alpha_1, \alpha_2, \ldots, \alpha_n$ such that $\mathscr{K} = \bigcup_{i=1}^{n} M_{x_{\alpha i}} = M_y$ where $y = \bigcup_{i=1}^{n} x_{\alpha_i}$.

We have already noted [see Exercises 4.15, 13.5 and 14.2] that every binary relation R on a set X induces a residuated mapping ξ_R on $\mathbf{P}(X)$ by the prescription $\xi_R(M) = R(M)$ and that there is an interesting connection between properties of the relation R and properties of the induced residuated map ξ_R. Much of the same sort of thing carries over in the context of Boolean algebras and Boolean relations. The next theorem illustrates this point.

THEOREM 21.9. *Let X be a Boolean space and let $\mathscr{A}$ be the Boolean algebra formed by the clopen subsets of $\mathscr{X}$. Then if $S \in B^*(X)$ and $f = \hat{\xi}_S$*

we have:

(1) *f is increasing if and only if S is reflexive;*
(2) *$f \circ f \leq f$ if and only if S is transitive;*
(3) *$f = f^*$ if and only if $S = S^t$;*
(4) *f is a residuated closure mapping if and only if S is both reflexive and transitive;*
(5) *f is a symmetric closure mapping if and only if S is an equivalence relation on X;*
(6) *f is decreasing if and only if $S = I_K$ for some $K \in \mathscr{A}$;*
(7) *f is weakly regular if and only if both S and S^t are functions (i.e. if and only if S is a homeomorphism of a clopen subset of X onto some clopen subset of X).*

The proof of the above result is left to the exercises at the end of the section on the grounds that it is completely analogous to the case of binary relations on a set (see Exercise 4.15).

COROLLARY. *If L is a complete infinitely distributive lattice then there exists a Boolean space X and an element T of $B^*(X)$ such that T is reflexive and transitive with* Res (L) *isomorphic to $T \circ B^*(X) \circ T$.*

Proof. This follows from Theorems 20.10 and 21.9.

EXERCISES

21.1. Let A be a Boolean algebra. Prove that for each $a \in A$ the mapping $x \to x \cap a$ is residuated with $x \to x \cup a'$ its residual.

21.2. Prove that every Boolean algebra may be coordinatized by an abelian Baer semigroup.

21.3. Prove Theorem 21.9. [*Hint.* To prove (7) assume xSy and xSz with $y \neq z$. Then there exists a clopen N such that $y \in N$ but $z \notin N$. Argue that $y \in N \Rightarrow x \in f^*(N)$ and $z \notin N \Rightarrow x \in (f^* \circ \imath)(N)$. Use Exercise 13.7(2) to arrive at a contradiction.]

21.4. Prove that the Boolean space associated with a given Boolean algebra in Theorem 21.8 is unique up to within homeomorphism. [*Hint.* Let X_i $(i = 1, 2)$ be Boolean spaces with $\mathscr{A}_i$ the algebra of clopen subsets of X_i. Let $f: \mathscr{A}_1 \to \mathscr{A}_2$ be an isomorphism. Define a relation S from X_1 to X_2 by

$$xSy \Leftrightarrow y \in \bigcap \{f(M);\, x \in M,\, M \in \mathscr{A}_1\}.$$

Argue that if xSy then $x \in M$, $M \in \mathscr{A}_1 \Leftrightarrow y \in f(M)$. Proceed as in part (7) of Exercise 21.3 to show that both S and S^t are functions. An obvious modification of the argument given in Example 21.2(4) will show both S and S^t to be continuous.]

21.5. Let X be a Boolean space with $\mathscr{A}$ its algebra of clopen subsets. Let $S \in B^*(X)$ and $f = \hat{\xi}_S$. Prove that f is a projection in Res $(\mathscr{A})$ if and only if S is symmetric and transitive as well as being reflexive on its domain. [*Hint.* Use Corollary 1 to Theorem 20.8.]

21.6. A residuated mapping f on a lattice L is said to be *quasi-multiplicative* if $(\forall x, y \in L)\ f[x \cap f(y)] = f(x) \cap f(y)$.

(1) Prove that every quasi-multiplicative residuated mapping is idempotent.

(2) Let L be a bounded section semicomplemented lattice. Prove that if the residuated mapping f on L is quasi-multiplicative then $(\forall x \in L)\ x = [x \cap f(\pi)] \cup [x \cap f^+(0)]$. Deduce that $(\forall x \in L)\ f(x) = f[x \cap f(\pi)]$. Prove further that a quasi-multiplicative residuated mapping is weakly increasing if and only if $f(\pi) \cap f^+(0) = 0$.

21.7. Let A be a Boolean algebra.

(1) Prove that a residuated mapping f on A is a quantifier [see Exercise 9.10] if and only if it is a symmetric closure map.

(2) Prove that a residuated mapping f on A is a projection if and only if it is weakly increasing and quasi-multiplicative.

[*Hint.* (1) If f is a symmetric closure map, argue first that $x \cap f(y) = 0 \Rightarrow f(x) \cap f(y) = 0$. Then let w be a complement of $f[x \cap f(y)]$ in $[0, f(x) \cap f(y)]$ and show that $w = 0$. (2) Use Theorems 20.7, 20.8 and part (1) of the exercise.]

CHAPTER 3

RESIDUATED ALGEBRAIC STRUCTURES

22. Residuated groupoids and semigroups; Molinaro equivalences

By an *ordered groupoid* we shall mean a groupoid G which is also an ordered set in which, for each $x \in G$, the translations λ_x, ϱ_x given by $\lambda_x(y) = xy$ and $\varrho_x(y) = yx$ are isotone mappings. We shall say that an ordered groupoid G is *residuated on the left* [resp. *right*] if each left [resp. right] translation on G is a residuated mapping; and *residuated* if it is residuated on both the left and right. In what follows we shall be concerned with residuated groupoids and semigroups, though some of the results hold when residuation occurs on one side only.

From the properties of residuated mappings derived in § 2 we see that if G is a residuated groupoid then, for any given $x, y \in G$, the sets

$$\{z \in G;\ xz \leq y\} \quad \text{and} \quad \{z \in G;\ zx \leq y\}$$

are not empty and admit maximum elements. These maximum elements are respectively $\lambda_x^+(y)$ and $\varrho_x^+(y)$. Henceforth we shall denote them using the notations $y\ .^{\cdot}\ x$ and $y\ ^{\cdot}.\ x$ respectively and call them the *right* [resp. *left*] *residual* of y by x. The residual $y\ .^{\cdot}\ x$ is thus characterized by the properties

(1) $x(y\ .^{\cdot}\ x) \leq y$;
(2) $xz \leq y \Rightarrow z \leq y\ .^{\cdot}\ x$.

Similarly, $y\ ^{\cdot}.\ x$ is characterized by the properties

(3) $(y\ ^{\cdot}.\ x)\,x \leq y$;
(4) $zx \leq y \Rightarrow z \leq y\ ^{\cdot}.\ x$.

Note that (1) is none other than $\lambda_x \circ \lambda_x^+ \leq \text{id}$ and that (3) is none other than $\varrho_x \circ \varrho_x^+ \leq \text{id}$. The corresponding properties $\lambda_x^+ \circ \lambda_x \geq \text{id}$ and $\varrho_x^+ \circ \varrho_x \geq \text{id}$ are then respectively

(5) $y \leq xy \mathbin{.\!^{\cdot}} x$;

(6) $y \leq yx \mathbin{^{\cdot}\!.} x$.

Let us now note that, given $a, b \in G$, we have

$$a \mathbin{.\!^{\cdot}} x \geq b \Leftrightarrow xb \leq a \Leftrightarrow x \leq a \mathbin{^{\cdot}\!.} b.$$

It follows from this that for each $a \in G$ the mapping ζ_a from G to its dual G^* described by $\zeta_a(x) = a \mathbin{.\!^{\cdot}} x$ is residuated with residual given by

$$\zeta_a^+(b) = a \mathbin{^{\cdot}\!.} b = \varrho_b^+(a).$$

The property $\zeta_y^+ \circ \zeta_y \geq \text{id}_G$ then gives

(7) $x \leq y \mathbin{^{\cdot}\!.} (y \mathbin{.\!^{\cdot}} x)$,

whereas $\zeta_y \circ \zeta_y^+ \leq \text{id}_{G^*}$ gives

(8) $x \leq y \mathbin{.\!^{\cdot}} (y \mathbin{^{\cdot}\!.} x)$.

Note that these also follow from (1), (4) and (2), (3) respectively.

Now since each of λ_x^+, ϱ_x^+ is isotone we have

(9) $a \leq b \Rightarrow (\forall x \in G) \quad a \mathbin{.\!^{\cdot}} x \leq b \mathbin{.\!^{\cdot}} x, \quad a \mathbin{^{\cdot}\!.} x \leq b \mathbin{^{\cdot}\!.} x$.

Furthermore, since

$$a \leq b \Rightarrow \lambda_a \leq \lambda_b \Rightarrow \lambda_b^+ \leq \lambda_a^+ \circ \lambda_a \circ \lambda_b^+ \leq \lambda_a^+ \circ \lambda_b \circ \lambda_b^+ \leq \lambda_a^+$$

we deduce that

(10) $a \leq b \Rightarrow (\forall x \in G) \quad x \mathbin{.\!^{\cdot}} b \leq x \mathbin{.\!^{\cdot}} a, \quad x \mathbin{^{\cdot}\!.} b \leq x \mathbin{^{\cdot}\!.} a$.

THEOREM 22.1. *If G is a residuated groupoid and $x, y \in G$, then*

(a) $x(y \mathbin{.\!^{\cdot}} x) = y \Leftrightarrow (\exists z \in G) \quad y = xz$;

(b) $(y \mathbin{^{\cdot}\!.} x)x = y \Leftrightarrow (\exists z \in G) \quad y = zx$;

(c) $xy \mathbin{.\!^{\cdot}} x = y \Leftrightarrow (\exists z \in G) \quad y = z \mathbin{.\!^{\cdot}} x$;

(d) $yx \,^{\boldsymbol\cdot}.\, x = y \Leftrightarrow (\exists z \in G) \quad y = z \,^{\boldsymbol\cdot}.\, x;$

(e) $x \,.^{\boldsymbol\cdot}\, (x \,^{\boldsymbol\cdot}.\, y) = y \Leftrightarrow (\exists z \in G) \quad y = x \,.^{\boldsymbol\cdot}\, z;$

(f) $x \,^{\boldsymbol\cdot}.\, (x \,.^{\boldsymbol\cdot}\, y) = y \Leftrightarrow (\exists z \in G) \quad y = x \,^{\boldsymbol\cdot}.\, z.$

Proof. If $f: A \to B$ is a residuated map then clearly

$$\begin{cases} x = (f \circ f^{+})(x) \Leftrightarrow (\exists y \in A)\ x = f(y); \\ x = (f^{+} \circ f)(x) \Leftrightarrow (\exists y \in B)\ x = f^{+}(y). \end{cases}$$

Applying these observations in turn to λ_x, ϱ_x, ζ_x and their residuals we obtain the result.

THEOREM 22.2. *If G is a residuated groupoid then the following conditions are equivalent:*

(1) *G is abelian;*

(2) $(\forall x, y \in G) \quad x \,.^{\boldsymbol\cdot}\, y = x \,^{\boldsymbol\cdot}.\, y.$

Proof. (1) holds if and only if $(\forall x \in G)\ \lambda_x = \varrho_x$. By the uniqueness of residual maps, this is equivalent to $(\forall x \in G)\ \overset{+}{\lambda_x} = \overset{+}{\varrho_x}$ which is (2).

Remark. In the abelian case, we write $x \,.^{\boldsymbol\cdot}\, y = x \,^{\boldsymbol\cdot}.\, y = x : y$.

THEOREM 22.3. *If G is a residuated groupoid then the following conditions are equivalent:*

(1) *G is a semigroup;*

(2) $(\forall x, y, z \in G) \quad (x \,.^{\boldsymbol\cdot}\, y) \,.^{\boldsymbol\cdot}\, z = x \,.^{\boldsymbol\cdot}\, yz;$

(3) $(\forall x, y, z \in G) \quad (x \,^{\boldsymbol\cdot}.\, y) \,^{\boldsymbol\cdot}.\, z = x \,^{\boldsymbol\cdot}.\, zy;$

(4) $(\forall x, y, z \in G) \quad (x \,.^{\boldsymbol\cdot}\, y) \,^{\boldsymbol\cdot}.\, z = (x \,^{\boldsymbol\cdot}.\, z) \,.^{\boldsymbol\cdot}\, y;$

(5) $(\forall x, y, z \in G) \quad \begin{cases} (x \,.^{\boldsymbol\cdot}\, y)\, z \leq xz \,.^{\boldsymbol\cdot}\, y; \\ y\,(x \,^{\boldsymbol\cdot}.\, z) \leq yx \,^{\boldsymbol\cdot}.\, z. \end{cases}$

Proof. G is a semigroup if and only if $(\forall y, z \in G)\ y\,(zx) = (yz)\,x$ and this is equivalent to $(\forall y, z \in G)\ \lambda_y \circ \lambda_z = \lambda_{yz}$. This is in turn equivalent to $(\forall y, z \in G)\ \overset{+}{\lambda_z} \circ \overset{+}{\lambda_y} = \overset{+}{\lambda_{yz}}$ which is none other than (2).

In a similar way, (1) is equivalent to $(\forall y, z \in G)\ \varrho_y \circ \varrho_z = \varrho_{zy}$ which is equivalent to $(\forall y, z \in G)\ \overset{+}{\varrho_z} \circ \overset{+}{\varrho_y} = \overset{+}{\varrho_{zy}}$ which is (3).

Now (1) is also equivalent to $(\forall y, z \in G)\ \lambda_y \circ \varrho_z = \varrho_z \circ \lambda_y$ which is equivalent to $(\forall y, z \in G)\ \overset{+}{\varrho_z} \circ \overset{+}{\lambda_y} = \overset{+}{\lambda_y} \circ \overset{+}{\varrho_z}$ and this is (4).

To establish the equivalence of (1) and (5), we note that if E is an ordered set and $f, g \in \text{Res}(E)$ then

$$f \circ g \leq g \circ f \Leftrightarrow g \circ f^+ \leq f^+ \circ g. \tag{*}$$

[In fact, $f \circ g \leq g \circ f \Rightarrow g \circ f^+ \leq f^+ \circ f \circ g \circ f^+ \leq f^+ \circ g \circ f \circ f^+ \leq f^+ \circ g$; and conversely $g \circ f^+ \leq f^+ \circ g \Rightarrow f \circ g \leq f \circ g \circ f^+ \circ f \leq f \circ f^+ \circ g \circ f \leq g \circ f$.] Now (1) holds if and only if $(\forall y, z \in G)\ \lambda_y \circ \varrho_z = \varrho_z \circ \lambda_y$ which is equivalent to the conditions $\lambda_y \circ \varrho_z \leq \varrho_z \circ \lambda_y$ and $\varrho_z \circ \lambda_y \leq \lambda_y \circ \varrho_z$. By (*) these are equivalent to $\varrho_z \circ \lambda_y^+ \leq \lambda_y^+ \circ \varrho_z$ and $\lambda_y \circ \varrho_z^+ \leq \varrho_z^+ \circ \lambda_y$. These are none other than the conditions given in (5).

We shall now give a few simple examples of residuated semigroups; a great many more will be given both in the text and in the exercises to follow.

EXAMPLE 22.1. Every Boolean algebra is residuated with respect to $\cap$. It is readily verified that for all x, z the set $\{y;\ x \cap y \leq z\}$ is not empty and admits a maximum element, namely $z : x = z \cup x'$.

EXAMPLE 22.2. Every ordered group is residuated. Again for all x, z the sets $\{y, xy \leq z\}$ and $\{y;\ yx \leq z\}$ are not empty and admit maximum elements $x^{-1}z$ and zx^{-1} respectively, so that $z \mathbin{.\!\cdot} x = x^{-1}z$ and $z \mathbin{\cdot\!.} x = zx^{-1}$.

EXAMPLE 22.3. The ordered semigroups $I(\Lambda)$ of Example 2.4 is residuated. It is readily seen that $\mathbf{a} : \mathbf{b}$ is the ideal $\{x \in \Lambda;\ (\forall b \in \mathbf{b})\ xb \in \mathbf{a}\}$.

EXAMPLE 22.4. For any semigroup E define a multiplication on the ordered set $\mathbf{P}(E)$ by

$$\begin{cases} XY = \{xy;\ x \in X, y \in Y\}; \\ X\varnothing = \varnothing = \varnothing X. \end{cases}$$

It is readily seen that $\mathbf{P}(E)$ becomes an ordered semigroup which is also residuated; we have

$$X \mathbin{.\!\cdot} Y = \{z \in E;\ (\forall y \in Y)\ yz \in X\}$$

and

$$X \mathbin{\cdot\!.} Y = \{z \in E;\ (\forall y \in Y)\ zy \in X\}$$

though these sets may of course be Ø. We shall have occasion later (§ 24 and § 29) to deal with this important residuated semigroup.

Our next goal is to introduce three important types of equivalence relation on a residuated groupoid. These arise in a natural way from the following result and its dual.

THEOREM 22.4. *Let E, F be ordered sets and let $f \in \text{Res}(E, F)$. If R_f denotes the equivalence relation associated with f then R_f is a closure equivalence on E and can be characterized as an equivalence relation with convex classes such that each class modulo R_f contains one and only one element of* $\text{Im} f^+$ *which is the greatest element in its class.*

Proof. Since $f = f \circ f^+ \circ f$ we have $(\forall x \in E)\ x \equiv (f^+ \circ f)(x)\ (R_f)$ and $x \leq (f^+ \circ f)(x)$. It follows that $(f^+ \circ f)(x)$ is the greatest element of x/R_f. To show that R_f is a closure equivalence, it is sufficient by virtue of Theorem 6.9 to show that R_f satisfies the link property. To do so, suppose that we have a diagram in E of the form

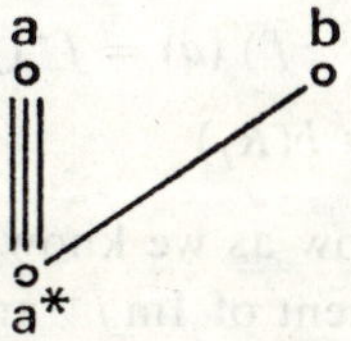

the equivalence being modulo R_f. Since $a^* \leq b$ we have $a \leq (f^+ \circ f)(a) = (f^+ \circ f)(a^*) \leq (f^+ \circ f)(b)$ whence there results the diagram

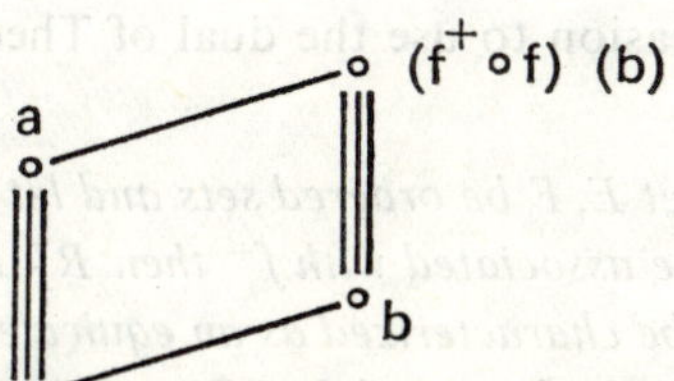

Thus R_f satisfies the link property.

It is clear that R_f has convex classes and that each class contains at least one element of $\operatorname{Im} f^+$, for $x \equiv f^+[f(x)]\,(R_f)$. Now if $f^+(y) \equiv f^+(z)\,(R_f)$ then $(f \circ f^+)(y) = (f \circ f^+)(z)$ whence $f^+(y) = (f^+ \circ f \circ f^+)(y) = (f^+ \circ f \circ f^+)(z) = f^+(z)$. Thus each class contains precisely one element of $\operatorname{Im} f^+$; and this element is maximum in its class.

Conversely, suppose that R is an equivalence relation on E such that R has convex classes and each class contains precisely one element of $\operatorname{Im} f^+$ which is maximum in its class. Given any $a \in E$ there then exists one and only one $f^+(y) \in E$ such that $a \equiv f^+(y)\,(R)$ and $a \leq f^+(y)$. Now

$$a \leq (f^+ \circ f)(a) \leq (f^+ \circ f \circ f^+)(y) = f^+(y)$$

and so the convexity of the classes gives

$$(f^+ \circ f)(a) \equiv f^+(y)\,(R).$$

Since each class modulo R contains precisely one element of $\operatorname{Im} f^+$, we deduce that $(f^+ \circ f)(a) = f^+(y)$. It follows this that

$$\begin{aligned} a \equiv b(R) &\Rightarrow a \equiv f^+(y) \equiv b(R) \\ &\Rightarrow (f^+ \circ f)(a) = f^+(y) = (f^+ \circ f)(b) \\ &\Rightarrow a \equiv b(R_f) \end{aligned}$$

and hence that $R \leq R_f$. Now as we know, each class modulo R_f contains one and only one element of $\operatorname{Im} f^+$ and so it follows that we must have $R = R_f$ [for if $R \neq R_f$ then $R < R_f$ and so at least one class modulo R_f splits up into several classes modulo R and, since each class modulo R contains precisely one element of $\operatorname{Im} f^+$, that class modulo R_f contains several elements of $\operatorname{Im} f^+$, which is impossible].

We shall have occasion to use the dual of Theorem 22.4; stated explicitly:

THEOREM 22.4*. *Let E, F be ordered sets and let $f \in \operatorname{Res}(E, F)$. If R_f^+ denotes the equivalence associated with f^+ then R_f^+ is a dual closure equivalence on F and can be characterized as an equivalence relation with convex classes such that each class modulo R_f^+ contains precisely one element of* $\operatorname{Im} f$ *which is the minimum element in its class.*

Let us now apply the above results to the case of a residuated groupoid.

Definition. Let G be a residuated groupoid. For each $x \in G$ we define

(a) *the Molinaro equivalence of type A associated with x* by

$$a \equiv b(A_x) \Leftrightarrow x \,.\!\cdot\, a = x \,.\!\cdot\, b; \quad a \equiv b({}_xA) \Leftrightarrow x \cdot\!. \, a = x \cdot\!. \, b;$$

(b) *the Molinaro equivalences of type F associated with x* by

$$a \equiv b(F_x) \Leftrightarrow xa = xb; \quad a \equiv b({}_xF) \Leftrightarrow ax = bx;$$

(c) *the Molinaro equivalences of type B associated with x* by

$$a \equiv b(B_x) \Leftrightarrow a \,.\!\cdot\, x = b \,.\!\cdot\, x; \quad a \equiv b({}_xB) \Leftrightarrow a \cdot\!. \, x = b \cdot\!. \, x.$$

Let us now recall that the maps $\lambda_x, \varrho_x : G \to G$ described by $\lambda_x(y) = xy$, $\varrho_x(y) = yx$ are residuated as are the maps $\lambda_x^+, \varrho_x^+ : G^* \to G^*$ described by $\lambda_x^+(y) = y \,.\!\cdot\, x$, $\varrho_x^+(y) = y \cdot\!. \, x$ and the maps $\zeta_x, \eta_x : G \to G^*$ described by $\zeta_x(y) = x \,.\!\cdot\, y$, $\eta_x(y) = x \cdot\!. \, y$. We note also that

$$A_x = R_{\zeta_x}; \; {}_xA = R_{\eta_x}; \; F_x = R_{\lambda_x}; \; {}_xF = R_{\varrho_x}; \; B_x = R_{\lambda_x^+}; \; {}_xB = R_{\varrho_x^+}.$$

Applying Theorem 22.4* in the case where $E = G$, $F = G^*$ and in turn $f = \zeta_x, \eta_x$ and remembering that a dual closure on G^* is simply a closure on G, we obtain:

THEOREM 22.5. *For each element x of a residuated groupoid G the equivalence A_x [resp. ${}_xA$] is a closure equivalence on G and can be characterized as an equivalence relation with convex classes such that each class modulo A_x [resp. ${}_xA$] contains one and only one left [resp. right] residual of x which is the greatest element in its class. The greatest element in the class of y modulo A_x [resp. ${}_xA$] is $x \cdot\!. \,(x \,.\!\cdot\, y)$ [resp. $x \,.\!\cdot\, (x \cdot\!. \, y)$].*

In a similar way, we can apply Theorem 22.4 in the case where $E = F = G$ and in turn $f = \lambda_x, \varrho_x$ to obtain:

THEOREM 22.6. *For each element x of a residuated groupoid G the equivalence F_x [resp. ${}_xF$] is a closure equivalence on G and can be characterized as an equivalence relation with convex classes such that each class modulo F_x [resp. ${}_xF$] contains one and only one right [resp. left] residual by x which is the greatest element in its class. The greatest element in the class of y modulo F_x [resp. ${}_xF$] is $xy \,.\!\cdot\, x$ [resp. $yx \cdot\!. \, x$].*

Finally, applying Theorem 22.4 in the case where $E = F = G^*$ and in turn $f = \lambda_x^+, \varrho_x^+$ we obtain:

THEOREM 22.7. *For each element x of a residuated groupoid G the equivalence B_x [resp. $_xB$] is a dual closure equivalence on G and can be characterized as an equivalence relation with convex classes such that each class modulo B_x [resp. $_xB$] contains one and only one right [resp. left] multiple of x which is minimum in its class. The minimum element in the class of y modulo B_x [resp. $_xB$] is $x\,(y \mathbin{.\!\cdot} x)$ [resp. $(y \mathbin{\cdot\!.} x)\,x$].*

Our aim now is to examine closure and dual closure equivalences on a residuated groupoid for possible compatibility with either multiplication or residuation. Such equivalences have interesting connections with the Molinaro equivalence. The following result is fundamental in the discussion.

THEOREM 22.8. *Given a diagram of sets and mappings of the form*

$$F \xrightarrow{f} F \xrightarrow{\theta} G \xrightarrow{g} G$$

in which $f \circ f = f$, the following conditions are equivalent:

(1) $x \equiv y(R_f) \Rightarrow \theta(x) \equiv \theta(y)\,(R_g)$;
(2) $g \circ \theta \circ f = g \circ \theta$.

If, moreover, F and G are ordered then, under the conditions shown, the following table gives equivalent formulations of (2):

	f a closure		*f a dual closure*	
	g a closure *θ isotone*	*g a dual closure* *θ antitone*	*g a closure* *θ isotone*	*g a dual closure* *θ antitone*
(2) ≡	$\theta \circ f \leq g \circ \theta$	$\theta \circ f \geq g \circ \theta$	$g \circ \theta \circ f \geq \theta$	$g \circ \theta \circ f \leq \theta$
	(a)	(b)	(c)	(d)

Proof. Suppose that (1) holds. Since $x \equiv f(x)\,(R_f)$ for each $x \in F$ we deduce that $\theta(x) \equiv \theta\,[f(x)]\,(R_g)$ whence we obtain (2). Conversely, using

(2) we deduce from $f(x) = f(y)$ that $(g \circ \theta)(x) = (g \circ \theta \circ f)(x) = (g \circ \theta \circ f)(y) = (g \circ \theta)(y)$ which gives (1).

Suppose now that F, G are ordered with f a closure map on F. If g is a closure map on G and θ is isotone, then since $g \geq \mathrm{id}$ we have $g \circ \theta \circ f \geq \theta \circ f$ which shows that (2) $\Rightarrow$ (a). Conversely, (a) implies that

$$g \circ \theta = g \circ g \circ \theta \geq g \circ \theta \circ f \geq g \circ \theta \quad [\theta \text{ isotone and } f \geq \mathrm{id}]$$

whence we have equality and (2). This then shows that if f, g are closures and θ is isotone, then (2) is equivalent to (a). We leave the rest of the table as an exercise for the reader.

The usefulness of the above result is reflected in the following.

THEOREM 22.9. *Let S be a residuated groupoid. If h is a closure map on S then the closure equivalence R_h is*

(a) *compatible on the left* [*resp. right*] *with multiplication if and only if*

$$(\forall x, y \in S) \;\; x \cdot h(y) \leq h(xy) \quad [\textit{resp.}\; h(x) \cdot y \leq h(xy)];$$

(b) *compatible on the right with* $.^{\cdot}$ [*resp.* $^{\cdot}.$] *if and only if*

$$(\forall x, y \in S) \;\; h(x) \,.^{\cdot}\, y \leq h(x \,.^{\cdot}\, y) \quad [\textit{resp.}\; h(x) \,^{\cdot}.\, y \leq h(x \,^{\cdot}.\, y)];$$

(c) *compatible on the left with* $.^{\cdot}$ [*resp.* $^{\cdot}.$] *if and only if*

$$(\forall x, y \in S) \;\; h[x \,.^{\cdot}\, h(y)] \geq x \,.^{\cdot}\, y \quad [\textit{resp.}\; h[x \,^{\cdot}.\, h(y)] \geq x \,^{\cdot}.\, y].$$

If, correspondingly, h is a dual closure map on S, then the dual closure equivalence R_h is

(d) *compatible on the left* [*resp. right*] *with multiplication if and only if*

$$(\forall x, y \in S) \;\; x \cdot h(y) \geq h(xy) \quad [\textit{resp.}\; h(x) \cdot y \geq h(xy)];$$

(e) *compatible on the right with* $.^{\cdot}$ [*resp.* $^{\cdot}.$] *if and only if*

$$(\forall x, y \in S) \;\; h(x) \,.^{\cdot}\, y \geq h(x \,.^{\cdot}\, y) \quad [\textit{resp.}\; h(x) \,^{\cdot}.\, y \geq h(x \,^{\cdot}.\, y)];$$

(f) *compatible on the left with* $.^{\cdot}$ [*resp.* $^{\cdot}.$] *if and only if*

$$(\forall x, y \in S) \;\; h[x \,.^{\cdot}\, h(y)] \leq x \,.^{\cdot}\, y \quad [\textit{resp.}\; h[x \,^{\cdot}.\, h(y)] \leq x \,^{\cdot}.\, y].$$

Proof. For each closure map h on S we have

(a) R_h is compatible on the left with multiplication if and only if

$$h(y) = h(z) \Rightarrow (\forall x \in S)\ (h \circ \lambda_x)\ (y) = (h \circ \lambda_x)\ (z).$$

Applying Theorem 22.8(a) with $F = G = S, f = g = h,\ \theta = \lambda_x$ we obtain the necessary and sufficient condition $\lambda_x \circ h \leq h \circ \lambda_x$ which gives $x \cdot h(y) \leq h\,(xy)$.

(b) R_h is compatible on the right with $.^{\cdot}$ if and only if

$$h(y) = h(z) \Rightarrow (\forall x \in S)\ (h \circ \lambda_x^+)\ (y) = (h \circ \lambda_x^+)\ (z).$$

Applying Theorem 22.8(a) with $F = G = S, f = g = h,\ \theta = \lambda_x^+$ we obtain the necessary and sufficient condition $\lambda_x^+ \circ h \leq h \circ \lambda_x^+$ which gives $h(y)\ .^{\cdot}\ x \leq h\,(y\ .^{\cdot}\ x)$.

(c) Apply Theorem 22.8(c) with $F = S^*,\ G = S, f = g = h,\ \theta = \zeta_x$.

In the corresponding case where h is a dual closure map, to prove:

(d) Apply Theorem 22.8(b) with $F = S^*, G = S, f = g = h, \theta = \lambda_x$.

(e) Apply Theorem 22.8(b) with $F = S^*,\ G = S, f = g = h,\ \theta = \lambda_x^+$.

(f) Apply Theorem 22.8(d) with $F = G = S,\ f = g = h,\ \theta = \zeta_x$.

THEOREM 22.10. *Let G be a residuated groupoid and let R be a closure equivalence on G. Denoting by f the associated closure map and by C the associated closure subset, the following conditions are equivalent:*

(1) *R is compatible on the right* [*resp. left*] *with multiplication;*

(2) $x \in C \Rightarrow (\forall y \in G)\quad x\ ^{\cdot}.\ y \in C\quad$ [*resp.* $x\ .^{\cdot}\ y \in C$];

(3) $R \leq \bigcap_{x \in C} A_x\quad$ [*resp.* $R \leq \bigcap_{x \in C} {}_xA$];

(4) $(\forall a, b \in G)\quad f(a)\ .^{\cdot}\ b = f(a)\ .^{\cdot}\ f(b)$
[*resp.* $f(a)\ ^{\cdot}.\ b = f(a)\ ^{\cdot}.\ f(b)$].

Proof. We shall show that (1) $\Leftrightarrow$ (2) and that (1) $\Rightarrow$ (3) $\Rightarrow$ (4) $\Rightarrow$ (1). Suppose that (1) holds and let $x \in C$. By the definition of C, $x = f(x)$. I) now $a = x\ ^{\cdot}.\ y$ then using Theorem 22.9(a) we have $f(a)\,y \leq f\,(ay$f $\leq f(x) = x$ so that $f(a) \leq x\ ^{\cdot}.\ y = a$. It follows that $f(a) = a$ and hence that $a \in C$. Conversely, if (2) holds, then from $y \leq yx\ ^{\cdot}.\ x \leq f\,(yx)\ ^{\cdot}.\ x \in C$ we deduce that $f(y) \leq f\,[f\,(yx)\ ^{\cdot}.\ x] = f\,(yx)\ ^{\cdot}.\ x$ and so $f(y)\,x \leq f\,(yx)$ whence R is compatible on the right with multiplication.

To show that (1) $\Rightarrow$ (3), let $a \equiv b(R)$ and let $x \in C$. By (1) we have $a(x \mathbin{.\cdot} b) \equiv b(x \mathbin{.\cdot} b)(R)$. Now $x \in C$ and so is maximum in its class modulo R so that $x/R \subseteq [\leftarrow, x]$. Since $b(x \mathbin{.\cdot} b) \leq x$ it follows from the above that $[a(x \mathbin{.\cdot} b)]/R \cap [\leftarrow, x] \neq \emptyset$. Since R is strongly upper regular we deduce from Theorem 6.10 that $[a(x \mathbin{.\cdot} b)]/R \subseteq [\leftarrow, x]$ whence $a(x \mathbin{.\cdot} b) \leq x$ and consequently $x \mathbin{.\cdot} b \leq x \mathbin{.\cdot} a$. In a similar way we can show that $x \mathbin{.\cdot} a \leq x \mathbin{.\cdot} b$. We have thus shown that $a \equiv b(R) \Rightarrow a \equiv b(A_x)$ for each $x \in C$; this is (3).

Suppose now that (3) holds. Then from $b \equiv f(b)(R)$ we deduce that, for each $x \in C$, $x \mathbin{.\cdot} b = x \mathbin{.\cdot} f(b)$. Since $x \in C$ if and only if $x = f(x)$, (4) follows.

Finally, if (4) holds then for any $a, b \in G$ we have

$$a \leq ba \mathbin{.\cdot} b \leq f(ba) \mathbin{.\cdot} b = f(ba) \mathbin{.\cdot} f(b)$$

whence $f(b)\,a \leq f(ba)$ and so (1) holds by Theorem 22.9(a).

It should be noted that we do not have equality in general in (3) of the previous theorem. For example, consider the ordered semigroup S consisting of a four-element chain $a < b < c < d$ with every product equal to a. It is clear that this is a residuated semigroup; every residual is equal to d. The partition $\{\{a, b\}, \{c, d\}\}$ corresponds to an equivalence relation R which is clearly a compatible closure equivalence with associated closure subset $C = \{b, d\}$. Now $A_b = A_d = \pi_S$ the universal equivalence on S. It follows that $R < \bigcap_{x \in C} A_x$.

Theorem 22.11. *Let G be a residuated groupoid and let R be a closure equivalence on G. Then R is compatible with multiplication and compatible on the right with $\mathbin{.\cdot}$ and $\mathbin{\cdot.}$ if and only if*

$$(\forall x, y \in G) \quad f(x) \mathbin{.\cdot} y = f(x \mathbin{.\cdot} y) \quad \text{and} \quad f(x) \mathbin{\cdot.} y = f(x \mathbin{\cdot.} y),$$

f being the associated closure mapping.

Proof. Suppose that R is compatible with multiplication and compatible on the right with $\mathbin{.\cdot}$ and $\mathbin{\cdot.}$. Given any $x, y \in G$ we deduce from $x \equiv f(x)(R)$ that $x \mathbin{.\cdot} y \equiv f(x) \mathbin{.\cdot} y(R)$ and $x \mathbin{\cdot.} y \equiv f(x) \mathbin{\cdot.} y(R)$. Since $f(x) \mathbin{.\cdot} y \in C$ and $f(x) \mathbin{\cdot.} y \in C$ [Theorem 22.10], it then follows that

$f(x) .^{\cdot} y = f(x .^{\cdot} y)$ and $f(x) ^{\cdot}. y = f(x ^{\cdot}. y)$. The conditions are therefore necessary.

Conversely, if the conditions are satisfied then by Theorem 22.9 we have that R is compatible on the right with $.^{\cdot}$ and $^{\cdot}.$. Moreover, these conditions also show that $f(x) .^{\cdot} y \in C$ and $f(x) ^{\cdot}. y \in C$ so that, by Theorem 22.10, R is also compatible with multiplication.

THEOREM 22.12. *If S is a residuated semigroup, then for each* $x \in S$

(1) A_x [*resp.* ${}_xA$] *is compatible on the right* [*resp. left*] *with multiplication;*

(2) F_x [*resp.* ${}_xF$] *is compatible on the right* [*resp. left*] *with multiplication;*

(3) B_x [*resp.* ${}_xB$] *is compatible on the right with* $^{\cdot}.$ [*resp.* $.^{\cdot}$].

Proof. The closure mapping associated with A_x is given by the prescription $h(a) = x ^{\cdot}. (x .^{\cdot} a)$. Using Theorem 22.3 we have $[x ^{\cdot}. (x .^{\cdot} a)]\, b \leq x ^{\cdot}. \{x .^{\cdot} [x ^{\cdot}. (x .^{\cdot} a)]\, b\} = x ^{\cdot}. ([x .^{\cdot} \{x ^{\cdot}. (x .^{\cdot} a)\}] .^{\cdot} b) = x ^{\cdot}. [(x .^{\cdot} a) .^{\cdot} b] = x ^{\cdot}. (x .^{\cdot} ab)$,
i.e. $h(a) \cdot b \leq h(ab)$. It follows by Theorem 22.9 that A_x is compatible on the right with multiplication. All of the other statements are proved in a similar way. [*Alternatively*, these results may be proved directly; for example, $x .^{\cdot} a = x .^{\cdot} b \Rightarrow (\forall c \in S)\, x .^{\cdot} ac = (x .^{\cdot} a) .^{\cdot} c = (x .^{\cdot} b) .^{\cdot} c = x .^{\cdot} bc$].

Our next result is the analogue of Theorem 22.10; we leave its proof to the reader.

THEOREM 22.13. *Let G be a residuated groupoid and let R be a dual closure equivalence on G. Denoting by f the associated dual closure map and by C the associated dual closure subset, the following conditions are equivalent:*

(1) *R is compatible on the right with* $^{\cdot}.$ [*resp.* $.^{\cdot}$];

(2) $x \in C \Rightarrow (\forall y \in G) \quad xy \in C \quad$ [*resp.* $yx \in C$];

(3) $R \leq \bigcap_{x \in C} B_x \quad$ [*resp.* $R \leq \bigcap_{x \in C} {}_xB$];

(4) $(\forall a, b \in G)\ a .^{\cdot} f(a ^{\cdot}. b) = f(a) .^{\cdot} f(a ^{\cdot}. b)$ [*resp.* $a ^{\cdot}. f(a .^{\cdot} b) = f(a) ^{\cdot}. f(a .^{\cdot} b)$].

[*Hint*. For (1) $\Rightarrow$ (3) consider $a \cdot. (a .\cdot x) \equiv b \cdot. (a .\cdot x) (R)$ and the dual of Theorem 6.10.]

THEOREM 22.14. *If S is a residuated semigroup, then for any $x \in S$:*

(1) $A_x \leq \bigcap_{t \in S} A_{x \cdot. t}$ *and* ${}_xA \leq \bigcap_{t \in S} {}_{x .\cdot t}A$;

(2) $F_x \leq \bigcap_{t \in S} F_{tx} \cap \bigcap_{t \in S} A_{t .\cdot x}$ *and* ${}_xF \leq \bigcap_{t \in S} {}_{xt}F \cap \bigcap_{t \in S} {}_{t .\cdot x}A$;

(3) $B_x \leq \bigcap_{t \in S} B_{xt}$ *and* ${}_xB \leq \bigcap_{t \in S} {}_{tx}B$.

Proof. The closure subset associated with A_x is the set of elements which are of the form $x \cdot. t$ for some $t \in S$. (1) therefore follows from the results of Theorems 22.12 and 22.10. Statements (2) and (3) are proved in a similar way, the extra part in (2) resulting from the implications

$$a \equiv b(F_x) \Rightarrow xa = xb \Rightarrow (\forall t \in S)\ txa = txb \Rightarrow (\forall t \in S)\ a \equiv b\,(F_{tx}).$$

[*Alternatively*, for example, $x .\cdot a = x .\cdot b \Rightarrow (\forall t \in G) \quad (x \cdot. t) .\cdot a = (x .\cdot a) \cdot. t = (x .\cdot b) \cdot. t = (x \cdot. t) .\cdot b$.]

THEOREM 22.15. *Let G be a residuated groupoid. If R is a closure equivalence on G which is compatible on the right [resp. left] with multiplication with associated closure subset C then*

$$\bigcap_{x \in C} F_x \leq \bigcap_{x \in C} {}_xA \quad \left[\text{resp. } \bigcap_{x \in C} {}_xF \leq \bigcap_{x \in C} A_x\right].$$

Correspondingly, if R is a dual closure equivalence on G which is compatible on the right with $\cdot.$ [resp. $.\cdot$] with associated dual closure subset C then

$$\bigcap_{x \in C} {}_xA \leq \bigcap_{x \in C} F_x \quad \left[\text{resp. } \bigcap_{x \in C} A_x \leq \bigcap_{x \in C} {}_xF\right].$$

Proof. Let $a \equiv b \left(\bigcap_{x \in C} F_x\right)$ and, for any $m \in C$ let $t_1 = m \cdot. a$ and $t_2 = m \cdot. b$. By Theorem 22.10 we have $t_1, t_2 \in C$. Now on the one hand $t_2 a = t_2 b \leq m$ and so $t_2 \leq m \cdot. a = t_1$; and on the other $t_1 b = t_1 a \leq m$ and so $t_1 \leq m \cdot. b = t_2$. Thus $t_1 = t_2$ and so $a \equiv b\,({}_mA)$. Since this holds for each $m \in C$, the first result follows. The others are proved similarly.

THEOREM 22.16. *If G is a residuated groupoid then*

$$\text{(a)} \bigcap_{x \in G} A_x = \bigcap_{x \in G} {}_xF; \quad \text{(b)} \bigcap_{x \in G} {}_xA = \bigcap_{x \in G} F_x; \quad \text{(c)} \bigcap_{x \in G} B_x = \bigcap_{x \in G} {}_xB.$$

Proof. Consider the relation of equality on G. This is clearly both a closure and a dual closure on G which is compatible with both multiplication and residuation. The properties (a), (b) then follow immediately from the results in Theorem 22.15.

As for (c), let $a \equiv b \left(\bigcap_{x \in G} B_x\right)$ so that $a \mathbin{.^{\cdot}} x = b \mathbin{.^{\cdot}} x$ for each $x \in G$. Given $x \in G$ let $a \mathbin{.^{\cdot}} x = b \mathbin{.^{\cdot}} x = p$ and consider the elements $p_1 = a \mathbin{^{\cdot}.} p$ and $p_2 = b \mathbin{^{\cdot}.} p$. We have $a \mathbin{.^{\cdot}} p_1 = a \mathbin{.^{\cdot}} (a \mathbin{^{\cdot}.} p) = p$ whence $b \mathbin{.^{\cdot}} p_1 = p$ and so $p_1 \leq b \mathbin{^{\cdot}.} (b \mathbin{.^{\cdot}} p_1) = b \mathbin{^{\cdot}.} p = p_2$. In a similar way we can show that $p_2 \leq p_1$ and so we have $p_1 = p_2$. We have thus shown that if $a \equiv b \left(\bigcap_{x \in G} B_x\right)$ and if p is a right residual of a or of b then $a \equiv b\ ({}_pB)$.

Suppose now that y is any element of G and let $a \mathbin{^{\cdot}.} y = z_1$ and $a \mathbin{.^{\cdot}} z_1 = z_2$. Then $a \mathbin{^{\cdot}.} z_2 = a \mathbin{^{\cdot}.} (a \mathbin{.^{\cdot}} z_1) = z_1$ and $y \leq a \mathbin{.^{\cdot}} z_1 = z_2$. It follows that $b \mathbin{^{\cdot}.} z_2 \leq b \mathbin{^{\cdot}.} y$. But from the previous paragraph we have $b \mathbin{^{\cdot}.} z_2 = a \mathbin{^{\cdot}.} z_2 = z_1 = a \mathbin{^{\cdot}.} y$. Hence $a \mathbin{^{\cdot}.} y \leq b \mathbin{^{\cdot}.} y$. In a similar way we can show that $b \mathbin{^{\cdot}.} y \leq a \mathbin{^{\cdot}.} y$ whence we deduce that $a \equiv b\ ({}_yB)$. Since y was chosen arbitrarily in G, we thus have $\bigcap_{x \in G} B_x \leq \bigcap_{x \in G} {}_xB$. Interchanging left and right residuals throughout, we can obtain the reverse inclusion. This establishes (c).

We end the present section by considering a particular situation in which equality does hold in Theorem 22.10(3). For this purpose, we require the following result.

THEOREM 22.17. *Let G be a residuated groupoid and let R be a closure equivalence on G which is compatible with multiplication. Then G/R is a residuated groupoid.*

Proof. Since R is compatible (left and right) with multiplication, it is clear that G/R is a groupoid. Since R is strongly upper regular we can order G/R in the usual way, namely

$$x/R \preccurlyeq_R y/R \Leftrightarrow (\forall x^* \in x/R)\ (\exists y^* \in y/R)\ x^* \leq y^*.$$

If we denote by f the associated closure map, then we note that this order is the same as that defined by

$$x/R \leq y/R \Leftrightarrow f(x) \leq f(y).$$

To show that G/R is residuated, let x/R and y/R be given arbitrarily. Since $x\,[f(y) \,.^{\boldsymbol\cdot}\, x] \leq f(y)$ implies $f\{x\,[f(y) \,.^{\boldsymbol\cdot}\, x]\} \leq f(y)$ we see that

$$x/R \cdot [f(y) \,.^{\boldsymbol\cdot}\, x]/R \leq y/R.$$

Moreover, $xz/R \leq y/R$ implies $xz \leq f(xz) \leq f(y)$ which gives $z \leq f(y) \,.^{\boldsymbol\cdot}\, x$ and hence $z/R \leq [f(y) \,.^{\boldsymbol\cdot}\, x]/R$. It therefore follows that

$$y/R \,.^{\boldsymbol\cdot}\, x/R = [f(y) \,.^{\boldsymbol\cdot}\, x]/R.$$

In a similar way we can show that $y/R \,^{\boldsymbol\cdot}.\, x/R = [f(y) \,^{\boldsymbol\cdot}.\, x]/R$.

THEOREM 22.18. *Let G be a residuated groupoid. If R is a closure equivalence on G which is compatible with multiplication and if every element of C, the associated closure subset, is both a left and a right residual of itself then* $\bigcap_{x\in C} A_x = R = \bigcap_{x\in C} {}_xA$.

Proof. Let f denote the associated closure mapping. For each $x \in C$ we have $x = f(x)$ and, by Theorem 22.1, $x \,.^{\boldsymbol\cdot}\, (x \,^{\boldsymbol\cdot}.\, x) = x = x \,^{\boldsymbol\cdot}.\, (x \,.^{\boldsymbol\cdot}\, x)$. Using Theorems 22.17 and 22.10(4) we have, for each $a \in G$,

$$\begin{aligned} a/R \,.^{\boldsymbol\cdot}\, (a/R \,^{\boldsymbol\cdot}.\, a/R) = a/R \,.^{\boldsymbol\cdot}\, [f(a) \,^{\boldsymbol\cdot}.\, a]/R &= \{f(a) \,.^{\boldsymbol\cdot}\, [f(a) \,^{\boldsymbol\cdot}.\, a]\}/R \\ &= \{f(a) \,.^{\boldsymbol\cdot}\, [f(a) \,^{\boldsymbol\cdot}.\, f(a)]\}/R \\ &= f(a)/R \\ &= a/R \end{aligned}$$

and similarly $a/R \,^{\boldsymbol\cdot}.\, (a/R \,.^{\boldsymbol\cdot}\, a/R) = a/R$. Thus in the residuated groupoid G/R each element is both a left and a right residual of itself. Now let $b \equiv c \left(\bigcap_{x\in C} A_x\right)$. Since $f(b) \in C$ we have $f(b) \,.^{\boldsymbol\cdot}\, b = f(b) \,.^{\boldsymbol\cdot} c$ whence we have $b/R \,.^{\boldsymbol\cdot}\, b/R = b/R \,.^{\boldsymbol\cdot}\, c/R$ and so

$$c/R \leq b/R \,^{\boldsymbol\cdot}.\, (b/R \,.^{\boldsymbol\cdot}\, c/R) = b/R \,^{\boldsymbol\cdot}.\, (b/R \,.^{\boldsymbol\cdot}\, b/R) = b/R.$$

In a similar way we can show that $b/R \leq c/R$. Hence $b/R = c/R$ and it follows that $\bigcap_{x \in C} A_x \leq R$. The required equality then follows by Theorem 22.10(3). A similar argument yields $R = \bigcap_{x \in C} {}_xA$.

Remark. It should be noted that the hypothesis on C in Theorem 22.18 is satisfied in the case where every element of G is both a left and a right residual of itself; i.e. whenever each $x \in G$ is maximum in its class modulo A_x and ${}_xA$. This happens in particular when G has a neutral element; for, denoting such an element by 1, the equalities $\lambda_1 = \varrho_1 = \text{id}$ give $\lambda_1^+ = \varrho_1^+ = \text{id}$ and hence $(\forall x \in G)\ x \mathbin{.\!^{\cdot}} 1 = x = x \mathbin{^{\cdot}\!.} 1$. In each of the above cases the relation of equality is clearly a compatible closure equivalence with associated closure subset G itself. We deduce that in any such groupoid $\bigcap_{x \in G} A_x$ and $\bigcap_{x \in G} {}_xA$ reduce to equality. Another consequence of the previous result is that if G contains a maximum element π then the universal equivalence π_G is a compatible closure equivalence having $\{\pi\}$ as closure subset, so that $\pi_G = A_\pi = {}_\pi A$.

EXERCISES

22.1. Consider the ordered groupoid G described by the following Hasse diagram and Cayley table

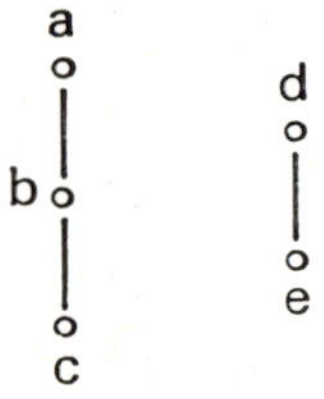

	a	b	c	d	e
a	a	b	c	e	e
b	a	b	c	e	e
c	c	c	c	e	e
d	d	d	e	c	c
e	e	e	e	c	c

Show that G is residuated and compile tables of residuals. Determine the partitions associated with each of the Molinaro equivalences and verify the result of Theorem 22.16. Show also that the equivalences $\bigcap_{x \in G} A_x$, $\bigcap_{x \in G} F_x$, $\bigcap_{x \in G} B_x$ are distinct.

22.2. Consider the ordered (abelian) semigroup defined by

$$S = \{a_1, a_2, a_3, \ldots\} \qquad a_i a_j = a_{i+j}.$$
$$a_1 > a_2 > a_3 > \cdots$$

Show that S is residuated, find a formula for the residuals and determine the partitions associated with the Molinaro equivalences.

22.3. Let G be a residuated groupoid. Prove that for each $x \in G$ the set of right [resp. left] multiples of x is equipotent to the set of right [resp. left] residuals by x. Show also that the set of right residuals of x is equipotent to the set of left residuals of x.

22.4. Show that in an ordered group every Molinaro equivalence reduces to equality.

22.5. Let B be a Boolean algebra. Prove that, for each $x \in B$,

$$\text{(a) } A_{x'} = F_x; \quad \text{(b) } y \equiv z(B_x) \Leftrightarrow y' \equiv z'(A_{x'}).$$

Given any $x, y \in B$ show that $y/A_x = [y \cap x', y \cup x]$.

22.6. If a, b are elements of a residuated groupoid G such that $a \cup b$ exists, show that so also does $(x \mathbin{.^{\cdot}} a) \cap (x \mathbin{.^{\cdot}} b)$ for each $x \in G$ and that $(x \mathbin{.^{\cdot}} a) \cap (x \mathbin{.^{\cdot}} b) = x \mathbin{.^{\cdot}} (a \cup b)$. If G is a $\cup$-semilattice, show that G is *$\cup$-semireticulated* in the sense that $(\forall a, b, c \in G)\ a(b \cup c) = ab \cup ac,\ (b \cup c)a = ba \cup ca$. Show also that each equivalence of type A and each equivalence of type F is compatible with $\cup$. If G is a lattice, show that the property $(\forall a, b, c \in G)\ (a \cap b) \mathbin{.^{\cdot}} c = (a \mathbin{.^{\cdot}} c) \cap (b \mathbin{.^{\cdot}} c)$ also holds and deduce that each equivalence of type B is compatible with $\cap$.

22.7. Let G be a residuated groupoid. Prove that the following conditions concerning $x \in G$ are equivalent:

(a) $(\forall y \in G)\ xy = yx$;
(b) $(\forall y \in G)\ y \mathbin{.^{\cdot}} x = y \mathbin{^{\cdot}.} x$.

22.8. Let G be a residuated groupoid. If R is a dual closure equivalence on G with associated dual closure map f and dual closure subset C, prove that the following conditions are equivalent:

(1) R is compatible on the *left* with $^{\cdot}.$ [resp. $.^{\cdot}$];
(2) $R \leq \bigcap_{x \in C} F_x$ $\left[\text{resp. } R \leq \bigcap_{x \in C} {}_xF\right]$;
(3) $(\forall x, y \in G)\ f(x) \cdot y = f(x)f(y)$ [resp. $x \cdot f(y) = f(x)f(y)$].

22.9. Supply complete details of all the analogous proofs in this section.

23. The zigzag equivalence

In this section we shall introduce a particularly simple equivalence relation which we shall use to obtain further information concerning the structure of residuated groupoids. Let us begin by considering the following remarks:

(a) there exist ordered sets on which no multiplication can be defined such that they be residuated [for example, the set $E = \{x, y, z\}$ with $y < x$, $z < x$, $y \parallel z$];

(b) there exist ordered sets on which several multiplications can be defined such that they be residuated [for example, $E = \{x, y, z\}$ with $z < y < x$ is residuated under each of the multiplications

	x	y	z
x	z	z	z
y	z	z	z
z	z	z	z

	x	y	z
x	x	y	z
y	y	y	z
z	z	z	z

];

(c) there exist groupoids which, even though they can be ordered in an isotone manner, can nevertheless not be residuated [for example, take $G = \{x, y\}$ with $xx = xy = x$, $yx = yy = y$ and $y < x$];

(d) there exist groupoids which can be ordered in several ways such that they be residuated [for example, $G = \{x, y, z, t\}$ with $(\forall a, b \in G)\ ab = t$ can be ordered in 12 different ways in order that it be residuated].

This being the case, we ask the following question: What can one say about a residuated structure as far as it being an ordered set is concerned? In seeking an answer to this question, we shall impose several restrictions on the multiplication and observe the different forms permissible for each of the structures in the following diagram:

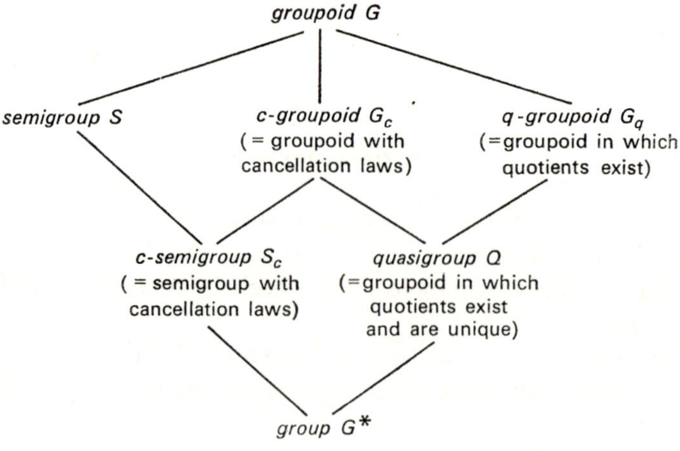

Definition. Let E be an ordered set. By the *zigzag equivalence* on E we shall mean the relation Z defined on E by

$$a \equiv b(Z) \Leftrightarrow \begin{cases} \text{there exist } x_1, x_2, \ldots, x_n \in E \text{ such} \\ \text{that } a \nparallel x_1, \ldots, x_i \nparallel x_{i+1}, \ldots, x_n \nparallel b. \end{cases}$$

It is clear that Z is an equivalence relation on E. In any Hasse diagram, the classes modulo Z are the disjoint portions. For example, if an ordered set E is given by the Hasse diagram

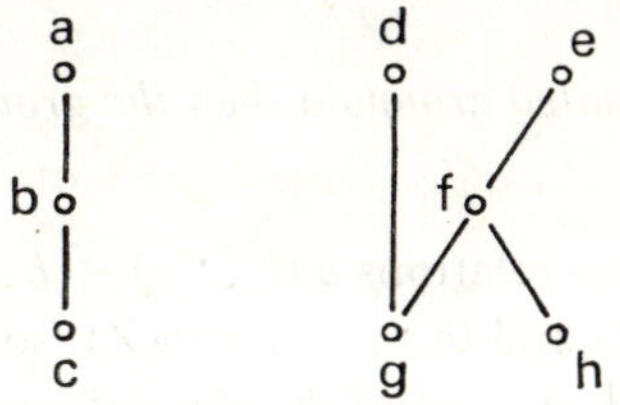

then the classes modulo Z are $\{a, b, c\}$, $\{d, e, f, g, h\}$, $\{i\}$, $\{j\}$.

THEOREM 23.1. *If G is an ordered groupoid then the zigzag equivalence Z is strongly regular on G and is compatible with multiplication. Moreover, if G is residuated then Z is compatible with residuation.*

Proof. It is clear from the definition of Z that this equivalence satisfies Theorem 6.1 and hence is regular on G. Now if $a_1 \equiv a_2(Z)$, then for any $b \nparallel a_2$ we have $a_1 \equiv b(Z)$; hence Z satisfies both the link property and its dual and so is strongly regular on G. To show that Z is compatible with multiplication, let $a_1 \equiv a_2(Z)$ so that a_1 and a_2 are connected by a finite zigzag chain

$$a_1 = x_1 \nparallel x_2 \nparallel \cdots \nparallel x_{n-1} \nparallel x_n = a_2.$$

By the isotonicity of multiplication, it follows that for each $b \in G$

$$a_1 b = x_1 b \nparallel x_2 b \nparallel \cdots \nparallel x_n b = a_2 b$$

and so $a_1 b \equiv a_2 b\ (Z)$. Thus Z is compatible on the left with multiplication. Similarly it is compatible on the right.

Suppose now that G is residuated. Let $a \equiv a^*(Z)$ and $b \equiv b^*(Z)$. Then there exist $a_1, \ldots, a_n$ and $b_1, \ldots, b_m$ such that

$$a = a_1 \Vert a_2 \Vert \cdots \Vert a_n = a^* \quad \text{and} \quad b = b_1 \Vert b_2 \Vert \cdots \Vert b_m = b^*.$$

From the properties of residuals we deduce that

$$\begin{cases} a \mathbin{.^{\cdot}} b = a_1 \mathbin{.^{\cdot}} b \Vert a_2 \mathbin{.^{\cdot}} b \Vert \cdots \Vert a_n \mathbin{.^{\cdot}} b = a^* \mathbin{.^{\cdot}} b, \\ a^* \mathbin{.^{\cdot}} b = a^* \mathbin{.^{\cdot}} b_1 \Vert a^* \mathbin{.^{\cdot}} b_2 \Vert \cdots \Vert a^* \mathbin{.^{\cdot}} b_m = a^* \mathbin{.^{\cdot}} b^* \end{cases}$$

whence we have $a \mathbin{.^{\cdot}} b \equiv a^* \mathbin{.^{\cdot}} b^*(Z)$. A similar result holds for left residuals.

THEOREM 23.2. *If G is a residuated groupoid then the groupoid G/Z is a quasi-group homomorphic to G.*

Proof. Since G is residuated, the relations $a(b \mathbin{.^{\cdot}} a) \leq b$ and $(b \mathbin{^{\cdot}.} a)a \leq b$ imply that $a(b \mathbin{.^{\cdot}} a) \equiv b(Z)$ and $(b \mathbin{^{\cdot}.} a)a \equiv b(Z)$, so that if $\mathscr{A}$ denotes the class of a modulo Z and $\mathscr{B}$ denotes the class of b modulo Z then the class $\mathscr{X}$ of $b \mathbin{.^{\cdot}} a$ modulo Z satisfies $\mathscr{A}\mathscr{X} = \mathscr{B}$ and the class $\mathscr{Y}$ of $b \mathbin{^{\cdot}.} a$ modulo Z satisfies $\mathscr{Y}\mathscr{A} = \mathscr{B}$. It follows that quotients exist in G/Z. We now show that these quotients are unique. Let $\mathscr{A}, \mathscr{B}, \mathscr{C}, \mathscr{D} \in G/Z$ be such that $\mathscr{A}\mathscr{B} = \mathscr{A}\mathscr{C} = \mathscr{D}$ and let us show that $\mathscr{B} = \mathscr{C}$. Since G is residuated the residuals $d \mathbin{.^{\cdot}} a$ exist for all $d \in \mathscr{D}$ and all $a \in \mathscr{A}$ and by Theorem 23.1 all these residuals belong to the same class modulo Z. Let this class be $\mathscr{E}$ and consider the product $ab = d$ where $a \in \mathscr{A}, b \in \mathscr{B}, d \in \mathscr{D}$. We have $b \leq d \mathbin{.^{\cdot}} a \in \mathscr{E}$ whence $b \in \mathscr{E}$ and consequently $\mathscr{B} = \mathscr{E}$ since Z is an equivalence relation. Considering in a similar way a product $ac = d^*$ where $a \in \mathscr{A}$, $c \in \mathscr{C}$, $d^* \in \mathscr{D}$ an analogous proof shows that $\mathscr{C} = \mathscr{E}$. We have thus established that the equation $\mathscr{A}\mathscr{X} = \mathscr{D}$ has a unique solution. In a similar way so also does $\mathscr{Y}\mathscr{A} = \mathscr{D}$ and hence G/Z is a quasigroup. Finally, it is clear that the canonical map $\natural_Z : G \to G/Z$ is a homomorphism.

COROLLARY. *G/Z is a loop if and only if $(\forall a, b \in G)\ a \mathbin{.^{\cdot}} a \equiv b \mathbin{^{\cdot}.} b(Z)$.*

Proof. The necessary and sufficient condition that G/Z be a loop is that it contain a neutral element. This is clearly equivalent to the condition stated.

THEOREM 23.3. *If a residuated groupoid G contains a maximal element then that element is maximum in its class modulo Z.*

Proof. Let $\bar{a}$ be maximal in G. We show first that for any $x \in G$

$$[\leftarrow, x] \cap [\leftarrow, \bar{a}] \neq \emptyset \Rightarrow x \leq \bar{a}.$$

In fact, let x be such that $[\leftarrow, x] \cap [\leftarrow, \bar{a}] \neq \emptyset$. Clearly x and $\bar{a}$ are in the same class modulo Z. Let this class be $\mathscr{A}$ and let $\mathscr{B} = \mathscr{A}\mathscr{A}$. For any element $a \in [\leftarrow, x] \cap [\leftarrow, \bar{a}]$ we have

$$(\forall b \in \mathscr{B})\ b \cdot\!.\ \bar{a} \leq b \cdot\!.\ a \quad \text{and} \quad b \cdot\!.\ x \leq b \cdot\!.\ a.$$

Considering therefore the element $b^* = \bar{a}^2$ we have, since $\bar{a}$ is maximal,

$$\bar{a} = b^* \cdot\!.\ \bar{a} = b^* \cdot\!.\ a.$$

It follows from the above that $b^* \cdot\!.\ x \leq b^* \cdot\!.\ \bar{a}$ whence $(b^* \cdot\!.\ x)\, \bar{a} \leq b^*$ and so, $\bar{a}$ being maximal, $\bar{a} = b^* .\!\cdot (b^* \cdot\!.\ x) \geq x$.

This being the case, consider any element $a^* \in \mathscr{A}$ other than $\bar{a}$. [If no such element exists then clearly $\mathscr{A} = \{\bar{a}\}$ and there is nothing to prove.] Suppose that there exists in any finite zigzag chain connecting $\bar{a}$ to a^* a first element, a_k say, which satisfies $a_k \notin [\leftarrow, \bar{a}]$. Then we have necessarily $[\leftarrow, a_k] \cap [\leftarrow, \bar{a}] \neq \emptyset$ since the element preceding a_k in the zigzag chain belongs to this set. By applying the result of the previous paragraph we deduce that $a_k \leq \bar{a}$ which is contrary to the hypothesis. It follows that, in any finite zigzag chain connecting $\bar{a}$ to a^*, there is no first element which is not less than or equal to $\bar{a}$. Consequently all the elements in any such chain are less than or equal to $\bar{a}$ and in particular $a^* \leq \bar{a}$. Since a^* was chosen arbitrarily in $\mathscr{A}$ we conclude that $\bar{a}$ is maximum in $\mathscr{A}$.

THEOREM 23.4. *Let G be a residuated groupoid. Then*

(1) *if G contains a descending chain which is unbounded below, each class modulo Z contains at least one such chain;*

(2) *if G contains an ascending chain which is unbounded above, each class modulo Z contains at least one ascending chain which is unbounded above and at least one descending chain which is unbounded below.*

Proof. Let $a_1 \geq a_2 \geq a_3 \geq \cdots$ denote a descending chain, unbounded below, in the class $\mathscr{A}$ modulo Z. Let $\mathscr{B}$ be any class modulo Z. Then there exists one and only class $\mathscr{C}$ modulo Z such that $\mathscr{C}\mathscr{B} = \mathscr{A}$ and

$$(\forall c \in \mathscr{C}) \quad a_1 \mathbin{.\dot{}} c \geq a_2 \mathbin{.\dot{}} c \geq a_3 \mathbin{.\dot{}} c \geq \cdots$$

Let $b_i = a_i \mathbin{.\dot{}} c$ for each index i and let us show that the chain given by $b_i \geq b_{i+1}$ $(i = 1, 2, 3, \ldots)$ is unbounded below. Suppose in fact that there existed an element $b \in \mathscr{B}$ such that $(\forall n)\ b \leq b_n$; then we would have $(\forall n)\ cb \leq a_n$ and the chain $a_i \geq a_{i+1}$ $(i = 1, 2, 3, \ldots)$ would be bounded below by cb, contrary to the hypothesis. It follows that $\mathscr{B}$ contains a descending chain which is unbounded below and since $\mathscr{B}$ is arbitrary the same is true for all classes modulo Z.

Suppose now that $a_1 \leq a_2 \leq a_3 \leq \cdots$ is an ascending chain, unbounded above, in the class $\mathscr{A}$ modulo Z. Let $\mathscr{C}$ be any class modulo Z. Then there exists one and only one class $\mathscr{B}$ modulo Z such that $\mathscr{B}\mathscr{A} = \mathscr{C}$ and

$$(\forall b \in \mathscr{B}) \quad ba_1 \leq ba_2 \leq ba_3 \leq \cdots.$$

Let $c_i = ba_i$ for each index i and let us show that the chain $c_i \leq c_{i+1}$ $(i = 1, 2, 3, \ldots)$ is unbounded above. Suppose in fact that there existed an element $c \in \mathscr{C}$ such that $(\forall n)\ c_n \leq c$. Then we would have $(\forall n)\ ba_n \leq c$ whence $(\forall n)\ a_n \leq c \mathbin{.\dot{}} b$ and the chain $a_i \leq a_{i+1}$ $(i = 1, 2, 3, \ldots)$ would be bounded above by $c \mathbin{.\dot{}} b$, contrary to the hypothesis. It follows that every class modulo Z contains an ascending chain which is unbounded above.

Moreover, for each class $\mathscr{C}$ modulo Z there is one and only one class $\mathscr{D}$ modulo Z such that $\mathscr{A}\mathscr{D} = \mathscr{C}$ and

$$(\forall c \in \mathscr{C}) \quad c \mathbin{.\dot{}} a_1 \geq c \mathbin{.\dot{}} a_2 \geq c \mathbin{.\dot{}} a_3 \geq \cdots$$

Define $d_i = c \mathbin{.\dot{}} a_i$ for each index i. The chain $d_i \geq d_{i+1}$ $(i = 1, 2, 3, \ldots)$ is not bounded below [for if it were then there would exist $d \leq c \mathbin{.\dot{}} a_n$ for each n, whence $a_n \leq c \mathbin{\dot{}.} d$ and the chain $a_i \leq a_{i+1}$ $(i = 1, 2, 3, \ldots)$ would be bounded above]. Since $\mathscr{D}$ contains a descending chain which is unbounded below, the result follows from part (1).

Collecting the above results, we can now prove:

THEOREM 23.5. *If the residuated groupoid G contains a maximal element then each class modulo Z contains a maximum element.*

Proof. Suppose that $\bar{a}$ is maximal in the class $\mathscr{A}$ modulo Z. By Theorem 23.3, $\bar{a}$ is the maximum element of $\mathscr{A}$. It follows that $\mathscr{A}$ contains no ascending chain which is unbounded above and hence by Theorem 23.4 that no class modulo Z can contain such a chain. By Zorn's axiom, each class therefore contains a maximal element which, by virtue of Theorem 23.3, is maximum in its class.

Let us now see what is implied by the existence of a minimal element in a residuated groupoid.

THEOREM 23.6. *If the residuated groupoid G contains a minimal element then every class modulo Z is an upper directed set.*

Proof. Let $\underline{x}$ be minimal in G and consider first of all any two elements a_1, a_2 of G such that $[\leftarrow, a_1] \cap [\leftarrow, a_2] \neq \emptyset$. We know that there exists $y \in G$ such that $a_1 y = \underline{x}$ (namely, $y = \underline{x} \mathbin{.\cdot} a_1$). Let $a \in [\leftarrow, a_1] \cap [\leftarrow, a_2]$; then by the isotone property, and remembering that $\underline{x}$ is minimal, we have $\underline{x} = a_1 y = ay \leq a_2 y$ whence $a_1 \leq a_2 y \mathbin{\cdot .} y$. But we know that $a_2 \leq a_2 y \mathbin{\cdot .} y$; it therefore follows that $[a_1, \rightarrow] \cap [a_2, \rightarrow] \neq \emptyset$.

This being the case, let $\mathscr{B}$ be any class modulo Z and let β_1, β_2 be any two elements of $\mathscr{B}$. By the definition of Z there are finite zigzag chains joining β_1 to β_2. Choose one of minimal length, say

$$\beta_1 = b_1 \nparallel b_2 \nparallel \cdots \nparallel b_n = \beta_2.$$

Now amongst these elements there is a finite number, N say, of elements b_t such that $b_{t-1} \leq b_t$ and $b_{t+1} \leq b_t$. Denoting such elements by $b_{\bar{t}}$ we consider the finite sequence

$$b_{\bar{1}} \parallel b_{\bar{2}} \parallel \cdots \parallel b_{\bar{N}},$$

where the non-comparability results from the minimality of the length of the chain. Now from the definition of $b_{\bar{t}}$ we have $[\leftarrow, \beta_1] \cap [\leftarrow, b_{\bar{1}}] \neq \emptyset$. The result of the first paragraph above therefore gives $[\beta_1, \rightarrow] \cap [b_{\bar{1}}, \rightarrow] \neq \emptyset$. Consider any element $b_{1*} \in [\beta_1, \rightarrow] \cap [b_{\bar{1}}, \rightarrow]$; since $[\leftarrow, b_{\bar{1}}] \cap [\leftarrow, b_{\bar{2}}] \neq \emptyset$ we deduce that $[\leftarrow, b_{1*}] \cap [\leftarrow, b_{\bar{2}}] \neq \emptyset$ so that, by the above result, $[b_{1*}, \rightarrow] \cap [b_{\bar{2}}, \rightarrow] \neq \emptyset$ and consequently $[\beta_1, \rightarrow] \cap [b_{\bar{2}}, \rightarrow]$

$\neq \emptyset$. Consider now $b_{2*} \in [\beta_1, \rightarrow] \cap [b_{\bar{2}}, \rightarrow]$; since $[\leftarrow, b_{\bar{2}}] \cap [\leftarrow, b_{\bar{3}}] \neq \emptyset$ we have $[\leftarrow, b_{2*}] \cap [\leftarrow, b_{\bar{3}}] \neq \emptyset$ so that, by the above result, $[b_{2*}, \rightarrow] \cap [b_{\bar{3}}, \rightarrow] \neq \emptyset$ and consequently $[\beta_1, \rightarrow] \cap [b_{\bar{3}}, \rightarrow] \neq \emptyset$. Consider now any element $b_{3*} \in [\beta_1, \rightarrow] \cap [b_{\bar{3}}, \rightarrow]$, etc. After a finite number (in fact N) applications of this process, we arrive at $[\beta_1, \rightarrow] \cap [b_{\bar{N}}, \rightarrow] \neq \emptyset$. Since we also have $[\leftarrow, b_{\bar{N}}] \cap [\leftarrow, \beta_2] \neq \emptyset$ a final application of the process yields $[\beta_1, \rightarrow] \cap [\beta_2, \rightarrow] \neq \emptyset$ and this completes the proof.

THEOREM 23.7. *If the residuated groupoid G contains a minimal element then that element is minimum in its class modulo Z.*

Proof. Let $\underline{a}$ be minimal in G and let $\mathscr{A}$ be its class modulo Z. Let x be any element of $\mathscr{A}$. Since $\mathscr{A}$ is upper directed by Theorem 23.6, there exists $z \in [x, \rightarrow] \cap [\underline{a}, \rightarrow]$ and since there exists t such that $tz = \underline{a}$ (namely $t = \underline{a} \cdot . z$) we have $tx = t\underline{a} = \underline{a}$. In other words, for any $x \in \mathscr{A}$ there exists an element, which we shall denote by t_x, such that $t_x x = \underline{a}$ and $t_x \leq \underline{a} \cdot . \underline{a}$.

Consider now any element $y \in \mathscr{A}$. Since G is residuated, there exists $x \in \mathscr{A}$ such that $(\underline{a} \cdot . \underline{a}) x \leq y$. It follows by the isotone property that $px \leq y$ for all $p \leq \underline{a} \cdot . \underline{a}$ and in particular that $\underline{a} = t_x x \leq y$. Since y was chosen arbitrarily in $\mathscr{A}$, it follows that $\underline{a}$ is the minimum element of $\mathscr{A}$.

THEOREM 23.8. *If the residuated groupoid G contains a minimal element then every class modulo Z contains both a maximum element and a minimum element.*

Proof. Let $\underline{a}$ be minimal in G and let $\mathscr{A}$ be its class modulo Z. By Theorem 23.7, $\underline{a}$ is minimum in $\mathscr{A}$. It follows that $\mathscr{A}$ contains no descending chains which are unbounded below and so, by Theorem 23.4(2), no class modulo Z contains an ascending chain which is unbounded above. All ascending chains in G being bounded above, it follows by Zorn's axiom that G contains maximal elements and so, by Theorem 23.5, each class modulo Z contains a maximum element. Moreover, since a is minimum in $\mathscr{A}$, it follows by Theorem 23.4(1) that no class modulo Z can contain a descending chain which is unbounded below. Again by Zorn's axiom each class modulo Z therefore contains minimal elements. The result is completed by appealing to Theorem 23.7.

The previous results give us the general form of residuated groupoids; we summarize in the following:

THEOREM 23.9. *If the ordered groupoid G is residuated then each class modulo Z contains either:*

(1) *a maximum element and a minimum element; or*
(2) *a maximum element and no minimal elements; or*
(3) *no maximal elements and no minimal elements.*

It should also be noted from the above results that Z is a closure equivalence if and only if one of the classes modulo Z admits a maximum element; and that Z is both a closure and a dual closure equivalence if and only if one of the classes admits a minimum element. Theorem 23.9 may thus be restated in the form:

THEOREM 23.9*. *If G is a residuated groupoid then the zigzag equivalence Z on G is either a closure equivalence or both a closure equivalence and a dual closure equivalence or neither.*

The three types of residuated groupoid as described in Theorem 16.9 are in general distinct. This can be shown by means of examples and for this we refer the reader to Exercises 22.1, 23.1 and 23.2.

THEOREM 23.10. *In a residuated groupoid the Molinaro equivalences are finer than the zigzag equivalence.*

Proof. This follows from the observations

$$\text{(i) } a \equiv b(A_x) \Rightarrow a \leq x \,^{\cdot}.\, (x \,.^{\cdot}\, a) = x \,^{\cdot}.\, (x \,.^{\cdot}\, b) \geq b \Rightarrow a \equiv b(Z);$$
$$\text{(ii) } a \equiv b(B_x) \Rightarrow a \geq x\,(a \,.^{\cdot}\, x) = x\,(b \,.^{\cdot}\, x) \leq b \Rightarrow a \equiv b(Z);$$
$$\text{(iii) } a \equiv b(F_x) \Rightarrow a \leq xa \,.^{\cdot}\, x = xb \,.^{\cdot}\, x \geq b \Rightarrow a \equiv b(Z).$$

THEOREM 23.11. *A residuated groupoid G contains a maximal element if and only if*

$$(\exists x \in G)\ A_x = Z \quad [\textit{resp. } {}_xA = Z].$$

Proof. Suppose that $\bar{x}$ is maximal (hence maximum) in the class $\mathscr{X}$ modulo Z. Let $\mathscr{A}$ be any class modulo Z. There exists one and only one class $\mathscr{B}$ modulo Z such that $\mathscr{A}\mathscr{B} = \mathscr{X}$; let $\bar{b}$ be the maximum element of this class. Since $(\forall a \in \mathscr{A})\ a\bar{b} \le \bar{x}$ we have $(\forall a \in \mathscr{A})\ \bar{b} = \bar{x} \,.\!\cdot\, a$. It follows that $a \equiv a^*(Z) \Rightarrow a \equiv a^*(A_{\bar{x}})$ whence $Z \le A_{\bar{x}}$. Appealing to Theorem 23.10, we then have $Z = A_{\bar{x}}$. Conversely, if there is an element $x \in G$ such that $Z = A_x$ then since each class modulo A_x admits a maximum element so also does each class modulo Z.

THEOREM 23.12. *The following conditions are equivalent and are necessary and sufficient for a residuated groupoid to admit a minimal element:*

(1) $(\exists x \in G)\quad F_x = Z\quad$ [*resp.* ${}_xF = Z$];
(2) $(\exists x \in G)\quad B_x = Z\quad$ [*resp.* ${}_xB = Z$].

Proof. If G contains a minimal element then each class modulo Z contains a maximum element and a minimum element (Theorem 23.8). Consider $\mathscr{B}\mathscr{A} = \mathscr{C}$ with $\underline{b}$ minimum in $\mathscr{B}$, $\bar{a}$ maximum in $\mathscr{A}$ and $\underline{c}$ minimum in $\mathscr{C}$. We have necessarily $\underline{b}\bar{a} = \underline{c}$; for if we had $\underline{b}\bar{a} = c > \underline{c}$ then we would have $(\forall b \in \mathscr{B})\ b\bar{a} \ge c > \underline{c}$ and consequently there would not exist $b \in G$ such that $b\bar{a} \le \underline{c}$, so that G would not be residuated. From this equality we deduce, using the fact that $\underline{c}$ is the minimum element of $\mathscr{C}$, that $(\forall a \in \mathscr{A})\ \underline{b}a = \underline{c}$. It follows that $a \equiv a^*(Z) \Rightarrow a \equiv a^*(F_{\underline{b}})$ whence $Z \le F_{\underline{b}}$ and so $Z = F_{\underline{b}}$ by Theorem 23.10. Conversely, if there is an element $x \in G$ such that $F_x = Z$, let $\mathscr{X}$ be the class of x modulo Z and let $\mathscr{A}$ be any class modulo Z. Writing $\mathscr{X}\mathscr{A} = \mathscr{Y}$ we have, since $F_x = Z$,

$$(\exists y^* \in \mathscr{Y})\ (\forall a \in \mathscr{A})\ xa = y^*.$$

Now if y is any element of $\mathscr{Y}$ there exists an element a^* $(= y \,.\!\cdot\, x)$ such that $xa^* \le y$ and so it follows that $y^* \le y$ whence y^* is the minimum element of $\mathscr{Y}$ and hence is minimal in G.

The corresponding assertion concerning the equivalence of type B is proved as follows. Considering $\mathscr{C}\mathscr{B} = \mathscr{A}$, we have as in the above $\bar{c}\underline{b} = \underline{a}$ so that $(\forall a \in \mathscr{A})\ \bar{c}\underline{b} \le a$ and consequently $(\forall a \in \mathscr{A})\ \bar{c} = a \,\cdot\!.\, \underline{b}$. It follows that $Z \le B_{\underline{b}}$ and hence that $Z = B_{\underline{b}}$. The converse is clear.

Introducing the notation max G [resp. min G] to denote the set of maximal [resp. minimal] elements of G, the following result is immediate from the previous proof:

THEOREM 23.13. *If the residuated groupoid G contains a maximal element $\bar{x}$, then*

$$\max G = \{\bar{x} \mathbin{.\cdot} a;\ a \in G\} = \{\bar{x} \mathbin{\cdot .} a;\ a \in G\}.$$

Correspondingly, if G contains a minimal element $\underline{y}$ then

$$\max G = \{a \mathbin{.\cdot} \underline{y};\ a \in G\} = \{a \mathbin{\cdot .} \underline{y};\ a \in G\};$$

$$\min G = \{a\underline{y};\ a \in G\} = \{\underline{y}a;\ a \in G\}.$$

Let us now examine the situation when G is a semigroup.

THEOREM 23.14. *If the ordered semigroup S is residuated then S/Z is a group.*

Proof. Since Z is compatible with multiplication by Theorem 23.1, it follows that S/Z is a semigroup. Being a quasigroup by Theorem 16.2, S/Z is therefore a group.

It can be shown by means of examples that restricting the multiplication to be associative does not alter the general form of G as an ordered set; see Exercises 23.3, 23.4 and 23.5. The general form of residuated semigroups may therefore be enunciated as in Theorem 23.9.

Turning now to the case where G is a c-groupoid (i.e. one in which the cancellation laws hold) we have the following results, of which the first is an immediate consequence of the definition:

THEOREM 23.15. *A residuated groupoid G is a c-groupoid if and only if every equivalence of type F on G reduces to equality.*

THEOREM 23.16. *A residuated c-groupoid cannot contain a minimal element without the equivalence Z reducing to equality.*

Proof. Suppose that G contains a minimal element $\underline{x}$. Let $\mathscr{X}$ be its class modulo Z. Let $y \equiv \underline{x}(Z)$; then since by Theorem 23.6 there exists $z \in [\underline{x}, \rightarrow] \cap [y, \rightarrow]$, there exists t (namely $t = \underline{x} \mathbin{\cdot .} z$) such that $t\underline{x} = ty$ $[= \underline{x}]$. It follows by the cancellation law that $\underline{x} = y$. Since y was chosen arbitrarily in $\mathscr{X}$ we conclude that $\mathscr{X} = \{\underline{x}\}$. Since each class modulo Z contains a minimal element, we deduce from this that Z reduces to equality.

Exercises 23.6 and 23.7 show that no further simplification of Theorem 23.9 arises in the case of c-groupoids. The general form of residuated c-groupoids is thus as follows.

THEOREM 23.17. *If a c-groupoid is residuated then either the equivalence Z reduces to equality or each class modulo Z contains a maximum element and no minimal elements or no maximal elements and no minimal elements.*

Let us now pass to the case of a q-groupoid; i.e., a groupoid G in which $(\forall a, b \in G)\ (\exists x, y \in G)\ ax = b,\ ya = b.$

THEOREM 23.18. *A residuated groupoid is a q-groupoid if and only if each equivalence of type B reduces to equality.*

Proof. The sufficiency of the condition follows from the fact that

$$(\forall a, b \in G) \quad a\,(b \,.\!\cdot\, a) \equiv b(B_a); \quad (b \cdot\!.\, a)\, a \equiv b({}_aB).$$

Conversely, if G is a q-groupoid then every element is both a left and a right multiple of every other element. Thus every element is minimum in its class modulo every equivalence of type B. The condition is therefore also necessary.

THEOREM 23.19. *A residuated q-groupoid cannot contain a maximal element without the equivalence Z reducing to equality.*

Proof. Suppose that G is a residuated q-groupoid and that $\bar{a}$ is maximal in G. By Theorem 23.18 we have

$$(\forall b, b^* \in G) \quad b\,(\bar{a} \,.\!\cdot\, b) = \bar{a} = b^*\,(\bar{a} \,.\!\cdot\, b^*). \tag{*}$$

In particular, suppose that b, b^* belong to the same class modulo Z. Then since $A_{\bar{a}} = Z$ by Theorem 23.11 we have $\bar{a} \,.\!\cdot\, b = \bar{a} \,.\!\cdot\, b^* = c$ say, so that by (*) $b \equiv b^*({}_cF)$. Since this holds for each class modulo Z we deduce that $Z = {}_cF$ and hence by Theorem 23.12 that each class modulo Z contains a minimum element. Now let $\underline{x}$ be any minimal element of G. By Theorem 23.13 the minimal elements of G are simply the multiples of $\underline{x}$. But since $B_{\underline{x}}, {}_{\underline{x}}B$ are equality, every element is a multiple of $\underline{x}$ and so is minimal in G. It follows that Z is equality.

The general form of residuated q-groupoids is as follows, their existence being assured by Exercise 23.8.

THEOREM 23.20. *If a q-groupoid is residuated then either the equivalence Z reduces to equality or each class modulo Z contains no maximal elements and no minimal elements.*

The general form of residuated c-semigroups is deduced from that of residuated semigroups and that of residuated c-groupoids. Its enunciation is as in Theorem 23.17 and examples of each type are given in Exercises 23.9 and 23.10. The general form of residuated quasigroups is deduced from that of residuated c-groupoids and that of residuated q-groupoids. Its enunciation is as in Theorem 23.20. An example of a residuated quasigroup is to be found in Exercise 23.11. We also have the following results concerning residuated quasigroups, of which the first is immediate.

THEOREM 23.21. *A residuated groupoid G is a quasigroup if and only if all the equivalences of types B and F reduce to equality.*

THEOREM 23.22. *If G is a residuated quasigroup then every equivalence of type A reduces to equality.*

Proof. Given any $a, c \in G$ there exists a unique $b \in G$ such that $ab = c$. Consider the set of elements $x \in G$ such that $ax \leq c$. We have $ax \leq ab$ and so $x \leq ab \,.\!\cdot\, a = b$ since F_a is equality. It follows from this that $b = c \,.\!\cdot\, a$. In a similar way, $a = c \cdot\!.\, b$. Thus $a = c \cdot\!.\, b = c \cdot\!.\, (c \,.\!\cdot\, a)$. Since a, c are arbitrary, it follows that each equivalence of type A is equality.

Definition. An ordered groupoid will be called $\cup$-*semireticulated* if it is a $\cup$-semilattice in which the following distributive laws hold

$$(\forall a, b, c \in G) \quad a(b \cup c) = ab \cup ac; \quad (b \cup c)\, a = ba \cup ca.$$

THEOREM 23.23. *Let Q be an ordered quasigroup. If Q is a $\cup$-semilattice then Q is residuated if and only if it is $\cup$-semireticulated.*

Proof. If Q is residuated then, each translation being a residuated mapping, Q is $\cup$-semireticulated by Theorem 5.2 (see also Exercise 22.3). Conversely, let Q be $\cup$-semireticulated. Given any $a, b \in Q$ there exists a unique $c \in Q$ such that $ac = b$. Let us show that this element c is the greatest of the elements $x \in Q$ such that $ax \leq b$. Given any x satisfying $ax \leq b$, consider the element $z = c \cup x$. We have

$$az = a(c \cup x) = ac \cup ax = b \cup ax = b = ac$$

whence $z = c$ by the cancellation law and so $x \leq c$.

Definition. By a *reticulated groupoid* we shall mean a $\cup$-semireticulated groupoid which is a lattice.

THEOREM 23.24. *Every $\cup$-semireticulated quasigroup is reticulated.*

Proof. If Q is $\cup$-semireticulated then by the previous theorem Q is residuated. Given any $a \in Q$, consider the mapping $f_a : Q \to Q$ given by

$$(\forall x \in Q)\ f_a(x) = a \mathbin{.\!\cdot} x.$$

Since A_a is equality by Theorem 23.22, f_a is injective. Moreover, since ${}_aA$ is also equality every element of Q is a right residual of a and so f_a is surjective. Thus f_a is a bijection; and since it satisfies

$$x \leq y \Leftrightarrow f_a(y) \leq f_a(x),$$

it follows that Q is isomorphic to its dual and so is a lattice.

As far as groups are concerned, we have seen in Example 22.2 that every ordered group is residuated with $b \mathbin{.\!\cdot} a = a^{-1}b$ and $b \mathbin{\cdot\!.} a = ba^{-1}$. The general form of residuated groups is as in Theorem 23.20. We also have the following result.

THEOREM 23.25. *Every $\cup$-semilattice ordered group is reticulated and as a lattice is distributive.*

Proof. Let G be a $\cup$-semilattice ordered group. Being residuated, it is then $\cup$-semireticulated by Theorem 23.23 and hence is reticulated by Theorem 23.24. Now intersection in G is given by

$$(\forall a, b \in G)\quad a \cap b = b\,(a \cup b)^{-1}\,a. \qquad (*)$$

In fact, from

$$x \leq y \Leftrightarrow 1 = xx^{-1} \leq yx^{-1} \Leftrightarrow y^{-1} \leq y^{-1}yx^{-1} = x^{-1}$$

we deduce that for any a, b in G, $a^{-1} \geq (a \cup b)^{-1}$ and $b^{-1} \geq (a \cup b)^{-1}$. It follows that $b\,(a \cup b)^{-1}a$ is a lower bound for $\{a, b\}$. Now if $x \leq a, b$ then $a^{-1}, b^{-1} \leq x^{-1}$ and so $a^{-1} \cup b^{-1} \leq x^{-1}$. But since G is reticulated $a^{-1} \cup b^{-1} = a^{-1}\,(b \cup a)\,b^{-1}$. Hence we have $x \leq b\,(a \cup b)^{-1}a$. This establishes the equality (*). To show that G is distributive as a lattice, we use the result of Theorem 9.1. Suppose that $a \cup b = a \cup c$ and that

$a \cap b = a \cap c$; then from (*) we have

$$b = (a \cap b)\, a^{-1}\, (a \cup b) = (a \cap c)\, a^{-1}\, (a \cup c) = c$$

as required.

We end the present section with a structure theorem which follows from the results of the previous discussion.

Definition. By a *proper* Molinaro equivalence on a residuated groupoid G we shall mean an equivalence of type A, B or F which is distinct from equality and from the zigzag equivalence.

THEOREM 23.26. *Let G be a residuated groupoid with a neutral element. If G has no proper Molinaro equivalences then there are but two possibilities:*

(1) *the classes modulo Z have at most two elements and the class of* 1 *is isomorphic to the Boolean algebra* $\{0, 1\}$; *or*

(2) *G is a loop; and if the class of* 1 *consists only of* 1 *then the loop ordering is the trivial ordering* $a \not\parallel b \Leftrightarrow a = b$.

Proof. First of all, if every Molinaro equivalence reduces to equality then G is a loop by virtue of Theorem 23.21; and if the class of 1 consists only of 1 itself, then 1 is minimal in G and so, by Theorem 23.13, every element of G is minimal and consequently Z is equality, the trivial ordering.

Suppose therefore that not every Molinaro equivalence reduces to equality. By Theorem 23.10, Z is not equality and there exists, by hypothesis, at least one equivalence of type A, B or F which coincides with Z. It follows by virtue of Theorems 23.11, 23.12 and 23.5 that each class modulo Z admits a maximum element. Suppose that $\bar{a}$ is the maximum element in the class of 1 modulo Z. From $1 \leq \bar{a}$ we have $\bar{a} = \bar{a}1 \leq \bar{a}\bar{a}$ so that, $\bar{a}$ being maximal, $\bar{a} = \bar{a}\bar{a}$ and consequently $1 \equiv \bar{a}(F_{\bar{a}})$. Now if $F_{\bar{a}} = Z$ we have $(\forall x \equiv \bar{a}(Z))\ \bar{a}x = \bar{a}\bar{a}$ whence it follows that $\bar{a}$ is also minimum in its class modulo Z [for since $\bar{a}\bar{a} = \bar{a}$ we have $(\forall x \equiv \bar{a}(Z))$ $\bar{a}x = \bar{a}$ and if there existed $y \equiv \bar{a}(Z)$ with $y < \bar{a}$ then there would not exist $x \in G$ such that $\bar{a}x \leq y$, so that G would not be residuated]. It follows from this that if $F_{\bar{a}} = Z$ then the class of 1 modulo Z reduces to $\{1\}$ and as we have seen above this implies that Z is equality, contrary to the hypothesis. Hence we cannot have $F_{\bar{a}} = Z$, whence $F_{\bar{a}}$ must be equality. It then follows that $1 = \bar{a}$ so that 1 is maximum in its class modulo Z. Since we always have $(\forall x \in G)\ 1 \le x \,.\!\cdot\, x$, it then follows that $(\forall x \in G)$ $1 = x \,.\!\cdot\, x$. Consider now any class $\mathscr{X}$ modulo Z. Let $\bar{x}$ be the maximum element of $\mathscr{X}$ and consider $x_1 \le x_2 < \bar{x}$. We have $x_2 \,.\!\cdot\, x_1 \ge x_2 \,.\!\cdot\, x_2 = 1$ whence, 1 being maximal, it follows that $x_1 \equiv x_2\,(A_{x_2})$. But since $x_2 \,.\!\cdot\, x_2 = 1$ we also have the equality $x_2 \cdot\!.\, (x_2 \,.\!\cdot\, x_2) = x_2 \cdot\!.\, 1 = x_2$ so that x_2 is maximum in its class modulo A_{x_2} and so $x_2 \not\equiv \bar{x}(A_{x_2})$. We deduce from this that $A_{x_2} \neq Z$ and so A_{x_2} must be equality, whence $x_1 = x_2$. Consequently, any element which is covered by $\bar{x}$ is necessarily minimal in $\mathscr{X}$ and such an element must be minimum in $\mathscr{X}$ by virtue of Theorem 23.7. The proof is completed by noting that if the class containing 1 is $\{x, 1\}$ then $x < 1$ gives $x^2 \le x$ and this forces $x^2 = x$; consequently $\{x, 1\}$ is isomorphic to the two-element Boolean algebra.

EXERCISES

23.1. Consider the ordered set defined by

$$\begin{cases} G = \{a_i^\lambda,\ b_j^\mu;\ \lambda, \mu = 0, 1, \ldots, 5;\ i, j = 1, 2, 3, \ldots\} \\ a_i^\lambda \le b_j^\mu \le a_k^\nu \Leftrightarrow \lambda = \mu = \nu,\ i > j \ge k. \end{cases}$$

Endow G with the following multiplication:

(a) choose as G/Z the following quasigroup

	$\mathscr{A}^0$	$\mathscr{A}^1$	$\mathscr{A}^2$	$\mathscr{A}^3$	$\mathscr{A}^4$	$\mathscr{A}^5$
$\mathscr{A}^0$	$\mathscr{A}^1$	$\mathscr{A}^2$	$\mathscr{A}^4$	$\mathscr{A}^5$	$\mathscr{A}^0$	$\mathscr{A}^3$
$\mathscr{A}^1$	$\mathscr{A}^2$	$\mathscr{A}^5$	$\mathscr{A}^0$	$\mathscr{A}^4$	$\mathscr{A}^3$	$\mathscr{A}^1$
$\mathscr{A}^2$	$\mathscr{A}^4$	$\mathscr{A}^0$	$\mathscr{A}^3$	$\mathscr{A}^2$	$\mathscr{A}^1$	$\mathscr{A}^5$
$\mathscr{A}^3$	$\mathscr{A}^5$	$\mathscr{A}^3$	$\mathscr{A}^1$	$\mathscr{A}^0$	$\mathscr{A}^4$	$\mathscr{A}^2$
$\mathscr{A}^4$	$\mathscr{A}^0$	$\mathscr{A}^1$	$\mathscr{A}^2$	$\mathscr{A}^3$	$\mathscr{A}^5$	$\mathscr{A}^4$
$\mathscr{A}^5$	$\mathscr{A}^3$	$\mathscr{A}^4$	$\mathscr{A}^5$	$\mathscr{A}^1$	$\mathscr{A}^2$	$\mathscr{A}^0$

(*)

(b) for element-wise multiplication, define

$$a_i^\lambda a_j^\mu = a_i^\lambda b_j^\mu = a_{ij}^{\lambda\mu};\quad b_i^\lambda a_j^\mu = b_i^\lambda b_j^\mu = b_{ij}^{\lambda\mu}$$

where $\mathscr{A}^{\lambda\mu}$ is the product $\mathscr{A}^\lambda\mathscr{A}^\mu$ as determined by (*). Show that G is a residuated groupoid in which, if $\{i/j\}$ denotes the integer N such that $N - 1 < i/j \le N$ and $\mathscr{A}^{\lambda \,.\cdot\, \mu}$

is the class $\mathscr{A}^p$ such that $\mathscr{A}^\mu \mathscr{A}^p = \mathscr{A}^\lambda$,

$$\begin{cases} a_i^\lambda \mathbin{.\cdot} a_j^\mu = a_i^\lambda \mathbin{.\cdot} b_j^\mu = b_i^\lambda \mathbin{.\cdot} b_j^\mu = a_{\{i/j\}}^{\lambda.\cdot\mu}; \\ b_i^\lambda \mathbin{.\cdot} a_j^\mu = a_{\{i/j\}+1}^{\lambda.\cdot\mu}, \end{cases}$$

$$\begin{cases} a_i^\lambda \mathbin{\cdot.} a_j^\mu = a_i^\lambda \mathbin{\cdot.} b_j^\mu = a_{\{i/j\}}^{\lambda\cdot.\mu}; \\ b_i^\lambda \mathbin{\cdot.} a_j^\mu = b_i^\lambda \mathbin{\cdot.} b_j^\mu = b_{\{i/j\}}^{\lambda\cdot.\mu}. \end{cases}$$

23.2. Consider the ordered set defined by

$$\begin{cases} G = \{(x, y)^\lambda;\ \lambda = 0, 1, \ldots, 5;\ x, y \text{ integers with } x \leq 0\}; \\ (x, y)^\lambda \leq (x', y')^\mu \Leftrightarrow \lambda = \mu,\ x \leq x',\ y \leq y'. \end{cases}$$

Endow G with the following multiplication:

(a) as the groupoid G/Z choose the quasigroup (*) given in Exercise 23.1;

(b) for element-wise multiplication define

$$(x, y)^\lambda\, (u, v)^\mu = (\min\{x, u\},\ y + v^*)^{\lambda\mu}$$

where $\lambda\mu$ is as in Exercise 23.1 and v^* denotes the greatest multiple of a given fixed integer $N > 1$ which is less than or equal to v; i.e. $v^* = kN < v \leq (k + 1)N$. Establish the properties $d^* = (N - 1 + d^*)^*$, $b^* + d^* = (b + d^*)^*$, $b \leq b^* + N - 1$ and deduce that G is residuated with

$$\begin{cases} (c, d)^\lambda \mathbin{\cdot.} (a, b)^\mu = \begin{cases} (0, d - b^*)^{\lambda\cdot.\mu} & \text{if } a \leq c; \\ (c, d - b^*)^{\lambda\cdot.\mu} & \text{if } a > c, \end{cases} \\ (c, d)^\lambda \mathbin{.\cdot} (a, b)^\mu = \begin{cases} (0, (d - b)^* + N - 1)^{\lambda.\cdot\mu} & \text{if } a \leq c; \\ (c, (d - b)^* + N - 1)^{\lambda.\cdot\mu} & \text{if } a > c. \end{cases} \end{cases}$$

23.3. Consider the following Hasse diagram and Cayley table:

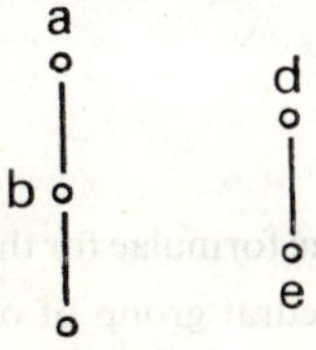

	a	b	c	d	e
a	b	b	c	e	e
b	c	c	c	e	e
c	c	c	c	e	e
d	d	d	e	c	c
e	e	e	e	c	c

Show that these define a non-abelian ordered semigroup S. Show that S is residuated by compiling tables of residuals.

23.4. Modify Exercise 23.1 by taking for G/Z any group of order 6. Show that this yields a non-abelian residuated semigroup of type two with analogous formulae for residuals.

23.5. Modify Exercise 23.2 by taking G/Z to be any group of order 6. Show that this yields a non-abelian residuated semigroup of the third type.

23.6. Consider the ordered set defined by

$$\begin{cases} G = \{a_i^\lambda; \quad \lambda = 0, 1, \cdots, 5; \quad i = 1, 2, 3, \ldots\}; \\ a_i^\lambda \leq a_j^\mu \Leftrightarrow \lambda = \mu, i \geq j. \end{cases}$$

Endow G with the following multiplication:

(a) for G/Z take the quasigroup (*) of Exercise 23.1;
(b) $a_i^\lambda a_j^\mu = a_{i+j}^{\lambda\mu}$.

Show that this defines a residuated c-groupoid in which

$$a_i^\lambda \,.\cdot\, a_j^\mu = \begin{cases} a_1^{\lambda.\cdot\mu} & \text{if} \quad i < j + 1; \\ a_{i-j}^{\lambda.\cdot\mu} & \text{if} \quad i \geq j + 1, \end{cases}$$

with similar formulae for left residuals.

23.7. Consider the ordered set defined by

$$\begin{cases} G = \{a_{2n,i}^\lambda; \lambda = 0, 1, \ldots, 5; n = 0, \pm 1, \pm 2, \ldots; i = 1, 2, 3, \ldots\}; \\ a_{2n,i}^\lambda \leq a_{2m,j}^\mu \Leftrightarrow \lambda = \mu, n \leq m, i \leq j. \end{cases}$$

Endowing G with the following multiplication:

(a) G/Z: the quasigroup of Exercise 23.1;
(b) $a_{2n,i}^\lambda a_{2m,j}^\mu = a_{2n+m,i+j}^{\lambda\mu}$,

show that G becomes a residuated c-groupoid and determine formulae for the residuals.

23.8. Consider the ordered set given by

$$\begin{cases} G = \{a_i^\lambda; \lambda = 0, 1, \ldots, 5; i = 0, \pm 1, \pm 2, \ldots\}; \\ a_i^\lambda \leq a_j^\mu \Leftrightarrow \lambda = \mu, i \leq j. \end{cases}$$

Endow G with the following multiplication:

(a) G/Z: the quasigroup of Exercise 23.1;

$$\text{(b)} \begin{cases} a_{2n}^\lambda a_{2m-1}^\mu = a_{2n-1}^\lambda a_{2m-1}^\mu = a_{2n-1}^\lambda a_{2m}^\mu = a_{2n-2}^\lambda a_{2m}^\mu; \\ a_i^\lambda a_i^\mu = a_i^{\lambda\mu}. \end{cases}$$

Show that G becomes a residuated q-groupoid and determine formulae for the residuals.

23.9. Modify Exercise 23.6 by taking for G/Z the dihedral group of order 6 (the smallest non-abelian group); show that the resulting structure is a residuated c-semigroup.

23.10. Modify Exercise 23.7 as in the previous exercise; show that the resulting structure is a residuated c-semigroup.

23.11. Modify Exercise 23.7 by allowing the suffix i to take also the values $0, -1, -2, \ldots$ Show that the resulting structure is that of a residuated quasigroup. Determine how the formulae for residuals change in respect of those found in Exercise 23.7.

23.12. Prove that an ordered group G is reticulated if and only if, for each $x \in G$, $x \cup 1$ exists.

23.13. If G is an ordered group, prove that for all $a, b \in G$ the principal filters $[a, \rightarrow]$, $[b, \rightarrow]$ are isomorphic.

23.14. An element a of a residuated groupoid is said to be:

(1) *equiresidual* if $(\forall x \in G)\ a \mathbin{.\cdot} x = a \mathbin{\cdot.} x$;
(2) *of type* α if $(\forall x \in G)\ x \mathbin{.\cdot} a = x \mathbin{\cdot.} a$;
(3) *of type* β if $(\forall x \in G)\ a \mathbin{.\cdot} x = x \mathbin{\cdot.} a$;
(4) *of type* γ if $(\forall x \in G)\ x \mathbin{.\cdot} a = a \mathbin{\cdot.} x$;
(5) *of type* δ if $(\forall x \in G)\ a \mathbin{.\cdot} x = x \mathbin{.\cdot} a$;
(6) *of type* ε if $(\forall x \in G)\ a \mathbin{\cdot.} x = x \mathbin{\cdot.} a$.

Refer to Exercise 22.7 for a characterization of elements of type α. Prove that if a residuated groupoid G contains an element of one of the types $\beta, \gamma, \delta, \varepsilon$ then each class modulo Z contains a maximum element and a minimum element. Let G be a residuated groupoid and let $a \in G$ be in the class $\mathscr{A}$ modulo Z. Prove that a is of type β if and only if:

(1) each class modulo Z has a maximum element and a minimum element;
(2) for all $\mathscr{B}, \mathscr{C} \in G/Z$ such that $\mathscr{B}\mathscr{C} = \mathscr{A}$ we have $\mathscr{C}\mathscr{A} = \mathscr{B}$;
(3) $\overline{\beta\gamma} \leq a$ for all maximal elements $\overline{\beta}, \overline{\gamma}$ such that $\overline{\beta\gamma} \in \mathscr{A}$;
(4) $(\forall x \in G)\ xa$ is minimal in G.

Deduce in a similar way characterizations of elements of types $\gamma, \delta, \varepsilon$. By means of examples, show that the above six types of elements are in general distinct.

23.15. Let G be a residuated groupoid such that G/Z is a group with neutral element $\mathscr{E}$. If $a \in G$ is of type β, prove that:

(1) G/Z is involutive [in that $(\forall \mathscr{A} \in G/Z)\ \mathscr{A}^2 = \mathscr{E}$];
(2) a is also equiresidual and of type ε;
(3) each element of $[a, \rightarrow]$ is equiresidual.

23.16. If G is a residuated groupoid with a neutral element and if $a \in G$ is of one of the types $\beta, \gamma, \delta, \varepsilon$ show that the class of a modulo Z is $\{a\}$.

23.17. Let S be a residuated semigroup with neutral element 1. An element $a \in S$ is said to be *of order* n if a smallest positive integer n exists such that $a^n = 1$. Let $a \in S$ be of order n. Prove that, if p is any positive integer and $x = a^p$, the equivalences F_x, ${}_xF$, B_x, ${}_xB$ reduce to equality. Deduce that if s, t are positive integers then the following conditions concerning $a \in S$ are equivalent:

(1) $a^{s+t} = 1$;
(2) $(\forall x \in S)\ x \mathbin{.\cdot} a^t = a^s x$;
(3) $(\forall x \in S)\ x \mathbin{\cdot.} a^t = x a^s$.

23.18. Prove that in a residuated semigroup with neutral element 1 the following conditions concerning $a \in S$ are equivalent:

(1) $\lambda_a^+ = \lambda_a$;
(2) $\varrho_a^+ = \varrho_a$;

(3) $(\forall x \in S)\ x \mathbin{.^{\cdot}} a = ax$;
(4) $(\forall x \in S)\ x \mathbin{^{\cdot}.} a = xa$;
(5) $a^2 = 1$.

23.19. Prove that in a residuated semigroup with neutral element 1 the following conditions concerning $a \in S$ are equivalent:

(1) $\lambda_a^+ = \varrho_a$;
(2) $\varrho_a^+ = \lambda_a$;
(3) $(\forall x \in S)\ axa = x$;
(4) $(\forall x \in S)\ x \mathbin{.^{\cdot}} a = xa$;
(5) $(\forall x \in S)\ x \mathbin{^{\cdot}.} a = ax$;
(6) $a^2 = 1$ and $(\forall x \in S)\ ax = xa$.

23.20. Consider the four element set $G = \{a, b, c, d\}$. Show that there are four ways in which G can be endowed with a multiplication and an ordering in such a way that it becomes a non-abelian residuated groupoid (or semigroup) in which:

(1) a is equiresidual;
(2) b is of all six types in Exercise 23.14;
(3) c is equiresidual and of types γ, δ;
(4) d is of type α.

23.21. Let G be an abelian residuated groupoid. For each $x \in G$ let λ_x, ζ_x be the mappings described by $(\forall y \in G)\ \lambda_x(y) = xy$ and $\zeta_x(y) = x : y$. We say that G satisfies the property:

R_1 if $(\forall x \in G)\ \lambda_x^+$ is residuated;
R_2 if $(\forall x \in G)\ \lambda_x^+$ is dually residuated;
R_3 if $(\forall x \in G)\ \zeta_x$ is residuated;
R_4 if $(\forall x \in G)\ \zeta_x$ is dually residuated.

Prove that in G the properties R_2 and R_3 are equivalent and are satisfied if and only if G is a quasigroup in which Z reduces to equality.

We shall say that G is *super-residuated on the right (left)* if it satisfies $R_1(R_4)$. If G is super-residuated on the right (left) prove that each equivalence of type $A(B)$ is both a closure and a dual closure equivalence and is strongly regular. If G is super-residuated on the right prove that either Z reduces to equality or each class modulo Z contains no maximal elements and no minimal elements.

Now let G be an abelian residuated groupoid in which each class modulo Z is totally ordered. Prove that G is super-residuated (on the left and right) if and only if:

(1) each class modulo Z contains no maximal elements and no minimal elements;
(2) all equivalences of types A, B are both closure equivalences and dual closure equivalences.

Consider the ordered set described by

$$\begin{cases} G = \{a_{p,i};\ p = 0, \pm 1, \pm 2, \ldots,\ i = 1, 2, \ldots, N\}; \\ a_{p,i} \leq a_{q,j} \Leftrightarrow \text{either } p < q \text{ or } p = q \text{ and } i \geq j. \end{cases}$$

Endow G with the following multiplication:

$$a_{p,i} \cdot a_{q,j} = a_{p+q,\ \min\{i,j\}}.$$

Show that G is a residuated semigroup which is also super-residuated.

24. Group homomorphic images of ordered semigroups; Querré semigroups

As we have seen in Theorem 23.14, for any residuated semigroup S the quotient semigroup S/Z is a (trivially ordered) group which is an isotone homomorphic image of S. It is natural to ask the general question as to just when an ordered semigroup admits an isotone homomorphic image which is a group. In this section we shall obtain an answer to this question.

We begin by asking the reader to refer back to Example 22.4 where we observed that for each semigroup S the power set $\mathbf{P}(S)$ can be considered as a residuated semigroup. It is precisely in this residuated semigroup that we shall be working and, for this purpose, we recall that residuals are given by

$$X \,.\!\cdot\, Y = \{z \in S;\ (\forall y \in Y)\ yz \in X\}, \quad X \,\cdot\!.\, Y = \{z \in S;\ (\forall y \in Y)\ zy \in X\}.$$

If H is a non-empty subset of S we shall say that H is *reflexive* if $xy \in H \Leftrightarrow yx \in H$; i.e. if $(\forall x \in S)\ H \,.\!\cdot\, \{x\} = H \,\cdot\!.\, \{x\}$, in which case we shall use the notation $H : \{x\}$. Such a subset will be called *neat* if $(\forall x \in S)$ $H : \{x\} \neq \varnothing$. Suppose now that H is a reflexive neat subset of S. Define an equivalence relation R_H on S by

$$a \equiv b(R_H) \Leftrightarrow H : \{a\} = H : \{b\}.$$

We call R_H the *Dubreil equivalence* associated with H. This equivalence is compatible with multiplication since if $a \equiv b(R_H)$ then, for each $x \in S$,

$$y \in H : \{xa\} \Leftrightarrow yxa \in H \Leftrightarrow yx \in H : \{a\} = H : \{b\} \Leftrightarrow yxb \in H$$
$$\Leftrightarrow y \in H : \{xb\},$$

so that $H : \{xa\} = H : \{xb\}$ and hence $xa \equiv xb\,(R_H)$; and in a similar way we can show that $ax \equiv bx\ (R_H)$. We can thus form the quotient semigroup S/R_H. Define a relation $\leq$ on S/R_H by

$$x/R_H \leq y/R_H \Leftrightarrow H:\{y\} \subseteq H:\{x\}.$$

Clearly $\leq$ is an ordering. Moreover,

$$\begin{aligned} a/R_H \leq b/R_H \Rightarrow H:\{b\} \subseteq H:\{a\} & \\ \Rightarrow (\forall x \in S)\ H:\{bx\} = (H:\{b\}) \,.^{\cdot}\, \{x\} & \\ \subseteq (H:\{a\}) \,.^{\cdot}\, \{x\} = H:\{ax\}, & \end{aligned}$$

from which we deduce that S/R_H is an ordered semigroup.

If we now impose on H the property that it be an order ideal of S then the canonical epimorphism $\natural_H : S \to S/R_H$ becomes isotone; for if $a \leq b$ in S, then $xa \leq xb$ implies, if $xb \in H$, that $xa \in H$ so that we obtain $H:\{b\} \subseteq H:\{a\}$. Thus, if H is a reflexive neat order ideal of S we can construct a semigroup S/R_H which is an isotone homomorphic image of S. Let us now examine under what conditions S/R_H becomes a group.

For this purpose, consider the set

$$E_H = \{y \in S;\ H:\{y\} = H\}.$$

Supposing for a moment that this set is not empty, we note that any element of S which is equivalent modulo R_H to an element of E_H is itself an element of E_H; and any two elements in E_H are equivalent modulo R_H. Hence E_H forms one of the classes modulo R_H. Moreover, from the fact that if $y \in E_H$ then

$$H:\{xy\} = (H:\{y\}) \,^{\cdot}.\, \{x\} = H:\{x\},$$

$$H:\{yx\} = (H:\{y\}) \,.^{\cdot}\, \{x\} = H:\{x\}$$

we see immediately that E_H becomes the neutral element of S/R_H. Thus, if $E_H \neq \emptyset$, S/R_H is a semigroup with a neutral element. In order to have S/R_H a group, we require the following concept.

Definition. We shall say that a subset H of an ordered semigroup S is *strongly neat* if both H and E_H are non-empty reflexive neat subsets of S.

If now in the above H is strongly neat then for each $x \in S$ the set $E_H : \{x\}$ is not empty; and for any element $y \in E_H : \{x\}$ we have $xy \in E_H$ so that $xy/R_H = E_H$ and likewise $yx/R_H = E_H$. This shows that for each $x \in S$ the class x/R_H has an inverse in S/R_H whence S/R_H becomes a group. [Note that

$$y \in (x/R_H)^{-1} \Leftrightarrow y/R_H = (x/R_H)^{-1} \Leftrightarrow yx/R_H = E_H \Leftrightarrow yx \in E_H$$
$$\Leftrightarrow y \in E_H : \{x\}$$

and so the inverse class of x/R_H is none other than $E_H : \{x\}$.]

In summary, therefore, if H is a reflexive strongly neat order ideal of S, then S/R_H is an isotone homomorphic group image of S. We shall now occupy ourselves with the converse and show that *every* isotone homomorphic group image of S arises in this manner.

For this purpose, let G be an ordered group and let $h : S \to G$ be an isotone epimorphism. Consider the *negative cone* of G, defined to be the subset $N = \{x \in G; x \leq 1\}$. Let $H = h^{\leftarrow}(N)$. If $y \in H$ with $x \leq y$ then, h being isotone, $h(x) \leq h(y) \leq 1$ and so $x \in H$. Hence H is an order ideal of S. That H is reflexive follows from the observation that

$$xy \in H \Leftrightarrow h(x)\, h(y) = h\,(xy) \leq 1$$
$$\Leftrightarrow h(x) \leq [h(y)]^{-1}$$
$$\Leftrightarrow h\,(yx) = h(y)\, h(x) \leq 1$$
$$\Leftrightarrow yx \in H.$$

That H is neat follows from the fact that h is surjective; for, given any $x \in S$, there exists $y \in S$ such that $h(y) = [h(x)]^{-1}$ and $h\,(xy) = h(x)\, h(y) = 1$ so that $xy \in H$. Now $x \in H : \{y\} \Leftrightarrow h\,(xy) \leq 1 \Leftrightarrow h(x) \leq [h(y)]^{-1}$ and so, h being surjective,

$$E_H = \{y \in S; H : \{y\} = H\} = \{y \in S; h(x) \leq [h(y)]^{-1} \Leftrightarrow h(x) \leq 1\}$$
$$= \{y \in S; h(y) = 1\}.$$

Consequently, the argument used above to show that H is neat also shows that E_H is neat. Thus H is strongly neat. Finally, we note that since h is surjective

$$
\begin{aligned}
H:\{a\} = H:\{b\} &\Leftrightarrow (h\,(xa) \leq 1 \Leftrightarrow h\,(xb) \leq 1)\\
&\Leftrightarrow (h(x) \leq [h(a)]^{-1} \Leftrightarrow h(x) \leq [h(b)]^{-1})\\
&\Leftrightarrow [h(a)]^{-1} = [h(b)]^{-1}\\
&\Leftrightarrow h(a) = h(b),
\end{aligned}
$$

and so we can define a mapping $\zeta_h: S/R_H \to G$ by the prescription $\zeta_h\,(x/R_H) = h(x)$. Clearly ζ_h is an isomorphism and so $S/R_H \simeq G$.

The following result summarizes the situation:

THEOREM 24.1. *Let S be an ordered semigroup. If H is a reflexive strongly neat order ideal of S and R_H is the associated Dubreil equivalence, then S/R_H is an isotone homomorphic group image of S. Moreover, every isotone homomorphic group image of S arises in this manner.*

Definition. By an *anticone* of an ordered semigroup S we shall mean a reflexive strongly neat order ideal H of S which is also a subsemigroup of S containing E_H.

With this terminology we have the following.

COROLLARY. *The set of isotone homomorphisms which map S onto an ordered group is equipotent to the set of anticones of S.*

Proof. For each isotone homomorphism h of S onto an ordered group G let $H = h^{\leftarrow}(N)$ where N is the negative cone of G. We know that H is a reflexive strongly neat order ideal of S. It is in fact an anticone since if $h(x) \leq 1$ and $h(y) \leq 1$ then $h\,(xy) = h(x)\,h(y) \leq 1$ so H is also a subsemigroup of S which clearly contains $E_H = \{x \in S;\ h(x) = 1\}$. Since as was shown above h is completely determined by H, and conversely, it suffices to show that if H is an anticone of S then $H = \natural_H^{\leftarrow}(N)$ where N is the negative cone of S/R_H. Now

$$\natural_H^{\leftarrow}(N) = \{x \in S;\ x/R_H \leqslant E_H\} = \{x \in S;\ H \subseteq H:\{x\}\}$$

and since H is a semigroup we have, for each $x \in H$, $\{x\}\,H \subseteq H$ and so $H \subseteq H:\{x\}$ whence $H \subseteq \natural_H^{\leftarrow}(N)$. On the other hand, if $x \in \natural_H^{\leftarrow}(N)$ then $\{x\}\,H \subseteq H$ and so for all $y \in H$ we have $xy \in H$. In particular, let

$y \in E_H \subseteq H$; then we obtain $x \in H:\{y\} = H$. Hence $\natural_H^{\leftarrow}(N) \subseteq H$ and we have the desired equality.

Remark. It follows from the above that, if H is an anticone, then

$$H:H = H:\bigcup_{x \in H}\{x\} = \bigcap_{x \in H} H:\{x\} = \bigcap_{x \in E_H} H:\{x\} = H.$$

In what follows, we shall denote by Δ the set of Dubreil equivalences associated with the set Γ of anticones of S.

Definition. An ordered semigroup S will be called a *Querré semigroup* if and only if there is associated with S an ordered group G and an isotone epimorphism $f: S \to G$ such that, for any ordered group K and isotone epimorphism $g: S \to K$, there is a unique epimorphism (not necessarily isotone) $h: G \to K$ such that the commutativity relation $h \circ f = g$ holds in the triangle

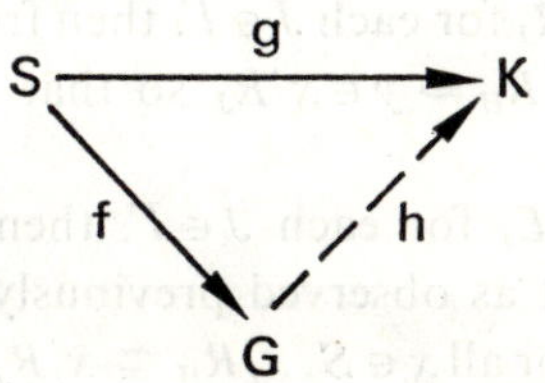

Such a group G we shall call the *greatest isotone homomorphic group image of S*.

THEOREM 24.2. *Let S be an ordered semigroup. Then the following are equivalent:*

(1) *S is a Querré semigroup;*

(2) *Δ has a minimum element;*

(3) *$\{E_J; J \in \Gamma\}$ has a minimum element.*

Proof. (1) $\Rightarrow$ (2): Let $G = S/R_H$ be the greatest isotone homomorphic group image of S. Then in any diagram of the form

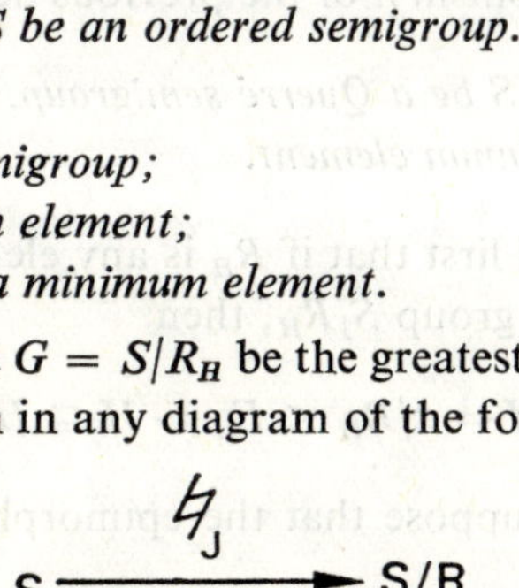

there is a unique homomorphism $h: S/R_H \to S/R_J$ such that $h \circ \natural_H = \natural_J$. Clearly h is given by $h(x/R_H) = x/R_J$ whence it follows that $x/R_H = y/R_H \Rightarrow x/R_J = y/R_J$; in other words, $R_H \leq R_J$. Since this holds for each $J \in \Gamma$, R_H is the minimum element of Δ.

(2) $\Rightarrow$ (1): Let R_H be the minimum element of Δ. Let K be any ordered group which is an isotone homomorphic image of S. By Theorem 24.1, K is of the form S/R_J and, by hypothesis, $R_H \leq R_J$. Now the latter gives

$$x/R_H = y/R_H \Rightarrow x \equiv y(R_H) \Rightarrow x \equiv y(R_J) \Rightarrow x/R_J = y/R_J,$$

and so we can define a mapping $h: S/R_H \to S/R_J$ by the prescription $h(x/R_H) = x/R_J$. This mapping is clearly an epimorphism and is unique with respect to the property $h \circ \natural_H = \natural_J$. Hence G/R_H is the greatest isotone homomorphic group image of S and so S is a Querré semigroup.

(2) $\Rightarrow$ (3): If $R_H \leq R_J$ for each $J \in \Gamma$, then from $y/R_H = x/R_H \Rightarrow y/R_J = x/R_J$ we have $y \in x/R_H \Rightarrow y \in x/R_J$ so that $x/R_H \subseteq x/R_J$ whence in particular $E_H \subseteq E_J$.

(3) $\Rightarrow$ (2): If $E_H \leq E_J$ for each $J \in \Gamma$, then for any $x \in S$ we have $E_H : \{x\} \subseteq E_J : \{x\}$. But as observed previously $E_H : \{x\} = (x/R_H)^{-1}$. It therefore follows that, for all $x \in S$, $x/R_H \subseteq x/R_J$ and hence that $R_H \leq R_J$.

Definition. We shall say that a Querré semigroup is *normal* if and only if each unique epimorphism h of the previous definition is isotone.

THEOREM 24.3. *Let S be a Querré semigroup. Then S is normal if and only if Γ admits a minimum element.*

Proof. Let us recall first that if R_H is any element of Δ and E_H is the neutral element of the group S/R_H, then

$$x \in H \Leftrightarrow x/R_H \leq E_H \Leftrightarrow H \subseteq H : \{x\}.$$

This being the case, suppose that the epimorphism $h: S/R_H \to S/R_J$ is isotone; then

$$x \in H \Rightarrow x/R_H \leq E_H \Rightarrow x/R_J = h(x/R_H) \leq h(E_H) = E_J \Rightarrow x \in J,$$

and so $H \subseteq J$. Conversely, if H is the minimum element of Γ, then for any

$J \in \Gamma$ we have

$$x/R_H \leq E_H \Rightarrow x \in H \Rightarrow x \in J \Rightarrow x/R_J \leq E_J.$$

We thus have a group homomorphism h which is such that $x \leq 1 \Rightarrow h(x) \leq 1$. It follows from this that h is isotone; for $h(y^{-1}) = [h(y)]^{-1}$ and so

$$\begin{aligned} x \leq y \Rightarrow xy^{-1} \leq 1 & \\ & \Rightarrow h(x)\,[h(y)]^{-1} = h(x)\,h(y^{-1}) = h\,(xy^{-1}) \leq 1 \\ & \Rightarrow h(x) \leq h(y). \end{aligned}$$

Definitions. If S is an ordered semigroup then for each $a, b \in S$ we define the *quasi-residuals of a by b* to be the sets

$$\langle a \,.\!\cdot\, b\rangle = \{x \in S;\ bx \leq a\}, \quad \langle a \,\cdot\!.\, b\rangle = \{x \in S;\ xb \leq a\}.$$

If these sets are not empty whatever the choice of $a, b \in S$, then we say that S is *quasi-residuated* [cf. § 2]. By a *principal subsemigroup* of S we shall mean any quasi-residual of the form $\langle a \,\cdot\!.\, a\rangle$ or $\langle a \,.\!\cdot\, a\rangle$. [It is readily seen that the latter quasi-residuals are subsemigroups and order ideals of S.]

THEOREM 24.4. *If H is any anticone of the ordered semigroup S then*

$$\bigcup_{a \in S} \langle a \,\cdot\!.\, a\rangle \subseteq H \quad \textit{and} \quad \bigcup_{a \in S} \langle a \,.\!\cdot\, a\rangle \subseteq H.$$

Proof. Suppose that $\langle a \,\cdot\!.\, a\rangle \neq \emptyset$, for example, and let $t \in \langle a \,\cdot\!.\, a\rangle$. Then from $ta \leq a$ we have $t/R_H \cdot a/R_H \leq a/R_H$ and so $t/R_H \leq E_H$ whence $t \in H$.

Definition. By the *core* of an ordered semigroup S we shall mean the set-theoretic union of all its principal subsemigroups. We shall use the notation $)S($ to denote the core of S.

THEOREM 24.5. *If $)S(\neq \emptyset$ then $)S($ is a reflexive order ideal of S.*

Proof. If $xy \in)S($, then for some $t \in S$ either $xyt \leq t$ or $txy \leq t$ whence either $yxyt \leq yt$ or $txyx \leq tx$ so that either $yx \in \langle yt \,\cdot\!.\, yt\rangle$ or $yx \in \langle tx \,.\!\cdot\, tx\rangle$. In either case $yx \in)S($ and so $)S($ is reflexive. Being the set-theoretic union of order ideals of S, $)S($ is also an order ideal of S.

We shall make use of the following result in obtaining an example of a normal Querré semigroup.

THEOREM 24.6. *If* $)S($ *is an anticone and* $E_{)S(}$ *coincides with the set* $T = \{x \in S; (\exists y \in S)\ xy = y = yx\}$, *then S is a normal Querré semigroup.*

Proof. If $)S($ is an anticone then it is the smallest anticone by virtue of Theorem 24.4. For each $x \in T$ we have, for some $y \in S$, $xy = y = yx$, and so, on passing to quotients, we see that $x \in E_J$ for each anticone J. Thus if $E_{)S(} = T$ we have $E_{)S(} \subseteq E_J$ for each anticone J. It therefore follows by Theorem 24.2 that S is a Querré semigroup and, $)S($ being the smallest anticone, the result follows by Theorem 24.3.

EXAMPLE 24.1. An element a of a semigroup S is said to be *regular* if and only if there exists an element $x \in S$ such that $a = axa$. We say that S itself is regular if every element of S is regular. Elements a, b in S are said to be *inverses* of each other if and only if $a = aba$ and $b = bab$. We note first that $a \in S$ is regular if and only if it has an inverse. [In fact, if there exists b such that $a = aba$ then a is regular. Conversely, if $a = axa$ then, writing $xax = b$, we have $aba = a(xax)a = ax(axa) = axa = a$ and also $bab = (xax)a(xax) = x(axa)(xax) = xa(xax) = x(axa)x = xax = b$, so that b is an inverse of a.] By an *inverse semigroup* we mean a semigroup S every element of which admits a unique inverse. The following conditions are equivalent and are necessary and sufficient for a semigroup S to be an inverse semigroup:

(1) S is regular and any two idempotents of S commute;
(2) every principal right [resp. left] ideal of S has a unique idempotent generator.

[In fact, if S is an inverse semigroup then clearly S is regular. The set of idempotents in S is not empty; for from $a = axa$ we deduce that $ax = axax$. Let, therefore, e, f be idempotents in S. Let a be the (unique) inverse of ef so that $(ef)a(ef) = ef$ and $a(ef)a = a$. Let $b = ae$; then $(ef)b(ef) = efae^2f = efaef = ef$ and $b(ef)b = ae^2fae = aefae = ae = b$, so that by the uniqueness of inverses we have $a = b = ae$. In a similar way we can show that $fa = a$. Consequently, $a^2 = (ae)(fa) = a(ef)a = a$. It follows that a is an inverse of itself and so, by the uniqueness, $a = ef$.

Thus ef is also an idempotent. In a similar way we can show that fe is idempotent. Now ef and fe are inverses of each other; for $(ef)(fe)(ef) = ef^2e^2f = efef = ef$ and, by symmetry, $(fe)(ef)(fe) = fe$. Thus ef and fe are each inverses of $a = ef$, and since inverses are unique we deduce that $ef = fe$. The condition (1) is therefore necessary. Now let us show that (1) $\Rightarrow$ (2). If (1) holds then each $a \in S$ is regular so that, for some $x \in S$, $a = axa$; and as we have seen the element $e = ax$ is an idempotent of S such that $ea = a$. Now in general S has no neutral element so the right ideal generated by a non-empty subset T of S is $T \cup TS$; in particular, the principal right ideal generated by $\{t\}$ is $\{t\} \cup \{t\}S$. It follows from the above that we have $\{a\} \cup \{a\}S = \{e\} \cup \{e\}S$, whence every principal right ideal admits an idempotent generator. Suppose now that e, f are idempotents which generate the same principal right ideal: $\{e\} \cup \{e\}S = \{f\} \cup \{f\}S$. Then there exists $y \in S$ such that $ey = ff = f$ and so $ef = e(ey) = ey = f$. Similarly, we have $fe = e$. By the hypothesis (1) we deduce that $e = f$ and property (2) follows. Now suppose that (2) holds and let us show that this implies that S is an inverse semigroup. If e is an idempotent then from $\{a\} \cup \{a\}S = \{e\} \cup \{e\}S = \{e\}S$ we deduce that there exists $x \in S$ such that $a = ex$, so that $ea = e^2x = ex = a$; and there exists $y \in S$ such that $ay = ee = e$. It follows that $aya = ea = a$ and so a is regular. Since a is arbitrary, it follows that S is regular. It remains, therefore, to show that inverses are unique. For this purpose, let b, c be inverses of a so that $aba = a$, $bab = b$, $aca = a$, $cac = c$. Since ab and ac are idempotents, these conditions give

$$\{ab\} \cup \{ab\}S = \{ab\}S = \{a\}S = \{ac\}S = \{ac\} \cup \{ac\}S.$$

The standing hypothesis (2) then yields $ab = ac$. In a similar way, we have $ba = ca$ and consequently $b = bab = bac = cac = c$ as required.]

In an inverse semigroup the unique inverse of a is written a^{-1}. In such a semigroup we have $(a^{-1})^{-1} = a$ and $(ab)^{-1} = b^{-1}a^{-1}$. [In fact the first is clear by the uniqueness of inverses. As for the second, the fact that idempotents commute gives $ab(b^{-1}a^{-1})ab = a(bb^{-1})(a^{-1}a)b = aa^{-1}abb^{-1}b = ab$ and $b^{-1}a^{-1}(ab)b^{-1}a^{-1} = b^{-1}(a^{-1}a)(bb^{-1})a^{-1} = b^{-1}bb^{-1}a^{-1}aa^{-1} = b^{-1}a^{-1}$, whence $b^{-1}a^{-1}$ is the (unique) inverse of ab.]

Having established these preliminaries, let us now show how an inverse semigroup can be ordered. Let us observe first that the following conditions are equivalent in such a semigroup:

$$(\alpha)\ aa^{-1} = ab^{-1};\quad (\beta)\ a^{-1}a = a^{-1}b;\quad (\gamma)\quad ab^{-1}a = a;$$

$$(\alpha^*)\ aa^{-1} = ba^{-1};\quad (\beta^*)\ a^{-1}a = b^{-1}a;\quad (\gamma^*)\ a^{-1}ba^{-1} = a^{-1}.$$

[In fact, each condition (x^*) is equivalent to (x), as may be seen by taking inverses. We shall show that $(\alpha) \Rightarrow (\gamma)$, $(\gamma^*) \Rightarrow (\beta)$, $(\beta^*) \Rightarrow (\alpha)$, whence the result will follow. That $(\alpha) \Rightarrow (\gamma)$ is immediate on multiplying the equality (α) on the right by a. Now (γ^*) implies that $a^{-1}b$ is an idempotent. As idempotents commute, (γ^*) then implies $a^{-1}a = a^{-1}ba^{-1}a = a^{-1}aa^{-1}b = a^{-1}b$, which is (β). Finally, if (β^*) holds then ab^{-1} is idempotent since $(ab^{-1})(ab^{-1}) = a(b^{-1}a)b^{-1} = a(a^{-1})b^{-1} = ab^{-1}$, from which it follows that $aa^{-1} = a(a^{-1}a)a^{-1} = a(b^{-1}a)a^{-1} = (ab^{-1})(aa^{-1}) = aa^{-1}ab^{-1} = ab^{-1}$ and hence (α) holds.]

This being the case, define the relation $\leq$ on S by setting

$$a \leq b \Leftrightarrow aa^{-1} = ab^{-1}.$$

It is clear that $\leq$ is reflexive on S. It is also anti-symmetric; for from $a \leq b$ and $b \leq a$ we have $a = ab^{-1}a$, $ab^{-1} = bb^{-1}$ and $b^{-1}a = b^{-1}b$, whence $a = (ab^{-1})a = (bb^{-1})a = b(b^{-1}a) = bb^{-1}b = b$. Finally, $\leq$ is transitive; for from $a \leq b$ and $b \leq c$ we have $ac^{-1}a = aa^{-1}ac^{-1}a = aa^{-1}bc^{-1}a = aa^{-1}bb^{-1}a = aa^{-1}aa^{-1}a = a$, whence $a \leq c$. Thus $\leq$ is an ordering on S. Now S is an ordered semigroup since if $a \leq b$ then, for any $x \in S$,

$$\begin{cases} (xa)(xb)^{-1} = xab^{-1}x^{-1} = xaa^{-1}x^{-1} = (xa)(xa)^{-1}; \\ (ax)^{-1}(bx) = x^{-1}a^{-1}bx = x^{-1}a^{-1}ax = (ax)^{-1}(ax), \end{cases}$$

so that $xa \leq xb$ and $ax \leq bx$.

This ordered semigroup is quasi-residuated since, given any $a, b \in S$, $ab^{-1} \in \langle a \cdot . \, b\rangle$ and $b^{-1}a \in \langle a \, . \cdot b\rangle$. [For example, $ab^{-1}b(ab^{-1}b)^{-1} = ab^{-1}bb^{-1}ba^{-1} = ab^{-1}ba^{-1} = a(ab^{-1}b)^{-1}$ and so $ab^{-1}b \leq a$.]

Now let I be the set of idempotents in S. Every element of I is of the form $y^{-1}y$; in fact, if $x \in I$ then from $x^2 = x$ we deduce $x = xxx$ and so $x = x^{-1}$ giving $x = xx = x^{-1}x$; and conversely we have seen that every element of the form $y^{-1}y$ is idempotent. From the inequalities $ab^{-1}b \leq a$ and $bb^{-1}a \leq a$ we then deduce that

$$(\forall x \in I)\,(\forall a \in S) \quad ax \leq a \quad \text{and} \quad xa \leq a,$$

so that I is a lower bound for the set of principal subsemigroups of S.

Consider now the set

$$I^* = \{x \in S;\ (\exists e \in I)\ e \leq x\}.$$

Since, as was shown earlier, I is a subsemigroup of S, so also is I^*; in fact, from $e \leq x, f \leq y$ $(e, f \in I)$ we have $ef \leq xy$ and since $ef \in I$ we deduce that $xy \in I^*$. The semigroup I^* is reflexive; for

$$\begin{aligned} xy \in I^* &\Rightarrow (\exists e \in I) \quad e \leq xy \\ &\Rightarrow (\exists e \in I) \quad yey^{-1} \leq yxyy^{-1} \leq yx \\ &\Rightarrow yx \in I^* \quad \text{since} \quad yey^{-1} \in I. \end{aligned}$$

Let us now show that I^* is an order ideal of S. Suppose that $x \in I^*$ and $y \leq x$. From $x \in I^*$ we have, for some $e \in I$, $e \leq x$ so that $ee^{-1} = ex^{-1}$. Taking inverses and using the fact that e is idempotent (and hence is its own inverse) we obtain $e = xe^{-1} = xe$. Thus from $y \leq x$ we deduce that $y^{-1}y = y^{-1}x$ so that $y^{-1}ye = y^{-1}xe = y^{-1}e \leq y^{-1}$. Now

$$a \leq b \Leftrightarrow a = ab^{-1}a \Leftrightarrow a^{-1} = a^{-1}ba^{-1} \Leftrightarrow a^{-1} \leq b^{-1},$$

and so it follows from the above that $ey^{-1}y \leq y$. But $ey^{-1}y \in I$ and so we have $y \in I^*$ as required.

To show that I^* is strongly neat we observe that for each $x \in S$ we have $xx^{-1} \in I \subseteq I^*$ and so I^* is neat. Since $xx^{-1} \in I^*$ and I^* is clearly a subsemigroup of S, we have $\{xx^{-1}\}\, I^* \subseteq I^*$ and so, on the one hand, $I^* \subseteq I^* : \{xx^{-1}\}$. But if $y \in I^* : \{xx^{-1}\}$ then $yxx^{-1} \in I^*$ and so there is an idempotent e such that $e \leq yxx^{-1} \leq y$ whence $y \in I^*$. We have thus shown that $I^* : \{xx^{-1}\} \subseteq I^*$. The resulting equality $I^* : \{xx^{-1}\} = I^*$ now shows that E_{I^*} is neat. Hence I^* is strongly neat.

Now

$$I^* : I^* = I^* : \bigcup_{x \in I^*} \{x\} = \bigcap_{x \in I^*} I^* : \{x\} = I^*$$

since for all $x \in I^*$ we have, I^* being a subsemigroup, $I^* \subseteq I^* : \{x\}$ and for each idempotent xx^{-1} we have $xx^{-1} \in I^*$ with $I^* : \{xx^{-1}\} = I^*$. We thus have $x \in E_{I^*} \Rightarrow I^* : \{x\} = I^* \Rightarrow x \in I^* : I^* = I^*$ so that $E_{I^*} \subseteq I^*$. This completes the proof that I^* is an anticone of S.

We now show that in fact $E_{I^*} = I^*$. For this, let $x \in I^*$ and let $y \in I^* : \{x\}$. Then $yx \in I^*$ and so there is an idempotent f such that $f \leq x$ whence $xf = f$ and so $ef \leq yxf = yf \leq y$. Thus $y \in I^*$ and we have shown in this way that if $x \in I^*$ then $I^* : \{x\} \subseteq I^*$. But the converse inclusion clearly holds since I^* is an anticone. Hence if $x \in I^*$ then $x \in E_{I^*}$ and so $I^* \subseteq E_{I^*}$ and the desired equality follows.

Now since I^* is an anticone we have $)S(\subseteq I^*$ by Theorem 24.4. But if $x \in I^*$ then $e = xe$ for some $e \in I$, whence $x \in)S($. Hence $I^* =)S($.

Finally, let us consider the set $T = \{x \in S; (\exists y \in S)\ xy = y = yx\}$. If $x \in T$, then, on passing to quotients, we see that $x \in E_{I^*} = I^* =)S($. Conversely, if $x \in)S($ then $x \in I^*$ whence there exists an idempotent e such that $e = ex = xe$ and so $x \in T$. Thus $T =)S(= I^* = E_{I^*}$ and by applying Theorem 24.6 we obtain finally the fact that S is a normal Querré semigroup.

Let us now continue the thread of this example by characterizing the equivalence which yields the greatest isotone homomorphic group image.

THEOREM 24.7. *If S is an inverse semigroup and I is its set of idempotents then the following three relations are equivalent and are each responsible for the greatest isotone homomorphic group image of S:*

(1) $x \equiv y(M) \Leftrightarrow (\exists e \in I) \quad ex = ey$;
(2) $x \equiv y(H) \Leftrightarrow xy^{-1} \in I^*$;
(3) *the zigzag equivalence Z.*

Proof. Suppose first that $x \equiv y(M)$. Then for some $e \in I$ we have $ex = ey$ whence $xy^{-1} \geq exy^{-1} = eyy^{-1} \in I$ and so $xy^{-1} \in I^*$ and $x \equiv y(H)$. Conversely, if $x \equiv y(H)$, then $xy^{-1} \in I^*$, and so there exists $f \in I$ such that $f \leq xy^{-1}$. It follows that $fxy^{-1} = f$ [for $f^{-1}f = f^{-1}xy^{-1}$ and $f = f^{-1}$]. Now let $e = fxy^{-1}yx^{-1}$; then $e = fxy^{-1}(xy^{-1})^{-1} \in I$ and, as idempotents commute, $ef = e$. Now

$$ex = e^2x = efxy^{-1}yx^{-1}x = efxx^{-1}xy^{-1}y = efxy^{-1}y = efy = ey$$

and so $x \equiv y(M)$. This then shows that M and H are equivalent.

Let us now show that $R_{I^*} = H$. From the identity $y = yy^{-1}y$ we have $yy^{-1}/R_{I^*} = E_{I^*} = I^*$ and so

$$x \equiv y(R_{I^*}) \Leftrightarrow xy^{-1} \equiv yy^{-1}\,(R_{I^*}) \Leftrightarrow xy^{-1} \in I^*.$$

This then shows that $R_{I^*} = H$ and consequently S/H is the greatest isotone homomorphic group image of S.

Now let us show that $H = Z$. We begin by observing that

$$\begin{aligned} x \equiv y(H) &\Rightarrow (\exists e \in I) \quad e \leq xy^{-1} \\ &\Rightarrow (\exists e \in I) \quad ey \leq xy^{-1}y \leq x, \quad ey \leq y \\ &\Rightarrow x \equiv y(Z). \end{aligned}$$

On the other hand, we have

$$\text{(i)} \qquad t \leq a, b \Rightarrow tt^{-1} \leq ab^{-1} \Rightarrow ab^{-1} \in I^* \Rightarrow a \equiv b(H);$$

$$\begin{aligned} \text{(ii)} \qquad t \geq a, b &\Rightarrow at^{-1}b = aa^{-1}b \leq b, \quad at^{-1}b = ab^{-1}b \leq a \\ &\Rightarrow at^{-1}b \leq a, b \\ &\Rightarrow a \equiv b(H) \quad \text{[by (i)]}, \end{aligned}$$

so that if $x \equiv y(Z)$ then, by applying (i) and (ii) to any zig-zag chain joining x and y, we obtain $x \equiv y(H)$. This then shows that H and Z coincide and completes the proof.

EXERCISES

24.1. Let S be an ordered semigroup with a neutral element. In this exercise we show that S can be embedded in a normal Querré semigroup with a neutral element. For each integer p, let

$$[p] = \begin{cases} p & \text{if } p \geq 0; \\ 0 & \text{otherwise,} \end{cases}$$

and let $f_p : S \times S \rightarrow S$ be given by

$$f_p(x, y) = \begin{cases} x & \text{if } p > 0; \\ xy & \text{if } p = 0; \\ y & \text{if } p < 0. \end{cases}$$

Verify the identities

$$[m] + [n - [-m]] = [m + [n]];$$

$$f_{m+[n]}(f_n(x, y), z) = f_{n-[-m]}(x, f_m(y, z))$$

and use these to show that $\mathbf{N} \times S \times \mathbf{N}$ is a semigroup under the law of composition defined by

$$(m, x, n)(m^*, x^*, n^*) = (m + [m^* - n], f_{n-m^*}(x, x^*), n^* + [n - m^*]).$$

Show that (0, 1, 0) is the neutral element of this semigroup. Define the relation $\leq$ on $\mathbf{N} \times S \times \mathbf{N}$ by

$$(m, x, n) \leq (m^*, x^*, n^*) \Leftrightarrow m = m^*, x \leq x^*, n = n^*.$$

Show that $(\mathbf{N} \times S \times \mathbf{N}, \leq)$ is an ordered semigroup. For each $n \in \mathbf{N}$ define the mapping $\zeta_n : S \to \mathbf{N} \times S \times \mathbf{N}$ by $\zeta_n(x) = (n, x, n)$. Show that ζ_n is an isotone monomorphism. Let $S^* = \{(n, x, n); n \in \mathbf{N}, x \in S\}$. Show that S^* is an anticone of $\mathbf{N} \times S \times \mathbf{N}$ and that S^* coincides with the core of $\mathbf{N} \times S \times \mathbf{N}$. Conclude that $\mathbf{N} \times S \times \mathbf{N}$ is a normal Querré semigroup which contains an isomorphic copy of S.

24.2. Let G be any ordered group. In this exercise we show how to construct a normal Querré semigroup whose greatest isotone homomorphic group image is isomorphic to G. Let L be any idempotent semigroup. Show that L can be ordered by $x \leq y \Leftrightarrow xy = x = yx$. Endow $G \times L$ with the following ordering and multiplication:

$$\begin{cases} (g, x) \leq (h, y) \Leftrightarrow g \leq h, x \leq y; \\ (g, x)\,(h, y) = (gh, x). \end{cases}$$

Show that $G \times L$ is an ordered semigroup. Show also that the map $f: G \times L \to G$ described by $f((g, x)) = g$ is an isotone epimorphism. If N is the negative cone of G prove that $f^{\leftarrow}(N) =)G \times L($ and deduce that $G \times L$ is a normal Querré semigroup. Show further that $(g, x) \equiv (h, y)\ (R_{f^{\leftarrow}(N)}) \Leftrightarrow g = h$ and deduce that $(G \times L)/R_{f^{\leftarrow}(N)} \simeq G$.

24.3. Consider the set $\mathbf{R} \times \mathbf{Z}$ ordered in the usual cartesian manner and made into an ordered semigroup by the law of composition

$$(x, m) \oplus (y, n) = (x + y + m + n, 0).$$

Determine the core of this semigroup and show that it is an anticone. Hence show that the semigroup is a normal Querré semigroup the greatest isotone homomorphic group image of which is the additive group $\mathbf{R}$ ordered in the usual way.

25. Dubreil–Jacotin semigroups; *A*-nomal semigroups

Definition. We shall say that an anticone H of an ordered semigroup is *principal* if and only if it is of the form $H = [\leftarrow, h]$.

THEOREM 25.1. *If an ordered semigroup S admits a principal anticone $[\leftarrow, h]$ then this is the only principal anticone in S and $[\leftarrow, h] =)S($.*

Proof. From the proof of Theorem 24.1 we have, for any anticone H,

$$x \in H \Leftrightarrow H \subseteq H : \{x\}.$$

Setting $H = [\leftarrow, h]$, this translates into

$$\begin{aligned} x \in [\leftarrow, h] &\Leftrightarrow [\leftarrow, h] \subseteq [\leftarrow, h] : \{x\} = \langle h : x\rangle \\ &\Leftrightarrow h \in \langle h : x\rangle \\ &\Leftrightarrow x \in \langle h : h\rangle \end{aligned}$$

whence we have, by Theorem 24.4,

$$)S(\subseteq [\leftarrow, h] = \langle h : h\rangle \subseteq)S($$

and so $[\leftarrow, h] =)S($. This also establishes uniqueness.

Definition. By a ***Dubreil–Jacotin semigroup*** we shall mean an ordered semigroup which admits a (necessarily unique) principal anticone.

THEOREM 25.2. *An ordered semigroup is a Dubreil–Jacotin semigroup if and only if it satisfies the properties*

(1) $)S($ *is strongly neat;*
(2) $(\exists \xi \in S) \quad [\leftarrow, \xi] =)S($.

Proof. The conditions are necessary by Theorem 25.1. Conversely, suppose that (1) and (2) hold. From (2) we have, for some $t \in S$ for example, $\xi \in \langle t\,{}^{\cdot}.\,t\rangle$. It follows that $[\leftarrow, \xi] \subseteq \langle t\,{}^{\cdot}.\,t\rangle$ and hence, by (2), that $[\leftarrow, \xi] = \langle t\,{}^{\cdot}.\,t\rangle$. Now from $\xi t \leq t$ we have $\xi^2 t \leq \xi t \leq t$ and so $\xi^2 \in \langle t\,{}^{\cdot}.\,t\rangle = [\leftarrow, \xi]$. Thus $\xi^2 \leq \xi$ and so $\xi \in \langle \xi\,{}^{\cdot}.\,\xi\rangle$ and $\xi \in \langle \xi\,.{}^{\cdot}\,\xi\rangle$. It follows from this that $)S(= [\leftarrow, \xi] = \langle \xi\,{}^{\cdot}.\,\xi\rangle = \langle \xi\,.{}^{\cdot}\,\xi\rangle$ and is a subsemigroup of S. Adding to these results that of Theorem 24.6 we see that $)S($ is a reflexive strongly neat order ideal of S which is a subsemigroup of S. Since $)S(= [\leftarrow, \xi]$ is reflexive we have

$$(\forall x \in S) \quad \langle \xi\,.{}^{\cdot}\,x\rangle = [\leftarrow, \xi]\,.{}^{\cdot}\,\{x\} = [\leftarrow, \xi]\,{}^{\cdot}.\,\{x\} = \langle \xi\,{}^{\cdot}.\,x\rangle.$$

We express this by saying that ξ is *equi-quasiresidual* and in this case write $\langle \xi\,{}^{\cdot}.\,x\rangle = \langle \xi\,.{}^{\cdot}\,x\rangle = \langle \xi : x\rangle$. Now

$$x \in E_{)S(} \Leftrightarrow \langle \xi : x\rangle = [\leftarrow, \xi] : \{x\} = [\leftarrow, \xi]$$

$$\Leftrightarrow \xi : x \quad \text{exists and is } \xi.$$

Thus $x \in E_{)S(} \Rightarrow \xi : x = \xi \Rightarrow x\xi \leq \xi \Rightarrow x \in \langle \xi : \xi\rangle = [\leftarrow, \xi] =)S($. Hence $E_{)S(} \subseteq)S($ and so $)S($ is indeed an anticone of S. Since $)S($ is principal, S is then a Dubreil–Jacotin semigroup.

Definition. If S is an ordered semigroup and G is an ordered group then we shall say that an epimorphism $f : S \to G$ is *principal* if and only if it is isotone and such that the pre-image of the negative cone of G is a principal order ideal of S.

The following result summarizes what has gone before:

THEOREM 25.3. *An ordered semigroup S is a Dubreil–Jacotin semigroup if and only if it admits a principal epimorphic image which is a group. Such a group is necessarily unique up to isomorphism. If S is a Dubreil–Jacotin semigroup then)S(has a maximum element ξ which is equi-quasiresidual in the sense that*

$$(\forall x \in S) \quad \langle \xi \,.\!\cdot\, x \rangle = \langle \xi \,\cdot\!.\, x \rangle$$

and the unique principal homomorphic group of S is given by $S/\mathscr{A}_\xi$ *where* $\mathscr{A}_\xi$ *is the equivalence given by*

$$x \equiv y(\mathscr{A}_\xi) \Leftrightarrow \langle \xi : x \rangle = \langle \xi : y \rangle.$$

EXAMPLE 25.1. Consider the set

$$S = \left\{0,\ p - \frac{1}{n}; \qquad p, n \in Z, \quad n \geq 2\right\}.$$

The relation $\leq$ defined on S by

$$\begin{cases} p - \dfrac{1}{n} \leq q - \dfrac{1}{m} \Leftrightarrow p = q, \quad n \leq m; \\[2ex] p - \dfrac{1}{n} \leq 0 \Leftrightarrow p = 0, \end{cases}$$

is an ordering on S. Define a law of composition $\oplus$ on S by

$$\begin{cases} \left(p - \dfrac{1}{n}\right) \oplus \left(q - \dfrac{1}{m}\right) = p + q - \dfrac{1}{\min\{n, m\}}; \\[2ex] \left(p - \dfrac{1}{n}\right) \oplus 0 = p - \dfrac{1}{n} = 0 \oplus \left(p - \dfrac{1}{n}\right); \\[2ex] 0 \oplus 0 = 0. \end{cases}$$

It is clear that $\oplus$ is commutative, associative and isotone, so that $(S, \oplus)$ is an ordered semigroup. Now in this ordered semigroup we have certain residuals existing, namely

$$0 : 0 = 0; \qquad \left(p - \frac{1}{n}\right) : 0 = p - \frac{1}{n}; \qquad \left(p - \frac{1}{n}\right) : \left(p - \frac{1}{n}\right) = 0.$$

We also have

$$\left\langle 0 : p - \frac{1}{n} \right\rangle = \begin{cases} \left\{ -p - \frac{1}{t} ; \quad t \leq 2 \right\} & \text{if } p \neq 0; \\ [\leftarrow, 0] & \text{if } p = 0. \end{cases}$$

It follows from these observations that $)S(= [\leftarrow, 0]$. Now

$$\begin{aligned} E_{)S(} &= \{x \in S;\ \langle 0 : x \rangle = [\leftarrow, 0]\} \\ &= \{x \in S;\ 0 : x \text{ exists and is } 0\} \\ &= \{0\} \cup \left\{ -\frac{1}{n} ; \quad n \geq 2 \right\} \\ &= [\leftarrow, 0]. \end{aligned}$$

Since for each $p - \frac{1}{n}$ we have $\left(p - \frac{1}{n}\right) \oplus \left(-p - \frac{1}{t}\right) = -\frac{1}{\min\{n, t\}}$ < 0 it follows that $)S($ is strongly neat. Applying Theorem 25.2 we now see that S is a Dubreil–Jacotin semigroup. The unique principal homomorphic group image of S is $S/\mathscr{A}_0$ and, as is readily seen, $S/\mathscr{A}_0 \simeq \mathbf{Z}$ where $\mathbf{Z}$ is trivially ordered.

It is clear that a particular case of a principal homomorphism is exhibited by a residuated mapping $f: S \to G$. Our next result shows how this arises in a simple way.

THEOREM 25.4. *Let S be an ordered semigroup and let $f: S \to G$ be a principal epimorphism of S onto an ordered group G. The following conditions are then equivalent:*

(1) *f is residuated;*

(2) *the greatest element ξ of $)S($ is residuated.*

Proof. Suppose that (2) holds and let y be any element of G. Since f is surjective, there exists $t \in S$ such that $f(t) = y^{-1}$. Thus

$$\begin{aligned} f(x) \leq y &\Leftrightarrow f(xt) = f(x)f(t) = f(x)y^{-1} \leq 1 \\ &\Leftrightarrow xt \leq \xi \\ &\Leftrightarrow x \leq \xi : t \end{aligned}$$

whence it follows that f is residuated with $f^{+}(y) = \xi : t$.

Conversely, suppose that f is residuated. Then, f being surjective,

$$xt \leq \xi \Leftrightarrow f(x)f(t) = f(xt) \leq f(\xi) = 1$$
$$\Leftrightarrow f(x) \leq [f(t)]^{-1}$$
$$\Leftrightarrow x \leq f^{+}\, [f(t)]^{-1},$$

whence $\xi : t$ exists and is $f^{+}\, [f(t)]^{-1}$.

Definition. We shall say that a Dubreil–Jacotin semigroup is *strong* if the element ξ is residuated.

Before giving a convenient characterization of strong Dubreil–Jacotin semigroups, we prove a preliminary result which will also be of use to us later.

THEOREM 25.5. *Let S be an ordered semigroup. If $t \in S$ is residuated then each right residual of t is residuated on the right and each left residual of t is residuated on the left.*

Proof. We give the proof for left residuals. Since t is residuated on the left, given any $x, y \in S$ the set of elements $z \in S$ satisfying $zy \leq t \cdot\!.\, x$ is not empty; for $(t \cdot\!.\, yx)\, yx \leq t$ and so $(t \cdot\!.\, yx)\, y \leq t \cdot\!.\, x$. Now for any z satisfying $zy \leq t \cdot\!.\, x$ we have $zyx \leq t$ and so $z \leq t \cdot\!.\, yx$. This then shows that $(t \cdot\!.\, x) \cdot\!.\, y$ exists and is $t \cdot\!.\, yx$.

THEOREM 25.6. *An ordered semigroup S is a strong Dubreil–Jacotin semigroup if and only if it satisfies the property*

$$(\exists \xi \in S) \quad \xi \textit{ is residuated and } \quad [\leftarrow, \xi] =)S(.$$

Proof. The condition is clearly necessary. Conversely, suppose that it is satisfied and let us show that $[\leftarrow, \xi]$ is strongly neat. For each $x \in S$ we have, ξ being residuated, $(\xi : x)\, x \in [\leftarrow, \xi]$ and so $[\leftarrow, \xi]$ is neat. Now, as observed in the proof of Theorem 25.2, $x \in E_{)S(}$ if and only if $\xi : x$ exists and is ξ. Thus by Theorem 25.5 we have

$$\xi = \xi : \xi \leq \xi : (\xi : x)\, x = (\xi \cdot\!.\, x) \cdot\!.\, (\xi \cdot\!.\, x)$$
$$\in \langle (\xi \cdot\!.\, x) \cdot\!.\, (\xi \cdot\!.\, x) \rangle \subseteq)S(= [\leftarrow, \xi]$$

and so $\xi : (\xi : x)\, x = \xi$ whence $(\xi : x)\, x \in E_{)S(}$. Hence $E_{)S(}$ is also neat. The result now follows from Theorem 25.2.

The situation so far may be summarized as follows:

THEOREM 25.7. *An ordered semigroup S is a strong Dubreil–Jacotin semigroup if and only if it admits an ordered group as an image under a residuated epimorphism. Such a group is necessarily unique up to isomorphism. If S is a strong Dubreil–Jacotin semigroup, then)S(has a maximum element ξ which is equiresidual and the unique residuated homomorphic group image of S is given by the closure equivalence A_ξ.*

THEOREM 25.8. *Let S be an ordered semigroup and let R be an equivalence relation on S such that S/R is an isotone homomorphic group image of S. The following conditions are then equivalent:*

(1) *S is a strong Dubreil–Jacotin semigroup and R is responsible for the unique residuated homomorphic group image of S;*
(2) *one of the classes modulo R admits a maximum element which is residuated.*

Proof. That (1) ⇒ (2) is immediate from Theorem 25.7. To show that (2) ⇒ (1), let one of the classes modulo R admit a maximum element t which is residuated. Let e be any element of the unit class modulo R. From $et \equiv t(R)$ we deduce that $et \leq t$ and hence that $e \leq t \cdot . \, t$. It follows that $et \leq (t \cdot . \, t)\, t \leq t$. Now the classes modulo R are convex (for R is regular); we therefore deduce that $et \equiv (t \cdot . \, t)\, t(R)$ and so, S/R being cancellative, $e \equiv t \cdot . \, t(R)$. In a similar way we can show that $e \equiv t \, . \cdot t(R)$. This then shows that the unit class modulo R admits a maximum element, namely the element $\xi = t \, . \cdot t = t \cdot . \, t$. The element ξ is also residuated by virtue of Theorem 25.5. Now let x be any element of S, let its class modulo R be $\mathscr{X}$ and let x^* be any element of $\mathscr{X}^{-1}$. From $xx^* \equiv \xi(R)$ we have $xx^* \leq \xi$ so $x^* \leq \xi \, . \cdot x$, giving $xx^* \leq x\, (\xi \, . \cdot x) \leq \xi$. From the convexity of the classes we then deduce that $xx^* \equiv x\, (\xi \, . \cdot x)\, (R)$. This then shows that if $x \in \mathscr{X}$ then $\xi \, . \cdot x \in \mathscr{X}^{-1}$. Similarly, we can show that $\xi \cdot . \, x \in \mathscr{X}^{-1}$. It follows from this that $x\, (\xi \, . \cdot x) \in \mathscr{X}\mathscr{X}^{-1} = \mathscr{E}$, the unit class, and that $\xi \cdot . \, x\, (\xi \, . \cdot x) \in \mathscr{E}^{-1} = \mathscr{E}$. Now let $p \in \langle x \cdot . \, x \rangle$. We have $px \leq x$

$\leq \xi \cdot . (\xi . \cdot x)$ whence it follows that

$$p \leq [\xi \cdot . (\xi . \cdot x)] \cdot . x = \xi \cdot . x (\xi . \cdot x) \in \mathscr{E}.$$

But ξ is the maximum element of $\mathscr{E}$. Thus $p \leq \xi$ and hence $\langle x \cdot . x\rangle \subseteq [\leftarrow, \xi]$. Since we have $\xi^2 \equiv \xi(R)$ and hence $\xi^2 \leq \xi$ and so $\xi \leq \xi \cdot . \xi$, we conclude that $)S(= [\leftarrow, \xi]$ and hence that S is a strong Dubreil–Jacotin semigroup. That R coincides with A_ξ is shown as follows. R being compatible with multiplication, we have

$$\begin{aligned} x \equiv y(R) &\Rightarrow x (\xi : x) \equiv \xi \equiv y (\xi : x) (R) \\ &\Rightarrow y (\xi : x) \leq \xi \\ &\Rightarrow \xi : x \leq \xi : y \end{aligned}$$

and, similarly, $\xi : y \leq \xi : x$. Thus $x \equiv y(R) \Rightarrow x \equiv y(A_\xi)$ and so $R \leq A_\xi$. Since we have seen that $x \in \mathscr{X} \Rightarrow \xi : x \in \mathscr{X}^{-1}$, we have $\xi : (\xi : x) \in \mathscr{X}$. It follows that $x \equiv y(A_\xi) \Rightarrow x \equiv \xi : (\xi : x) = \xi : (\xi : y) \equiv y(R)$ and so $A_\xi \leq R$.

EXAMPLE 25.2. Let $\mathbf{R}_-$ denote the set of real numbers which are ≤ 0, and consider the set $S = \mathbf{R}_- \times \mathbf{Z}$ ordered in the usual cartesian manner. Define a multiplication on S by

$$(p, i)(q, j) = (-1, i + j).$$

It is readily seen that S is an (abelian) ordered semigroup. In this ordered semigroup we have

$$\langle (r, k) : (p, i)\rangle = \begin{cases} \varnothing & \text{if } r < -1; \\ [\leftarrow, (0, k-1)] & \text{if } r \geq -1. \end{cases}$$

It follows that for each (r, k) we have $\langle (r, k) : (r, k)\rangle = \varnothing$ or $[\leftarrow, (0, 0)]$. Thus $)S(= [\leftarrow, (0, 0)]$. Moreover, $(0, 0)$ is residuated. By Theorem 25.6, S is a strong Dubreil–Jacotin semigroup. It is readily seen that $S/A_\xi \simeq \mathbf{Z}$.

THEOREM 25.9. *Let S be a residuated semigroup and let*

$$S^{\cdot\,\dot{}} = \{x . \cdot x;\ x \in S\}, \qquad S^{\dot{}\,\cdot} = \{x \cdot . x;\ x \in S\}.$$

Then $S^{\cdot\,\dot{}}$ and $S^{\dot{}\,\cdot}$ admit the same set of upper bounds.

Proof. Let $t \in S$ be an upper bound of $S^{.\,\cdot}$. Then we have

$$(\forall x, y \in S) \quad (y \,{}^{\cdot}.\, x) \,.{}^{\cdot}\, (y \,{}^{\cdot}.\, x) \leq t.$$

But, using Theorem 22.3(5), we have $(y \,{}^{\cdot}.\, x)(x \,{}^{\cdot}.\, x) \leq (y \,{}^{\cdot}.\, x)\, x \,{}^{\cdot}.\, x \leq y \,{}^{\cdot}.\, x$ and so

$$(\forall x, y \in S) \quad x \,{}^{\cdot}.\, x \leq (y \,{}^{\cdot}.\, x) \,.{}^{\cdot}\, (y \,{}^{\cdot}.\, x).$$

It therefore follows that t is also an upper bound for $S^{\cdot\,.}$. In a similar way we can establish the converse.

Definition. We shall say that a residuated semigroup S admits a *bimaximum element* ξ if and only if $\xi = \max S^{.\,\cdot} = \max S^{\cdot\,.}$.

THEOREM 25.10. *In a residuated semigroup S the following conditions are equivalent:*

(1) *S is a (strong) Dubreil–Jacotin semigroup;*
(2) *S admits a bimaximum element;*
(3) $\{x \in S;\, x^2 \leq x\}$ *admits a maximum element.*

Moreover, if S has a neutral element then each of the above conditions is equivalent to

(4) *S admits a greatest idempotent.*

Proof. Since residuals exist, we have

$$)S(= \bigcup\, [\leftarrow, x \,.{}^{\cdot}\, x] \cup \bigcup\, [\leftarrow, x \,{}^{\cdot}.\, x]. \qquad (*)$$

If (1) holds then $)S(= [\leftarrow, \xi]$ and so $(\forall x \in S)\; x \,.{}^{\cdot}\, x \leq \xi$ and $x \,{}^{\cdot}.\, x \leq \xi$ with $\xi = \xi \,{}^{\cdot}.\, \xi = \xi \,.{}^{\cdot}\, \xi$. It follows that ξ is the bimaximum element of S. Conversely, it is clear from (*) that if a bimaximum element ξ exists then $)S(= [\leftarrow, \xi]$ and (1) follows by Theorem 25.6.

Now let $J = \{x \in S;\, x^2 \leq x\}$. For each $x \in S$ we have

$$(x \,{}^{\cdot}.\, x)(x \,{}^{\cdot}.\, x) \leq (x \,{}^{\cdot}.\, x)\, x \,{}^{\cdot}.\, x \leq x \,{}^{\cdot}.\, x$$

and so $x \,{}^{\cdot}.\, x \in J$. Thus $S^{\cdot\,.} \subseteq J$ and likewise $S^{.\,\cdot} \subseteq J$. If now J has a maximum element e then from $e^2 \leq e$ we have $e \leq e \,{}^{\cdot}.\, e \in S^{\cdot\,.} \subseteq J$ whence $e = e \,{}^{\cdot}.\, e$ and likewise $e = e \,.{}^{\cdot}\, e$. It follows from this that e is the bimaximum element of S. Conversely, if ξ is the bimaximum element, then $\xi \in S^{.\cdot} \cap S^{\cdot .} \subseteq J$; and for every $x \in J$ we have $x \leq x \cdot . \, x \leq \max S^{\cdot .} = \xi$. Thus ξ is the maximum element of J.

Finally, suppose that S has a neutral element 1. From $1x \leq x$ we deduce $1 \leq x \cdot . \, x$ and hence that $x \cdot . \, x \leq (x \cdot . \, x)^2$. But we have seen above that $x \cdot . \, x \in J$. Hence $x \cdot . \, x$ is idempotent. Denoting the set of idempotents in S by I, we thus have $S^{\cdot .} \subseteq I$ and likewise $S^{.\cdot} \subseteq I$. Now if S admits a greatest idempotent e we have $e \leq e \cdot . \, e$ whence $e = e \cdot . \, e$ and likewise $e = e \, . \cdot e$. It follows that e is the bimaximum element of S. Conversely, if ξ is the bimaximum element of S, then $\xi \in S^{\cdot .} \cap S^{.\cdot} \subseteq I$ and so ξ is idempotent. Since ξ is the greatest element of J and since $I \subseteq J$, it follows that ξ is also the greatest element of I.

For the remainder of this section we shall restrict our attention to residuated Dubreil–Jacotin semigroups. As we have seen, in such a semigroup, the unique residuated homomorphic group image is given by the equivalence of type A associated with the (equiresidual) bimaximum element ξ. This equivalence is thus cancellative with respect to multiplication in the sense that

$$xa \equiv ya \, (A_\xi) \Rightarrow x \equiv y(A_\xi).$$

For the purpose of obtaining useful alternative characterizations of residuated Dubreil–Jacotin semigroups, we shall now investigate cancellative closure equivalences on a residuated semigroup. We shall make use of the following notation. The set of closure equivalences on S which are compatible on the right [resp. left] with multiplication will be denoted by $\Omega.$ [resp. $.\Omega$] and the set of closure equivalences on S which are cancellative on the right [resp. left] with multiplication will be denoted by $\chi.$ [resp. $.\chi$].

THEOREM 25.11. *Let S be a residuated semigroup. If R is a closure equivalence on S with associated closure mapping f then the following conditions are equivalent:*

(1) $R \in .\chi$ *[resp.* $R \in \chi.$*]*;
(2) $(\forall a, x \in S) \quad a \equiv f(xa) \, . \cdot x(R)$ *[resp.* $a \equiv f(ax) \cdot . \, x(R)$*]*;
(3) $f(ca) \leq f(cb) \Rightarrow f(a) \leq f(b)$ *[resp.* $f(ac) \leq f(bc) \Rightarrow f(a) \leq f(b)$*]*.

Proof. Suppose that (1) holds. From $xa \leq f(xa)$ we deduce that $a \leq f(xa) \, . \cdot x$ and so $xa \leq x[f(xa) \, . \cdot x] \leq f(xa)$. The classes modulo R

being convex, it follows that $xa \equiv x[f(xa) \,.\!^{\cdot}\, x]\,(R)$. Applying (1), we then obtain (2). Conversely, suppose that (2) holds and let $xa \equiv xb\,(R)$. Then $f(xa) = f(xb)$ and so $a \equiv f(xa) \,.\!^{\cdot}\, x = f(xb) \,.\!^{\cdot}\, x \equiv b(R)$, showing that (1) holds.

To show that (2) ⇒ (3), we observe that from $f(ca) \leq f(cb)$ we have, using (2), $f(a) = f[f(ca) \,.\!^{\cdot}\, c] \leq f[f(cb) \,.\!^{\cdot}\, c] = f(b)$. Conversely, since $x[f(xa) \,.\!^{\cdot}\, x] \leq f(xa)$ we have $f\{x[f(xa) \,.\!^{\cdot}\, x]\} \leq f[f(xa)] = f(xa)$ so that, by (3), $f[f(xa) \,.\!^{\cdot}\, x] \leq f(a)$. But $a \leq f(xa) \,.\!^{\cdot}\, x$ and so $f(a) \leq f[f(xa) \,.\!^{\cdot}\, x]$. It follows that $f(a) = f[f(xa) \,.\!^{\cdot}\, x]$ and this establishes (2).

COROLLARY. $R \in .\chi \Rightarrow (\forall x \in S) \quad F_x \leq R$.

Proof. If $R \in .\chi$ then by the above result we have

$$(\forall a, x \in S) \quad a \equiv f(xa) \,.\!^{\cdot}\, x(R)$$

and the convexity of the classes modulo R gives

$$(\forall a, x \in S) \quad a \equiv xa \,.\!^{\cdot}\, x(R),$$

which may be expressed in the form $f = f \circ \varphi_x$, where φ_x is the closure mapping associated with F_x. It follows by Theorem 4.4 that $F_x \leq R$.

THEOREM 25.12. *If S is a residuated semigroup and R is a closure equivalence on S with associated closure mapping f, the following conditions are equivalent:*

(1) $R \in .\Omega \cap .\chi$ [*resp.* $R \in \Omega. \cap \chi.$];

(2) $(\forall a, x \in S) \quad f(a) = f(xa) \,.\!^{\cdot}\, x$ [*resp.* $f(a) = f(ax) \,^{\cdot}\!.\, x$].

Proof. Suppose that (1) holds. Then from $R \in .\chi$ we deduce, using Theorem 25.11, that

$$(\forall a, x \in S) \quad a \equiv f(xa) \,.\!^{\cdot}\, x(R).$$

But from $R \in .\Omega$ we deduce, using Theorem 22.10, that $f(xa) \,.\!^{\cdot}\, x$ belongs to the closure subset associated with R, so that

$$(\forall a, x \in S) \quad f(a) = f[f(xa) \,.\!^{\cdot}\, x] = f(xa) \,.\!^{\cdot}\, x.$$

Conversely, suppose that (2) holds. The equality $f(a) = f(xa) \,.\!^{\cdot}\, x$ implies, on the one hand, that $xf(a) \leq f(xa)$, so that, by Theorem 22.9, $R \in .\Omega$;

and on the other it implies that $a \equiv f(xa) \,.^{\cdot}\, x(R)$ so that, by Theorem 25.11, we also have $R \in .\chi$.

THEOREM 25.13. *If S is a residuated semigroup and x is an arbitrary element of S, the following conditions are equivalent:*

(1) $A_x \in .\Omega \cap \Omega. \cap .\chi$ [*resp.* ${}_xA \in .\Omega \cap \Omega. \cap \chi.$];
(2) $(\forall t \in S)\quad A_x = A_{x.^{\cdot}t}$ [*resp.* ${}_xA = {}_{x^{\cdot}.t}A$].

Proof. Note that by Theorem 22.12 we have $A_x \in \Omega.$ for each $x \in S$. Applying Theorem 25.12, we have $A_x \in .\Omega \cap .\chi$ if and only if

$$(\forall a, t \in S)\quad x \,^{\cdot}.\, (x \,.^{\cdot}\, a) = [x \,^{\cdot}.\, (x \,.^{\cdot}\, ta)] \,.^{\cdot}\, t.$$

Now the right-hand side of the above is, by Theorem 22.3, none other than

$$(x \,.^{\cdot}\, t) \,^{\cdot}.\, [(x \,.^{\cdot}\, t) \,.^{\cdot}\, a].$$

Fixing momentarily x, t the equality

$$(\forall a \in S)\quad x \,^{\cdot}.\, (x \,.^{\cdot}\, a) = (x \,.^{\cdot}\, t) \,^{\cdot}.\, [(x \,.^{\cdot}\, t) \,.^{\cdot}\, a]$$

is clearly equivalent to the statement $A_x = A_{x.^{\cdot}t}$. Hence (1) and (2) are equivalent.

THEOREM 25.14. *A residuated semigroup S is a Dubreil–Jacotin semigroup if and only if* $\chi. \cup .\chi \neq \varnothing$.

Proof. If S is a Dubreil–Jacotin semigroup, then clearly $A_\xi \in .\chi$. Conversely, suppose that $R \in .\chi$. Then, just as in the proof of the corollary to Theorem 25.11, we have

$$(\forall a, x \in S)\qquad a \equiv xa \,.^{\cdot}\, x(R),$$

so that

$$(\forall b, x \in S)\quad f(b) \equiv xf(b) \,.^{\cdot}\, x(R).$$

But $f(b)$ is maximum in its class modulo R and $f(b) \leq xf(b) \,.^{\cdot}\, x$. It follows that

$$(\forall b, x \in S)\quad f(b) = xf(b) \,.^{\cdot}\, x,$$

and so

$$\begin{aligned}(\forall b, x \in S)\quad f(b) \,^{\cdot}.\, f(b) &= [xf(b) \,.^{\cdot}\, x] \,^{\cdot}.\, f(b)\\ &= [xf(b) \,^{\cdot}.\, f(b)] \,.^{\cdot}\, x\\ &\geq x \,.^{\cdot}\, x.\end{aligned}$$

Thus $S^{\cdot\cdot}$ (and likewise $S^{\cdot}\cdot$) is bounded above. Now from the proof of Theorem 25.9,

$$[f(b) \cdot . f(b)] .\cdot [f(b) \cdot . f(b)] \geq f(b) \cdot . f(b),$$

and so a bimaximum element exists, namely $\xi = [f(b) \cdot . f(b)] .\cdot [f(b) \cdot . f(b)]$. It follows by Theorem 25.10 that S is a Dubreil–Jacotin semigroup.

Definition. If S is a residuated semigroup we say that $x \in S$ is *right A-nomaloid* [resp. *left A-nomaloid*] if and only if S/A_x [resp. $S/{}_xA$] is a group. We say that x is *A-nomaloid* if it is A-nomaloid on both the right and the left. These notions coincide when x is *A-symmetric* in the sense that $A_x = {}_xA$ and, more particularly, when x is equiresidual or S is abelian.

THEOREM 25.15. *If S is a residuated semigroup then the following conditions concerning $x \in S$ are equivalent:*

(1) *x is A-nomaloid on the right* [*resp. left*];
(2) *S is a Dubreil–Jacotin semigroup and $A_x = A_\xi$* [*resp.* ${}_xA = {}_\xi A$];
(3) $(\forall t \in S) \quad A_x = A_{x.\cdot t} = A_{x\cdot .t}$ [*resp.* ${}_xA = {}_{x.\cdot t}A = {}_{x\cdot .t}A$].

Proof. The equivalence of (1) and (2) follows immediately from the result of Theorem 25.8. Suppose now that (2) holds. From $A_x = A_\xi$ we deduce that every left residual of x is a residual of ξ and conversely, so that $(\forall t \in S)(\exists p \in S)\ x \cdot . t = \xi : p$. Now by Theorem 25.13 we have $A_{\xi:p} = A_\xi$ and by the hypothesis $A_\xi = A_x$. It follows that $(\forall t \in S)\ A_{x\cdot .t} = A_x$. Moreover, since $A_x = A_\xi$ we have $A_x \in .\Omega \cap \Omega. \cap .\chi$ and so, again by Theorem 25.13, $(\forall t \in S)\ A_x = A_{x.\cdot t}$. This then shows that (2) $\Rightarrow$ (3). Conversely, if (3) holds, then by Theorems 25.13 and 25.14 it follows that S is a Dubreil–Jacotin semigroup and therefore admits a bimaximum element ξ. Since by hypothesis $A_{x\cdot .\xi} = A_x \in .\Omega \cap \Omega. \cap .\chi$, we have, by Theorem 25.13, $A_{x\cdot .\xi} = A_{(x\cdot .\xi).\cdot(x\cdot .\xi)}$. Now $(x \cdot . \xi) .\cdot (x \cdot . \xi) = [x .\cdot (x \cdot . \xi)] \cdot . \xi \geq \xi \cdot . \xi = \xi$ and so, ξ being the bimaximum element, we deduce that $(x \cdot . \xi) .\cdot (x \cdot . \xi) = \xi$. Combining the above observations, we obtain $A_x = A_\xi$. This then establishes (2) and completes the proof.

Definition. If S is a residuated semigroup then we shall say that $x \in S$

is *right* [resp. *left*] *A-nomal* if it is right [resp. left] A-nomaloid and is the greatest element in its class modulo A_x [resp. ${}_xA$].

THEOREM 25.16. *In a residuated semigroup S the following conditions are equivalent:*

(1) *$x \in S$ is right A-nomal;*
(2) *$x \in S$ is left A-nomal.*

Proof. We show first that the condition (2) is equivalent to the conditions

(a) $(\exists k \in S) \quad x = x \,.^{\cdot}\, xk;$

(b) $(\forall t \in S) \quad x \,.^{\cdot}\, x = (x \,.^{\cdot}\, t) \,{}^{\cdot}.\, (x \,.^{\cdot}\, t).$

In fact, suppose that (a) and (b) hold. From (b) we deduce that

$$(\forall t \in S) \quad x \,.^{\cdot}\, x = [x \,{}^{\cdot}.\, (x \,.^{\cdot}\, t)] \,.^{\cdot}\, t \geq t \,.^{\cdot}\, t$$

and so a bimaximum element exists, namely $\xi = x \,.^{\cdot}\, x$. Now by Theorem 22.10 we have ${}_xA \leq {}_{x.^{\cdot}x}A$. It therefore follows from (a) that ${}_xA = {}_{x.^{\cdot}x}A$; for (a) implies that every right residual of x (which is maximum in its class modulo ${}_xA$) is a right residual of $x \,.^{\cdot}\, x$ and so is maximum in its class modulo ${}_{x.^{\cdot}x}A$. It follows from the above observations that ${}_xA = {}_\xi A$ and so, by Theorem 25.15, x is A-nomaloid on the left. Using (a) again, we see that x is A-nomal on the left. Conversely, suppose that x is A-nomal on the left. Then in the first place we have

$$(\forall t \in S) \quad {}_xA = {}_{x.^{\cdot}t}A = {}_{x^{\cdot}.t}A.$$

Since x is maximum in its class modulo ${}_xA$ it is also maximum in its class modulo ${}_{x.^{\cdot}x}A$. Consequently there exists $k \in S$ such that $x = (x \,.^{\cdot}\, x) \,.^{\cdot}\, k = x \,.^{\cdot}\, xk$, so that (a) holds. Now x is also maximum in its class modulo every ${}_{x^{\cdot}.t}A$ and so, for each $t \in S$,

$$\begin{aligned} x \,.^{\cdot}\, x &= \{(x \,{}^{\cdot}.\, t) \,.^{\cdot}\, [(x \,{}^{\cdot}.\, t) \,{}^{\cdot}.\, x]\} \,.^{\cdot}\, x \\ &= (x \,{}^{\cdot}.\, t) \,.^{\cdot}\, [(x \,{}^{\cdot}.\, t) \,{}^{\cdot}.\, x]\, x \\ &\geq (x \,{}^{\cdot}.\, t) \,.^{\cdot}\, (x \,{}^{\cdot}.\, t) \\ &= [x \,.^{\cdot}\, (x \,{}^{\cdot}.\, t)] \,{}^{\cdot}.\, t \\ &\geq t \,{}^{\cdot}.\, t. \end{aligned}$$

It follows that $x \mathbin{.\!^{\cdot}} x$ is an upper bound for $S^{\cdot}$ and indeed that $x \mathbin{.\!^{\cdot}} x = \xi$. Using (a) and the fact that ξ is equiresidual, we then have

$$\begin{aligned}(\forall t \in S) \quad (x \mathbin{.\!^{\cdot}} t) \mathbin{^{\cdot}\!.} (x \mathbin{.\!^{\cdot}} t) &= (\xi : kt) \mathbin{^{\cdot}\!.} (\xi : kt)\\ &= \xi \mathbin{^{\cdot}\!.} (\xi \mathbin{^{\cdot}\!.} kt)\, kt\\ &\geq \xi \mathbin{^{\cdot}\!.} \xi\\ &= \xi,\end{aligned}$$

from which it follows that

$$(\forall t \in S) \quad (x \mathbin{.\!^{\cdot}} t) \mathbin{^{\cdot}\!.} (x \mathbin{.\!^{\cdot}} t) = \xi = x \mathbin{.\!^{\cdot}} x,$$

which is (b).

This being the case, we see that if x is A-nomal on the left then $x \mathbin{.\!^{\cdot}} x = \xi$ and $(\exists k \in S)\ x = \xi : k$. Consequently

$$x \mathbin{^{\cdot}\!.} x = (\xi : k) \mathbin{^{\cdot}\!.} (\xi : k) = \xi \mathbin{^{\cdot}\!.} (\xi \mathbin{^{\cdot}\!.} k)\, k \geq \xi \mathbin{^{\cdot}\!.} \xi = \xi,$$

so that we also have $x \mathbin{^{\cdot}\!.} x = \xi$. Thus, for each $t \in S$,

$$\begin{aligned}(x \mathbin{^{\cdot}\!.} t) \mathbin{.\!^{\cdot}} (x \mathbin{^{\cdot}\!.} t) &= [(\xi : k) \mathbin{^{\cdot}\!.} t] \mathbin{.\!^{\cdot}} [(\xi : k) \mathbin{^{\cdot}\!.} t]\\ &= (\xi : tk) \mathbin{.\!^{\cdot}} (\xi : tk)\\ &= \xi \mathbin{.\!^{\cdot}} tk\, (\xi \mathbin{.\!^{\cdot}} tk)\\ &\geq \xi \mathbin{.\!^{\cdot}} \xi\\ &= \xi,\end{aligned}$$

whence

$$(\forall t \in S) \quad (x \mathbin{^{\cdot}\!.} t) \mathbin{.\!^{\cdot}} (x \mathbin{^{\cdot}\!.} t) = \xi = x \mathbin{^{\cdot}\!.} x.$$

Since this is the condition which is dual to (b), we conclude that x is also A-nomal on the right. A similar proof shows that (1) $\Rightarrow$ (2).

Remark. Because of the previous result, we shall use the term *A-nomal* to describe an element which is A-nomal on the left or on the right.

Definition. We shall say that a semigroup is *A-nomal* if it is residuated and admits an A-nomal element. It is clear from Theorem 25.15 that the notions of A-nomal semigroup and residuated Dubreil–Jacotin semigroup coincide. For the purpose of later classifications of residuated semigroups, we shall use the term A-nomal henceforth.

THEOREM 25.17. *Let S be an A-nomal semigroup. Then $x \in S$ is A-nomal if and only if it is a residual of the bimaximum element ξ. Moreover, the set of A-nomal elements of S forms a group with respect to the law of composition $(\xi : x) \circ (\xi : y) = \xi : yx$. This group is isomorphic to S/A_ξ and an A-nomal element is equiresidual if and only if its class modulo A_ξ belongs to the centre of S/A_ξ.*

Proof. It is clear from the proof of the previous result that if $x \in S$ is A-nomal then x is a residual of ξ. Conversely, if $x = \xi : y$ then we have $A_x = A_{\xi:y} = A_\xi$ and so, by Theorem 25.15, x is A-nomaloid on the right. Being a residual of ξ, x is maximum in its class modulo A_ξ, hence maximum in its class modulo A_x and consequently A-nomal.

Now since A_ξ is compatible with multiplication we have no trouble in verifying that the assignment $(\xi : x) \circ (\xi : y) = \xi : yx$ yields a law of composition on the set G° of A-nomal elements. Consider now the mapping $f: G^\circ \to S/A_\xi$ described by setting $f(\xi : x) = (x/A_\xi)^{-1}$. This mapping is clearly a bijection. Now S/A_ξ is ordered to the prescription

$$\begin{aligned} x/A_\xi \leq y/A_\xi &\Leftrightarrow)S(: \{y\} \subseteq)S(: \{x\} \\ &\Leftrightarrow \langle \xi : y \rangle \subseteq \langle \xi : x \rangle \\ &\Leftrightarrow \xi : y \leq \xi : x, \end{aligned}$$

whence it follows that f is isotone. Moreover,

$$\begin{aligned} f[(\xi : x) \circ (\xi : y)] = f(\xi : yx) &= (yx/A_\xi)^{-1} = (x/A_\xi)^{-1} (y/A_\xi)^{-1} \\ &= f(\xi : x) f(\xi : y) \end{aligned}$$

and so f is also a homomorphism. It follows that f is an isomorphism and so G° is a group with neutral element ξ.

Finally, the A-nomal element $\xi : x$ is equiresidual if and only if

$$(\forall y \in S) \quad (\xi : x) \,.\!^{\cdot}\, y = (\xi : x) \,^{\cdot}\!.\, y.$$

Now using the fact that ξ is equiresidual, the left hand side of the above is $\xi \mathbin{.\cdot} xy$ and the right-hand side is $\xi \mathbin{\cdot.} xy$. The condition that $\xi : x$ be equiresidual is therefore

$$(\forall y \in S) \quad (\xi : x) \circ (\xi : y) = (\xi : y) \circ (\xi : x),$$

in other words that $\xi : x$ belong to the centre of G°. By virtue of the above isomorphism, this is equivalent to saying that $(x/A_\xi)^{-1}$ belongs to the centre of S/A_ξ. The proof is completed by remarking that the class of $\xi : x$ modulo A_ξ is none other than $(x/A_\xi)^{-1}$, a point which was observed in the proof of Theorem 25.8.

EXAMPLE 25.3. Consider the residuated semigroup as described in Exercise 23.5. The unit class modulo Z of this semigroup is a residuated subsemigroup and is given by

$$\begin{cases} E = \{(x, y);\ x, y \text{ integers with } x \leq 0\}; \\ (x, y) \leq (x', y') \Leftrightarrow x \leq x',\ y \leq y', \end{cases}$$

the multiplication being given by

$$(x, y)(u, v) = (\min\{x, u\},\ y + v^*),$$

where $v^* = kN \leq v < (k+1)N$ with N a fixed integer >1. The residuals are given by the formulae

$$\begin{cases} (c, d) \mathbin{\cdot.} (a, b) = \begin{cases} (0, d - b^*) & \text{if } a \leq c; \\ (c, d - b^*) & \text{if } a > c, \end{cases} \\[2ex] (c, d) \mathbin{.\cdot} (a, b) = \begin{cases} (0, (d - b)^* + N - 1) & \text{if } a \leq c; \\ (c, (d - b)^* + N - 1) & \text{if } a > c. \end{cases} \end{cases}$$

In this residuated semigroup we have

$$(c, d) \mathbin{\cdot.} (c, d) = (0, d - d^*), \quad (c, d) \mathbin{.\cdot} (c, d) = (0, N - 1)$$

and so S has a bimaximum element, namely $(0, N-1)$. By Theorem 25.17 the A-nomal elements are those of the form $(0, N-1) : (a, b)$

$= (0, N - 1 - b^*)$. The classes modulo A_ξ with $N = 4$ for example are as follows:

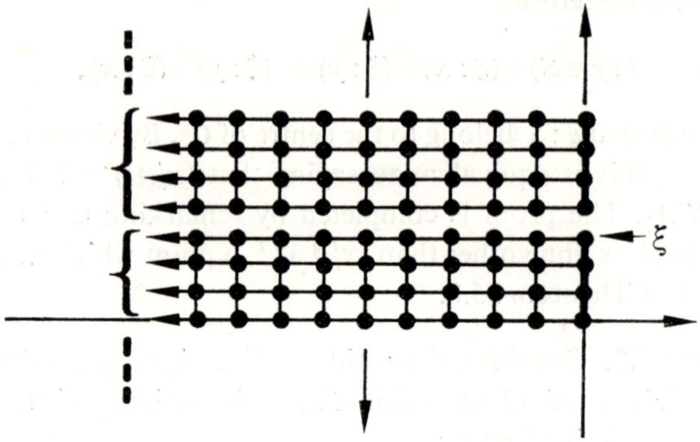

EXAMPLE 25.4. Let I be a commutative integral domain and let K be its field of fractions (so that we can consider the elements of K as of the form a/b where $a, b \in I$ with $b \neq 0$). By a *fractionary ideal* of I we mean any I-submodule $\mathbf{a}$ of the I-module K such that the elements of $\mathbf{a}$ admit a common denominator $d \neq 0$ in I; more precisely, if $\mathbf{a}$ has the property $(\exists d \in I \setminus \{0\})\ d\mathbf{a} \subseteq I$. Thus if $\mathbf{a}$ is a fractionary ideal we have $\mathbf{a} = (1/d)\,\mathbf{b}$ where $\mathbf{b}$ is an ordinary ideal of I. For example, every ordinary ideal of I is a fractionary ideal (take $d = 1$). Every finitely generated I-submodule $\mathbf{a}$ of K is also a fractionary ideal; for if $\{a_1, \ldots, a_n\}$ is a system of generators of $\mathbf{a}$ then each a_i can be written in the form $a_i = b_i/d_i$, where $b_i, d_i \in I$ with $d_i \neq 0$, and if we define $d = d_1 d_2 \ldots d_n$ then clearly $d \neq 0$ and $\mathbf{a} \subseteq (1/d)\,I$. In particular, if $\mathbf{a}$ has but one generator, say $x = a/d\,(d \neq 0)$, then Ix is a fractionary ideal called the *principal fractionary ideal generated by x*. It is clear that the set of all fractionary ideals of I, ordered by set inclusion, forms a lattice-ordered semigroup under the laws

$$(\mathbf{a}, \mathbf{b}) \to \mathbf{a} + \mathbf{b} \text{ [union]}, \quad (\mathbf{a}, \mathbf{b}) \to \mathbf{a} \cap \mathbf{b}, \quad (\mathbf{a}, \mathbf{b}) \to \mathbf{ab}.$$

In particular the set $PF^*(I)$ of all non-zero principal fractionary ideals forms an ordered group (the neutral element being $I1 = I$ and the inverse of Ix being Ix^{-1}). This ordered group is dually isomorphic to the quotient group K^*/U where $K^* = K\setminus\{0\}$ and U is the group of invertible elements of I. [To be more explicit, if we let $I^* = I\setminus\{0\}$ and write $x|y \Leftrightarrow (\exists p \in I^*)\ xp = y$ then the relation $\equiv$ defined by

$$x \equiv y \Leftrightarrow x|y \text{ and } y|x$$

is an equivalence relation which is none other than the relation $xy^{-1} \in U$. We can thus order K^*/U by setting

$$x/U \leq y/U \Leftrightarrow x|y;$$

and since $x|y \Leftrightarrow Ix \supseteq Iy$, the dual isomorphism follows.] Now let $F^*(I)$ denote the set of non-zero fractionary ideals of I. We note that $F^*(I)$ is a residuated semigroup. [To see this, it is sufficient to show that if $\mathbf{a}, \mathbf{b} \in F^*(I)$ then $\mathbf{a} : \mathbf{b} = \{x \in K;\ x\mathbf{b} \subseteq \mathbf{a}\}$ is also an element of $F^*(I)$. For this purpose, let $d \neq 0$ be such that $\mathbf{a} \subseteq (1/d)\,I$ and let $b \in \mathbf{b}\setminus\{0\}$; then $db\,(\mathbf{a} : \mathbf{b}) \subseteq d\mathbf{a} \subseteq I$. Moreover, if $a \in \mathbf{a}\setminus\{0\}$ and $d'\mathbf{b} \subseteq I$ then $ad'\mathbf{b} \subseteq \mathbf{a}$ so that $\mathbf{a} : \mathbf{b} \neq \emptyset$.] Since for each $\mathbf{a} \in F^*(I)$ there exists $d \neq 0$ such that $\mathbf{a} \subseteq Id^{-1}$, the set of principal fractionary ideals which contain $\mathbf{a}$ is not empty. Define a relation R on $F^*(I)$ by setting

$$\mathbf{a} \equiv \mathbf{b}(R) \Leftrightarrow \Pr(\mathbf{a}) = \Pr(\mathbf{b})$$

where $\Pr(\mathbf{a})$ denotes the set of principal fractionary ideals of I which contain $\mathbf{a}$. Since $F^*(I)$ is residuated, we observe that

$$Ix \in \Pr(\mathbf{a}) \Leftrightarrow x^{-1}\mathbf{a} \subseteq I \Leftrightarrow x^{-1} \in I : \mathbf{a}$$

and so it follows that the relation R defined above is none other than $R = A_I$. We say that $a \in F^*(I)$ is a *divisorial ideal* if and only if $a = a^\circ$ where by a° we mean the intersection of all the principal fractionary ideals which contain $\mathbf{a}$. It is clear that for each $\mathbf{a} \in F^*(I)$ we have $\mathbf{a} \subseteq \mathbf{a}^\circ$ and $\mathbf{a} \equiv \mathbf{a}^\circ(R)$. It follows that the divisorial ideals are none other than the greatest elements in the classes modulo A_I. Let us now show that the following conditions are equivalent:

(1) $F^*(I)/A_I$ is a group (whence, by Theorem 25.8, $F^*(I)$ is an A-nomal semigroup in which the A-nomal elements are the divisorial ideals);

(2) I is *completely integrally closed* in the sense that if $x \in K$ is such that all the powers x^n $(n \geq 0)$ are contained in a finitely generated I-submodule of K then $x \in I$.

Suppose first that $F^*(I)/A_I$ is a group. Let $s \in K$ be such that $I[x]$ is contained in a finitely generated I-submodule M of K. Since M is an element of $F^*(I)$, so also is $I[x]$. Let $I[x] = \mathbf{a}$; then we have $x\mathbf{a} \subseteq \mathbf{a}$ and $Ix\mathbf{a} \subseteq \mathbf{a}$ so that, $F^*(I)/A_I$ being a group with neutral element $I1/A_I = I/A_I$, we have $Ix/A_I \leq I/A_I$. It follows that

$$Ix = (Ix)^\circ \subseteq I^\circ = (I1)^\circ = I1 = I$$

and hence that $x = 1x \in I$. We have thus shown that if $F^*(I)/A_I$ is a group, then I is completely integrally closed. Conversely, suppose that I satisfies (2). To show that $F^*(I)/A_I$ is a group, it is sufficient to establish the following identity in the case where $\mathbf{a}$ is divisorial:

$$\mathbf{a}/A_I \cdot (I : \mathbf{a})/A_I = I/A_I;$$

and since $\mathbf{a}\,(I : \mathbf{a}) \subseteq I$ it is sufficient, in view of the fact that $A_I = R$, to show that every principal fractionary ideal which contains $\mathbf{a}\,(I : \mathbf{a})$ also contains I. Suppose then that $\mathbf{a}\,(I : \mathbf{a}) \subseteq Ix^{-1}$ and let $y \in K^*$ be such that $\mathbf{a} \subseteq Iy$. Then $y^{-1}\mathbf{a} \subseteq (I : \mathbf{a})\,\mathbf{a} \subseteq Ix^{-1}$ and so $x\mathbf{a} \subseteq Iy$. Thus every principal fractionary ideal which contains $\mathbf{a}$ also contains $x\mathbf{a}$. Since, by hypothesis, $\mathbf{a}$ is divisorial, we deduce that $x\mathbf{a} \subseteq \mathbf{a}$. Consequently, for each positive integer n, we have $x^n\mathbf{a} \subseteq \mathbf{a}$. Now let x_1, x_2 be elements of K^* such that $x_1 \in \mathbf{a} \subseteq Ix_2$. Then for each positive integer n we have $x^n x_1 \in Ix_2$ which gives $x^n \in Ix_2x_1^{-1}$. Applying the standing hypothesis, we deduce that $x \in I$ so that $Ix \subseteq I$ and $I \subseteq Ix^{-1}$. This then establishes the required property.

EXAMPLE 25.5. Let S be a semigroup and define a multiplication on $\mathbf{P}(S)$ by $XY = \{xy;\, x \in X, y \in Y\}$, $X\emptyset = \emptyset = \emptyset X$. Ordering $\mathbf{P}(S)$ by set inclusion, we obtain an ordered semigroup which is residuated; for example, we have $X \,.\!\cdot\, Y = \{z \in S;\, (\forall y \in Y)\; zy \in X\}$, though this may be $\emptyset$. It is clear that $\mathbf{P}(S)$ is an A-nomal semigroup with bimaximum element $\xi = S$. In this case $\mathbf{P}(S)/A_\xi$ is trivial in the sense that it consists of a single element. We shall therefore consider a residuated subsemigroup of $\mathbf{P}(S)$ which contains neither S nor $\emptyset$. Given non-empty $X, D \in \mathbf{P}(S)$ we shall say that X is

$$D\text{-}transportable \text{ if } \quad D \,.^{\cdot}\, X \neq \emptyset \quad \text{and} \quad D^{\cdot}.\, X \neq \emptyset;$$

and that X is

$$D\text{-}neat \text{ if } \quad X \,.^{\cdot}\, D \neq \emptyset, \quad X^{\cdot}.\, D \neq \emptyset \quad \text{and} \quad (X \,.^{\cdot}\, D)^{\cdot}.\, D \neq \emptyset.$$

Finally, we shall say that X is a *D-complex* if it is non-empty and both D-transportable and D-neat.

We begin by observing that:

If D is a subsemigroup of S which is equiresidual in $\mathbf{P}(S)$ then for any D-transportable subset X of $\mathbf{P}(S)$ the subsets XD, DX and DXD are D-complexes.

In fact, from $D^2 \subseteq D$ we have $D \subseteq D : D$ and so

(1) $\emptyset \subset D^{\cdot}.\, X \subseteq (D : D)^{\cdot}.\, X = D : DX;$
(2) $\emptyset \subset (X \,.^{\cdot}\, D) D \subseteq XD \,.^{\cdot}\, D;$
(3) $\emptyset \subset X \subseteq XD^{\cdot}.\, D;$
(4) $\emptyset \subset X \,.^{\cdot}\, D \subseteq (X \,.^{\cdot}\, D) D^{\cdot}.\, D \subseteq (XD \,.^{\cdot}\, D)^{\cdot}.\, D,$

which shows that XD is a D-complex; similarly, so also are DX and DXD.

Let us now show that:

If D is a subsemigroup of S which is equiresidual in $\mathbf{P}(S)$ and such that $D : S = \emptyset$, then the set $C(D)$ of D-complexes is a residuated subsemigroup of $\mathbf{P}(S)$ in which residuals coincide with the corresponding residuals in $\mathbf{P}(S)$. Moreover, $\emptyset \notin C(D)$ and $S \notin C(D)$.

It is clear that neither $\emptyset$ nor S can be D-complexes. Moreover, $C(D) \neq \emptyset$; for $D^2 \subseteq D$ gives $D \subseteq D : D$ and hence $D \subseteq (D : D) : D$ so that $D \in C(D)$. Now let $X, Y \in C(D)$; then

(1) $\emptyset \subset (D : Y)(D : X) \subseteq (D : Y)[(D : D)^{\cdot}.\, X] = (D : Y)[(D : X) \,.^{\cdot}\, D]$
$\subseteq D\,[(D : X) \,.^{\cdot}\, D] \,.^{\cdot}\, Y \subseteq (D : X) \,.^{\cdot}\, Y = D : XY;$
(2) $\emptyset \subset X(Y^{\cdot}.\, D) \subseteq XY^{\cdot}.\, D;$
(3) $\emptyset \subset (X \,.^{\cdot}\, D)\, Y \subseteq XY \,.^{\cdot} D;$
(4) $\emptyset \subset (X \,.^{\cdot}\, D)\,(Y^{\cdot}.\, D) \subseteq X(Y^{\cdot}.\, D) \,.^{\cdot}\, D \subseteq (XY^{\cdot}.\, D) \,.^{\cdot}\, D,$

whence it follows that $XY \in C(D)$ and hence that $C(D)$ is a subsemigroup of $\mathbf{P}(S)$. Also,

$$(5)\ \emptyset \subset (D:Y)(X\,.^{\cdot}\,D) \subseteq D(X\,.^{\cdot}\,D)\,.^{\cdot}\,Y \subseteq X\,.^{\cdot}\,Y;$$

$$(6)\ \emptyset \subset (D:X)\,Y \subseteq (D:X)\,[X\,^{\cdot}.\,(X\,.^{\cdot}\,Y)] \subseteq (D:X)\,X\,^{\cdot}.\,(X\,.^{\cdot}\,Y) \subseteq D:(X\,.^{\cdot}\,Y);$$

$$(7)\ \emptyset \subset (D:Y)\,[(X\,.^{\cdot}\,D)\,^{\cdot}.\,D] \subseteq (D:Y)(X\,.^{\cdot}\,D)\,^{\cdot}.\,D \subseteq [D(X\,.^{\cdot}\,D)\,^{\cdot}.\,Y]\,^{\cdot}.\,D \subseteq (X\,.^{\cdot}\,Y)\,^{\cdot}.\,D;$$

$$(8)\ \emptyset \subset (D:Y)(X\,.^{\cdot}\,D) \subseteq [(D:D)\,^{\cdot}.\,Y](X\,.^{\cdot}\,D) = (D:YD)(X\,.^{\cdot}\,D) \subseteq D(X\,.^{\cdot}\,D)\,.^{\cdot}\,YD \subseteq (X\,.^{\cdot}\,Y)\,.^{\cdot}\,D;$$

$$(9)\ \emptyset \subset (D:Y)\,[(X\,^{\cdot}.\,D)\,.^{\cdot}\,D] \subseteq (D:YD)\,[(X\,^{\cdot}.\,D)\,.^{\cdot}\,D] \subseteq (X\,^{\cdot}.\,D)\,.^{\cdot}\,YD = [(X\,.^{\cdot}\,Y)\,.^{\cdot}\,D]\,^{\cdot}.\,D,$$

whence it follows that $X\,.^{\cdot}\,Y \in C(D)$. Similarly, we can show that $X\,^{\cdot}.\,Y \in C(D)$ and so $C(D)$ is a residuated subsemigroup of $\mathbf{P}(S)$ in which residuals coincide with the corresponding residuals in $\mathbf{P}(S)$.

By a *principal D-transportable subset* we shall mean a D-transportable subset of the form $X = (x) = \{x, x^2, x^3, \ldots, x^n, \ldots\}$. Let us now prove:

If D is a subsemigroup of S which is equiresidual in $\mathbf{P}(S)$ *and such that* $D:S = \emptyset$ *then the following conditions are equivalent:*

(a) $C(D)$ *is an A-nomal semigroup with bimaximum element D;*

(b) *every principal D-transportable subset of* $\mathbf{P}(S)$ *is contained in D.*

Suppose that (b) holds. Let M be any D-complex and let $x \in M\,.^{\cdot}\,M$. Then $Mx \subseteq M$ and so, for each positive integer n, $Mx^n \subseteq M$. It follows that $X = \{x, x^2, \ldots, x^n, \ldots\} \subseteq M\,.^{\cdot}\,M$ and hence that X is D-transportable; for $\emptyset \subset D:(M\,.^{\cdot}\,M) \subseteq D:X$. By the hypothesis (b) we deduce that $x \in D$ and hence that $M\,.^{\cdot}\,M \subseteq D \subseteq D:D$. The statement (a) then follows from Theorem 25.10. Conversely, suppose that (a) holds and let $X = \{x, x^2, \ldots, x^n, \ldots\}$ be any principal D-transportable subset. Since $xX \subseteq X$ we have $xXD \subseteq XD$. But, as was shown previously, XD is a D-complex. It follows by (a) that $x \in XD\,^{\cdot}.\,XD \subseteq D$ and so $X \subseteq D$ as required.

Finally, let us note that $C(D)$ is A-nomal in the case where D is *unitary* in the sense that it satisfies the property

$$\text{if} \quad dx \in D \quad \text{with} \quad d \in D \quad \text{then} \quad x \in D. \qquad (*)$$

For, given any D-transportable subset of the form $X = \{x, x^2, \ldots, x^n, \ldots\}$ we have $D : X \neq \emptyset$, and so there exists an element a such that $aX \subseteq D$. For any positive integer p we therefore have $ax^p = d \in D$ and hence $dx = ax^{p+1} \in aX \subseteq D$. We deduce from (*) that $x \in D$ and hence that $X \subseteq D$. It then follows from the equivalence of (a), (b) above that $C(D)$ is A-nomal with bimaximum element D.

EXERCISES

25.1. Let T be the subset of $\mathbf{R} \times \mathbf{R}$ given by

$$T = \{(0, 0)\} \cup \{(x, y);\ x < 0, y \in \mathbf{Z}\}.$$

Show that, under the ordering inherited from $\mathbf{R} \times \mathbf{R}$ and the multiplication defined by

$$(p, i)(q, j) = (\min\{p, q\}, i + j),$$

T forms an ordered semigroup in which

$$\langle (p, i) : (q, j) \rangle = \begin{cases} \{(t, i - j);\ t < 0\} & \text{if } q \leq p \text{ and } i \neq j; \\ [\leftarrow, (0, 0)] & \text{if } q \leq p \text{ and } i = j; \\ [\leftarrow, (p, i - j)] & \text{if } q > p. \end{cases}$$

Deduce that T is a Dubreil–Jacotin semigroup, but is not strong.

25.2. Endow the ordered set T of the previous exercise with the following multiplication:

$$(p, i)(q, j) = (-1, i + j).$$

Show that T becomes an ordered semigroup in which

$$\langle (p, i) : (q, j) \rangle = \begin{cases} \emptyset & \text{if } p < -1; \\ [\leftarrow, (0, 0)] & \text{if } p \geq -1 \text{ and } i = j; \\ \{(t, i - j);\ t < 0\} & \text{if } p \geq -1 \text{ and } i \neq j. \end{cases}$$

Deduce that T is a Dubreil–Jacotin semigroup, but is not strong. Now consider the set $S = T \cup \{(0, n);\ n = \pm 1, \pm 2, \ldots\}$ and endow S with the same multiplication as defined above. Show that S is a strong Dubreil–Jacotin semigroup.

25.3. Prove that an inverse semigroup is a Dubreil–Jacotin semigroup if and only if the unit class modulo Z admits a maximum element.

25.4. Let S be an A-nomal semigroup. Prove that the following conditions concerning $x \in S$ are equivalent:

(1) $A_x \leq A_\xi$;
(2) $\xi = x^{\cdot} . (x . ^{\cdot} \xi)$.

Writing $x^* = x \,.\cdot\, \xi$, show that if $x \,.\cdot\, x^* = x \cdot.\, x^*$ then $A_x \leq A_\xi$. Deduce that in an abelian A-nomal semigroup every equivalence of type A is finer that A_ξ. By referring back to Example 25.1, show that this is not necessarily the case when S is non-abelian. More precisely, show that in that example ${}_{(c,d)}A \leq {}_\xi A$ for all $(c, d) \in S$ but that $A_{(c,d)} \leq A$ if and only if $d \equiv N - 1 \pmod{N}$.

25.5. Let S be an A-nomal semigroup and let $E = \{x \in S; x \equiv \xi(A_\xi)\}$. Prove that A_ξ may be described by

$$a \equiv b(A_\xi) \Leftrightarrow (\exists x, y \in E)\ ax = yb.$$

25.6. If S is a residuated semigroup which admits a maximal element, prove that S is an A-nomal semigroup in which $A_\xi = Z$.

25.7. In this exercise we give a method of constructing, for any given ordered group G, an A-nomal semigroup S such that $S/A_\xi \simeq G$. Let L be an $\cap$-semilattice which is residuated with respect to $\cap$ [e.g. any Boolean algebra]. Show that L has a maximum element π_L. Endow $G \times L$ with the following ordering and multiplication:

$$\begin{cases} (g, x) \leq (h, y) \Leftrightarrow g \leq h,\ x \leq y; \\ (g, x)\,(h, y) = (gh, x \cap y). \end{cases}$$

Show that $G \times L$ forms in this way an A-nomal semigroup with bimaximum element $(1_G, \pi_L)$. Show that the A-nomal elements are precisely those of the form (g, π_L) where $g \in G$ and deduce that

$$(G \times L)/A_\xi \simeq G.$$

25.8. Let G be an ordered group and let N be its negative cone. Prove that

$$(\forall x \in G)\quad x^{-1}N = Nx^{-1}$$

and deduce that N is equiresidual in $\mathbf{P}(G)$. Show also that $N : G = \emptyset$. Prove that for any subset X of G the following conditions are equivalent:

(1) X is bounded above in G;
(2) X is N-transportable.

An ordered group G is said to be *completely integrally closed* if whenever any subset of the form $X = \{x, x^2, \ldots, x^n, \ldots\}$ admits an upper bound then it admits 1_G as an upper bound. Prove that the following conditions are equivalent:

(3) G is completely integrally closed;
(4) the set $C(N)$ of N-complexes is an A-nomal semigroup with bimaximum element N.

26. Particular types of A-nomal semigroups

In this and the following two sections we shall be concerned with a systematic classification of particular types of A-nomal semigroups. We shall use the notation $\Omega_{\cdot\cdot x}$ [resp. $\Omega_{\cdot\,\cdot x}$] to denote the set of closure equivalences on a residuated semigroup S which are compatible on the right with respect to residuation on the right [resp. left]; and the notation $\chi_{.\cdot x}$ [resp. $\chi_{\cdot .x}$] to denote the set of closure equivalences which are cancellative on the right with respect to residuation on the right [resp. left].

THEOREM 26.1. *Let S be an A-nomal semigroup with bimaximum element ξ. The following conditions on ξ are equivalent:*

(1) $A_\xi \in \Omega_{.\cdot x} \cap \Omega_{\cdot .x}$;

(2) $(\forall x \in S) \quad x \,.^{\cdot}\, \xi \equiv x \equiv x \,^{\cdot}.\, \xi(A_\xi)$;

(3) $A_\xi \in \chi_{.\cdot x} \cap \chi_{\cdot .x}$.

Proof. Suppose that (1) holds. If f denotes the closure mapping associated with A_ξ we have, by Theorem 22.11,

$$(\forall x, y \in S) \quad f(x) \,.^{\cdot}\, y = f(x \,.^{\cdot}\, y), \quad f(x) \,^{\cdot}.\, y = f(x \,^{\cdot}.\, y).$$

In particular,

$$(\forall x \in S) \quad f(x) \,.^{\cdot}\, \xi = f(x \,.^{\cdot}\, \xi) \equiv x \,.^{\cdot}\, \xi(A_\xi).$$

Now since $f(x) \,.^{\cdot}\, \xi = [\xi : (\xi : x)] \,.^{\cdot}\, \xi = (\xi : \xi) \,^{\cdot}.\, (\xi : x) = \xi : (\xi : x) = f(x)$ we deduce that $(\forall x \in S)$ $x \equiv x \,.^{\cdot}\, \xi(A_\xi)$. Similarly, we can show that $x \equiv x \,^{\cdot}.\, \xi(A_\xi)$ and this shows that (1) $\Rightarrow$ (2).

Now suppose that (2) holds. Then we make the following five observations:

(α) $\qquad (\forall_x \in S) \quad A_x \leqslant A_\xi; \quad {}_xA \leq A_\xi;$

[In fact, if $x \,.^{\cdot}\, \xi = x^*$, then $\xi \leq x \,^{\cdot}.\, (x \,.^{\cdot}\, \xi) = x \,^{\cdot}.\, x^*$. But by (2) we have, modulo A_ξ, $x \,^{\cdot}.\, x^* \equiv (x \,^{\cdot}.\, x^*) \,.^{\cdot}\, \xi = [x \,^{\cdot}.\, (x \,.^{\cdot}\, \xi)] \,.^{\cdot}\, \xi = (x \,.^{\cdot}\, \xi) \,^{\cdot}.\, (x \,.^{\cdot}\, \xi) \leq \xi$. Thus $x \,^{\cdot}.\, x^* = \xi$ and so, by Exercise 25.4, $A_x \leq A_\xi$. Similarly, we can show that ${}_xA \leq A_\xi$.]

(β) $\quad (\forall x \in S) \, (\exists \xi_1, \xi_2 \equiv \xi(A_\xi)) \quad x \,.^{\cdot}\, \xi_1 = x \,^{\cdot}.\, \xi_2 = f(x);$

[In fact, let t be any A-nomal element. Since by (α) we have $A_x \leq A_\xi = A_t$, it follows that t is maximum in its class modulo A_x and so $x \,^{\cdot}.\, (x \,.^{\cdot}\, t) = t$. Consequently, $x \,^{\cdot}.\, t\,(x \,.^{\cdot}\, t) = t \,^{\cdot}.\, t = \xi = x \,^{\cdot}.\, (x \,.^{\cdot}\, \xi)$, and so $t(x \,.^{\cdot}\, t) \equiv x \,.^{\cdot}\, \xi({}_xA)$. Using ($\alpha$) again, we have $t(x \,.^{\cdot}\, t) \equiv x \,.^{\cdot}\, \xi \equiv x(A_\xi)$. In particular, consider $t = f(x) = \xi : (\xi : x)$; we obtain $f(x)\,[x \,.^{\cdot}\, f(x)] \equiv x$

$\equiv f(x)\,(A_\xi)$ whence it follows that $x\,.\!\cdot f(x) \equiv \xi(A_\xi)$. Writing $\xi_2 = x\,.\!\cdot f(x)$, the equality $x \cdot\!.\, \xi_2 = f(x)$ then follows from the fact that $f(x)$ is maximum in its class modulo A_x. The statement concerning ξ_1 is proved similarly.]

$$(\beta) \qquad (\forall x \in S)\,(\forall \xi', \xi'' \equiv \xi(A_\xi)) \quad x\,.\!\cdot \xi' \equiv x \cdot\!.\, \xi'' \equiv x(A_\xi);$$

[We note first that if $y\,.\!\cdot \xi_1 = f(x)$, then $y \equiv x(A_\xi)$, for $y\,.\!\cdot \xi_1 f(x) = f(x)\,.\!\cdot f(x) = \xi$ since $f(x)$ is A-nomal, so that $y \cdot\!.\, \xi = y \cdot\!.\, [y\,.\!\cdot \xi_1 f(x)] \equiv \xi_1 f(x)\,(A_y)$ and (α) gives, together with (2), $x \equiv f(x) \equiv \xi_1 f(x) \equiv y\,.\!\cdot \xi \equiv y(A_\xi)$. Now by ($\beta$) there exists ξ_1 such that $x\,.\!\cdot \xi_1 = f(x)$, and since $f(x)$ is A-nomal we have $(\forall \xi'' \equiv \xi(A_\xi))\, f(x) \cdot\!.\, \xi'' = f(x) \cdot\!.\, \xi = f(x)$; consequently $(x \cdot\!.\, \xi'') \cdot\!.\, \xi_1 = (x \cdot\!.\, \xi_1) \cdot\!.\, \xi'' = f(x) \cdot\!.\, \xi'' = f(x)$ and so, by the previous remark, $x \cdot\!.\, \xi'' \equiv x(A_\xi)$.]

$$(\delta) \qquad x\,.\!\cdot y \equiv \xi(A_\xi) \Leftrightarrow x \equiv y(A_\xi);$$

Let $x\,.\!\cdot y = \xi_1 \equiv \xi(A_\xi)$. Then by ($\alpha$) and ($\gamma$) we have $y \equiv x \cdot\!.\, (x\,.\!\cdot y) = x \cdot\!.\, \xi_1 \equiv x(A_\xi)$.]

$$(\varepsilon) \qquad (\forall x \in S) \quad x\,.\!\cdot x \equiv \xi \equiv x \cdot\!.\, x(A_\xi).$$

[By (α) we have

$$(\forall x \in S) \quad (x \cdot\!.\, x) \cdot\!.\, [(x \cdot\!.\, x)\,.\!\cdot \xi] = \xi = x \cdot\!.\, (x\,.\!\cdot \xi)$$

so that, by (α) and (2),

$$(\forall x \in S) \quad [(x \cdot\!.\, x)\,.\!\cdot \xi]\, x \equiv x\,.\!\cdot \xi \equiv x(A_\xi)$$

which in turn gives

$$(\forall x \in S) \quad (x \cdot\!.\, x)\,.\!\cdot \xi \equiv \xi(A_\xi)$$

and the result follows on applying (δ).]

Combining the above observations, we see first that, by (ε),

$$(\forall x, y \in S) \quad (y\,.\!\cdot x)\,.\!\cdot (y\,.\!\cdot x) \equiv \xi(A_\xi).$$

Now the left-hand side of this is $y\,.\!\cdot x\,(y\,.\!\cdot x)$, and so, by ($\delta$),

$$(\forall x, y \in S) \quad x\,(y\,.\!\cdot x) \equiv y(A_\xi). \qquad (*)$$

It follows from this that $y \mathbin{.^{\cdot}} x = z \mathbin{.^{\cdot}} x \Rightarrow y \equiv z(A_\xi)$, so that each equivalence ${}_xB$ is contained in A_ξ. Furthermore, from (*) we also have

$$y \mathbin{.^{\cdot}} x \equiv z \mathbin{.^{\cdot}} x(A_\xi) \Rightarrow y \equiv z(A_\xi)$$

which shows that $A_\xi \in \chi_{.\cdot x}$. Similarly, we can show that $A_\xi \in \chi_{\cdot .x}$ and this concludes the proof of (2) $\Rightarrow$ (3).

Finally, suppose that (3) holds. From the identity $x(y \mathbin{.^{\cdot}} x) \mathbin{.^{\cdot}} x = y \mathbin{.^{\cdot}} x$ we have $x(y \mathbin{.^{\cdot}} x) \mathbin{.^{\cdot}} x \equiv y \mathbin{.^{\cdot}} x(A_\xi)$ and so (*) holds. Consequently,

$$\begin{aligned} y \equiv z(A_\xi) &\Rightarrow (\forall x \in S) \quad x(y \mathbin{.^{\cdot}} x) \equiv x(z \mathbin{.^{\cdot}} x)(A_\xi) \\ &\Rightarrow (\forall x \in S) \quad y \mathbin{.^{\cdot}} x \equiv z \mathbin{.^{\cdot}} x(A_\xi), \end{aligned}$$

i.e. $A_\xi \in \Omega_{.\cdot x}$. Similarly, we can show that $A_\xi \in \Omega_{\cdot .x}$ and this establishes (1).

Definition. We shall say that a semigroup is *A-nomally closed* if it is an A-nomal semigroup which satisfies any of the equivalent properties given in the previous theorem. Let us remark that this notion can be split into the (non-equivalent) notions of A-nomal closure on the left [$A_\xi \in \Omega_{\cdot .x}$] and A-nomal closure on the right [$A_\xi \in \Omega_{.\cdot x}$]. Whilst we shall discuss only those semigroups which are bilaterally A-nomally closed, we shall give an example later of a semigroup which is A-nomally closed on one side only.

THEOREM 26.2. *A residuated semigroup is A-nomally closed if and only if there is an A-symmetric element* $t \in S$ *which is maximum in its class modulo* A_t *and such that* $A_t \in \chi_{.\cdot x} \cap \chi_{\cdot .x}$.

Proof. If S is A-nomally closed, then clearly the element ξ has the stated properties. Conversely, from $A_t \in \chi_{.\cdot x} \cap \chi_{\cdot .x}$ we deduce that

$$(\forall x, y \in S) \quad x(y \mathbin{.^{\cdot}} x) \equiv y \equiv (y \mathbin{{}^{\cdot}.} x)\, x\, (A_t).$$

In particular let $y = t \mathbin{{}^{\cdot}.} t$; then we have $x[(t \mathbin{{}^{\cdot}.} t) \mathbin{.^{\cdot}} x] \equiv t \mathbin{{}^{\cdot}.} t(A_t)$ and so $(t \mathbin{.^{\cdot}} x) \mathbin{.^{\cdot}} [(t \mathbin{.^{\cdot}} x) \mathbin{{}^{\cdot}.} t] = t \mathbin{.^{\cdot}} x[(t \mathbin{{}^{\cdot}.} t) \mathbin{.^{\cdot}} x] = t \mathbin{.^{\cdot}} (t \mathbin{{}^{\cdot}.} t) = t$ whence every right residual of t is a right residual of $t \mathbin{.^{\cdot}} x$. Since the converse clearly holds, we deduce that $(\forall x \in S)\ {}_tA = {}_{t .\cdot x}A$. Choosing $y = t$ we also obtain

$$(\forall x \in S) \quad t \mathbin{.^{\cdot}} t = t \mathbin{.^{\cdot}} (t \mathbin{{}^{\cdot}.} x)\, x = [t \mathbin{.^{\cdot}} (t \mathbin{{}^{\cdot}.} x)] \mathbin{.^{\cdot}} x \geq x \mathbin{.^{\cdot}} x,$$

and so S is an A-nomal semigroup with bimaximum element $t \mathbin{.\!\cdot} t$. It follows that $A_t = {}_tA = {}_{t\cdot\cdot t}A = {}_\xi A = A_\xi$ and the result follows from Theorem 26.1.

EXAMPLE 26.1. Every residuated semigroup having a maximal element (in particular, every finite residuated semigroup) is A-nomally closed. In fact A_ξ is none other than Z in this case and, as was shown in Theorem 23.1, $Z \in \Omega_{\cdot\cdot x} \cap \Omega_{\cdot\cdot x}$.

EXAMPLE 26.2. The A-nomal semigroup of Example 25.1 is not A-nomally closed since it does not satisfy the condition (2) of Theorem 26.1. [In fact $(0, N-1):(a, b) = (0, N-1-b^*)$ and so we have

$$(a, b) \equiv (\alpha, \beta)\,(A_\xi) \Leftrightarrow b^* = \beta^*.$$

Now $(a, b) \mathbin{.\!\cdot} (0, N-1) = (a, b)$; and $(a, b) \mathbin{\cdot\!.} (0, N-1) = (a, (b-N+1)^* + N - 1)$, this being equivalent to (a, b) modulo A_ξ if and only if

$$b^* = [(b-N+1)^* + N - 1]^* = (b - N + 1)^*.$$

This equality does not hold for all b; for example, take $b = 0$.] However, this semigroup is A-nomally closed on the left since $A_\xi \in \Omega_{\cdot\cdot x}$. [In fact, let $(a, b) \equiv (\alpha, \beta)\,(A_\xi)$; then $b^* = \beta^*$ and since

$$(b - y^*)^* = b^* - y^* = \beta^* - y^* = (\beta - y^*)^*$$

it follows that $(a, b) \mathbin{\cdot\!.} (x, y) \equiv (\alpha, \beta) \mathbin{\cdot\!.} (x, y)\,(A_\xi)$.]

Definition. We shall say that a semigroup S is *A-totally closed* if it is an A-nomal semigroup in which $(\forall x \in S)\; x \mathbin{.\!\cdot} x = \xi = x \mathbin{\cdot\!.} x$.

THEOREM 26.3. *Every A-totally closed semigroup is A-nomally closed.*

Proof. If S is A-totally closed then clearly

$$(\forall x \in S) \quad (x \mathbin{.\!\cdot} x) \mathbin{\cdot\!.} \xi = \xi = (x \mathbin{\cdot\!.} x) \mathbin{.\!\cdot} \xi.$$

The first of these equalities gives $\xi = (x \mathbin{\cdot\!.} \xi) \mathbin{.\!\cdot} x$ so that $x\xi \leq y \mathbin{\cdot\!.} \xi$ and hence $x\xi^2 \leq (x \mathbin{\cdot\!.} \xi)\,\xi \leq x$. Now clearly $x \equiv x\xi^2\,(A_\xi)$ and so, the classes being convex, we have $x \equiv (x \mathbin{\cdot\!.} \xi)\,\xi \equiv x \mathbin{\cdot\!.} \xi(A_\xi)$. In a similar way we can show that $x \equiv x \mathbin{.\!\cdot} \xi(A_\xi)$. Since this holds for all $x \in S$ we conclude by Theorem 26.1 that S is A-nomally closed.

Remark. The converse of Theorem 26.3 does not hold in general. To see this, all we have to do is exhibit an A-nomally closed semigroup which is not A-totally closed. Such a semigroup is that of Exercises 23.3; for it is clearly A-nomally closed (Example 26.1) but is not A-totally closed since $b \,.\!\cdot\, b = b \neq \xi = a$.

THEOREM 26.4. *Every A-nomal semigroup contains an A-totally closed subsemigroup.*

Proof. Let S be A-nomal and consider the subset

$$T = \{x \in S;\ x \,.\!\cdot\, x = \xi = x \,\cdot\!.\, x\}.$$

We observe first that $T \neq \emptyset$ since it clearly contains every A-nomal element. Now T is a subsemigroup of S, since if $x, y \in T$ then

$$\begin{cases} \xi = y \,.\!\cdot\, y \leq (xy \,.\!\cdot\, x) \,.\!\cdot\, y = xy \,.\!\cdot\, xy \leq \xi; \\ \xi = x \,\cdot\!.\, x \leq (xy \,\cdot\!.\, y) \,\cdot\!.\, x = xy \,\cdot\!.\, xy \leq \xi, \end{cases}$$

and so $xy \in T$. That T is residuated follows from the fact that if $x, y \in T$, then we have

$$\begin{cases} \xi = y \,.\!\cdot\, y \leq [x \,\cdot\!.\, (x \,.\!\cdot\, y)] \,.\!\cdot\, y = (x \,.\!\cdot\, y) \,\cdot\!.\, (x \,.\!\cdot\, y) \leq \xi; \\ \xi = x \,.\!\cdot\, x \leq x \,.\!\cdot\, y\,(x \,.\!\cdot\, y) = (x \,.\!\cdot\, y) \,.\!\cdot\, (x \,.\!\cdot\, y) \leq \xi; \end{cases}$$

from which it follows that $x \,.\!\cdot\, y \in T$. Similarly, we can show that $x \,\cdot\!.\, y \in T$. Thus T is a residuated subsemigroup of S. By its definition, T is clearly A-totally closed since $\xi : \xi = \xi$ and so $\xi \in T$.

Definition. We shall say that a semigroup is *A-integrally closed* if it is an A-nomal semigroup in which $(\forall x \in S)\ x \,.\!\cdot\, \xi = x = x \,\cdot\!.\, \xi$.

THEOREM 26.5. *A residuated semigroup S is A-integrally closed if and only if*

(1) *S has a neutral element* 1;
(2) $(\forall x \in S)$ $x \,.\!\cdot\, x = 1$ [*resp.* $x \,\cdot\!.\, x = 1$].

Proof. Suppose that S is A-integrally closed. Then

$$x \equiv y(B_\xi) \Rightarrow x = x \,.\!\cdot\, \xi = y \,.\!\cdot\, \xi = y,$$

so that the equivalence B_ξ reduces to equality. It follows that

$$(\forall x \in S) \quad x = \xi\,(x \,.\!\cdot\, \xi) = \xi x.$$

In a similar way we can show that $x\xi = x$ and so it follows that ξ is the neutral element 1. Moreover, since $1 \leq x \,.\!\cdot\, x \leq \xi$ we have $x \,.\!\cdot\, x = 1$.

Conversely, suppose that (1) and (2) hold. By (1) we have, for each $x \in S$, $x \,.\!\cdot\, 1 = x = x \cdot\!.\, 1$ and by (2) we have $x \,.\!\cdot\, x = 1 = 1 \,.\!\cdot\, 1$ so it follows that 1 is the bimaximum element of S and hence that S is A-integrally closed.

Corollary 1. *Every A-integrally closed semigroup is A-totally closed.*

Proof. This is immediate from the definition and Theorem 26.1.

Corollary 2. *An A-totally closed semigroup is A-integrally closed if and only if it has a neutral element.*

Proof. Necessity is obvious. If S is A-totally closed with a 1 then $1 = 1 \,.\!\cdot\, 1 = \xi$ and so S is A-integrally closed.

Definition. By an *r-subsemigroup* of a residuated semigroup S we shall mean a subsemigroup T which is residuated in such a way that the residuals in T coincide with the corresponding residuals in S.

Theorem 26.6. *Let S be an A-nomal semigroup with a neutral element* 1. *If S is not A-integrally closed then S admits a greatest A-integrally closed r-subsemigroup, namely the subset* $K_\xi = \{x \,.\!\cdot\, \xi \in S;\ x \,.\!\cdot\, \xi = x \cdot\!.\, \xi\}$.

Proof. Let us note first that, as was shown in the proof of Theorem 25.10, ξ is idempotent. Clearly $\{\xi\}$ then forms an A-integrally closed r-subsemigroup. Now consider K_ξ. Let $a = x \cdot\!.\, \xi \in K_\xi$. Then $a = x \cdot\!.\, \xi = x \cdot\!.\, \xi^2 = (x \cdot\!.\, \xi) \cdot\!.\, \xi = a \cdot\!.\, \xi$ so that $a\xi \leq a$. But since $1 \leq \xi$ we have $a \leq a\xi$ and so it follows that $a = a\xi$. Similarly, using right residuals, we can show that $a = \xi a$. Thus ξ is the neutral element for K_ξ. Now K_ξ is a subsemigroup of S. In fact, if $a = x \cdot\!.\, \xi \in K_\xi$ and $b = y \cdot\!.\, \xi \in K_\xi$ then from $a\xi = a$ we have $ba\xi = ba$ so that $ba \leq ba \cdot\!.\, \xi \leq ba \cdot\!.\, 1 = ba$, giving $ba = ba \cdot\!.\, \xi$. Similarly, from $\xi b = b$ we have $ba = ba \,.\!\cdot\, \xi$. It follows that $ba \in K_\xi$. Let us now show that K_ξ is an r-subsemigroup of S. If $a, b \in K_\xi$ then from $\xi a = a$ we have $b \cdot\!.\, a = b \cdot\!.\, \xi a = (b \cdot\!.\, a) \cdot\!.\, \xi$ and from $a\xi = a$ we have $b \cdot\!.\, a = b \cdot\!.\, a\xi = (b \cdot\!.\, \xi) \cdot\!.\, a = (b \,.\!\cdot\, \xi) \cdot\!.\, a$

$= (b \cdot . a) . \cdot \xi$. This shows that $b \cdot . a \in K_\xi$, and by a similar method we can show that $b . \cdot a \in K_\xi$. To show that K_ξ is A-integrally closed, we observe that for each $a \in K_\xi$ we have $a \cdot . a = \xi a \cdot . \xi a = (\xi a \cdot . a) \cdot . \xi \geq \xi \cdot . \xi = \xi$ and so $a \cdot . a = \xi$. Since ξ is the neutral element of K_ξ it follows by Theorem 26.5 that K_ξ is A-integrally closed.

Now let G be any r-subsemigroup of S which has a neutral element 1_G and which is A-integrally closed. For any $x \in G$ we have $1_S \leq x . \cdot x = 1_G \leq \xi$ and so $\xi \leq \xi 1_G \leq \xi^2 = \xi$ whence $\xi = \xi 1_G$ and, similarly, $\xi = 1_G \xi$. Thus $\xi \leq \xi : 1_G \leq \xi : 1_S = \xi$ and so $\xi = \xi : 1_G$. It follows that

$$\xi \in K_{1_G} = \{x . \cdot 1_G \in S;\ x . \cdot 1_G = x \cdot . 1_G\}.$$

Now we can show that K_{1_G} is an A-integrally closed r-subsemigroup of S in exactly the same way as we did for K (the proof being valid since $1_S \leq 1_G$). It follows that $\xi : \xi = 1_G$ and hence that $\xi = 1_G$. Consequently, $G \subseteq K_{1_G} = K_\xi$ and the result follows.

EXAMPLE 26.3. If S is a residuated semigroup with neutral element 1, then S/A_1 is a group if and only if S is A-integrally closed. In fact, if S/A_1 is a group then, by Theorem 25.8, S is A-nomal and $A_1 = A_\xi$. This means that 1 is A-nomaloid on the right, so that $1 \cdot . 1 = 1$ is A-nomal. It follows that $1 = \xi$ since they are in the same class modulo A_ξ. Thus S is A-integrally closed. The converse is obvious. As an illustration of this, let us refer back to Example 25.2. There we showed that if I is integrally closed, then $F^*(I)/A_I$ is a group (and conversely). Since I is the neutral element for $F^*(I)$, the previous remark allows us to restate the result in the following form: *a commutative integral domain I is completely integrally closed if and only if the semigroup $F^*(I)$ of non-zero fractionary ideals of I is A-integrally closed.*

EXERCISES

26.1. Prove that an A-nomal semigroup S is A-nomally closed if and only if

$$(\forall x \in S)\ (x \cdot . x) . \cdot \xi \equiv \xi \equiv (x . \cdot x) \cdot . \xi\ (A_\xi).$$

26.2. An A-nomal semigroup S is said to be *A-totally closed on the left* [resp. *right*] if

$$(\forall x \in S)\ (x . \cdot x) \cdot . \xi \equiv x \cdot . x = \xi (A_\xi)\ [\text{resp. } (x \cdot . x) . \cdot \xi \equiv x . \cdot x = \xi (A_\xi)].$$

If S is A-totally closed on the left [resp. right], prove that S is A-nomally closed.

For each integer j let j° be the integer such that $j \equiv j^\circ \pmod{n}$ and $0 \le j^\circ < n$, where n is a fixed integer > 1. Define a multiplication on $\mathbf{Z} \times \mathbf{Z}$, ordered in the usual way, by

$$(p, i)\,(q, j) = (p + q,\, i + j - j^\circ).$$

Show that in this way $\mathbf{Z} \times \mathbf{Z}$ becomes a residuated semigroup in which

$$\begin{cases} (p, i) \,{}^{\cdot}.\, (q, j) = (p - q,\, i - j + j^\circ); \\ (p, i) \,.^{\cdot}\, (q, j) = (p - q,\, i - j - (i - j)^\circ + n - 1). \end{cases}$$

Deduce that this semigroup is A-totally closed on the left.

26.3. Let S be an A-nomally closed semigroup. Prove that the equivalence A_ξ may be described by

$$x \equiv y(A_\xi) \Leftrightarrow (\forall \xi_1, \xi_2 \equiv \xi(A_\xi))\ x \,.^{\cdot}\, \xi_1 = y \,.^{\cdot}\, \xi_2.$$

Using the property (β) of Theorem 26.1 and the fact that each equivalence of type B is contained in A_ξ, deduce that

$$A_\xi = \prod_{x \in S} B_x = \prod_{x \in S} {}_xB,$$

where Π denotes transitive product.

26.4. If S is an abelian A-nomal semigroup which is a lattice, prove that A_ξ is compatible with $\cap$. Writing $|x, y| = (x : y) \cap (y : x) \cap \xi$, show that S is A-nomally closed if and only if

$$\left.\begin{aligned} \bigcap_{i=1}^{n} |x_i, y_i| \le |x, y| \\ (i = 1, \ldots, n)\ x_i \equiv y_i(A_\xi) \end{aligned}\right\} \Rightarrow x \equiv y(A_\xi).$$

26.5. Let S be an A-nomal semigroup. If S is $\cup$-semireticulated, prove that so also is the A-totally closed subsemigroup T of Theorem 26.4. If S is also a lattice, show that so also is T.

26.6. Prove that every residuated cancellative semigroup with a neutral element is A-integrally closed.

26.7. Prove that every residuated semigroup with a neutral element which is maximal is A-integrally closed.

26.8. Consider the ordered semigroup S described by the following Hasse diagram and Cayley table:

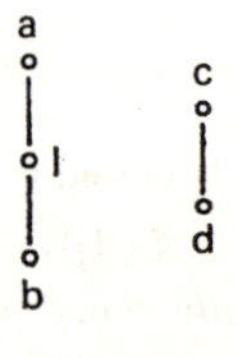

	a	l	b	c	d
a	a	a	b	c	d
l	a	l	b	c	d
b	b	b	b	d	d
c	c	c	d	a	b
d	d	d	d	b	b

Show that S is A-nomally closed but neither A-totally closed nor A-integrally closed. Show also that the greatest A-integrally closed r-subsemigroup of S is $K_a = \{a, b, c, d\}$. [Note that $\{a, b\}$ is also an A-integrally closed r-subsemigroup.]

26.9. Let S be an A-nomal semigroup with neutral element 1. If S is $\cup$-semireticulated show that so also is K_ξ (Theorem 26.6). If S is also a lattice, show that so also is K_ξ.

26.10. Show that the semigroup $G \times L$ of Exercise 25.7 is A-integrally closed.

27. *F*-nomality

In this and the following section we shall consider further particular types of A-nomal semigroups.

Definition. An element x of a residuated semigroup S will be called *F-nomaloid on the right* [resp. *left*] if and only if $(\forall t \in S)\ F_x = F_{xt}$ [resp. ${}_xF = {}_{tx}F$). We shall say that $x \in S$ is *F-nomal on the right* [resp. *left*] if it is F-nomaloid on the right [resp. left] and maximum in its class modulo F_x [resp. ${}_xF$].

Unlike the case of A-nomal elements, we shall show later that the notions of F-nomal on the right and F-nomal on the left are in general distinct.

THEOREM 27.1. *In a residuated semigroup S the following conditions are equivalent:*

(1) $x \in S$ *is F-nomaloid on the right* [*resp. left*];

(2) $F_x \in .\Omega \cap \Omega. \cap .\chi$ [*resp.* ${}_xF \in \Omega. \cap .\Omega \cap \chi.$].

Proof. By Theorem 22.12 we have $F_x \in \Omega.$ for every $x \in S$. Now, by Theorem 25.12, we have $F_x \in .\Omega \cap .\chi$ if and only if

$$(\forall a, b \in S) \quad xa \cdot\!\! \cdot\, x = (xba \cdot\!\! \cdot\, x) \cdot\!\! \cdot\, b = xba \cdot\!\! \cdot\, xb,$$

which is clearly equivalent to saying that $(\forall b \in S)\ F_x = F_{xb}$.

THEOREM 27.2. *If S is a residuated semigroup and $x \in S$ is F-nomaloid on the right* [*resp. left*], *then* $(\forall y \in S)\ F_y \leq F_x$ [*resp.* ${}_yF \leq {}_xF$].

Proof. By Theorem 22.13 we have $(\forall y \in S)\ F_y \leq F_{xy} = F_x$.

COROLLARY. *If $x \in S$ is F-nomaloid on the right* [*resp. left*] *then we also have* $(\forall t \in S)\ F_x = F_{tx}$ [*resp.* ${}_xF = {}_{xt}F$].

Proof. This is immediate from Theorem 27.2 and 22.13.

Definition. We shall say that a semigroup S is *F-nomal on the left* [resp.

right] if it admits an element which is F-nomal on the left [resp. right]. A semigroup which is F-nomal on both sides will be called simply *F-nomal.*

THEOREM 27.3. *If a semigroup is F-nomal on the right (resp. left) then S is A-nomal.*

Proof. If $x \in S$ is F-nomal on the right for example then by Theorem 27.1 we have $F_x \in .\chi$. It then follows by Theorem 25.14 that S is A-nomal.

EXAMPLE 27.1. Let S be a residuated cancellative semigroup. Since every equivalence of type F reduces to equality, it follows that every element of S is F-nomal on the right and on the left.

EXAMPLE 27.2. If a residuated semigroup contains a minimum element m then by Theorem 23.13 every multiple of m coincides with m so that m is the zero element (and conversely). Clearly m is F-nomaloid on both the left and right.

EXAMPLE 27.3. Consider the ordered set described by

$$\begin{cases} S = \{(x, y);\ x, y \text{ integers with } x \leq 0\}; \\ (x, y) \leq (x', y') \Leftrightarrow x \leq x', \quad y \leq y'. \end{cases}$$

Endow S with a multiplication as follows: let N, M be fixed integers greater than 1 and for each integer p define p^*, $p^\wedge$ by the inequalities $p^* = kN \leq p < (k + 1)\,N$, $p^\wedge = tM \leq p < (t + 1)\,M$; now define

$$(p, i)\,(q, j) = (\min\{p^* + q,\ p + q^*\},\ i + j^\wedge).$$

This multiplication makes S into an ordered semigroup. In fact, let $x = [(p, i)\,(q, j)]\,(r, s)$ and let k_1, k_2, k_3 be such that $k_1N = p^*$, $k_2N = q^*, k_3N = r^*$. Now $(k_1 + k_2)\,N \leq k_1N + q < (k_1 + k_2 + 1)N$ and $(k_1 + k_2)\,N \leq p + k_2N < (k_1 + k_2 + 1)\,N$; consequently

$$(k_1 + k_2)\,N \leq \min\{p^* + q,\ p + q^*\} < (k_1 + k_2 + 1)\,N.$$

It follows that $x = (\lambda, \mu)$, where

$$\begin{cases} \lambda = \min\{(k_1 + k_2)\,N + r,\quad k_3N + \min\{k_1N + q,\ p + k_2N\}\}; \\ \mu = i + j^\wedge + k^\wedge. \end{cases}$$

Now the expression for λ may be written in the symmetric form

$$\lambda = \min\{(k_1 + k_2)N + r, \quad (k_3 + k_1)N + q, \quad (k_2 + k_3)N + p\}$$

and that for μ may be written $\mu = i + (j + k^\wedge)^\wedge$. It follows from this that the above multiplication is associative. It is also clearly isotone. Let us now show that S is residuated. From the definition of multiplication we have $(p, i)(q, j) \leq (r, k)$ if and only if

$$\min\{p^* + q, p + q^*\} \leq r \quad \text{and} \quad i + j^\wedge \leq k.$$

Let us first see, given $q \leq 0$, how $\min\{p^* + q, p + q^*)$ varies with $p \leq 0$. [We are interested only in negative values of p, q by the definition of S.] Define

$$p^\circ = p^* + (q - q^*).$$

Then $p^\circ \geq p^*$ and $(p^\circ)^* = p^* + (q - q^*)^* = p^* + q^* - q^* = p^*$. Thus $p^\circ + q^* = p^* + q$ and if $p^\circ \leq x \leq p^* + N - 1$ then $p^\circ + q^* \leq x + q^* \leq p^* + N - 1 + q^*$ so that $\min\{x^* + q, x + q^*\} = \min\{p^* + q, x + q^*\} = p^* + q$. On the other hand, if $p^* \leq y \leq p^\circ - 1$, say $y = p^\circ - t$, then $\min\{y^* + q, y + q^*\} = \min\{p^* + q, p^* + q - q^* - t + q^*\} = p^* + q - t$. The graph of the function

$$p \to \min\{p^* + q, p + q^*\}$$

restricted to the interval $[p^*, p^* + N - 1]$ is therefore

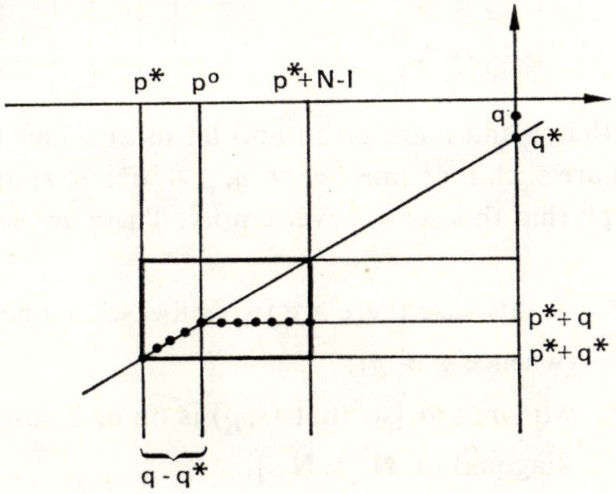

Having seen this, the graph of the function is as follows:

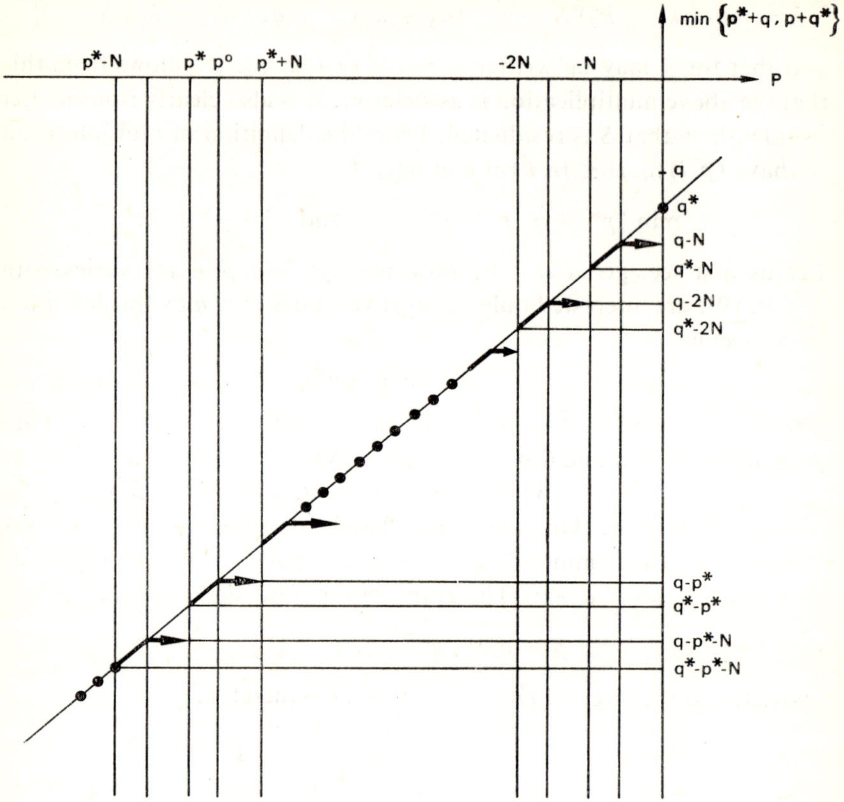

Suppose now that p and r are given and let us consider the set of elements q which are such that $\min\{p^* + q, p + q^*\} \leq r$. It is clear from the above graph that this set is never empty. There are several cases to consider.

(a) $r^* \geq p^*$: in this case there are two subcases, namely

(i) $r^* > p^*$ (whence $r > p$);

(ii) $r^* = p^*$ with $r \leq p$ [so that (r, p) is on or below the principal diagonal of $\mathbf{N}_- \times \mathbf{N}_-$].

It is clear that in each of these cases the maximum value of q which is possible is $q = 0$, the corresponding graph being

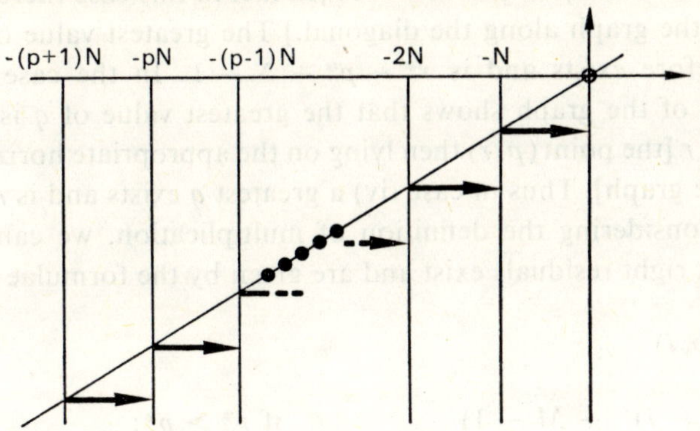

(b) $r^* < p^*$: in this case there are also two subcases, namely

(iii) $r - r^* \geq p - p^*$;

(iv) $r - r^* < p - p^*$.

These cases correspond respectively to the cases where the point (p, r) appears (iii) above or on, or (iv) below the diagonal of

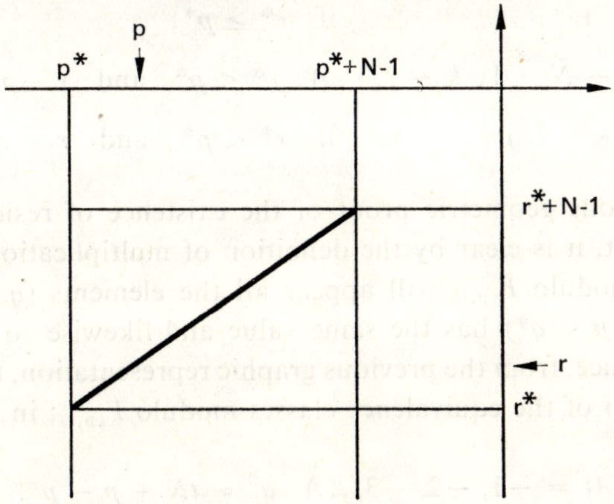

Now since $r^* < p^*$ we can choose q such that $q^* = r^* - p^*$. By considering the graph given previously, we see that in case (iii) the maximum possible q satisfies $q - q^* = N - 1$. [In fact in this case there are $N - 1$ points of the graph along the diagonal.] The greatest value of q in this case therefore exists and is $r^* - p^* + N - 1$. In the case (iv), consideration of the graph shows that the greatest value of q is such that $p^* + q = r$ [the point (p, r) then lying on the appropriate horizontal portion of the graph]. Thus in case (iv) a greatest q exists and is $r - p^*$.

By reconsidering the definition of multiplication, we can therefore assert that right residuals exist and are given by the formulae

$$(r, k) \,.\!\cdot\, (p, i)$$

$$= \begin{cases} (0,\ (k - i)^\wedge + M - 1) & \text{if } r^* \geq p^*; \\ (r^* - p^* + N - 1,\ (k - i)^\wedge + M - 1) & \text{if } r^* < p^* \text{ and } r - r^* \geq p - p^*; \\ (r - p^*,\ (k - i)^\wedge + M - 1) & \text{if } r^* < p^* \text{ and } r - r^* < p - p^*. \end{cases}$$

Interchanging the rôles of p, q in the previous discussion, we see that left residuals also exist and are given by the formulae

$$(r, k) \cdot\!.\, (p, i)$$

$$= \begin{cases} (0,\ k - i^\wedge) & \text{if } r^* \geq p^*; \\ (r^* - p^* + N - 1,\ k - i^\wedge) & \text{if } r^* < p^* \text{ and } r - r^* \geq p - p^*; \\ (r - p^*,\ k - i^\wedge) & \text{if } r^* < p^* \text{ and } r < r^* - p - p^*. \end{cases}$$

The previous geometric proof of the existence of residuals is very useful. In fact, it is clear by the definition of multiplication that in the same class modulo $F_{(p,i)}$ will appear all the elements (q, j) for which $\min(p^* + q, p + q^*)$ has the same value and likewise so does $j^\wedge$. We therefore deduce, from the previous graphic representation, the following representation of the equivalence classes modulo $F_{(p,i)}$; in this we have written

$$(t = -1, -2, -3, \ldots) \quad q_t^\circ = tN + p - p^*.$$

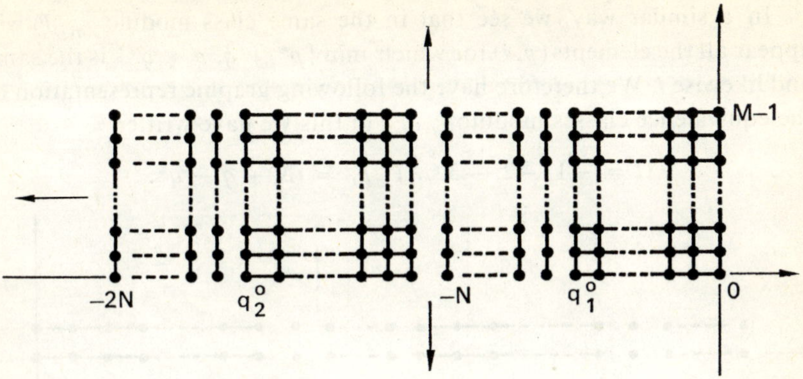

In particular, the elements (p, i) in which p is such that $p = p^*$ give the following partition modulo $F_{(p,i)}$:

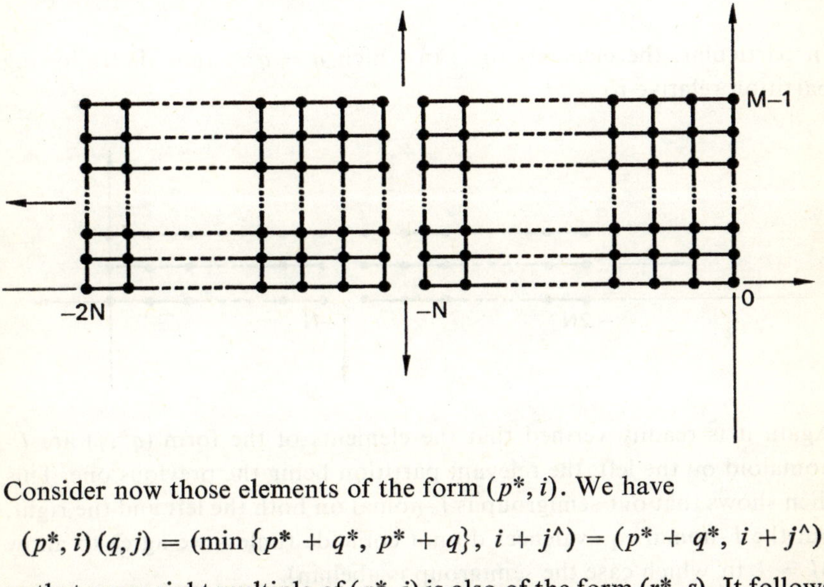

Consider now those elements of the form (p^*, i). We have

$$(p^*, i)(q, j) = (\min\{p^* + q^*, p^* + q\}, i + j^\wedge) = (p^* + q^*, i + j^\wedge),$$

so that every right multiple of (p^*, i) is also of the form (r^*, s). It follows that each element of the form (p^*, i) is F-nomaloid on the right, for the partitions relative to $F_{(p^*,i)}$ and, for any (q,j), $F_{(p^*,i)(q,j)}$ are the same (namely the immediately preceding one).

In a similar way, we see that in the same class modulo ${}_{(q,j)}F$ will appear all the elements (p, i) for which $\min\{p^* + q, p + q^*\}$ is the same and likewise i. We therefore have the following graphic representation of the equivalence classes modulo ${}_{(q,j)}F$; in this we have written

$$(t = -1, -2, -3, \ldots) \quad p_t^\circ = tN + q - q^*.$$

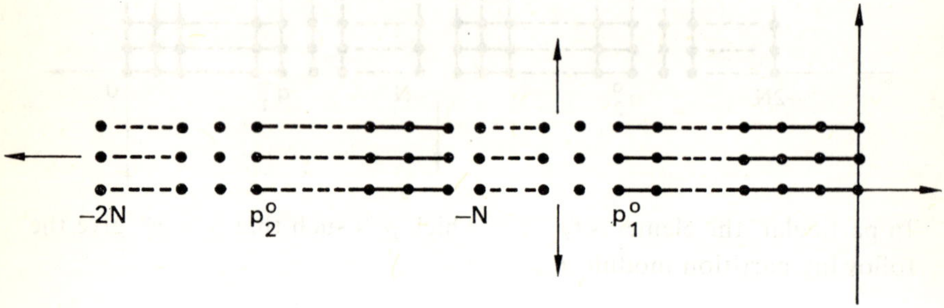

In particular, the elements (q, j) in which $q = q^*$ admit the following partition relative to ${}_{(q,j)}F$:

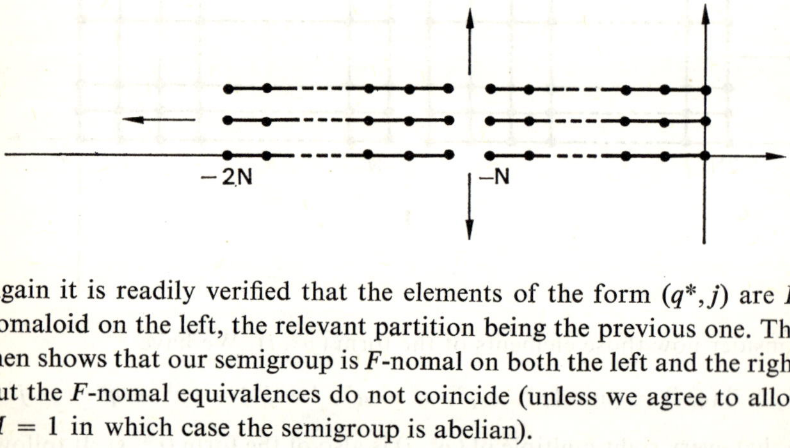

Again it is readily verified that the elements of the form (q^*, j) are F-nomaloid on the left, the relevant partition being the previous one. This then shows that our semigroup is F-nomal on both the left and the right, but the F-nomal equivalences do not coincide (unless we agree to allow $M = 1$ in which case the semigroup is abelian).

Definitions. We shall say that a semigroup is *F^*-nomal* if it is F-nomal on both the left and the right and such that the F-nomal equivalences coincide. By an *F-nomally closed semigroup* we shall mean an F^*-nomal semigroup which is A-nomally closed. Furthermore, we shall say that a semigroup is *F-totally closed* if it is F-nomally closed and A-totally closed; and *F-integrally closed* if it is F-totally closed and A-integrally closed.

These definitions may be remembered by the following scheme:

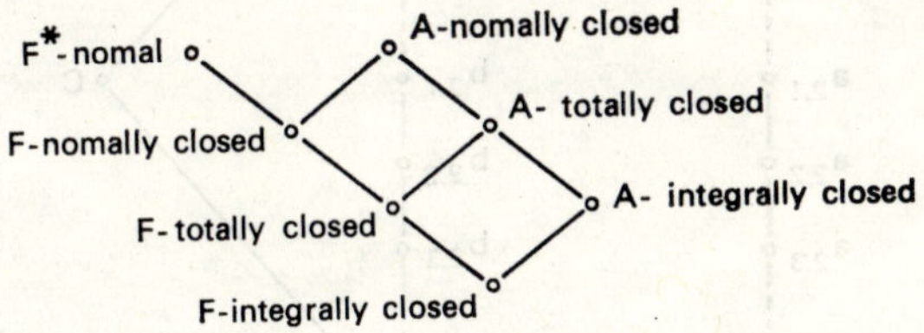

The exercises which follow show that in general these types of semigroup are distinct.

EXERCISES

27.1. Let S be the ordered set of Example 27.3. Endow S with the following multiplication:

$$(p, i)(q, j) = (p^* + q^*, i + j^\wedge).$$

Show that S becomes an F^*-nomal semigroup in which every element is F-nomaloid on both the left and the right. Determine the associated partitions and also that of the A-nomal equivalence A_ξ.

27.2. An element x of a residuated semigroup S is said to be *F-symmetric* if $F_x = {}_xF$. Prove that S is F^*-nomal if and only if it contains an F-symmetric element x such that $F_x \in \chi. \cap .\chi$.

27.3. Consider the ordered (abelian) semigroup S defined by the following Hasse diagram (see page 300) and multiplication:

$$\begin{cases} a_{p,i}a_{q,j} = b_{p,i}b_{q,j} = a_{p+q,\,\min\{i,j\}}; \\ a_{p,i}b_{q,j} = b_{q,j}a_{p,i} = b_{p+q,\,\min\{i,j\}}; \\ (\forall x)\; cx = xc = xb_{1,1}. \end{cases}$$

Show that S is residuated and establish formulae for the residuals. Deduce that the elements of the form $a_{p,1}$ and $b_{p,1}$ are F-nomal and hence that S is F-nomally closed. Show further that $S\backslash\{c\}$ is an F-totally closed semigroup and that $S\backslash\{c\} \cup \{1\}$ where 1 is a neutral element $\geq a_{1,1}$ is an F-integrally closed semigroup.

27.4. Let S be an F^*-nomal semigroup and consider the subset $T = \{x \in S;$ $x \mathbin{.\cdot} x = \xi = x \mathbin{\cdot .} x\}$. If $y \in S$ is F-nomal, show that $y \in T$. Deduce that every F^*-nomal

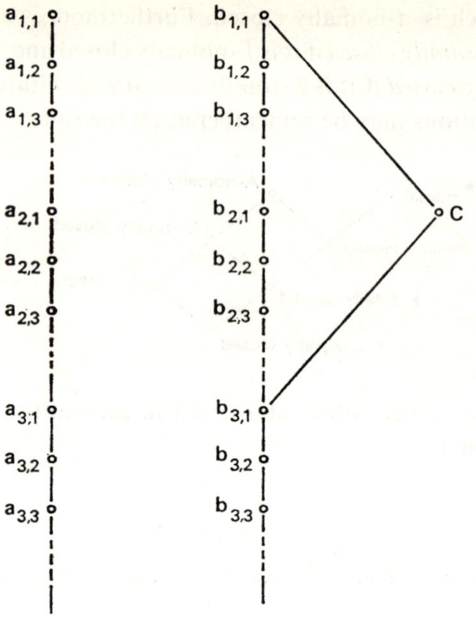

semigroup contains an F-totally closed subsemigroup. Illustrate by referring to the previous exercise.

27.5. Show that every residuated cancellative semigroup with a neutral element is F-integrally closed.

28. B-nomality

Definitions. An element x of a residuated semigroup S will be called *B-nomaloid on the right* [resp. *left*] if and only if $(\forall t \in S)\ B_x = B_{tx}$ [resp. ${}_xB = {}_{xt}B$]. We say that $x \in S$ is *B-nomal on the right* [resp. *left*] if x is B-nomaloid on the right [resp. left] and minimum in its class modulo $B_x[{}_xB]$.

Note that we are dealing with dual closure equivalences here. In order to carry out an investigation which is comparable to the case involving the equivalences of type A, we require the following general results. We shall use the notation ${}^{\cdot}\Omega$ $[{}^{\cdot}\chi]$ to denote the set of dual closure equivalences on a residuated semigroup S which are compatible [resp. cancellative] on the left with multiplication, etc.

THEOREM 28.1. *If S is a residuated semigroup and K is a dual closure equivalence on S with associated dual closure mapping f, then the following conditions are equivalent:*

(1) $K \in \chi^{\cdot .x}$ [*resp.* $K \in \chi^{. \cdot x}$];

(2) $(\forall a, x \in S) \quad a \equiv xf(a \,.^{\cdot}\, x)\,(K) \quad$ [*resp.* $a \equiv f(a \,^{\cdot}.\, x)\, x\,(K)$].

Proof. If (1) holds then $f(a \,.^{\cdot}\, x) \leq xf(a \,.^{\cdot}\, x) \,.^{\cdot}\, x \leq x(a \,.^{\cdot}\, x) \,.^{\cdot}\, x = a \,.^{\cdot}\, x$ and so the convexity of the classes modulo K gives $a \,.^{\cdot}\, x \equiv xf(a \,.^{\cdot}\, x) \,.^{\cdot}\, x\,(K)$, whence (2) follows. Conversely, if (2) holds then clearly

$$a \,.^{\cdot}\, x \equiv b \,.^{\cdot}\, x(K) \Rightarrow a \equiv b(K)$$

and so (1) holds.

THEOREM 28.2. *If S is a residuated semigroup and K is a dual closure equivalence on S with associated dual closure mapping f, then the following conditions are equivalent:*

(1) $K \in \Omega^{\cdot .x} \cap \chi^{\cdot .x}$ [*resp.* $K \in \Omega^{. \cdot x} \cap \chi^{. \cdot x}$];

(2) $(\forall a, x \in S) \quad f(a) = xf(a \,.^{\cdot}\, x) \quad$ [*resp.* $f(a) = f(a \,^{\cdot}.\, x)\, x$].

Proof. Suppose that (1) holds. Then from $K \in \Omega^{\cdot .x}$ we have, using Theorem 22.9(e), $f(a \,.^{\cdot}\, x) \leq f(a) \,.^{\cdot}\, x$ so that $xf(a \,.^{\cdot}\, x) \leq f(a)$. On the other hand, from $K \in \chi^{\cdot .x}$ we have, by Theorem 28.1 and the fact that $f(a)$ is the minimum element in the class of a modulo K, $f(a) \leq xf(a \,.^{\cdot}\, x)$. This, then, shows that (1) $\Rightarrow$ (2). Conversely, if (2) holds, then clearly $a \equiv xf(a \,.^{\cdot}\, x)\,(K)$ and $f(a \,.^{\cdot}\, x) \leq f(a) \,.^{\cdot}\, x$. It follows by Theorems 28.1 and 22.9(e) that (1) holds.

We can now use these results to characterize B-nomaloid elements.

THEOREM 28.3. *Let S be a residuated semigroup. The following conditions concerning $y \in S$ are equivalent:*

(1) *y is B-nomaloid on the right* [*resp. left*];

(2) $B_y \in \Omega^{\cdot .x} \cap \chi^{\cdot .x}$ [*resp.* ${}_yB \in \Omega^{. \cdot x} \cap \chi^{. \cdot x}$].

Proof. By applying Theorem 28.2 we see that (2) holds if and only if

$$(\forall a, x \in S) \quad y\,(a \mathbin{.^{\cdot}} y) = xy\,[(a \mathbin{.^{\cdot}} x) \mathbin{.^{\cdot}} y] = xy\,(a \mathbin{.^{\cdot}} xy),$$

which is equivalent to saying that $(\forall x \in S)\ B_y = B_{xy}$; i.e. that y is B-nomaloid on the right.

Remark. Note that we always have, for any element y of a residuated semigroup S, $B_y \in \Omega^{\cdot .x}$ and ${}_yB \in \Omega^{. \cdot x}$.

THEOREM 28.4. *If a B-nomal equivalence on the right (resp. left) exists in a residuated semigroup S then it is unique and contains every equivalence of type B on the right (resp. left). Moreover, S is an A-nomal semigroup.*

Proof. Let β be B-nomaloid on the right, so that $(\forall t \in S)\ B_\beta = B_{t\beta}$. Now by Theorem 22.14 we have $(\forall t \in S)\ B_t \leq \bigcap_{x \in S} B_{tx}$ and so in particular $B_t \leq B_{t\beta}$. It follows that $(\forall t \in S)\ B_t \leq B_\beta$ and this shows the uniqueness of B_β. Now let β be B-nomal on the right. Being minimum in its class modulo B_β, the element β is also minimum in its class modulo every equivalence B_x, so that

$$(\forall x \in S) \quad \beta = x\,(\beta \mathbin{.^{\cdot}} x).$$

It follows that

$$(\forall x \in S) \quad \beta \mathbin{^{\cdot}.} \beta = \beta \mathbin{^{\cdot}.} x\,(\beta \mathbin{.^{\cdot}} x) = [\beta \mathbin{^{\cdot}.} (\beta \mathbin{.^{\cdot}} x)] \mathbin{^{\cdot}.} x \geq x \mathbin{^{\cdot}.} x$$

and so a bimaximum element exists, namely $\xi = \beta \mathbin{^{\cdot}.} \beta$.

THEOREM 28.5. *Let S be a residuated semigroup which admits a B-nomal equivalence on the left and a B-nomal equivalence on the right. Then these equivalences coincide.*

Proof. Let $x \in S$ be B-nomaloid on the right and let $y \in S$ be B-nomaloid on the left. By Theorem 28.3 we have ${}_yB \in \Omega^{\cdot .x}$. Now the dual closure subset associated with ${}_yB$ consists of all the left multiples of y and so, by Theorem 22.13, we have ${}_yB \leq B_{ty}$ for each $t \in S$. Since x is B-nomaloid on the right, we have $B_{ty} \leq B_x$ and consequently ${}_yB \leq B_x$. A dual argument gives $B_x \leq {}_yB$ whence we have equality.

Definition. We shall say that an element x of a residuated semigroup S is *B-nomal* if it is B-nomal on the left and B-nomal on the right. In this case we have, by the previous result, $B_x = {}_xB$ and we call this the B-nomal equivalence. [In particular, if $y \in S$ is B-nomaloid on the right and $z \in S$ is B-nomaloid on the left then yz is B-nomal.]

THEOREM 28.6. *If the residuated semigroup S contains a B-nomal equivalence B_β on the right (resp. left) then*

(1) *every class modulo A_ξ contains one and only one B-nomal element on the right (resp. left);*
(2) *every class modulo B_β contains one and only one A-nomal element.*

Proof. (1) Since $(\forall x \in S)\ A_\xi = A_{\xi:x}$, every residual of ξ is a left [resp. right] residual of $\xi : x$. Let $\beta \in S$ be B-nomal on the right. Every right multiple of β is B-nomal on the right and given any $\lambda \in S$ there exists $\mu \in S$ such that $\xi : \lambda = (\xi : \beta) \,.\!\cdot\, \mu$. Thus for each $\lambda \in S$ there exists $\mu \in S$ such that $\lambda \equiv \beta\mu\,(A_\xi)$. It follows that each class modulo A_ξ contains at least one B-nomal element on the right. To show that each class modulo A_ξ contains at most one such element, we observe that if α_* is A-nomal and β_* is B-nomal on the right, then

$$\beta_* \equiv \alpha_*(A_\xi) \Rightarrow \beta_* \equiv \alpha_*(B_\beta). \qquad (*)$$

In fact if $\beta_* \equiv \alpha_*(A_\xi)$ then since $A_{\alpha_*} = A_\xi$ we have $\alpha_* \,.\!\cdot\, \beta_* = \alpha_* \,.\!\cdot\, \alpha_* = \xi = \beta_* \,.\!\cdot\, \beta_*$ [Theorem 28.4] so that $\alpha_* \equiv \beta_*(B_{\beta_*})$. Since $B_{\beta_*} = B_\beta$ it follows that $\alpha_* \equiv \beta_*(B_\beta)$. Suppose then that β_*, β_{**} are B-nomal on the right with $\beta_* \equiv \beta_{**}(A_\xi)$. Let α_* be the maximum element in this class modulo A_ξ. From the previous observation, we have $\beta_* \equiv \alpha_* \equiv \beta_{**}(B_\beta)$ and so we conclude that $\beta_* = \beta_{**}$ since each class modulo B_β contains only one B-nomal element on the right.

(2) Let us note first that every class modulo B_β contains at least one A-nomal element. In fact by (*) to each B-nomal element on the right β_* there corresponds an A-nomal element α_* such that $\alpha_* \equiv \beta_*(B_\beta)$; α_* is the greatest element in the class of β_* modulo A_ξ. To show that each class modulo B_β contains at most one A-nomal element, we observe that

if β_* is B-nomal on the right and α_* is A-nomal then

$$\beta_* \equiv \alpha_*(B_\beta) \Rightarrow \beta_* \equiv \alpha_*(A_\xi). \tag{**}$$

In fact if $\beta_* \equiv \alpha_*(B_\beta)$ then since $B_\beta = B_{\beta_*}$ we have $\beta_* . \cdot \beta_* = \alpha_* . \cdot \beta_*$. Now $\alpha_* . \cdot \beta_* = \xi = \alpha_* . \cdot \alpha_*$ and so it follows that $\alpha_* . \cdot \beta_* = \alpha_* . \cdot \alpha_*$ and so $\beta_* \equiv \alpha_* (A_{\alpha^*} = A_\xi)$. It then follows from this that every class modulo B_β contains precisely one A-nomal element.

THEOREM 28.7. *If $\beta \in S$ is B-nomal on the right then $A_\xi = F_\beta$.*

Proof. From $x \equiv y(A_\xi)$ we have $\beta x \equiv \beta y\,(A_\xi)$ so that, βx and βy being B-nomal on the right we have, by Theorem 28.6, $\beta x = \beta y$ whence $x \equiv y(F_\beta)$. Thus $A_\xi \leq F_\beta$. Conversely, $F_\beta \leq A_\xi$ since $A_\xi \in .\chi$.

COROLLARY. *If $\beta \in S$ is B-nomal on the right then β is F-nomaloid on the right. If S is B-nomal then S is F*-nomal.*

Proof. This follows from the equality $A_\xi = F_\beta$ and Theorems 27.1 and 25.13.

THEOREM 28.8. *If S admits an element β which is B-nomal on the right, then S is a group if and only if S is left cancellative.*

Proof. The condition is clearly necessary. To show that it is also sufficient, we observe from the above that $A_\xi = F_\beta$ and since F_β reduces to equality so also does A_ξ whence S is a group.

Denoting by Cen (S) the centre of S we now have:

THEOREM 28.9. *Let S be an A-nomal semigroup. A necessary and sufficient condition that S be B-nomal is*

$$(\exists \beta \in Cen\,(S))\,(\forall \xi^* \equiv \xi(A_\xi)) \quad \beta\xi^* = \beta.$$

Proof. Let $\beta \in S$ be B-nomal. By Theorem 28.7 we have $A_\xi = F_\beta = {}_\beta F$ and so

$$(\forall \xi^* \equiv \xi(A_\xi)) \quad \beta\xi^* = \beta\xi = \beta\,(\beta . \cdot \beta) = \beta.$$

In particular, this holds for the B-nomal element β_* which is in the class of ξ modulo A_ξ (cf. Theorem 28.6). Now every left and right multiple of β_* is B-nomal and so, since $\beta_* x \equiv x\beta_*\,(A_\xi)$, we deduce from Theorem 28.6 that $(\forall x \in S)\ \beta_* x = x\beta_*$ whence $\beta_* \in$ Cen (S).

Conversely, suppose that the condition holds. From the equality $\beta\xi = \beta = \xi\beta$ we deduce that $\xi \leq \beta \,.\!\cdot\, \beta$ and $\xi \leq \beta \,\cdot\!.\, \beta$ so that $\beta \,.\!\cdot\, \beta = \xi = \beta \,\cdot\!.\, \beta$. Now for each $t \in S$ we have $t\,(\xi \,.\!\cdot\, t) \equiv \xi \equiv (\xi \,\cdot\!.\, t)\, t(A_\xi)$ and so

$$(\forall t \in S) \quad t\,(\beta \,.\!\cdot\, \beta t) \equiv \xi \equiv (\beta \,\cdot\!.\, t\beta)\, t\,(A_\xi).$$

Applying the hypothesis, we deduce that

$$(\forall t \in S) \quad t\,(\beta \,.\!\cdot\, \beta t)\,\beta = \beta = \beta\,(\beta \,\cdot\!.\, t\beta)\, t.$$

It follows that every multiple of β is both a left and a right multiple of every element of S. Consequently, every equivalence of type B is contained in $B_\beta = {}_\beta B$ [cf. Ex. 22.7]. Since we always have $(\forall t \in S)\ B_\beta \leq B_{\beta t}$ it follows that $(\forall t \in S)\ B_\beta = B_{\beta t} = B_{t\beta}$ and hence that β is B-nomaloid. It is in fact B-nomal since $\beta = \beta\xi = \beta\,(\beta \,.\!\cdot\, \beta)$.

COROLLARY. *If* Cen $(S) = \emptyset$ *then no* $\beta \in S$ *can be B-nomal.*

EXAMPLE 28.1. Let N be a fixed positive integer and consider the ordered set S described by

$$\begin{cases} S = \{(p, i) \in \mathbf{Z} \times \mathbf{Z};\quad p \in [-N, 0]\}; \\ (p, i) \leq (q, j) \Leftrightarrow p \leq q, \quad i \leq j. \end{cases}$$

Endow S with the following multiplication

$$(p, i)\,(q, j) = (\min\{p, q\},\ i + j^\wedge)$$

where $j^\wedge = kM \leq j < (k+1)\,M$, M being a fixed integer greater than 1. It is readily verified that S becomes a residuated semigroup with residuals given as follows:

$$\begin{cases} (p, i) \,\cdot\!.\, (q, j) = \begin{cases} (0,\ i - j^\wedge) & \text{if } p \geq q; \\ (p,\ i - j^\wedge) & \text{if } p < q; \end{cases} \\[2ex] (p, i) \,.\!\cdot\, (q, j) = \begin{cases} (0,\ (i - j)^\wedge + M - 1) & \text{if } p \geq q; \\ (p,\ (i - j)^\wedge + M - 1) & \text{if } p < q. \end{cases} \end{cases}$$

Consider now the elements of the form $(-N, t^\wedge)$. We have

$$(p, i) \equiv (r, s) \left({}_{(-N,t^\wedge)}B\right) \Leftrightarrow i - t^\wedge = s - t^\wedge \Leftrightarrow i = s,$$

so the corresponding partition is

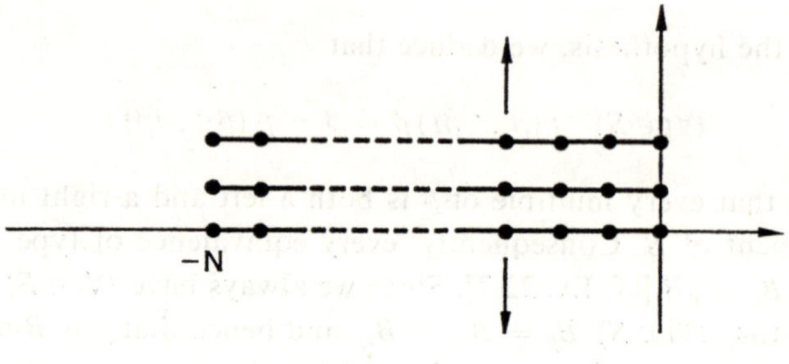

Now for any $(q, j) \in S$ we have

$$(-N, t^\wedge)(q, j) = (-N, t^\wedge + j^\wedge) = (-N, (t + j^\wedge)^\wedge)$$

and so each equivalence of type B on the left associated with $(-N, t^\wedge)(q, i)$ also gives rise to the above partition. It follows that the elements $(-N, t^\wedge)$ are B-nomaloid on the left. Being minimal in their respective classes, they are thus B-nomal on the left. However, S is not B-nomal on the right. In fact, the partition relative to $B_{(q,j)}$ is

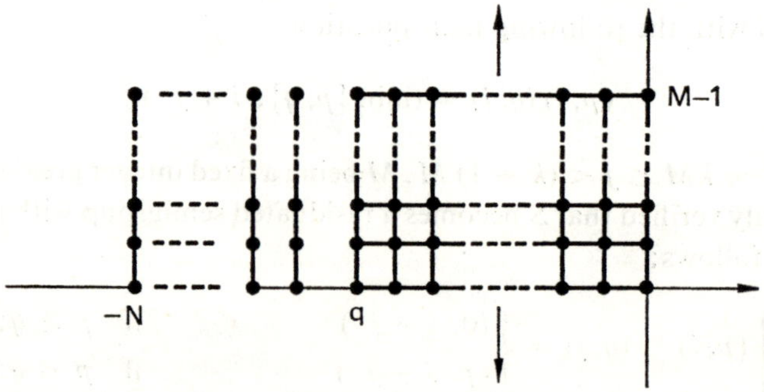

and since $M > 1$ this can never coincide with the left B-nomal equivalence. It follows by Theorem 28.5 that S is not B-nomal on the right.

Alternatively, one could remark that in this example Cen $(S) = \emptyset$, so the result follows by the corollary to Theorem 28.9.

THEOREM 28.10. *Let S be a residuated semigroup and let $\beta \in S$ be B-nomal. Then the following conditions are equivalent:*

(1) $A_\xi = B_\beta$;
(2) *S is F-nomally closed.*

Proof. Suppose first that S is F-nomally closed. Then S is A-nomally closed and $B_\beta \leq A_\xi$ [cf. the proof of Theorem 26.1]. Let $x \equiv y(A_\xi)$; then by Exercises 26.3 there exist ξ_1, ξ_2 in the class of ξ modulo A_ξ such that $x . \cdot \xi_1 = y . \cdot \xi_2$. Thus $x . \cdot \xi_1 \beta = y . \cdot \xi_2 \beta$. But $_\beta F = A_\xi$ and $\xi_1 \beta = \xi\beta = (\beta \cdot . \beta)\beta = \beta$ and likewise $\xi_2 \beta = \beta$. Thus $x . \cdot \beta = y . \cdot \beta$ and $x \equiv y(B_\beta)$. This then shows that $A_\xi \leq B_\beta$ and (1) follows.

Conversely, suppose that (1) holds. By Theorem 28.3 we have

$$A_\xi \in \Omega^{. \cdot x} \cap \chi^{. \cdot x} \cap \Omega^{\cdot . x} \cap \chi^{\cdot . x}$$

and so S is A-nomally closed by Theorem 26.1. Being F^*-nomal by the corollary to Theorem 28.7, S is then F-nomally closed.

This result allows us to define particular types of B-nomal semigroup just as we defined particular types of F-nomal semigroup. We define these by means of the following scheme:

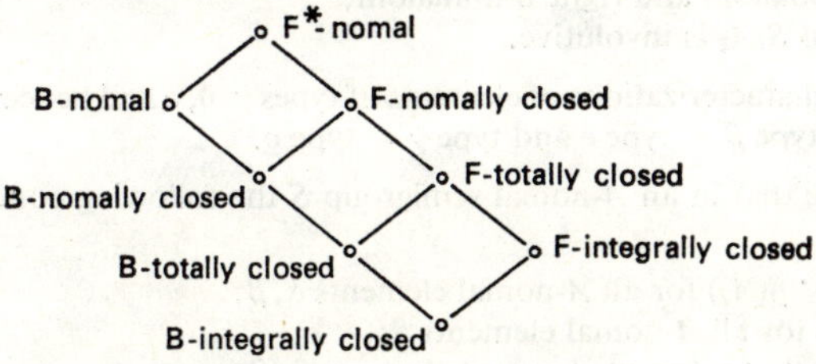

The examples which follow in the exercises show that these types of semigroup are, in general, distinct.

EXERCISES

28.1. Let S be the ordered set of Example 28.1. Define a multiplication on S by the prescription $(p, i)\,(q, j) = (\min\{p, q\}, i + j)$. Show that S becomes an abelian B-nomal semigroup.

28.2. Prove that every residuated semigroup with a minimal element (in particular every finite residuated semigroup) is B-nomal and that in this case the A-nomal, F-nomal and B-nomal equivalences all coincide with the zigzag equivalence Z. Deduce that such a semigroup is B-nomally closed.

28.3. Let S be a B-nomal semigroup. Let $T = \{x \in S;\ x \,.\!\cdot\, x = \xi = x \,\cdot\!.\, x\}$. Prove that T is a B-totally closed subsemigroup of S.

28.4. If S is a B-nomal semigroup with neutral element and $\beta \in S$ is B-nomal, prove that $\beta \in K_\xi$, where K_ξ is defined as in Theorem 26.6. Deduce that every B-nomal semigroup with a neutral element admits a greatest B-integrally closed subsemigroup.

28.5. Show that every ordered group is B-integrally closed.

28.6. Show that in a Boolean algebra B the only A-nomaloid element is π_B and the only B-nomaloid element is 0_B. What about the F-nomaloid elements?

28.7. Let S be a residuated semigroup with a neutral element 1. Show that S is an ordered group if and only if 1 is B-nomal.

28.8. Let S be a residuated semigroup with a maximal element. Prove that S has a minimal element if and only if S is B-nomal.

28.9. If S is a B-nomal semigroup with $\beta \in S$ B-nomal, prove that S is B-nomally closed if and only if

$$(\forall x, y \in S) \quad y \equiv yx \,\cdot\!.\, x \,({}_\beta B).$$

28.10. Referring back to Exercise 23.14 for notation, prove that an element a of a residuated semigroup S is of type β if and only if

(1) a is A-nomaloid and right B-nomaloid;
(2) the group S/A_ξ is involutive.

Deduce similar characterizations of elements of types γ, δ, ε and hence show that in the semigroup case type β = type ε and type γ = type δ.

28.11. Prove that in an A-nomal semigroup S the following conditions are equivalent:

(1) $\alpha\beta \equiv \alpha \,.\!\cdot\, \beta (A_\xi)$ for all A-nomal elements α, β;
(2) $\xi : \beta = \beta$ for all A-nomal elements β;
(3) $\alpha \,\cdot\!.\, \beta = \beta \,.\!\cdot\, \alpha$ for all A-nomal elements α, β;
(4) S contains a maximal element and S/Z is involutive.

Deduce that if S is B-nomal and S/A_ξ is involutive then S contains a maximal element and a minimal element and hence is B-nomally closed.

28.12. Consider in turn all of the residuated semigroups discussed in the text and classify them in terms of nomality.

29. Isotone homomorphic Boolean images of ordered semigroups

In § 25 we began a discussion of the conditions under which an ordered semigroup could be mapped onto an ordered group by an isotone homomorphism. A natural analogue of this is the following: *under what conditions does an ordered semigroup admit an isotone epimorphic image which is a Boolean algebra?* Our goal in this section will be to provide an answer to this question. We shall therefore now be concerned with configurations of the form $f: S \to B$, where S is an ordered semigroup, B is a Boolean algebra and f is an isotone epimorphism [in that $(\forall x, y \in S)\ f(xy) = f(x) \cap f(y)$].

Definition. By a *double ideal* of an ordered semigroup S we shall mean a non-empty subset H of S which is an order ideal of S and a semigroup ideal of S [the latter being expressed by $HS \subseteq H$ and $SH \subseteq H$ or, equivalently, $H \mathbin{.\!^{\cdot}} H = S = H \mathbin{^{\cdot}\!.} H$].

Let us begin by considering a double ideal H which is reflexive and such that $(\forall x \in S)\ H:\{x\} = H:\{x^2\}$. In this case we have

$$\begin{aligned} x \in H:\{ab\} \Rightarrow abx \in H \Rightarrow abxb \in H \Rightarrow xbab \in H \\ \Rightarrow axbab \in H \\ \Rightarrow babax \in H \\ \Rightarrow x \in H:\{(ba)^2\} = H:\{ba\} \end{aligned}$$

from which it follows immediately that

$$(\forall a, b \in S) \quad H:\{ab\} = H:\{ba\}. \tag{1}$$

Now suppose that $x \equiv y(R_H)$, where R_H is the Dubreil equivalence associated with H. If z is any element of S, we have

$$p \in H:\{zx\} \Leftrightarrow pz \in H:\{x\} = H:\{y\} \Leftrightarrow p \in H:\{zy\}.$$

This, together with (1), shows that R_H is compatible with multiplication and that S/R_H is an abelian semigroup. Now define the relation $\leq$ on S/R_H by

$$x/R_H \leq y/R_H \Leftrightarrow H:\{y\} \subseteq H:\{x\}.$$

It is clear that $\leq$ is an ordering and, H being an order ideal, the canonical surjection $\natural_H$ is isotone. Since H is also a semigroup ideal, we also have

$$p \in H:\{x\} \Rightarrow (\forall y \in S) \quad pxy \in H \Rightarrow (\forall y \in S) \quad p \in H:\{xy\}$$

from which it follows that $(\forall x, y \in S)\ xy/R_H \leq x/R_H$. Since S/R_H is abelian xy/R_H is then a lower bound for x/R_H, y/R_H in S/R_H. Now let z/R_H be any such lower bound. Then $H:\{x\} \subseteq H:\{z\}$ and $H:\{y\} \subseteq H:\{z\}$ and so

$$\begin{aligned} p \in H:\{xy\} \Rightarrow px \in H:\{y\} \subseteq H:\{z\} \Rightarrow zp \in H:\{x\} \subseteq H:\{z\} \\ \Rightarrow p \in H:\{z^2\} = H:\{z\}. \end{aligned}$$

We deduce from this that $z/R_H \leq xy/R_H$. This then proves that S/R_H is an $\curlywedge$-semilattice in which $x/R_H \curlywedge y/R_H = xy/R_H$. It is immediate that $\natural_H$ is now an epimorphism.

Now this semilattice contains a minimum element. For, consider the set

$$G_H = \{x \in S;\ H:\{x\} = S\}.$$

Since H is a semigroup ideal we have, for any $h \in H$, $\{h\}\, S \subseteq H$ and so $S = H:\{h\}$ whence $G_H \neq \emptyset$. Moreover, G_H is a class modulo R_H since any element of S which is equivalent modulo R_H to an element of G_H is also an element of G_H and all the elements in G_H are equivalent modulo R_H. Since for all $y \in S$ we have $H:\{y\} \subseteq S$ it follows that G_H is indeed the minimum element of S/R_H. It is also clear that $G_H = H:S$.

Now let us impose on H the condition that it satisfy

$$(\forall x \in S)\,(\exists x^\circ \in S) \quad H:(H:\{x\}) = H:\{x^\circ\}. \tag{2}$$

In this case we can define a mapping $i: S/R_H \to S/R_H$ by the prescription $i(x/R_H) = x^\circ/R_H$. Now

$$\begin{aligned} x/R_H \leq y/R_H &\Rightarrow H:\{y\} \subseteq H:\{x\} \\ &\Rightarrow H:\{x^\circ\} = H:(H:\{x\}) \subseteq H:(H:\{y\}) = H:\{y^\circ\} \\ &\Rightarrow i(y/R_H) = y^\circ/R_H \leq x^\circ/R_H = i(x/R_H) \end{aligned}$$

and so the mapping i is antitone. Furthermore, from the fact that

$$H:\{x\} = H:[H:(H:\{x\})]$$

we deduce that $i \circ i = \mathrm{id}$ and so i is an involution on S/R_H, an immediate consequence of which is that S/R_H is a bounded lattice.

Since from (2) we have $x \in H:\{x^\circ\}$ we see that $xx^\circ \in H$ and therefore $x/R_H \curlywedge i(x/R_H) = xx^\circ/R_H = G_H$. Consequently i is in fact an orthocomplementation on S/R_H.

Suppose now that x/R_H and y/R_H are complements in S/R_H. Then $xy/R_H = G_H$ and so $H:\{xy\} = S$ whence in particular $x^2y \in H$ so that $y \in H:\{x^2\} = H:\{x\}$. Thus $H:\{x^\circ\} = H:(H:\{x\}) \subseteq H:\{y\}$. Now $i(x/R_H)$ and $i(y/R_H)$ are also complements so in a similar way we have $y^\circ \in H:\{x^\circ\}$ and hence $H:\{x\} = H:(H:\{x^\circ\}) \subseteq H:\{y^\circ\}$ so that $H:\{x^\circ\} = H:(H:\{x\}) \supseteq H:(H:\{y^\circ\}) = H:\{y\}$. We deduce that $H:\{y\} = H:\{x^\circ\}$ and hence that complements in S/R_H are unique. An application of Theorem 18.12 now shows that S/R_H is a Boolean algebra.

In summary so far, therefore, if we define a *base* of S to be a non-empty subset H satisfying the properties

(1) H is a reflexive double ideal of S;
(2) $(\forall x \in S) \quad H:\{x\} = H:\{x^2\}$;
(3) $(\forall x \in S)(\exists x^\circ \in S) \quad H:(H:\{x\}) = H:\{x^\circ\}$,

then for each base H the Dubreil equivalence R_H is such that S/R_H is an isotone homomorphic Boolean image of S. We shall now prove the converse, namely that every isotone homomorphic Boolean image of S arises in this manner. For this purpose, let S be an ordered semigroup and let $f: S \to B$ be an isotone epimorphism of S onto a Boolean algebra B. Define $\mathrm{Ker} f = \{x \in S; f(x) = 0\}$ and note that since f is surjective $\mathrm{Ker} f$ is not empty. We show as follows that $\mathrm{Ker} f$ is a base of S. First, if $x \in \mathrm{Ker} f$ and $y \in S$, then $f(xy) = f(x) \cap f(y) = 0 \cap f(y) = 0$ and so $xy \in \mathrm{Ker} f$. In a similar way we have $yx \in \mathrm{Ker} f$, and so $\mathrm{Ker} f$ is a semigroup ideal of S. Clearly $x \in \mathrm{Ker} f$ and $y \leq x$ imply that $y \in \mathrm{Ker} f$ and so $\mathrm{Ker} f$ is a double ideal. Now

$$p \in \mathrm{Ker} f\, ^{\cdot}.\, \{x\} \Leftrightarrow f(p) \cap f(x) = f(px) = 0 \Leftrightarrow f(p) \leq [f(x)]' \quad (\dagger)$$

and it follows immediately from this that $\mathrm{Ker} f$ is reflexive. Since $f(x^2) = f(x) \cap f(x) = f(x)$ for each $x \in S$ we also have $\mathrm{Ker} f:\{x\}$

$= \mathrm{Ker}\, f : \{x^2\}$ for each $x \in S$. Writing $\mathrm{Ker}\, f = I$ we see from (†) that

$$I : \{x\} = \{p \in S;\ f(p) \leq [f(x)]'\}$$

whence, making use of (†) again and the fact that f is surjective,

$$\begin{aligned} I : (I : \{x\}) &= \{z \in S;\ (\forall p \in I : \{x\})\ f(z) \leq [f(p)]'\} \\ &= \{z \in S;\ (\forall p \in I : \{x\})\ f(p) \leq [f(z)]'\} \\ &= \{z \in S;\ [f(x)]' \leq [f(z)]'\} \\ &= \{z \in S;\ f(z) \leq f(x)\} \\ &= I : \{t\} \quad \text{where } t \text{ is such that} \quad f(t) = [f(x)]'. \end{aligned}$$

This then shows that $\mathrm{Ker}\, f$ is a base of S.
Now, again from (†) and the fact that f is surjective, we have

$$\begin{aligned} \mathrm{Ker}\, f : \{x\} = \mathrm{Ker}\, f : \{y\} &\Leftrightarrow \{f(p) \leq [f(x)]' \Leftrightarrow f(p) \leq [f(y)]'\} \\ &\Leftrightarrow [f(x)]' = [f(y)]' \\ &\Leftrightarrow f(x) = f(y). \end{aligned}$$

We can therefore define a mapping $\zeta : B \to S/R_{\mathrm{Ker}\, f}$ by the prescription $\zeta\, [f(x)] = x/R_{\mathrm{Ker}\, f}$. Since

$$\mathrm{Ker}\, f : \{x\} \subseteq \mathrm{Ker}\, f : \{y\} \Leftrightarrow f(x) \geq f(y),$$

it follows that ζ is an isomorphism.

We can now summarize the above as follows:

THEOREM 29.1. *Let S be an ordered semigroup. If H is a base of S and R_H is the associated Dubreil equivalence, then S/R_H is an isotone homomorphic Boolean image of S. Moreover, every isotone homomorphic Boolean image of S arises in this manner.*

Definition. We shall say that a base H is *strong* if it is such that $H = H . \cdot S = H \cdot . S$.

With this terminology, we have the following:

COROLLARY. *The set of isotone homomorphisms which map S onto a Boolean algebra is equipotent to the set of strong bases of S.*

Proof. For each isotone homomorphism f of S onto a Boolean algebra B the base $\operatorname{Ker} f$ is strong since, on the one hand,

$$\begin{aligned} p \in \operatorname{Ker} f : S &\Leftrightarrow (\forall y \in S) \quad py \in \operatorname{Ker} f \\ &\Leftrightarrow (\forall y \in S) \quad f(p) \leq [f(y)]' \end{aligned}$$

and, on the other, f being surjective, there exists $y \in S$ such that $f(y) = \pi$, the maximum element of B. Consequently $p \in \operatorname{Ker} f : S \Leftrightarrow f(p) = 0 \Leftrightarrow p \in \operatorname{Ker} f$ and so $\operatorname{Ker} f : S = \operatorname{Ker} f$.

Since, as was shown above, f is completely determined by $\operatorname{Ker} f$ (and conversely), it suffices to show that if H is a base then $H : S$ is a strong base and $R_H = R_{H:S}$. Now

$$\operatorname{Ker} \natural_H = \{x \in S;\ x/R_H = G_H\} = G_H = H : S$$

and so $H : S$ is indeed a strong base. That $R_H = R_{H:S}$ follows the fact that

$$\begin{aligned} x/R_H = y/R_H \Leftrightarrow \natural_H(x) = \natural_H(y) &\Leftrightarrow \operatorname{Ker} \natural_H : \{x\} = \operatorname{Ker} \natural_H : \{y\} \\ &\Leftrightarrow (H : S) : \{x\} = (H : S) : \{y\} \\ &\Leftrightarrow x/R_{H:S} = y/R_{H:S}. \end{aligned}$$

Let us now impose on S the condition that it be a $\cup$-semireticulated semigroup; i.e. is also a $\cup$-semilattice in which multiplication is distributive over union. By a homomorphism in this case we shall mean a mapping $f : S \to B$ such that $(\forall x, y \in S) f(xy) = f(x) \cap f(y)$ and $f(x \cup y) = f(x) \cup f(y)$. In such a semigroup we have, for any $\cup$-subsemilattice H which is also an order ideal, $H : \{x \cup y\} = H : \{x\} \cap H : \{y\}$. For $p \in H : \{x \cup y\} \Leftrightarrow px \cup py = p(x \cup y) \in H \Leftrightarrow px \in H$ and $py \in H \Leftrightarrow p \in H : \{x\} \cap H : \{y\}$. Thus R_H is compatible with union; for if $x \equiv y(R_H)$ and z is any element of S, then

$$H : \{x \cup z\} = H : \{x\} \cap H : \{z\} = H : \{y\} \cap H : \{z\} = H : \{y \cup z\}.$$

It follows that if H satisfies the properties (1) and (2) of a base and if H is both a $\cup$-subsemilattice and an order ideal of S, then S/R_H is a lattice in which $x/R_H \curlywedge y/R_H = xy/R_H$ and $x/R_H \curlyvee y/R_H = (x \cup y)/R_H$. Moreover, from the property $x(y \cup z) = xy \cup xz$ we see, on passing to quotients, that S/R_H is a distributive lattice. It is natural to inquire under what conditions it is a Boolean algebra. Suppose, in fact, that this were the case. Then H must also satisfy property (3) of a base and so we have

$$\begin{aligned} y \in H:\{x \cup x^\circ\} &\Leftrightarrow y \in H:\{x\} \quad \text{and} \quad y \in H:\{x^\circ\} \\ &\Leftrightarrow H:\{x^\circ\} \subseteq H:\{y\} \quad \text{and} \quad H:\{x\} \subseteq H:\{y\} \\ &\Leftrightarrow y/R_H \leq x^\circ/R_H \quad \text{and} \quad y/R_H \leq x/R_H \\ &\Leftrightarrow y/R_H \leq x^\circ/R_H \curlywedge x/R_H = G_H \\ &\Leftrightarrow y \in G_H = H:S. \end{aligned}$$

Consequently,

$$(\forall x \in S)\,(\exists x^\circ \in S) \quad H:\{x \cup x^\circ\} = H:S. \tag{α}$$

Moreover,

$$\begin{aligned} H:\{xx^\circ\} &= (H:\{x^\circ\}) \cdot\!. \{x\} = [H:(H:\{x\})] \cdot\!. \{x\} \\ &= (H:\{x\}) \cdot\!. (H:\{x\}) = S. \end{aligned} \tag{β}$$

Conversely, if these conditions hold, then $E_H = \{a \in S;\ H:\{a\} = H:S\} \neq \emptyset$ and, as before, we can show that E_H is the maximum element of S/R_H. It follows from (α) and (β) that x°/R_H is a complement of x/R_H in S/R_H. Hence S/R_H is a Boolean algebra. Remembering that a base H is strong if and only if $H = H:S$, we can sum the situation up in the following theorem:

THEOREM 29.2. *Let S be a $\cup$-semireticulated semigroup. There is a bijection between the set of homomorphisms of S onto a Boolean algebra and the set of subsets H of S having the properties*

(1) *H is a reflexive double ideal of S which is a $\cup$-subsemilattice;*
(2) $(\forall x \in S)$ $H:\{x\} = H:\{x^2\}$;
(3) $(\forall x \in S)\,(\exists x^\circ \in S)$ $H:\{xx^\circ\} = S$ *and* $H:\{x \cup x^\circ\} = H$.

Proof. In view of the previous remarks, it suffices to note that if $f: S \to B$ is a homomorphism then $\operatorname{Ker} f$ satisfies (1) and that if H satisfies the condition (3) then

$$H : S = H : \bigcup_{x \in S} \{x\} = \bigcap_{x \in S} H : \{x\} = H.$$

We shall leave a discussion of maximum homomorphic Boolean images to the exercises for this section. The conditions encountered so far are in general difficult to handle, so we shall proceed, as we did with group images, to consider a particular case obtained by strengthening the notion of a homomorphism. The reader will recall that when dealing with group images we met with a condition which was a nuisance because of its complexity, namely the condition that the core of S be strongly neat. This condition disappeared altogether whenever we required the bimaximum element to be residuated; and this is equivalent to saying that f is residuated (Theorem 25.4). As the following results show, if we pass directly to residuated homomorphisms an equally pleasant state of affairs exists for Boolean images.

THEOREM 29.3. *Let S be an ordered semigroup, B a Boolean algebra and $f: S \to B$ an isotone epimorphism. The following conditions are equivalent:*

(1) *f is residuated;*

(2) Ker *f has a maximum element t which is equiresidual.*

Proof. Let f be residuated. Then clearly Ker f admits a maximum element. Let this element be t; then we have

$$\begin{aligned} xy \leq t &\Leftrightarrow f(x) \cap f(y) = f(xy) \leq f(t) = 0 \\ &\Leftrightarrow f(y) \leq [f(x)]' \\ &\Leftrightarrow y \leq f^{+}[f(x)]'. \end{aligned}$$

Thus $t \,.\!\cdot\, x$ exists and is $f^{+}[f(x)]'$. In a similar way we can show that $t \cdot\!.\, x$ exists and is also $f^{+}[f(x)]'$.

Conversely, if Ker $f = [\leftarrow, t]$ with t equiresidual, then f being surjective, for each $y \in B$ there exists $y^* \in S$ such that $f(y^*) = y'$ and so

$$\begin{aligned} f(x) \leq y &\Leftrightarrow f(xy^*) = f(x) \cap f(y^*) = f(x) \cap y' = 0 \\ &\Leftrightarrow xy^* \leq t \\ &\Leftrightarrow x \leq t : y^*. \end{aligned}$$

It follows that f is residuated.

Definition. An element t of a residuated semigroup S will be called *right quasi-integral* if $\langle t \,.^{\cdot}\, t\rangle = S$, *left quasi-integral* if $\langle t \,^{\cdot}.\, t\rangle = S$ and *quasi-integral* if $\langle t \,.^{\cdot}\, t\rangle = S = \langle t \,^{\cdot}.\, t\rangle$.

THEOREM 29.4. *If $x \in S$ is quasi-integral and residuated, then*

(1) *S has a maximum element, namely $\pi = x \,.^{\cdot}\, x = x \,^{\cdot}.\, x$;*
(2) *$(\forall y \in S)$ $x \,.^{\cdot}\, y$ is right quasi-integral and $x \,^{\cdot}.\, y$ is left quasi-integral.*

Proof. (1) is immediate. As for (2), we observe that if $q = x \,.^{\cdot}\, y$ then $yq \leq x$ and so, for each $z \in S$, $yqz \leq xz \leq x$ whence $qz \leq x \,.^{\cdot}\, y = q$ and so $S = \langle q \,.^{\cdot}\, q\rangle$.

THEOREM 29.5. *An ordered semigroup S admits a Boolean algebra as image under a residuated homomorphism if and only if it admits an element t such that*

(1) *t is quasi-integral;*
(2) *t is equiresidual;*
(3) $(\forall x \in S)$ $\quad t : x = t : x^2$.

Each residuated homomorphic Boolean image of S is of the form S/A_t for such an element t and there is a bijection between the set of residuated homomorphisms of S onto a Boolean algebra and the set of elements $t \in S$ satisfying (1), (2), (3), *and*

(4) $t = t : (t : t)$.

Proof. Suppose first that S admits a Boolean algebra B as image under a residuated homomorphism f. Then $\operatorname{Ker} f = [\leftarrow, t]$ is a base of S. By Theorem 29.3, t is equiresidual. Since $[\leftarrow, t]$ is an ideal of S, we have $(\forall x \in S)$ $xt \leq t$ and $tx \leq t$ whence t is also quasi-integral. The property (2) in the definition of a base then yields property (3) of the theorem. The conditions are therefore necessary.

Conversely, let $t \in S$ satisfy (1), (2), (3) and consider $H = [\leftarrow, t]$. By (1), H is an ideal of S. By (2), H is reflexive. Thus (1), (2), (3) imply that H satisfies conditions (1), (2) in the definition of a base. Let us now show that the condition (3) in the definition of a base is also implied by (1), (2), (3) above. First we note that

$$[\leftarrow, t]:([\leftarrow, t]:\{x\}) = [\leftarrow, t]:\langle t:x\rangle = [\leftarrow, t]: \bigcup_{y\in\langle t:x\rangle} \{y\} = \bigcap_{y\in\langle t:x\rangle} \langle t:y\rangle.$$

Now since $\langle t:x\rangle$ admits a maximum element, namely the element $t:x$, this intersection is none other than $\langle t:(t:x)\rangle$. This then shows that property (3) is satisfied with $x^\circ = t:x$. The Theorem now follows by Theorem 29.1. All we have to do as far as the last part is concerned is to observe that a base of the form $[\leftarrow, t]$, where t satisfies (1), (2), (3), is strong if and only if

$$[\leftarrow, t] = [\leftarrow, t]:S = [\leftarrow, t]:\bigcup_{x\in S}\{x\} = \bigcap_{x\in S}\langle t:x\rangle.$$

But S has a maximum element, namely $t:t$ (Theorem 29.4). This intersection therefore reduces to $\langle t:(t:t)\rangle$ and so the above equality holds if and only if t also satisfies (4).

Taking multiplication in S to be commutative and idempotent, we deduce from Theorem 29.5 the following particular case.

THEOREM 29.6. *Let S be an $\cap$-semilattice. Then there is a bijection between the set of residuated homomorphisms of S onto a Boolean algebra and the set of elements $t\in S$ which are residuated. Every residuated epimorphic Boolean image of S is of the form S/A_t for each such element t.*

Proof. Every element of S is idempotent and quasi-integral. Moreover, if $x\in S$ is residuated then a maximum element exists, namely $\pi = x:x$. Since π is then the neutral element we have $x:(x:x) = x:\pi = x$. It follows from these observations that the conditions in the previous theorem are in this case equivalent to t being residuated.

Let us note that if t satisfies the conditions (1), (2), (3) of Theorem 29.5, then the Boolean algebra S/A_t is ordered according to the prescription

$$x/A_t \le y/A_t \Leftrightarrow t:y \le t:x \Leftrightarrow t:(t:x) \le t:(t:y),$$

and since A_t is a closure equivalence this is equivalent to $x \le t:(t:y)$. It follows that the set $R(t)$ of residuals of t forms a Boolean algebra which is isomorphic to S/A_t. For our future use, we shall end this section by determining explicitly the laws of this Boolean algebra.

Since t is quasi-integral and equiresidual, it follows by Theorem 29.4 that every element of $R(t)$ is quasi-integral. [Moreover, by Theorem 25.5, every element of $R(t)$ is also equiresidual.] Thus, given any $a, b \in R(t)$, we have

$$t:(t:ab) \leq t:(t:a) = a \quad \text{and} \quad t:(t:ab) \leq t:(t:b) = b,$$

so that $t:(t:ab)$ is a lower bound for $\{a, b\}$ in $R(t)$. If $x \in R(t)$ is any such lower bound then from $x \leq a$ and $x \leq b$ we have $x^2 \leq ab$ and so, using (3), $x = t:(t:x) = t:(t:x^2) \leq t:(t:ab)$. It follows from this that intersection in $R(t)$ is given by

$$a \curlywedge b = t:(t:ab) = t:(t:ba).$$

In a similar way we have

$$t:(t:a)(t:b) \geq t:(t:a) = a \quad \text{and} \quad t:(t:a)(t:b) \geq t:(t:b) = b.$$

If $x \in R(t)$ is any upper bound for $\{a, b\}$ in $R(t)$, then $t:x \leq t:a$ and $t:x \leq t:b$ so that $x = t:(t:x) = t:(t:x)^2 \geq t:(t:a)(t:b)$. We have thus shown that unions in $R(t)$ are given by

$$a \curlyvee b = t:(t:a)(t:b) = t:(t:b)(t:a).$$

Now as was observed in the proof of Theorem 29.5, the element $a^\circ = t:a$ satisfies the property (3) in the definition of a base and so it follows from the proof of Theorem 29.1 that a° is the complement of a in $R(t)$. This fact may also be shown directly using the above formulae; for the reader will have no trouble in showing that the maximum element of $R(t)$ is the element $t:t$ and the minimum element of $R(t)$ is the element $t:(t:t)$.

EXERCISES

29.1. Consider the ordered semigroup described by the following Cayley table and Hasse diagram:

	x	y	o
x	y	o	o
y	o	o	o
o	o	o	o

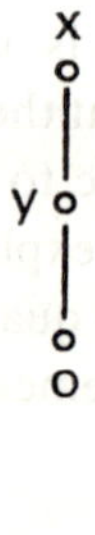

Show that the subset $H = \{0\}$ satisfies the properties (1) and (3) of a base but does not satisfy (2). Deduce that although S/R_H is a Boolean algebra, $\natural_H$ is not an isotone epimorphism. Show also that S is residuated and that S/A_0 is a residuated homomorphic Boolean image of S.

29.2. Let B, X be Boolean algebras. Define a *Boolean homomorphism* to be a mapping $f: B \to X$ such that, for all $x, y \in B$,

$$(1)\ f(x \cap y) = f(x) \cap f(y);\quad (2)\ f(x \cup y) = f(x) \cup f(y);\quad (3)\ f(x') = [f(x)]'.$$

Show that if f satisfies (1) and (2) then f satisfies (3) if and only if $f(0) = 0$ and $f(\pi) = \pi$. Show also that if f satisfies (1) and (3) then it also satisfies (2).

29.3. Define an ordered semigroup S to have a maximum isotone homomorphic Boolean image if and only if there is associated with S a Boolean algebra B and an isotone epimorphism $f: S \to B$ such that, for any Boolean algebra X and isotone epimorphism $g: S \to X$, there is a unique $\cap$-epimorphism $\zeta: B \to X$ such that $\zeta \circ f = g$. Show that S admits a maximum isotone homomorphic Boolean image if and only if the set Δ of Dubreil equivalences associated with the bases of S admits a minimum element.

29.4. Define the maximum isotone homomorphic Boolean image of an ordered semigroup to be *standard* if each epimorphism ζ in its definition is a Boolean epimorphism. Show that an ordered semigroup S admits a standard isotone homomorphic Boolean image if and only if:

(1) the set Γ of strong bases of S admits a minimum element H;
(2) $(\forall J \in \Gamma)\ H:(H:\{x^\circ\}) = H:\{x\} \Rightarrow J:(J:\{x^\circ\}) = J:\{x\}$.

29.5. Consider the following Hasse diagram and Cayley table:

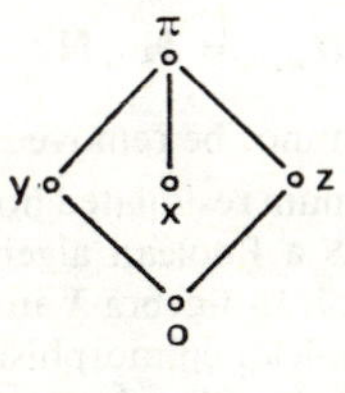

	o	y	x	z	π
o	o	o	o	o	o
y	o	y	o	y	y
z	o	o	z	z	z
x	o	y	z	π	π
π	o	y	z	π	π

Show that these define an ordered semigroup S whose bases are $\{0\}$, $[\leftarrow, y]$, $[\leftarrow, z]$, $\{0, y, z, \pi\}$, S. Which of these bases are strong? Show that S admits a standard maximum isotone homomorphic Boolean image.

29.6. Consider the $\cap$-semilattice as suggested by the following diagram:

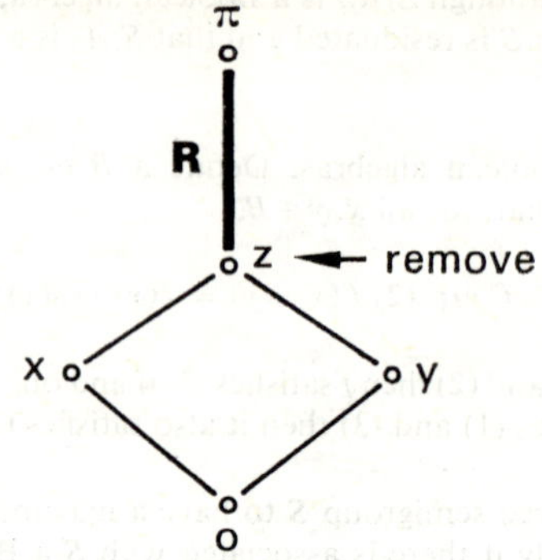

Show that the bases of S are $\{0\}$, $[\leftarrow, x]$, $[\leftarrow, y]$, $\{0, x, y\}$, $[\leftarrow, r]$ for each $r \in \mathbf{R}$, S. Deduce that the condition (2) of Exercise 29.4 cannot be removed.

29.7. Define a $\cup$-semireticulated semigroup S to have a maximum homomorphic Boolean image if and only if there is associated with S a Boolean algebra B and an epimorphism $f: S \to B$ such that, for any Boolean algebra X and epimorphism $g: S \to X$, there is a unique lattice epimorphism [hence Boolean, by Exercise 29.2] $\zeta: B \to X$ such that $\zeta \circ f = g$. Prove that the following are equivalent:

(1) S admits a maximum homomorphic Boolean image;

(2) the set Δ of Dubreil equivalences associated with the bases of S admits a minimum element;

(3) the set Γ of bases of S admits a minimum element H which is such that $(\forall J \in \Gamma)$ $H: \{x\} = H \Rightarrow J: \{x\} = J$.

29.8. Consider the set $\mathbf{N} \times \mathbf{N}$ of ordered pairs of natural numbers. Order $\mathbf{N} \times \mathbf{N}$ in the usual cartesian way. Observe that we obtain a distributive lattice which we may regard as a $\cup$-semireticulated semigroup in which multiplication is intersection. Show that the bases of $\mathbf{N} \times \mathbf{N}$ are the finite rectangles $H_{n,m} = [0, n] \times [0, m]$ and the infinite rectangles

$$H_{n,\infty} = \bigcup_{m \in \mathbf{N}} H_{n,m}; \quad H_{\infty,m} = \bigcup_{n \in \mathbf{N}} H_{n,m}; \quad H_{\infty,\infty} = \mathbf{N} \times \mathbf{N}.$$

Deduce that the second condition in Exercise 29.7 (3) cannot be removed.

29.9. Define an ordered semigroup S to have a maximum residuated homomorphic Boolean image if and only if there is associated with S a Boolean algebra B and a residuated epimorphism $f: S \to B$ such that, for every Boolean algebra X and residuated epimorphism $g: S \to X$, there is a unique residuated Boolean epimorphism $\zeta: B \to X$ such that $\zeta \circ f = g$. Let S be an $\cap$-semilattice. Show that the following are equivalent:

(1) S admits a maximum residuated homomorphic Boolean image;

(2) the set of equivalences A_t associated with the residuated elements of S admits a minimum element;

(3) the set of residuated elements in S admits a minimum element p and the only residuated elements in S are the residuals of p.

29.10. (a) Show that the lattice

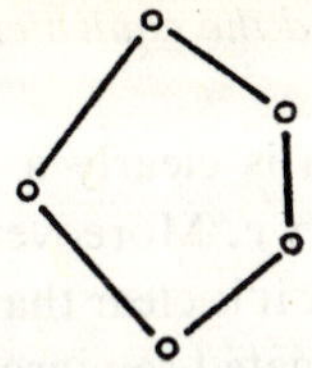

admits a maximum residuated homomorphic Boolean image.

(b) By considering the 3-element chain $0 < x < \pi$, show that the second condition of Exercise 29.9(3) cannot be removed.

30. Glivenko semigroups

Definition. By a *pseudo-residuated semigroup* we shall mean an ordered semigroup S with an equiresidual zero element 0. The residuals of 0 will be called the *pseudo-residuals* of S. By a *Glivenko semigroup* we shall mean a pseudo-residuated semigroup S which is such that S/A_0 is idempotent.

We note first that if S is a Glivenko semigroup, then the element 0 is endowed with the conditions (1), (2), (3) of Theorem 29.5 and hence S/A_0 is a Boolean algebra. If we write $0:x = x^*$ for each $x \in S$ and denote by S^{**} the set $R(0)$ of residuals of 0, then, according to the discussion given at the end of the previous section,

$$(\forall a, b \in S^{**}) \begin{cases} a \curlyvee b = 0:(0:a)(0:b) = (a^*b^*)^*; \\ a \curlywedge b = 0:(0:ab) = (ab)^{**}. \end{cases}$$

Moreover, the maximum element of S^{**} is $0:0 = 0^*$, the minimum element is $0:(0:0) = 0^{**}$ and the complement of $a \in S^{**}$ is a^*. As mentioned previously, every element of S^{**} is equiresidual; by the compatibility of A_0 with multiplication, we have

$$\begin{aligned} x^*:y = (0:x):y = 0:xy &= 0:[0:(0:x)]\,[0:(0:y)] \\ &= (0:x) \curlyvee (0:y) \\ &= x^* \curlyvee y^*. \end{aligned}$$

We shall require all of these facts in the results which follow.

THEOREM 30.1. *A pseudo-residuated semigroup is a Boolean algebra if and only if it is idempotent and the equivalence A_0 reduces to equality.*

Proof. A Boolean algebra is clearly a pseudo-residuated semigroup under the definition $xy = x \cap y$. Moreover, each element is idempotent and since $0 : x = x'$ for each x it is clear that A_0 reduces to equality. Conversely, if S is a pseudo-residuated semigroup which is idempotent, then so also is S/A_0. Thus S is a Glivenko semigroup and S/A_0 is a Boolean algebra. If A_0 reduces to equality, it follows that S is a Boolean algebra.

It should be noted that in a Glivenko semigroup the element 0 need not be the minimum element, nor even minimal, as the following example shows.

EXAMPLE 30.1. Consider the set S described by

$$S = \{\pi, x_i\ (i = 1, 2, 3, \ldots), 0^+, 0, y_j\ (j = 1, 2, 3, \ldots)\}.$$

Endow S with the following Cayley table and Hasse diagram:

	π x_1 x_2 x_3 $\cdots$	0^+ 0	y_1 y_2 y_3 $\cdots$
π x_1 x_2 x_3 $\vdots$	$\pi^2 = \pi$; $\pi x_i = x_i = x_i \pi$; $x_i x_j = x_{i+j}$	0	0
0^+ 0	0	0	0
y_1 y_2 y_3 $\vdots$	0	0	$y_i y_j = y_i$

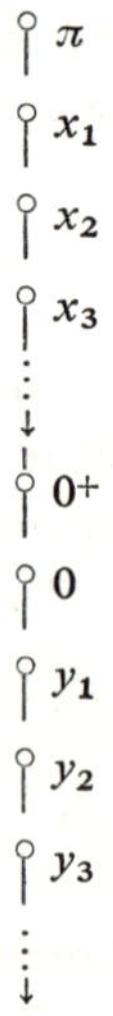

It is clear that S is an ordered semigroup. The element 0 is equiresidual; in fact, for each index i,

$$0:x_i = 0:\pi = 0^+ \quad \text{and} \quad 0:y_i = 0:0 = 0:0^+ = \pi.$$

It is readily seen that S/A_0 is idempotent, so that S is a Glivenko semigroup.

Let us now investigate some of the properties of Glivenko semigroups.

THEOREM 30.2. *If S is a Glivenko semigroup, then*

(1) $p \in [0, 0^{**}] \Rightarrow (\forall x \in S) \quad px = 0 = xp$;

(2) $0:x = 0^{**} \Rightarrow (\forall a \in S) \quad 0:xa = 0:a$;

(3) $(\forall x, y \in S) \quad x^*y^* \equiv x^* \curlywedge y^*(A_0)$.

Proof. (1) For each $x \in S$ we have, $0:0$ being the maximum element, $x0^{**} = x[0:(0:0)] \leq x[0:x] \leq 0$ and so if $p \in [0, 0^{**}]$ we obtain from this $0 = x0 \leq xp \leq x0^{**} \leq 0$ whence (1) follows.

(2) Let $p = 0:xa$; then $xap \leq 0$ and $ap \leq 0:x = 0^{**}$. Thus, for each $y \in S$, $yap \leq y0^{**} = 0$ [by (1)]. In particular, let $y = a$; we obtain $a^2p \leq 0$ and so $p \leq 0:a^2 = 0:a$. Now let $q = 0:a$; we have $aq \leq 0$ and so $xaq \leq x0 = 0$ whence $q \leq 0:xa$. It follows that $p = q$ and this gives (2).

(3) $x^* \curlywedge y^* = (x^*y^*)^{**}$.

THEOREM 30.3. *If S is a Glivenko semigroup then the mapping described by $x \to x^{**} = 0:(0:x)$ is a closure mapping of S onto S^{**} and the following conditions are equivalent:*

(1) $(\forall a, b \in S) \quad (ab)^{**} = a^{**}b^{**}$;

(2) *S^{**} is a subsemigroup of S;*

(3) *each element of S^{**} is idempotent.*

Furthermore, $a^{**} = b^{**}$ if there exists $d \in S$ such that $d^{**} = 0:0$ and $da = bd$. The converse of this is not in general true, but does hold if S is a $\cup$-semireticulated semigroup in which $(\forall x, y \in S)$ $x^2y = xy^2$.

Proof. It is clear that the mapping $x \to x^{**}$ is a closure mapping of S onto S^{**}. That (1) $\Rightarrow$ (2) is obvious. Conversely, since $a^{**}b^{**} \equiv ab$

$\equiv (ab)^{**}(A_0)$, we have (2) $\Rightarrow$ (1). To show that (2) $\Rightarrow$ (3), we observe that by Theorem 30.2(3) we have $x^*y^* = x^* \curlywedge y^*$ [for under the hypothesis (2), x^*y^* must be a pseudo-residual and hence maximum in its class modulo A_0]. Setting $y^* = x^*$ we obtain (3). Conversely, suppose that each element of S^{**} is idempotent. Since $x^{**} \geq (x^* \curlyvee y^*)^*$ and $y^{**} \geq (x^* \curlyvee y^*)^*$, we have $x^{**}y^{**} \geq [(x^* \curlyvee y^*)^*]^2 = (x^* \curlyvee y^*)^*$. But we know that $(x^{**}y^{**})^* = x^* \curlyvee y^*$, so that $x^{**}y^{**} \leq (x^{**}y^{**})^{**} = (x^* \curlyvee y^*)^*$. Thus $x^{**}y^{**} = (x^* \curlyvee y^*)^* = x^{**} \curlywedge y^{**}$. Writing x^* for x and y^* for y this becomes $x^*y^* = x^* \curlywedge y^*$ and this shows that S^{**} is a subsemigroup of S.

To prove the next assertion, we suppose that there exists $d \in S$ such that $d^{**} = 0:0$ and $da = bd$. Then

$$d^* = d^{***} = (0:0)^* = 0:(0:0) = 0^{**}.$$

Moreover, since S/A_0 is abelian, $0: db = 0: bd = 0: da$. It follows by Theorem 30.2(2) that $0: b = 0: a$ whence $a^{**} = b^{**}$.

That the converse of this does not hold in general may be seen by considering Example 30.1. There we have, for instance, $x_1^{**} = x_2^{**}$ [$= \pi$] and any element d satisfying $d^{**} = 0:0$ is either π or one of the x_i; the condition $dx_1 = x_2 d$ is then never satisfied, for $\pi x_1 = x_1 \neq x_2 = x_2 \pi$ and ($i = 1, 2, 3, \ldots$) $x_i x_1 = x_{i+1} \neq x_{i+2} = x_2 x_i$.

To show that the converse does hold under the conditions stated, we consider, for any pair of elements $a, b \in S$ which are such that $a^{**} = b^{**}$, the element $d = ba \cup b^*a^*$. Bearing in mind that $a^{**} = b^{**}$ is equivalent to $a^* = b^*$, we have

$$\begin{cases} d^* \leq (ba)^* = 0: ba = (0:a): b = (0:b): b = 0: b^2 = 0: b = b^*; \\ d^* \leq (b^*a^*)^* = [(b^*)^2]^* = b^{**}, \end{cases}$$

whence $d^* \leq b^* \curlywedge b^{**} = 0^{**}$. Since 0^{**} is the minimum element of S^{**} it follows that $d^* = 0^{**}$ and so $d^{**} = 0^*$. Furthermore,

$$bd = b\,(ba \cup b^*a^*) = b^2 a \cup bb^*a^*$$

and

$$da = (ba \cup b^*a^*)\,a = ba^2 \cup b^*a^*a.$$

Now $bb^* = b(0:b) \leq 0$ and so $bb^*a^* \leq 0a^* = 0$. But $b^* \geq 0^{**}$ and $a^* \geq 0^{**}$, so that $b^*a^* \geq 0^{**}0^{**} = 0$ [Theorem 30.2(1)] and consequently $bb^*a^* \geq b0 = 0$. Thus $bb^*a^* = 0$ and likewise $b^*a^*a = 0$. Under the hypothesis that $b^2a = ba^2$, we then obtain $bd = da$ as required.

Remark. Note that the above converse does not hold if we delete the condition $x^2y = xy^2$. This may be seen by referring to Example 30.1 which is $\cup$-semireticulated since the Hasse diagram is a chain.

THEOREM 30.4. *The equivalences of type A associated with the pseudo-residuals of a Glivenko semigroup S from a Boolean algebra which is isomorphic to the Boolean algebra S^{**} of pseudo-residuals.*

Proof. Denoting by T the set of equivalences of type A associated with the pseudo-residuals in S, we order T in the usual way, namely

$$A_{x^*} \leq A_{y^*} \Leftrightarrow (a \equiv b(A_{x^*}) \Rightarrow a \equiv b(A_{y^*})).$$

Now if $a \equiv b(A_{x^*})$ then

$$x^* \curlyvee a^* = x^* : a = x^* : b = x^* \curlyvee b^*.$$

Thus if $x^* \leq y^*$ we have

$$y^* \curlyvee a^* = y^* \curlyvee x^* \curlyvee a^* = y^* \curlyvee x^* \curlyvee b^* = y^* \curlyvee b^*,$$

so that $a \equiv b(A_{y^*})$. This then shows that $x^* \leq y^* \Rightarrow A_{x^*} \leq A_{y^*}$. To obtain the converse implication, we observe that

$$x^* : (x^* : 0) = x^* \curlyvee (x^* : 0)^* = x^* \curlyvee (x^* \curlyvee 0^*)^* = x^* \curlyvee 0^{**} = x^*.$$

Thus, since the greatest element in the class of 0 modulo A_{x^*} is $x^* : (x^* : 0)$, we have $A_{x^*} \leq A_{y^*} \Rightarrow x^* \leq y^*$; for from $A_{x^*} \leq A_{y^*}$ we deduce that the greatest element in the class of 0 modulo A_{x^*} is less than or equal to the greatest element in the class of 0 modulo A_{y^*}. It follows from the above observations that S^{**} and T are isomorphic under the mapping $x^* \to A_{x^*}$.

Definition. If S is a Glivenko semigroup then we shall say that $d \in S$ is *dense* if and only if $d^{**} = 0^*$.

As we shall see, the set of dense elements plays an important rôle in the properties of a particular type of Glivenko semigroup. For the present we mention only the following important fact.

THEOREM 30.5. *The set D of dense elements of a Glivenko semigroup S is a semigroup filter of S.*

Proof. Let $x, y \in D$; then by the compatibility of A_0 with multiplication, $(xy)^{**} = (x^{**}y^{**})^{**} = x^{**} \curlywedge y^{**} = 0^* \curlywedge 0^* = 0^*$ and so $xy \in D$. Also, if $x \in D$ with $y \geq x$, then $y^{**} \geq x^{**} = 0^*$ and so $y^{**} = 0^*$ whence $y \in D$. Thus D is a subsemigroup of S which is a filter of the ordered set S; i.e. a semigroup filter of S.

Definition. By a *Glivenko $\cap$-semilattice* we shall mean a Glivenko semigroup S which is an $\cap$-semilattice in which multiplication coincides with intersection.

THEOREM 30.6. *If S is a Glivenko $\cap$-semilattice then the mapping $(^{**}): S \to S^{**}$ is a closure mapping on S and a surjective homomorphism in the sense that it preserves intersections, pseudo-residuals, the zero element and (whenever they exist) unions.*

Proof. Intersection being the same as multiplication, property (3) of Theorem 30.3 holds, whence so also does property (1). Thus $(^{**})$ preserves intersections. Moreover, by Theorem 30.2(1) we have $0^{**} = 0^{**} \cap 0^{**} = 0^{**}0^{**} = 0$, so that $(^{**})$ also preserves the zero element. Finally, if $x \cup y$ exists in S then from $x \leq x \cup y$ and $y \leq x \cup y$ we obtain $x^* \geq (x \cup y)^*$, $y^* \geq (x \cup y)^*$ and so $x^* \cap y^* \geq (x \cup y)^*$. But $x \leq x^{**} \leq (x^* \cap y^*)^*$ and $y \leq y^{**} \leq (x^* \cap y^*)^*$ and so $x \cup y \leq (x^* \cap y^*)^*$ whence $(x \cup y)^* \geq (x^* \cap y^*)^{**}$. It follows from these observations that $(x \cup y)^* = (x^* \cap y^*)^{**} = (x^*y^*)^{**} = x^* \curlywedge y^*$ and consequently $(x \cup y)^{**} = (x^* \curlywedge y^*)^* = x^{**} \curlyvee y^{**}$.

Definition. By a *Glivenko $\cup$-semigroup* we mean a Glivenko semigroup which is also a $\cup$-semilattice.

THEOREM 30.7. *If S is a Glivenko $\cup$-semigroup then*

$$(\forall a, b \in S) \quad a^* \cup b^* \equiv a^* \curlyvee b^*(A_0).$$

Proof. Since $a^* \curlyvee b^* \geq a^*, b^*$ we have $a^* \curlyvee b^* \geq a^* \cup b^*$ so that, on the one hand, $(a^* \cup b^*)^* \geq (a^* \curlyvee b^*)^*$. But $a^*, b^* \leq a^* \cup b^*$ and so $a^{**}, b^{**} \geq (a^* \cup b^*)^*$ whence $(a^* \curlyvee b^*)^* = a^{**} \curlywedge b^{**} \geq (a^* \cup b^*)^*$. Thus $(a^* \cup b^*)^* = (a^* \curlywedge b^*)^*$.

THEOREM 30.8. *The Boolean algebra of pseudo-residuals of a Glivenko $\cup$-semigroup S is a $\cup$-subsemilattice of S if and only if*

$$(\forall a, b \in S) \quad a^* \cup b^* = (ab)^*.$$

Proof. Suppose that S^{**} is a $\cup$-subsemilattice of S. Then by Theorem 30.7 we have $a^* \cup b^* = a^* \curlyvee b^* = (a^{**}b^{**})^* = (ab)^*$. Conversely, if the condition holds then since $a^* \curlyvee b^* = (ab)^*$ we obtain $a^* \curlyvee b^* = (ab)^* = a^* \cup b^*$ and so S^{**} is a $\cup$-subsemilattice of S.

Definition. By a *Stone semigroup* we shall mean a Glivenko $\cup$-semigroup S in which $(\forall a \in S)\ a^* \cup a^{**} = 0^*$.

Note that not every Glivenko $\cup$-semigroup is a Stone semigroup, as is shown by the following example.

EXAMPLE 30.2. Let $S = \{\pi, x, a, b, 0\}$ with Hasse diagram

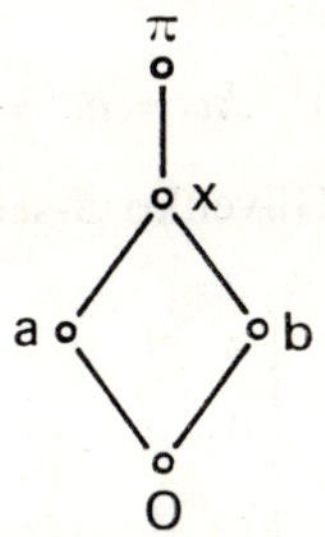

and multiplication given by $(\forall \alpha, \beta \in S)\ \alpha\beta = \alpha \cap \beta$. It is readily seen that S is a Glivenko $\cup$-semigroup but not a Stone semigroup since, for example, $a^* = b$ and $a^{**} = a$ so that $a^* \cup a^{**} = x \neq \pi = 0^*$.

THEOREM 30.9. *If, in the Glivenko $\cup$-semigroup S, the Boolean algebra S^{**} of pseudo-residuals forms a $\cup$-subsemilattice, then S is a Stone semigroup. The converse is not in general true.*

Proof. If S^{**} is a $\cup$-subsemilattice then, as we have just seen, we have the identity $a^* \cup b^* = a^* \curlyvee b^*$. Choosing $b = a^*$ we obtain $a^* \cup a^{**} = a^* \curlyvee a^{**} = 0^*$.

That the converse does not hold in general may be seen from the following:

EXAMPLE 30.3. Consider the ordered semigroup S described by the following Hasse diagram and multiplication:

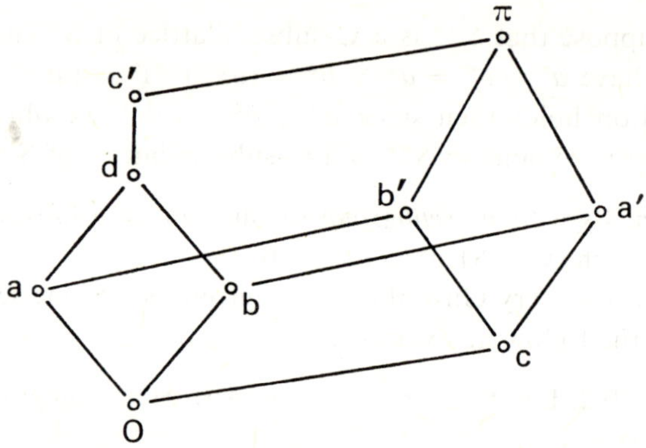

$$xy = x \cap y \quad \text{except that} \quad d\pi = dc' = \pi d = c'd = dd = c'.$$

It is readily verified that S is a Glivenko $\cup$-semigroup in which the pseudo-residuals are given by

$$x^* = \begin{cases} \pi & \text{if } x = 0; \\ 0 & \text{if } x = \pi; \\ c & \text{if } x = d; \\ x' & \text{otherwise,} \end{cases}$$

where the notation is conveniently chosen such that primes denote complements, so that for $x \neq d, \pi, 0$ we have $(x')' = x$. It follows that for each $x \in S$, $x^* \cup x^{**} = \pi = 0^*$ and so S is a Stone semigroup. However, the subset S^{**} is not a $\cup$-subsemilattice; for $a, b \in S^{**}$ whereas $a \cup b = d \notin S^{**}$.

Definition. By a *Glivenko lattice* we shall mean a Glivenko $\cap$-semilattice which is also a $\cup$-semilattice. The notion of a Glivenko lattice is thus synonymous with that of a *pseudo-complemented lattice* as defined in § 7. By a *Stone lattice* we shall mean a distributive Glivenko lattice in which the identity $x^* \cup x^{**} = 0^*$ holds.

THEOREM 30.10. *Let S be a distributive Glivenko lattice. Then the following conditions are equivalent:*

(1) *S is a Stone lattice;*
(2) $(\forall a, b \in S) \quad a^* \cup b^* = (a \cap b)^*$;
(3) *S^{**} is a sublattice.*

Proof. The equivalence of (2) and (3) follows from Theorem 30.8. That (3) $\Rightarrow$ (1) follows from Theorem 30.9. Suppose now that (1) holds. Then every element a^* of S^{**} is complemented in the lattice S [for $a^* \cap a^{**} = a^* \wedge a^{**} = 0^{**} = 0$ and $a^* \cup a^{**} = 0^{**}$]. Now S is distributive by hypothesis, so the complemented elements of S form a sublattice; for if $x, y \in S$ are complemented, then so also are $x \cap y$ and $x \cup y$, respective complements being $x' \cup y'$ and $x' \cap y'$. It therefore follows that (1) $\Rightarrow$ (3).

In the case of a Glivenko lattice which is distributive, we can give an interesting characterization of the equivalence relation [**] associated with the closure mapping (**). We require a few preliminaries which will be of use to us later also.

Definition. If L is an $\cap$-semilattice and J is a filter of L [i.e. a non-empty subset such that $x, y \in J \Rightarrow x \cap y \in J$ and $x \in J, y \geq x \Rightarrow y \in J$], we define the relation $\bigcup_{t \in J} F_t$ by

$$x \equiv y \left(\bigcup_{t \in J} F_t\right) \Leftrightarrow (\exists t \in J) \quad x \cap t = y \cap t.$$

Remark. It should be noted that if E is an arbitrary ordered set and $\{R_\alpha\}_{\alpha \in I}$ is a family of equivalence relations on E, then the relation $\bigcup_{\alpha \in I} R_\alpha$ defined by

$$x \equiv y \left(\bigcup_{\alpha \in I} R_\alpha\right) \Leftrightarrow (\exists \alpha \in I) \quad x \equiv y(R_\alpha)$$

is not in general an equivalence relation as transitivity fails (see Exercise 4.14). However, in the case of an abelian semigroup S [in particular, a semilattice], $\bigcup_{t \in J} F_t$ *is* an equivalence relation whenever J is a subsemigroup of S. To see that it is transitive in this case, we observe that if $xt_1 = yt_1$ and $yt_2 = zt_2$ where $t_1, t_2 \in J$ then $t = t_1 t_2 \in J$ and $xt = zt$. Thus in this case $\bigcup_{t \in J} F_t$ and $\prod_{t \in J} F_t$ coincide.

THEOREM 30.11. *If S is a distributive Glivenko lattice with dense filter D, then the closure equivalence* [**] *associated with the mapping* (**) *is given by* $[**] = \bigcup_{d \in D} F_d$.

Proof. Note that, S being a distributive lattice, it is a $\cup$-semireticulated semigroup under $xy = x \cap y$ and that the condition $x^2 y = xy^2$ holds. The result therefore follows immediately from Theorems 30.3 and 30.5.

EXERCISES

30.1. Let S be a Glivenko semigroup, S^{**} the Boolean algebra of pseudo-residuals and D its dense filter. Consider the equivalence relation R defined on $S \times S^{**}$ by

$$(x, a) \equiv (y, b)\ (R) \Leftrightarrow (x^* = y^* \quad \text{and} \quad a = b).$$

Show that $S \times S^{**}$ is a semigroup under the law of composition

$$((x, a), (y, b)) \rightarrow ((xy)^{**}, a \curlywedge b)$$

and that R is compatible with this law. Show that the quotient $(S \times S^{**})/R$ is pseudo-residuated and use Theorem 30.1 to show that it is a Boolean algebra. Show further that there is an isotone homomorphism $f: S \rightarrow (S \times S^{**})/R$ such that $\operatorname{Im} f \simeq S^{**}$ and $\operatorname{Ker}^* f = D$ where $\operatorname{Ker}^* f = \{x \in S; f(x) = \pi\}$.

30.2. Let L be a $\cup$-semilattice and consider the set $C(L)$ of equivalence relations on L which are compatible with union. Show that $C(L)$ is a complete lattice in which unions are transitive products. If $H, K \in C(L)$ are such that $H \leq K$ define the relation $H : K$ by

$$x \equiv y\ (H : K) \Leftrightarrow \begin{cases} \text{for all} \quad \alpha, \beta \in L \quad \text{such that} \quad \alpha \equiv \beta(K) \\ x \cup \alpha \equiv x \cup \beta(H) \Leftrightarrow y \cup \alpha \equiv y \cup \beta(H). \end{cases}$$

Show that

(1) $H : K \in C(L)$;
(2) $K \cap (H : K) = H$;

(3) if $J \in C(L)$ is such that $K \cap J = H$ then $J \leq H:K$.
Deduce that $C(L)$ forms a Glivenko lattice.

30.3. Without appealing to results on congruence relations, prove directly that the set $I(B)$ of ideals of a complete Boolean algebra B forms a Stone lattice.

31. Loipomorphisms

Definition. Let S, T be residuated abelian semigroups. We shall say that a mapping $f: S \to T$ is a *loipomorphism* if it is such that

(1) f is isotone;
(2) $(\forall x, y \in S)\quad f(xy) = f(x)f(y)$;
(3) $(\forall x, y \in S)\quad f(x:y) = f(x):f(y)$.

Thus a loipomorphism is an isotone homomorphism such that the subsemigroup $\operatorname{Im} f$ is stable under residuation with residuals in $\operatorname{Im} f$ given by (3).

The reader will note that we have given the above definition with the restriction that the semigroups in question were abelian. We shall maintain this assumption throughout the present section.

If S is a residuated abelian semigroup we shall be particularly interested in the subset $S^\wedge$ of S given by

$$S^\wedge = \bigcap_{x \in S} \langle x : x \rangle.$$

Clearly $S^\wedge$ is not empty if and only if S contains an element y such that $(\forall x \in S)\ xy \leq x$. In particular, this is the case if S has a neutral element.

For each $a \in S$ and each non-empty subset $D \subseteq S$ define

$$\{a\}_D = \bigcup_{d \in D} \langle a : d \rangle = \{x \in S;\ (\exists d \in D)\ xd \leq a\}.$$

It is clear that the relation R_D defined on S by

$$a \equiv b(R_D) \Leftrightarrow \{a\}_D = \{b\}_D$$

is an equivalence relation. It is equally clear that the relation $\leq$ defined on S/R_D by

$$a/R_D \leq b/R_D \Leftrightarrow \{a\}_D \subseteq \{b\}_D$$

is an ordering.

THEOREM 31.1. *Let S be an abelian residuated semigroup such that $S^\wedge \neq \emptyset$. For each subsemigroup D of $S^\wedge$ we have*

(1) $a/R_D \leq b/R_D \Leftrightarrow a \in \{b\}_D$;

(2) *R_D is compatible with multiplication;*

(3) *the quotient S/R_D is a residuated semigroup with a neutral element and the canonical surjection $\natural_D : S \to S/R_D$ is a loipomorphism.*

Proof. (1) Since $D \subseteq S^\wedge$ we have $(\forall a \in S)\,(\forall d \in D)\; ad \leq a$ and so $(\forall a \in S)\; a \in \{a\}_D$. It follows that

$$a/R_D \leq b/R_D \Rightarrow a \in \{a\}_D \subseteq \{b\}_D.$$

Conversely, if $a \in \{b\}_D$ then $(\exists d \in D)\; ad \leq b$ and so, D being a subsemigroup of $S^\wedge$,

$$x \in \{a\}_D \Rightarrow (\exists d^* \in D) \quad xd^* \leq a \Rightarrow (\exists d, d^* \in D) \quad xdd^* \leq ad \leq b$$
$$\Rightarrow x \in \{b\}_D$$

whence $\{a\}_D \subseteq \{b\}_D$ and so $a/R_D \leq b/R_D$.

(2) We observe that

$$\begin{aligned} a/R_D \leq b/R_D \Rightarrow a \in \{b\}_D &\Rightarrow (\exists d \in D) \quad ad \leq b \\ &\Rightarrow (\forall x \in S)\,(\exists d \in D) \quad axd \leq bx \\ &\Rightarrow (\forall x \in S) \quad ax \in \{bx\}_D \\ &\Rightarrow (\forall x \in S) \quad ax/R_D \leq bx/R_D. \end{aligned}$$

It follows immediately from this that

$$a \equiv b(R_D) \Rightarrow (\forall x \in S) \quad ax \equiv bx\,(R_D).$$

(3) It is clear from the proof of (2) that S/R_D is an ordered semigroup. We show as follows that it has a neutral element. For any $d \in D$ and any $a \in S$ we have trivially $ad \leq ad$ and so $a \in \{ad\}_D$ which gives $a/R_D \leq ad/R_D$. Now for any $d, d^* \in D$ and any $a \in S$ we also have $add^* \leq ad \leq a$ so that $ad \in \{a\}_D$ and hence $ad/R_D \leq a/R_D$. It follows that

$$(\forall a \in S)\,(\forall d \in D) \quad a/R_D = ad/R_D = a/R_D \cdot d/R_D$$

and so d/R_D is a neutral element for S/R_D. To show that S/R_D is residuated, we observe that

$$\begin{aligned} a/R_D \cdot x/R_D \leq b/R_D \Leftrightarrow ax \in \{b\}_D &\Leftrightarrow (\exists d \in D) \quad axd \leq b \\ &\Leftrightarrow (\exists d \in D) \quad xd \leq b:a \\ &\Leftrightarrow x \in \{b:a\}_D \\ &\Leftrightarrow x/R_D \leq (b:a)/R_D. \end{aligned}$$

It follows from this that residuals exist in S/R_D and are given by

$$b/R_D : a/R_D = (b:a)/R_D.$$

This formula also shows that the canonical surjection $\natural_D$ is a loipomorphism.

Under the hypotheses of Theorem 31.1, we can give a complete description of the equivalence classes modulo R_D and the pre-image under $\natural_D$ of the negative cone of S/R_D.

THEOREM 31.2. *Under the hypotheses of Theorem* 31.1 *we have:*

(1) $(\forall t \in S) \quad t/R_D = \bigcup_{n,m \in D} [tm, t:n]$;

(2) $(\forall d \in D)\ \natural_D^{\leftarrow} [\leftarrow, 1] = \{d\}_D$.

Proof. (1)

$$\begin{aligned} \{x\}_D = \{t\}_D \Leftrightarrow x \in \{t\}_D \quad \text{and} \quad t \in \{x\}_D \\ &\Leftrightarrow (\exists n, m \in D) \quad xn \leq t, \quad tm \leq x \\ &\Leftrightarrow (\exists n, m \in D) \quad tm \leq x \leq t:n \\ &\Leftrightarrow (\exists n, m \in D) \quad x \in [tm, \ t:n]. \end{aligned}$$

(2) Since d/R_D is the neutral element of S/R_D for any $d \in D$, we see that

$$x \in \natural_D^{\leftarrow} [\leftarrow, 1] \Leftrightarrow x/R_D \leq d/R_D \Leftrightarrow x \in \{d\}_D.$$

Definition. If T is a semigroup with neutral element 1 we define the 1-*kernel* of $f: S \to T$ by $\text{Ker}_1 f = \{x \in S; f(x) = 1\}$.

In what follows we shall write $\text{Ker}_1 f$ as simply $\text{Ker} f$ unless there is some danger of confusion.

THEOREM 31.3. *If S is a residuated abelian semigroup with the property that the subset $S^\wedge$ is not empty and is closed under residuation then for any subsemigroup D of $S^\wedge$ we have:*

(1) Ker $\natural_D$ *is a filter of* $S^\wedge$ *containing* D;
(2) $(\forall d \in D) \quad \{d\}_D = S^\wedge$;
(3) $R_D = R_{\mathrm{Ker}\,\natural_D}$.

Proof. (1) Since

$$x \in \mathrm{Ker}\,\natural_D \Leftrightarrow x/R_D = d/R_D \Leftrightarrow \{x\}_D = \{d\}_D \Leftrightarrow x \in d/R_D$$

we see from Theorem 31.2(1) that

$$\mathrm{Ker}\,\natural_D = \bigcup_{n,m \in D} [dm, d:n]. \tag{*}$$

It is clear from the above that $D \subseteq \mathrm{Ker}\,\natural_D$. Now $D \subseteq S^\wedge$ and so, since $S^\wedge$ is closed under residuation, we have $d, n \in D \Rightarrow d:n \in S^\wedge$. Consequently Ker $\natural_D \subseteq S^\wedge$. If $x \in \mathrm{Ker}\,\natural_D$ and $y \in S$ is such that $y \geq x$ then there exist $d, m \in D$ such that $dm \leq x \leq y \leq d:d$ and so $y \in \mathrm{Ker}\,\natural_D$.

(2) Since $yd \leq d$ for all $y \in S^\wedge$ and $d \in D$, we have $S^\wedge \subseteq \{d\}_D$. Conversely, if $x \in \{d\}_D$ then $(\exists d^* \in D)\ xd^* \leq d$ so that $x \leq d:d^*$. But by the hypothesis $d:d^* \in S^\wedge$. Hence $\{d\}_D \subseteq S^\wedge$ and (2) follows.

(3) Since $D \subseteq \mathrm{Ker}\,\natural_D$ we have

$$x \in \{a\}_D \Rightarrow (\exists d \in D \subseteq \mathrm{Ker}\,\natural_D) \quad xd \leq a \Rightarrow x \in \{a\}_{\mathrm{Ker}\,\natural_D}.$$

Conversely, using (*), we have

$$\begin{aligned} x \in \{a\}_{\mathrm{Ker}\,\natural_D} &\Rightarrow (\exists t \in \mathrm{Ker}\,\natural_D) \quad xt \leq a \\ &\Rightarrow (\exists d, m \in D) \quad xdm \leq xt \leq a \\ &\Rightarrow x \in \{a\}_D. \end{aligned}$$

This shows that $\{a\}_D = \{a\}_{\mathrm{Ker}\,\natural_D}$ for each $a \in S$ and so $R_D = R_{\mathrm{Ker}\,\natural_D}$.

Let us now examine the converse situation in which we are given residuated abelian semigroups S, T with T having a neutral element and a loipomorphism $f: S \to T$. In order to have Ker f a filter of $S^\wedge$ it is necessary to impose some restrictions. We therefore ask the reader to recall the terms *A-totally closed* and *A-integrally closed* as applied to a residuated semigroup. If S is an abelian A-totally closed semigroup then clearly $S^\wedge = [\leftarrow, \xi]$. If S is A-integrally closed then ξ becomes the neutral element of S.

THEOREM 31.4. *Let T be an abelian A-integrally closed semigroup. If S is an abelian residuated semigroup and $f: S \to T$ is a loipomorphism with the property that* $\operatorname{Ker} f \subseteq S^\wedge$, *then S is A-totally closed,* $\operatorname{Ker} f$ *is a filter of $S^\wedge$ and there is a unique bijective loipomorphism $\zeta: S/R_{\operatorname{Ker} f} \to \operatorname{Im} f$ such that $\zeta \circ \natural_{\operatorname{Ker} f} = f$.*

Proof. Since T is A-integrally closed, we have

$$(\forall x \in S) \quad f(x:x) = f(x):f(x) = 1$$

and so it follows from the hypothesis that $(\forall x \in S)\ x:x \in S^\wedge$. But by definition we have $S^\wedge = \bigcap_{x \in S} [\leftarrow, x:x]$. We deduce that there is an element $\xi \in S$ which is such that $(\forall x \in S)\ x:x = \xi$. Thus S is A-totally closed. That $\operatorname{Ker} f$ is a filter of $S^\wedge = [\leftarrow, \xi]$ then follows from the fact that if $x \in \operatorname{Ker} f$ and $x \leq y \leq \xi$ then $1 = f(x) \leq f(y) \leq f(\xi) = 1$ yields $y \in \operatorname{Ker} f$. Since $\operatorname{Ker} f$ is in particular a subsemigroup of $S^\wedge$ we can form the residuated quotient semigroup $S/R_{\operatorname{Ker} f}$ as in Theorem 31.1. Since S is totally closed and $\natural_{\operatorname{Ker} f}$ is a loipomorphism, $S/R_{\operatorname{Ker} f}$ is also A-totally closed. It is in fact A-integrally closed since it contains a neutral element. Now, writing $K = \operatorname{Ker} f$, we have

$$\{y\}_K \subseteq \{x\}_K \Rightarrow (\exists\, k \in K)\ yk \leq x \Rightarrow f(y) = f(y)f(k) = f(yk) \leq f(x).$$

It follows from this that we can define an isotone mapping $\zeta: S/R_K \to \operatorname{Im} f$ by the prescription $\zeta(x/R_K) = f(x)$. Clearly ζ is a surjective loipomorphism. To show that it is also injective, we note that

$$f(x) = f(y) \Rightarrow f(x:y) = f(x):f(y) = f(x):f(x) = 1$$

$$\Rightarrow x:y \in \operatorname{Ker} f = K.$$

The inequality $(x:y)\,y \leq x$ then shows that $y \in \{x\}_K$ and so $\{y\}_K \subseteq \{x\}_K$. In a similar way we can show that $x \in \{y\}_K$ and hence deduce that

$\{x\}_K = \{y\}_K$. Finally, ζ is clearly unique with respect to the property $\zeta \circ \natural_K = f$.

Remark. In the above proof we have shown in particular that the map ζ is a semigroup isomorphism. We note here that it is not in general an order isomorphism. For example, suppose that $(G, \leq)$ is an ordered group and let $(G, \preccurlyeq)$ be the same group ordered according to $a \preccurlyeq b \Leftrightarrow a = b$. Both $(G, \leq)$ and $(G, \preccurlyeq)$ are residuated with residuals in each case given by $a : b = ab^{-1}$. Consider the identity map on G as a mapping from $(G, \preccurlyeq)$ to $(G, \leq)$. It is clearly a loipomorphism whose kernel is simply $K = \{1\}$. Since we have

$$a/R_K \leq b/R_K \Leftrightarrow a \in \{b\}_K \Leftrightarrow a = a1 \preccurlyeq b \Leftrightarrow a = b,$$

we see that G/R_K exists and is a group which is isomorphic to G and order isomorphic to $(G, \preccurlyeq)$. It is now clear that the mapping ζ is a bijective loipomorphism but is not an order isomorphism unless $\leq$ is the same as $\preccurlyeq$.

THEOREM 31.5. *Let S, T, f be as in Theorem 31.4. If T admits a maximum element π, then:*

(1) *π coincides with the neutral element of T;*
(2) *S has a maximal element, namely ξ;*
(3) *ζ is also an order isomorphism.*

Proof. (1) For any $x \in T$ we have $x\pi \leq \pi$ and so $x \leq \pi : \pi = 1$. In particular we have $\pi \leq 1$ and so $\pi = 1$.

(2) Since f is isotone and 1 is the maximum element, we deduce from $f(\xi) = 1$ that $[\xi, \rightarrow] \subseteq \operatorname{Ker} f \subseteq S^\wedge = [\leftarrow, \xi]$. It follows readily from this that ξ is a maximal element of S.

(3) If $f(x) \leq f(y)$ then $f(y : x) = f(y) : f(x) \geq 1$ and so, since 1 is maximum, $y : x \in \operatorname{Ker} f$. The inequality $(y : x)\, x \leq y$ then shows that $x \in \{y\}_{\operatorname{Ker} f}$ and so $x/R_{\operatorname{Ker} f} \leq y/R_{\operatorname{Ker} f}$. This shows that ζ^{-1} is also isotone whence ζ is an order isomorphism.

At this stage we are led to make the following definitions.

Definitions. An ordered semigroup S is said to be *quasi-integral* if and only if $S = S^{\wedge}$; and *negatively ordered* if it is quasi-integral and admits a neutral element.

It is clear that a residuated quasi-integral semigroup is the same thing as an A-totally closed semigroup having a maximum element and that a residuated negatively ordered semigroup is the same as an A-integrally closed semigroup having a maximum element. These definitions allow us to combine all of the previous results in the following way.

THEOREM 31.6. *Let S be a residuated quasi-integral abelian semigroup. Then D is a filter of S if and only if D is the kernel of a loipomorphism of S onto a residuated negatively ordered abelian semigroup T.*

Proof. The condition is sufficient by virtue of Theorem 31.4. Conversely, suppose that D is a filter of S. Clearly S/R_D is a residuated negatively ordered semigroup which is a loipomorphic image of S. We show that $D = \text{Ker } \natural_D$. By Theorem 31.3 we have $D \subseteq \text{Ker } \natural_D$. To obtain the reverse inclusion, we note that since D is a filter of S we have $(\forall d, x \in D)$ $dn \leq d \Rightarrow d \leq d:n \Rightarrow d:n \in D$ and hence

$$\text{Ker } \natural_D = \bigcup_{n,m \in D} [dm, d:n] \subseteq D.$$

THEOREM 31.7. *Let S be a residuated quasi-integral abelian semigroup. Then a residuated abelian semigroup T is a negatively ordered loipomorphic image of S if and only if it is of the form S/R_D, where D is a subsemigroup of S. Moreover, there is a bijection between the set of negatively ordered loipomorphic images of S and the filters of S.*

Proof. By Theorem 31.1 and the fact that $S = S^{\wedge}$, S/R_D is a negatively ordered loipomorphic image of S for each subsemigroup D of S. Conversely, suppose that T is such an image. Since T is integrally closed and has a maximum element, we deduce from Theorems 31.4 and 31.5 that T is of the form S/R_D, where $D = \text{Ker} f$ is a subsemigroup of S.

As for the second part of the theorem, we note that S satisfies the conditions of Theorem 31.3 and so, for each subsemigroup D of S, there is a filter F [namely, $F = \text{Ker } \natural_D$] such that $S/R_D = S/R_F$. Now, as we saw in the proof of Theorem 31.6, for any filter G of S we have

$G = \text{Ker}\ \natural_G$. The result therefore follows from the observation that if F, G are filters of S such that $R_F = R_G$, then $F = \text{Ker}\ \natural_F = \text{Ker}\ \natural_G = G$.

THEOREM 31.8. *Let S be a residuated quasi-integral abelian semigroup. An equivalence relation R on S is compatible with both multiplication and residuation and is such that S/R has a neutral element if and only if R is of the form*

$$x \equiv y(R) \Leftrightarrow x \equiv y(R_D) \Leftrightarrow (x : y)\,(y : x) \in D,$$

where D is a filter of S.

Proof. Let D be a filter of S. Then the associated equivalence R_D is given by

$$\begin{aligned} x \equiv y(R_D) &\Leftrightarrow \{x\}_D = \{y\}_D \\ &\Leftrightarrow (\exists d_1, d_2 \in D) \quad xd_1 \leq y, \quad yd_2 \leq x \\ &\Leftrightarrow (\exists d_1, d_2 \in D) \quad d_1 \leq y : x, \quad d_2 \leq x : y \\ &\Leftrightarrow (x : y)\,(y : x) \in D, \end{aligned}$$

and by Theorem 31.1 the equivalence R_D is compatible with both multiplication and residuation and is such that the quotient semigroup has a neutral element.

Conversely, suppose that R is such an equivalence. Then S/R is a residuated negatively ordered loipomorphic image of S. By Theorems 31.4 and 31.5, S/R is then of the form S/R_D where D is a subsemigroup of S. But by Theorem 31.3 (3) we have $R_D = R_{\text{Ker}\,\natural_D}$ where, by Theorem 31.6, $\text{Ker}\ \natural_D$ is a filter of S. We conclude that

$$x \equiv y(R) \Leftrightarrow x \equiv y(R_{\text{Ker}\,\natural_D}) \Leftrightarrow (x : y)\,(y : x) \in \text{Ker}\ \natural_D .$$

Henceforth we shall commit the usual abuse of notation and write S/D in place of S/R_D.

We shall now impose on S the condition that it be a Glivenko semigroup. This has the effect of bringing to light an important example of a loipomorphism which we can use to obtain a neat characterization of the dense filter.

THEOREM 31.9. *Let S be a Glivenko semigroup. Suppose further that S is abelian, residuated and quasi-integral. Let S^{**} denote the Boolean algebra of pseudo-residuals in S and let D be the dense filter of S. Then the mapping $(^{**}): S \to S^{**}$ described by $x \to x^{**} = 0:(0:x)$ is a loipomorphism and $S^{**} \simeq S/D$.*

Proof. We note first that

$$(\forall x, y \in S) \quad (x:y)^* = (x^{**}:y)^*. \qquad (*)$$

In fact, since $xy \leq x$ we have $x \leq x:y$ and so $(x:y)^* \leq x^*$. Also, since $y^* = 0:y \leq x:y$ and so $(x:y)^* \leq y^{**}$, we have $(x:y)^* \leq x^* \curlywedge y^{**} = (x^{**} \curlyvee y^*)^* = (x^{**}:y)^*$. But, on the other hand, $x \leq x^{**}$ and so $x:y \leq x^{**}:y$ whence $(x^{**}:y)^* \leq (x:y)^*$. This then establishes (*).

Consider now the mapping (**). Clearly $S^{**} = \text{Im}\,(^{**})$ and (**) is a homomorphism since $(xy)^{**} = (x^{**}y^{**})^{**} = x^{**} \curlywedge y^{**}$. Now using the identity (*) we have $(x:y)^{**} = (x^{**}:y)^{**} = (x^{**} \curlyvee y^*)^{**} = x^{**} \curlyvee y^{***} = x^{**}:y^{**}$. It follows that (**) is a loipomorphism. Finally,

$$\text{Ker}\,(^{**}) = \{x \in S;\ x^{**} = 0^*\} = D.$$

Applying Theorems 31.4 and 31.5, we deduce that $S^{**} \simeq S/D$.

THEOREM 31.10. *Let S be an abelian residuated quasi-integral Glivenko semigroup. The dense filter D of S can be characterized as the smallest filter of S for which S/D is a Boolean algebra.*

Proof. By Theorem 31.9, S/D is indeed a Boolean algebra. Suppose then that J is a filter of S such that S/J is a Boolean algebra. Then every element of S/J must be maximum in its class modulo $A_{0/J}$ (Theorem 30.1) so, since the canonical mapping $\natural_J$ is a loipomorphism,

$$(\forall x \in S) \quad x/J = 0/J:[0/J:x/J] = 0/J:x^*/J = x^{**}/J.$$

In particular, this yields $x^{**}/J \leq x/J$ and so $x^{**} \in \{x\}_J$ whence

$$(\forall x \in S)\,(\exists j \in J) \quad x^{**}j \leq x.$$

Suppose now that $x \in S$ is such that $x^{**} \in J$. Then, J being a filter, we deduce from the above that $x \in J$. Now for any $x \in D$ we have $x^{**} = 0^*$ and since 0^* is the maximum element it belongs to every filter J. We conclude from this that $x \in D \Rightarrow x \in J$ whence $D \subseteq J$ as required.

EXERCISES

31.1. Under the hypotheses of Theorem 31.9, S/D is an isotone homomorphic Boolean image of S. Prove that the associated base is given by the class of 0 modulo A_0.

31.2. Let L be an $\cap$-semilattice which is residuated with respect to intersection. [A *Brouwer semilattice*: see the following section.] If, for each $a \in L$, the translation $x \to x \cap a$ is denoted by λ_a, show that each residual map λ_a^+ is a loipomorphism. Show also that if $S = \{\lambda_x^+ ; a \in L\}$ then $(L, \cap) \simeq (S, \circ)$.

31.3. Let A, B be Boolean algebras. By a *Boolean homomorphism* $f: A \to B$ we mean a lattice homomorphism which is such that $f(x') = [f(x)]'$ for each $x \in A$. Show that every Boolean homomorphism is a loipomorphism.

31.4. If a, b, x are elements of a Boolean algebra B, prove that

$$a \cup x = b \cup x \Leftrightarrow (a \cup b') \cap (a' \cup b) \geq x':$$

(a) by a direct method;
(b) by noting that $[x', \to]$ is a filter which is the kernel of the loipomorphism $\lambda_{x'}^+$.

31.5. Let A, B be Boolean algebras and let $f: A \to B$ be a lattice homomorphism. Prove that the following are equivalent:

(1) f is a loipomorphism;
(2) $f(\pi_A) = \pi_B$.

[*Hint.* Use Exercise 31.4.]

32. Brouwer semigroups; Brouwer semilattices

Definition. By a *Brouwer semigroup* we shall mean a residuated semigroup S in which every element x is quasi-integral, equiresidual and such that S/A_x is idempotent (and hence, by Theorem 29.5, a Boolean algebra).

THEOREM 32.1. *All Brouwer semigroups are abelian.*

Proof. Immediate from Theorem 22.2.

EXAMPLE 32.1. Every $\cap$-semilattice L which is residuated with respect to $\cap$ is a Brouwer semigroup under the definition $xy = x \cap y$. In fact it is clear that every element is quasi-integral and equiresidual; moreover, each quotient semigroup S/A_x is idempotent.

Definition. An $\cap$-semilattice which is residuated with respect to $\cap$ will be called a *Brouwer semilattice*. We shall see that these are very close relatives of Brouwer semigroups.

EXAMPLE 32.2. Consider the ordered abelian semigroup S described by the following Cayley table and Hasse diagram:

	x_1	x_2	x_3	0
x_1	x_2	x_2	0	0
x_2	x_2	x_2	0	0
x_3	0	0	0	0
0	0	0	0	0

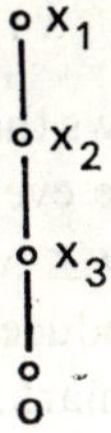

This ordered semigroup is residuated; the table of residuals is

	x_1	x_2	x_3	0
x_1	x_1	x_1	x_1	x_1
x_2	x_1	x_1	x_1	x_1
x_3	x_3	x_3	x_1	x_1
0	x_3	x_3	x_1	x_1

Now, on the one hand, we see that $x_1^2 = x_2^2 = x_2$ and $x_3^2 = 0^2 = 0$, and, on the other, $(\forall y \in S)\ x_1 \equiv x_2(A_y)$ and $x_3 \equiv 0(A_y)$. It follows from this that $(\forall x, y \in S)\ x \equiv x^2(A_y)$, so that each quotient semigroup S/A_y is idempotent. Every element being quasi-integral, S is, indeed, a Brouwer semigroup.

THEOREM 32.2. *A residuated semigroup S is a Brouwer semigroup if and only if it is abelian and such that, for each $x \in S$,*

(α) $B_x = F_x$;

(β) *S/F_x is idempotent.*

Proof. Suppose first that S is a Brouwer semigroup. Since each S/A_x is idempotent, we have

$$(\forall x, y \in S) \quad x:y = x:y^2 = (x:y):y,$$

which we can express in the form

$$(\forall x, y \in S) \quad x \equiv x:y(B_y). \tag{1}$$

Now we observe that

$$x:y \equiv z:y(B_y) \Rightarrow x:y^2 = z:y^2 \Rightarrow x:y = z:y,$$

so it follows that each class modulo B_y contains at most one residual by y. Now since every element of S is quasi-integral, we also have $(\forall x, y \in S)$ $x \leq xy:y \leq x:y$ and so, by (1) and the convexity of the classes modulo B_y, we deduce that $xy:y \equiv x:y(B_x)$ whence, by the immediately preceding remark,

$$(\forall x, y \in S) \quad xy:y = x:y. \tag{2}$$

It follows that

$$x \equiv z(F_y) \Rightarrow xy:y = zy:y \Rightarrow x:y = z:y \Rightarrow x \equiv z(B_y),$$

so that $(\forall y \in S)$ $F_y \leq B_y$. But we have shown that each class modulo B_y contains at most one residual by y and we know that each class modulo F_y contains precisely one residual by y. Hence we have $(\forall y \in S)$ $F_y = B_y$. It follows from this that (2) can be written in the form $(\forall x, y \in S)$ $xy \equiv x(F_y)$ or as $(\forall x, y \in S)$ $y^2 \equiv y(F_x)$, whence each quotient semigroup S/F_x is idempotent.

Conversely, suppose that S is abelian and that properties (α) and (β) are satisfied. By (β) we have $(\forall x, y \in S)$ $xy^2 = xy$ whence, by (α), we obtain $xy \equiv x(B_x)$. Now since $x \equiv y\,(x:y)\,(B_y)$ the convexity of the classes modulo B_y and the fact that each class modulo B_y contains precisely one multiple of y implies that $(\forall x, y \in S)$ $xy = y\,(x:y) \leq x$. This shows that each element of S is quasi-integral. It remains to show that each quotient semigroup S/A_x is idempotent. For this purpose, we note that from the identity $xy^2 = xy$ established above we have in particular $(\forall y \in S)\, y^3 = y^2$. Thus $(x:y^2):y = x:y^3 = x:y^2 = (x:y):y$ and therefore $x:y^2 \equiv x:y(B_y)$. But $B_y = F_y$ by hypothesis and each class modulo F_y has precisely one residual by y. We thus have $(\forall x, y \in S)\ x : y^2 = x : y$ and so each S/A_x is indeed idempotent.

COROLLARY. *If S is a Brouwer semigroup then for any $x, y, z \in S$ the following properties hold:*

(a) $x : x = y : y = \pi$ *(the maximum element of S)*;
(b) $y\,(x : y) = yx$;
(c) $(xy)^2 = xy$;
(d) $x : yz = (x : z) : (y : z)$;
(e) $xy : z \geq (x : z)\,(y : z) = (xy : z)^2$.

Proof. (a) Since every element of S is quasi-integral, this follows from Theorem 29.4.

(b) By the property (2) established in the theorem we have $xy \equiv x(B_y)$. But the minimum element in the class of x modulo B_y is $y\,(x : y)$. Thus $xy \equiv y\,(x : y)\,(B_y)$ from which (b) follows since each class modulo B_y contains precisely one multiple of y.

(c) By property (β) of the theorem we have $(\forall x, y \in S)\ xy^2 = xy$. Multiplication being commutative, there results $(xy)^2 = xy^2x = xyx = x^2y = xy$.

(d) By property (b) above, $(x : z) : (y : z) = x :\ z\,(y : z) = x : zy = x : yz$.

(e) Using Theorem 22.3(5) we have

$$(x : z)\,(y : z) \leq (x : z)\,y : z \leq (xy : z) : z = xy : z^2 = xy : z.$$

Thus, by (c) and the fact that each element is quasi-integral,

$$(x : z)\,(y : z) = [(x : z)\,(y : z)]^2 \leq (xy{:}z)^2 \leq xy : z.$$

But, again since each element is quasi-integral, $xy : z \leq x : z$ and $xy : z \leq y : z$, so that $(xy : z)^2 \leq (x : z)\,(y : z)$. It follows that

$$(xy : z)^2 = (x : z)\,(y : z) \leq xy : z.$$

Remark. It should be noted that equality does not hold in general in (e). For example, in Example 32.2 we have $x_3^2 : x_2 = 0 : x_2 = x_3$, whereas $(x_3 : x_2)\,(x_3 : x_2) = x_3x_3 = 0$. The equality does hold, however, whenever S is a Brouwer semilattice; for then $(x \cap y) : z \leq x : z$ and $(x \cap y) : z \leq y : z$ so that $(x \cap y) : z \leq (x : z) \cap (y : z)$.

The essential difference between a Brouwer semigroup and a Brouwer semilattice is the idempotency of the law of composition in the latter. We now investigate other manifestations of this difference.

THEOREM 32.3. *For a Brouwer semigroup S the following conditions are equivalent;*

(1) *S is a Brouwer semilattice;*
(2) $S^2 = S$;
(3) *S has a neutral element.*

Proof. That (1) ⇒ (3) is immediate from the fact that the maximum element π_S is the neutral element for intersection. To show that (3) ⇒ (2), let 1_S be the neutral element of S; then since $(\forall x, y \in S)\ xy^2 = xy$ we have $(\forall y \in S)\ y^2 = 1_S y^2 = 1_S y = y$. Finally, to show that (2) ⇒ (1) we observe that if (2) holds then for each $z \in S$ there exist $a, b \in S$ such that $z = ab$. By virtue of property (c) of the previous corollary, we then have $z^2 = (ab)^2 = ab = z$ and so if $z \leq x$ and $z \leq y$ we obtain $z = z^2 \leq xy$. It follows that $x \cap y$ exists and is none other than xy.

We can now give another quite natural definition of a Brouwer semigroup. Let us recap that to begin with we were interested in residuated mappings, then we studied algebraic structures in which every translation was a residuated mapping. Our next result extends the pattern of this general investigation.

THEOREM 32.4. *An ordered semigroup S is a Brouwer semigroup if and only if it is abelian and each translation is a residuated dual closure map.*

Proof. Suppose that S is a Brouwer semigroup. Then each translation is residuated and

$$(\forall x, y \in S) \quad xy^2 = xy \leq x \tag{*}$$

from which it follows immediately that each translation is also a dual closure mapping. Conversely, if S is abelian and each translation is a residuated dual closure map, then clearly S is residuated and (*) holds.

From this it follows that each element of S is quasi-integral and that

$$(\forall x, z \in S) \quad x : z = x : z^2$$

[for $zy \leq x$ if and only if $z^2 y \leq x$]. Thus for each $x \in S$ the quotient semigroup S/A_x is idempotent and so S is indeed a Brouwer semigroup.

Our next goal will be to examine very closely the structure of a Brouwer semigroup and show in particular that the ordering, except for the natural ordering of the idempotents, can be removed.

Let us note first that if S is an abelian semigroup with non-empty subset I of idempotents then I can be ordered in the following way:

$$e \leq f \Leftrightarrow ef = e.$$

This is known as the *natural order* on I. For each $e \in I$ define

$$S_e = \{x \in S;\ x^2 = e\}.$$

Clearly $S_e \neq \varnothing$ since it contains e; and if $e, f \in I$ are such that $e \neq f$, then $S_e \cap S_f = \varnothing$. We shall say that S is a *semilattice of* 0-*semigroups* if and only if S admits the partition

$$S = \bigcup_{e \in I} S_e \quad \text{with} \quad (\forall e, f \in I) \quad S_e S_f = \{ef\}.$$

Note that in this case each S_e is a subsemigroup of S in which every product is equal to e. Thus each S_e is a semigroup with zero element e and every product equal to e. This explains the terminology.

If L is any semilattice and $\{S_e;\ e \in L\}$ is a disjoint collection of non-empty sets each of which contains a distinguished element $0_e \in S_e$, then $S = \bigcup_{e \in L} S_e$ becomes a semilattice of 0-semigroups by defining

$$(\forall x \in S_e)\,(\forall y \in S_f) \quad xy = 0_{e \cap f}.$$

Note also that if a semigroup obtained in this way admits an ordering with respect to which it is quasi-integral then $0_e \leq 0_f \Leftrightarrow 0_e 0_f = 0_e$ (so that the ordering agrees with the natural order as far as the idempotents are concerned) and moreover $x \in S_e \Rightarrow 0_e = 0_e x \leq x$.

THEOREM 32.5. *Let S be an abelian semigroup. Then S is a semilattice of* 0-*semigroups if and only if each quotient semigroup S/F_x is idempotent.*

Proof. Let S be a semilattice of 0-semigroups, say $S = \bigcup_{e \in I} S_e$ where I is the set of idempotents. Then if $x \in S_e$, $y \in S_f$ we have

$$xy^2 \in S_e S_f S_f = \{ef^2\} = \{ef\} \quad \text{and} \quad xy \in S_e S_f = \{ef\}$$

whence $xy^2 = ef = xy$. Since this holds for all x, y we have each S/F_x idempotent.

Conversely, if each S/F_x is idempotent then clearly $xy^2 = xy$ for all $x, y \in S$ and so each product xy is idempotent. Let I denote the set of idempotents in S. For each $e \in I$ define $S_e = \{x \in S; x^2 = e\}$. Then

$$x \in S_e \Rightarrow (\forall y \in S) \quad yx = yx^2 = ye \Rightarrow x \equiv e \left(\bigcap_{y \in S} F_y\right)$$

and conversely

$$x \equiv e \left(\bigcap_{y \in S} F_y\right) \Rightarrow \begin{cases} x \equiv e(F_x) \Rightarrow xx = xe \\ x \equiv e(F_e) \Rightarrow ex = ee \end{cases}$$

$$\Rightarrow x^2 = xe = e^2 = e.$$

Thus S_e is none other than the class of e modulo $\bigcap_{y \in S} F_y$. Now if $e, f \in I$ are such that $e \equiv f\left(\bigcap_{y \in S} F_y\right)$, then we have in particular $e \equiv f(F_e)$ and $e \equiv f(F_f)$ so that $e = e^2 = ef = f^2 = f$. Thus each class modulo $\bigcap_{y \in S} F_y$ contains at most one idempotent. Since $xy = x^2 y$ we have $x \equiv x^2 \left(\bigcap_{y \in S} F_y\right)$ and so it follows that each class contains precisely one idempotent. We thus have the partition $S = \bigcup_{e \in I} S_e$. Now for any $e, f \in I$ we have, for $x \in S_e$ and $y \in S_f$, $xy = xy^2 = xf = x^2 f = ef$ and so $S_e S_f = \{ef\}$. This then shows that S is a semilattice of 0-semigroups.

Definition. We shall say that a semilattice of 0-semigroups is *Brouwerian* if and only if the semilattice of idempotents is Brouwerian.

THEOREM 32.6. *Let S be an abelian semigroup and let I be its set of idempotents. Then the following conditions are equivalent:*

(1) *S is a Brouwer semigroup;*

(2) *S is a Brouwer semilattice of 0-semigroups.*

Proof. Suppose that (1) holds. Then by Theorems 32.2 and 32.5 it follows that S is a semilattice of 0-semigroups. Given $e, f, g \in I$ we have, since $x \in I \Leftrightarrow x = y^2$ for some $y \in S$,

$$g \cap f = gf \leq e \Leftrightarrow g \leq e : f \Leftrightarrow g \leq (e : f)^2 \in I.$$

It follows from this that I is residuated with residuals given by

$$e \ \vdots\ f = (e : f)^2.$$

Conversely, suppose that (2) holds, so that $S = \bigcup_{e \in I} S_e$ is a partition of S. For each $e \in I$ choose an arbitrary element $p_e \in S_e$, distinct from e if possible. For $x, y \in S$ define the relation $\leq$ by

$$x \leq y \Leftrightarrow \begin{cases} \textit{either} & \text{(a) } x = y; \\ \textit{or} & \text{(b) } x \in I \quad \text{and} \quad x \leq y^2 \quad \text{in } I; \\ \textit{or} & \text{(c) } y \notin I, \quad y = p_{y^2} \quad \text{and} \quad x^2 \leq y^2 \quad \text{in } I. \end{cases}$$

We claim that this is an ordering on S. It is clearly reflexive. Suppose now that $x \leq y$ and $y \leq x$. If $x \neq y$ then we have either $x \in I$ and $y \in I$ or $x \notin I$ and $y \notin I$. The first of these gives $x = y$ by the anti-symmetry of the natural order on I; and in the second case we have $x^2 = y^2$ for the same reason, giving $x = p_{x^2} = p_{y^2} = y$. This contradiction establishes antisymmetry. Now suppose that $x \leq y$ and $y \leq z$ with $x \neq y$ and $y \neq z$. Since $x \notin I$ implies $y \notin I$, there are three possible cases. Firstly, if x and y both belong to I, then $x \leq y^2 = y \leq z^2$ in I and so $x \leq z$ in S. Secondly, if $x \in I$ and $y \notin I$ then $x \leq y^2 \leq z^2$ in I and so $x \leq z$ in S. Finally, if $x \notin I$ and $y \notin I$, then $z \notin I$, $z = p_{z^2}$ and $x^2 \leq y^2 \leq z^2$ in I whence $x \leq z$ in S. This then establishes transitivity.

To show that multiplication is isotone, we first note that since $S_e S_f = \{ef\}$ for all $e, f \in I$, we have $xy = x^2 y^2 \in I$ for all $x, y \in S$. Now

$$x \leq y \Rightarrow x^2 \leq y^2 \quad \text{in } I \Rightarrow zx = z^2 x^2 \leq z^2 y^2 \quad \text{in } I \Rightarrow zx \leq zy \quad \text{in } S.$$

To show that S is quasi-integral, we note that

$$xy = x^2 y^2 = x^2 \cap y^2 \leq x^2 \quad \text{in } I \Rightarrow xy \leq x \quad \text{in } S.$$

Let us now observe that

$$(\forall e \in I) \quad x^2 \leq p_e \Rightarrow x \leq p_e.$$

In fact if $p_e \in I$ this follows from (b); and when $p_e \notin I$ it follows from (c). As a consequence, p_e is the greatest element of S_e with $p_e^2 = e$. This being the case we now have, denoting residuation in I by $\vdots$,

$$\begin{aligned} xy \leq z \Leftrightarrow x^2y^2 \leq z^2 \Leftrightarrow x^2 &\leq z^2 \vdots y^2 \\ \Leftrightarrow x^2 &\leq p_{z^2 \vdots y^2} \\ \Leftrightarrow x &\leq p_{z^2 \vdots y^2}. \end{aligned}$$

This then shows that S is residuated with residuals given by

$$z : y = p_{z^2 \vdots y^2}.$$

Using this formula we see that

$$(\forall x, y \in S) \quad x : y = p_{x^2 \vdots y^2} = p_{x^2 \vdots y^4} = x : y^2$$

and obtain finally the fact that S is a Brouwer semigroup.

THEOREM 32.7. *Let S be a Brouwer semigroup with semilattice of idempotents I. Denoting by $\Box : S \to I$ the map described by $(\forall x \in S)\ \Box(x) = x^2$, we have*

(1) *$\Box$ is a loipomorphism;*
(2) *J is a filter of S if and only if $J = \Box^{\leftarrow}(K)$ where K is a filter of I;*
(3) *if L is a Brouwer semilattice then $f: S \to L$ is a loipomorphism if and only if $f = \psi \circ \Box$ where $\psi : I \to L$ is a loipomorphism.*

Proof. (1) Clearly $\Box$ is an isotone homomorphism. Now as was shown at the beginning of the proof of Theorem 32.6, residuation in I is given by $x \vdots y = (x : y)^2$. We thus have

$$\Box(x : y) = (x : y)^2 = x \vdots y = x \vdots y^2 = x^2 \vdots y^2 = \Box(x) \vdots \Box(y),$$

whence $\Box$ is a loipomorphism.

(2) Let J be a filter of S. Let $x, y \in \Box^{\rightarrow}(J)$; say $x = \Box(a)$ and $y = \Box(b)$ where $a, b \in J$. Since $ab \in J$ we have $x \cap y = \Box(a) \cap \Box(b) = \Box\,(ab)$

$\in \Box^{\rightarrow}(J)$. Moreover, if $x \in \Box^{\rightarrow}(J)$, say $x = \Box(z)$ where $z \in J$, and $y \in I$ is such that $y \geq x$ then since $\Box \circ \Box = \Box$ we have $\Box(x) = \Box\,[\Box(x)] = \Box(z)$ where $\Box(z) = z^2 \in J$ since $z \in J$. Thus

$$xy = (xy)^2 = \Box\,(xy) = \Box(x) \cap \Box(y) = \Box(x) \in J.$$

It follows from $xy \leq y$ that $y \in J$ and so $y = y^2 = \Box(y) \in \Box^{\rightarrow}(J)$. This then shows that $\Box^{\rightarrow}(J)$ is a filter of I. Now let us show that $J = \Box^{\leftarrow}\,[\Box^{\rightarrow}(J)]$. If $x \in \Box^{\leftarrow}\,[\Box^{\rightarrow}(J)]$ then $\Box(x) \in \Box^{\rightarrow}(J)$, say $\Box(x) = \Box(y)$ where $y \in J$. It follows that $x \geq x^2 = y^2 \in J$ and so $x \in J$. Thus $\Box^{\leftarrow}\,[\Box^{\rightarrow}(J)] \subseteq J$. The converse inclusion is clear.

Conversely, if $J = \Box^{\leftarrow}(K)$ where K is a filter of I then

$$x, y \in J \Rightarrow \Box(x),\ \Box(y) \in K \Rightarrow \Box\,(xy) = \Box(x) \cap \Box(y) \in K$$

$$\Rightarrow xy \in \Box^{\leftarrow}(K) = J.$$

Moreover, if $x \in J$ and $y \geq x$ then $x^2 \leq xy = x^2y^2 \leq x^2$ and so $\Box\,(xy) = \Box(x)$. Thus $\Box(x) \in K$; and $\Box(x) \cap \Box(y) = \Box\,(xy) = \Box(x)$ gives $\Box(y) \geq \Box(x)$ so $\Box(y) \in K$ and consequently $y \in \Box^{\leftarrow}(K) = J$. This then shows that J is a filter of S.

(3) If $f : S \to L$ is a loipomorphism then so also is $f|I : I \to L$, the restriction of f to I; for

$$f(x^2 \mathbin{\vdots} y^2) = f\,[(x^2 : y^2)^2] = f\,[x^2 : y^2] = f(x^2) : f(y^2).$$

Since $f(x) = f(x) \cap f(x) = f(x^2)$ we have $f = f|I \circ \Box$.

Conversely, if $f = \psi \circ \Box$ where $\psi : I \to L$ is a loipomorphism then

$$f(x : y) = f(x^2 : y^2) = \psi\,[(x^2 : y^2)^2] = \psi\,[x^2 \mathbin{\vdots} y^2] = \psi(x^2) : \psi(y^2)$$

$$= f(x) : f(y).$$

This completes the proof.

Because of the two previous results, we shall henceforth restrict our attention to Brouwer semilattices. It should be noted, however, that many of the results which follow may be expressed in terms of Brouwer semigroups.

We now recall the notation $\bigcup_{t \in J} F_t$ introduced at the end of § 30 and prove:

THEOREM 32.8. *If L is a Brouwer semilattice then an equivalence relation R on L is compatible with both* $\cap$ *and* : *if and only if R is of the form* $R = \bigcup_{t \in J} F_t$ *where J is a filter of L.*

Proof. By Theorem 31.6, R satisfies the compatibility conditions if and only if, for some filter J, R is given by

$$x \equiv y(R) \Leftrightarrow (x : y) \cap (y : x) \in J.$$

Now if $(x : y) \cap (y : x) \in J$, then using the property $x \cap (y : x) = x \cap y$ we have

$$\begin{aligned} x \cap (y : x) \cap (x : y) = x \cap y \cap (x : y) &= x \cap y \\ &= y \cap x \cap (y : x) \\ &= y \cap (x : y) \cap (y : x) \end{aligned}$$

and so there exists $t = (x : y) \cap (y : x) \in J$ such that $x \cap t = y \cap t$ whence $x \equiv y \left(\bigcup_{t \in J} F_t\right)$. Thus $R \leq \bigcup_{t \in J} F_t$. Conversely,

$$\begin{aligned} x \equiv y \left(\bigcup_{t \in J} F_t\right) &\Rightarrow (\exists t \in J) \quad x \cap t = y \cap t \\ &\Rightarrow (\exists t \in t) \quad x \cap t \leq y, \quad y \cap t \leq x \\ &\Rightarrow (\exists t \in J) \quad t \leq (y : x) \cap (x : y) \\ &\Rightarrow (x : y) \cap (y : x) \in J \end{aligned}$$

and so $\bigcup_{t \in J} F_t \leq R$, whence we have equality.

Definition. By a *Glivenko–Brouwer semilattice* we shall mean a Brouwer semilattice with a minimum element.

Suppose now that L is a Brouwer semilattice and for each $a \in L$ consider the filter $[a, \rightarrow]$. This is clearly a Glivenko–Brouwer subsemilattice of L relative to which we have:

THEOREM 32.9. *For each element a of a Brouwer semilattice L define* $(L:a) = \{x:a;\, x \in L\}$. *Then* $(L:a)$ *is a Brouwer semilattice and*

$$(L:a) \simeq L/[a, \rightarrow] = L/F_a.$$

Proof. By Exercise 31.2, each residual map λ_a^+ is a loipomorphism. Moreover,

$$\operatorname{Ker} \lambda_a^+ = \{x \in L;\, x:a = \lambda_a^+(x) = \pi\} = \{x \in L;\, a = a \cap \pi \leq x\} = [a, \rightarrow].$$

Applying Theorem 31.3 we obtain $(L:a) \simeq L/[a, \rightarrow]$. To establish the equality, we remember that by the usual abuse of notation we write $L/[a, \rightarrow]$ instead of L/R, where

$$R = \bigcup_{t \in [a, \rightarrow]} F_t.$$

Now for any $x, y \in L$ we have $x \leq y \Rightarrow F_y \leq F_x$. [For

$$a \equiv b(F_y) \Rightarrow y \cap a = y \cap b \Rightarrow x \cap a = (x \cap y) \cap a = x \cap (y \cap a)$$

$$= x \cap (y \cap b) = (x \cap y) \cap b = x \cap b \Rightarrow a \equiv b(F_x).]$$

It follows from this that $R = F_a$ and so $L/[a, \rightarrow] = L/F_a$.

THEOREM 32.10. *Let L be a Glivenko–Brouwer semilattice with dense filter D. Then the following conditions are equivalent:*

(1) *D is a Glivenko–Brouwer subsemilattice of L;*

(2) *there exists* $m \in D$ *such that* L/F_m *is a Boolean algebra.*

Proof. If (1) holds then D has a minimum element, m say. Now as we observed above $(\forall t \in D)\ F_t \leq F_m$ and so $\bigcup_{t \in D} F_t = F_m$. This yields $L/D = L/F_m$ and so L/F_m is a Boolean algebra (isomorphic to L^{**}).

Conversely, suppose that there exists $m \in D$ such that L/F_m is Boolean. Using Theorem 32.9 we see that $L/[m, \rightarrow]$ is Boolean. Applying Theorem 31.8 we deduce that $D \subseteq [m, \rightarrow]$ whence there results $D = [m, \rightarrow]$ since $m \in D$. It follows that D is a Glivenko–Brouwer semilattice.

THEOREM 32.11. *A Glivenko–Brouwer semilattice L is a Boolean algebra if and only if its only dense element is* π.

Proof. We note first that $(L:\pi) = \{x:\pi;\, x \in L\} = L$ and, by Theorem 32.9, $L \simeq L/\{\pi\}$. Thus if L is a Boolean algebra so also is $L/\{\pi\}$. But $\{\pi\}$ is a filter of L so by Theorem 31.8 we have $D \subseteq \{\pi\}$ whence $D = \{\pi\}$. Conversely, if $D = \{\pi\}$ then $L/D = L/F_\pi \simeq L$ and so L is Boolean.

Our aim now is to answer the following question: *In a Glivenko–Brouwer semilattice, precisely which filters are such that L/J is Boolean?* In order to characterize these filters, we require a few facts concerning the loipomorphism $(**) : L \to L^{**}$ given by the prescription $(**)(x) = x^{**}$.

THEOREM 32.12. *Let L be a Glivenko–Brouwer semilattice. If J is a filter of L, then $(**)^{\to}(J)$ is a filter of L^{**}; and if K is a filter of L^{**}, then $(**)^{\leftarrow}(K)$ is a filter of L.*

Proof. Let J be a filter of L and let $x^{**}, y^{**} \in (**)^{\to}(J)$. Then $x, y \in J$ and so, since $x \cap y \leq x \leq x^{**}$ and $x \cap y \leq y \leq y^{**}$, we have $x^{**} \cap y^{**} \geq x \cap y \in J$ so that $x^{**} \cap y^{**} \in J$ whence $x^{**} \cap y^{**} = (x^{**} \cap y^{**})^{**} \in (**)^{\to}(J)$. Also, if $x^{**} \in (**)^{\to}(J)$ and $y \in L^{**}$ is such that $y \geq x^{**}$ then $y \geq x \in J$ so that $y \in J$ and hence $y^{**} \in (**)^{\to}(J)$. Thus $(**)^{\to}(J)$ is a filter of L^{**}.

Now let K be a filter of L^{**}. Then

$$x, y \in (**)^{\leftarrow}(K) \Rightarrow x^{**}, y^{**} \in K \Rightarrow (x \cap y)^{**} = x^{**} \cap y^{**} \in K$$
$$\Rightarrow xy \in (**)^{\leftarrow}(K)$$

and

$$y \geq x \in (**)^{\leftarrow}(K) \Rightarrow y^{**} \geq x^{**} \in K \Rightarrow y^{**} \in K \Rightarrow y \in (**)^{\leftarrow}(K).$$

Thus $(**)^{\leftarrow}(K)$ is a filter of L.

Let us note that by Theorem 32.12 the loipomorphism $(**) : L \to L^{**}$ induces a mapping $(**)^{\to}$ from the set of filters of L to the set of filters of L^{**}. This mapping is clearly a surjective residuated map with residual given by $(**)^{\leftarrow}$. Note that since $(**)^{\to}$ is surjective then $(**)^{\leftarrow}$ is injective [Theorem 2.6].

THEOREM 32.13. *If L is a Glivenko-Brouwer semilattice and J is an ultrafilter of L then $(**)^{\to}(J)$ is an ultrafilter of L^{**}; and if K is an ultrafilter of L^{**} then $(**)^{\leftarrow}(K)$ is an ultrafilter of L.*

Proof. Suppose that J is an ultrafilter of L and let K be a filter of L^{**} such that $(^{**})^{\rightarrow}(J) \subseteq K \subseteq L^{**}$. Then we have $J \subseteq (^{**})^{\leftarrow}[(^{**})^{\rightarrow}(J)] \subseteq (^{**})^{\leftarrow}(K)$ where $(^{**})^{\leftarrow}(K) \neq L = (^{**})^{\leftarrow}(L^{**})$ since $(^{**})^{\leftarrow}$ is injective. Since $(^{**})^{\leftarrow}(K)$ is a filter of L, the maximality of J gives $J = (^{**})^{\leftarrow}[(^{**})^{\rightarrow}(J)] = (^{**})^{\leftarrow}(K)$. Since $(^{**})^{\leftarrow}$ is injective, we deduce that $(^{**})^{\rightarrow}(J) = K$ whence it follows that $(^{**})^{\rightarrow}(J)$ is an ultrafilter of L^{**}.

Suppose now that K is an ultrafilter of L^{**} and let H be a filter of L such that $(^{**})^{\leftarrow}(K) \subseteq H \subset L$. By Theorem 2.6 we have $(^{**})^{\rightarrow} \circ (^{**})^{\leftarrow} = \mathrm{id}$ and so $K = (^{**})^{\rightarrow}[(^{**})^{\leftarrow}(K)] \subseteq (^{**})^{\rightarrow}(H) \subseteq (^{**})^{\rightarrow}(L) = L^{**}$. Now we cannot have $(^{**})^{\rightarrow}(H) = L^{**}$; for, since H is a filter of L, $(^{**})^{\rightarrow}(H) = H^{**} = H \cap L^{**}$ and so the equality $H^{**} = L^{**}$ would yield $L^{**} \subseteq H$ whence $0 = 0^{**} \in H$ and consequently $H = L$, a contradiction. We thus have $K \subseteq (^{**})^{\rightarrow}(H) \subset L^{**}$ and the maximality of K yields $K = (^{**})^{\rightarrow}(H)$, from which we deduce that $(^{**})^{\leftarrow}(K) = (^{**})^{\leftarrow}[(^{**})^{\rightarrow}(H)] \supseteq H$. Hence we have $H = (^{**})^{\leftarrow}(K)$ and this shows that $^{**})^{\leftarrow}(K)$ is an ultrafilter of L.

The following result we give without proof; it follows by a standard application of the axiom of Zorn:

THEOREM 32.14. *In a Glivenko–Brouwer semilattice every proper filter is contained in an ultrafilter.*

We are now in a position to characterize the filters J of a Glivenko–Brouwer semilattice L for which L/J is Boolean.

THEOREM 32.15. *Let L be a Glivenko–Brouwer semilattice with dense filter D. For a filter J of L the following conditions are equivalent:*

(1) *L/J is a Boolean algebra;*
(2) $J = (^{**})^{\leftarrow}[(^{**})^{\rightarrow}(J)]$;
(3) *J is an intersection of ultrafilters;*
(4) $D \subseteq J$.

Proof. We shall show that (1) ⇒ (4) ⇒ (2) ⇒ (1) and that (2) ⇔ (3).
(1) ⇒ (4): this is immediate from Theorem 31.8.
(4) ⇒ (2): Suppose that $D \subseteq J$ and consider any element

$$x \in (^{**})^{\leftarrow}[(^{**})^{\rightarrow}(J)].$$

We have $x^{**} \in (^{**})^{\rightarrow}(J)$ so that, for some $y \in J$, $x^{**} = y^{**}$. Since J is a filter it follows that $x^{**} \in J$. Now by the formula (*) of Theorem 31.7 we have $(\forall x \in L)\ (x : x^{**})^{**} = (x^{**} : x^{**})^{**} = \pi^{**} = \pi$ and so $(\forall x \in L)\ x : x^{**} \in D \subseteq J$. Consequently

$$x = x^{**} \cap x = x^{**} \cap (x : x^{**}) \in J.$$

This then shows that $(^{**})^{\leftarrow}[(^{**})^{\rightarrow}(J)] \subseteq J$ whence there results equality and (2).

(2) $\Rightarrow$ (1): If (2) holds then $x^{**} \in (^{**})^{\rightarrow}(J) \Rightarrow x \in J$. To show that L/J is Boolean, it is sufficient to show that the equivalence of type A associated with $0/J$ reduces to equality [Theorem 30.1]. For this purpose, it is enough to show that

$$x^{**}/J = y^{**}/J \Rightarrow x/J = y/J.$$

Now

$$\begin{aligned} x^{**}/J = y^{**}/J &\Rightarrow (\exists d \in J) \quad x^{**} \cap d = y^{**} \cap d \\ &\Rightarrow (\exists d \in J) \quad d \leq (y^{**} \cap d) : x^{**} \leq y^{**} : x^{**} = (y : x)^{**} \\ &\Rightarrow (\exists d \in J) \quad d^{**} \leq (y : x)^{**} \\ &\Rightarrow (y : x)^{**} \in (^{**})^{\rightarrow}(J) \\ &\Rightarrow y : x \in J. \end{aligned}$$

In a similar way we can show that $x^{**}/J = y^{**}/J \Rightarrow x : y \in J$. Using Theorem 31.6 we can therefore say that

$$x^{**}/J = y^{**}/J \Rightarrow (x : y) \cap (y : x) \in J \Rightarrow x/J = y/J.$$

(2) $\Rightarrow$ (3): It follows by Theorem 21.7* that every filter of a Boolean algebra is the intersection of all the maximal filters containing it. Suppose that in L^{**} we have $(^{**})^{\rightarrow}(J) = \bigcap_{\alpha \in A} (^{**})^{\rightarrow}(M_\alpha)$ where each $(^{**})^{\rightarrow}(M_\alpha)$ is an ultrafilter of L^{**}. If (2) holds then we have

$$J = (^{**})^{\leftarrow}[(^{**})^{\rightarrow}(J)] = (^{**})^{\leftarrow}\Big(\bigcap_{\alpha \in A} (^{**})^{\rightarrow}(M_\alpha)\Big) = \bigcap_{\alpha \in A} (^{**})^{\leftarrow}[(^{**})^{\rightarrow}(M_\alpha)],$$

the right hand equality resulting from the fact that residual maps preserve intersections. Now since $(^{**})^{\rightarrow}(M_\alpha)$ is an ultrafilter of L^{**} the set

$M_\alpha = (^{**})^{\leftarrow}[(^{**})^{\rightarrow}(M_\alpha)]$ is an ultrafilter of L. We thus have $J = \bigcap_{\alpha\in A} M_\alpha$; i.e. J is an intersection of ultrafilters.

(3) $\Rightarrow$ (2): If J is an intersection of ultrafilters, say $J = \bigcap_{\alpha\in A} M_\alpha$, then for each $\alpha \in A$ we have $J \subseteq M_\alpha$ and so

$$(^{**})^{\leftarrow}[(^{**})^{\rightarrow}(J)] \subseteq (^{**})^{\leftarrow}[(^{**})^{\rightarrow}(M_\alpha)] = M_\alpha$$

(the equality resulting from the fact that every ultrafilter is maximal). It follows that $(^{**})^{\leftarrow}[(^{**})^{\rightarrow}(J)] \subseteq \bigcap_{\alpha\in A} M_\alpha = J$ whence we have equality and (2).

Definition. The two-element Boolean algebra has no filters other than itself and the set consisting of the greatest element. For this reason we call it the *simple* Boolean algebra.

THEOREM 32.16. *Let J be a filter of the Glivenko–Brouwer semilattice L. The following conditions are then equivalent:*

(1) *J is an ultrafilter of L;*
(2) *L/J is the simple Boolean algebra.*

Proof. We begin by noting that for any proper filter J of a Boolean algebra B the following assertions are equivalent [consider the dual of Theorem 21.5]:

(a) J is an ultrafilter;
(b) either $x \in J$ or $x^* \in J$ (but not both).

This being the case, suppose that J is an ultrafilter of L. By Theorem 32.15 we have $J = (^{**})^{\leftarrow}[(^{**})^{\rightarrow}(J)]$ and so J satisfies the property

$$y^{**} \in (^{**})^{\rightarrow}(J) \Rightarrow y \in J.$$

If now $x \in L \setminus J$ we deduce that $x^{**} \notin (^{**})^{\rightarrow}(J)$ so that, by (b),

$$x^* = x^{***} \in (^{**})^{\rightarrow}(J) = J \cap L^{**} \subseteq J.$$

Thus, since

$$\begin{aligned} x/J = 0/J &\Leftrightarrow (\exists t \in J) \quad x \cap t = 0 \cap t = 0 \\ &\Leftrightarrow (\exists t \in J) \quad t \leq 0 : x = x^* \\ &\Leftrightarrow x^* \in J, \end{aligned}$$

we see that L/J is simple.

Conversely, suppose that L/J is simple. Let K be a filter of L with $J \subset K$ and let $x \in K \setminus J$. Since L/J is simple we have $\natural_J(x) = 0/J$ and so

$$\natural_J(x^*) = \natural_J(0:x) = \natural_J(0) : \natural_J(x) = 0/J : 0/J = \pi/J,$$

whence $x^* \in \operatorname{Ker} \natural_J = J$. Consequently, $0 = x \cap (0:x) = x \cap x^* \in K$ and it follows that K is not proper. This shows that J is an ultrafilter.

COROLLARY. *The dense filter of a Glivenko–Brouwer semilattice L is an ultrafilter of L if and only if L^{**} is simple.*

As we have seen, the important features of a Glivenko–Brouwer semilattice are (1) the Boolean algebra L^{**} of pseudo-residuals and (2) the dense filter D. Our next, and final, goal is to determine all Glivenko–Brouwer semilattices which have a given Boolean algebra as algebra of pseudo-residuals and a given Brouwer semilattice as dense filter.

Definition. If B is a Boolean algebra and D is a Brouwer semilattice, we shall say that a mapping $f: B \times D \to D$ is *admissible* if and only if:

(1) for each $a \in B$ the mapping $f_a : D \to D$ described by $f_a(d) = f(a,d)$ is a loipomorphism with $f_a \geq \mathrm{id}_D$;
(2) $f_{\pi_B} = \mathrm{id}_D$ and $(\forall d \in D)\ \ f_{0_B}(d) = \pi_D$;
(3) $(\forall a, b \in B)\ \ f_{a \cap b} = f_a \circ f_b$.

THEOREM 32.17. *Let B be a Boolean algebra, L a Brouwer semilattice and $f: B \times L \to L$ an admissible map. Then the relation R_f defined on $B \times L$ by*

$$(\alpha, x) \equiv (\beta, y)\ (R_f) \Leftrightarrow (\alpha = \beta \text{ and } f_\alpha(x) = f_\alpha(y))$$

is an equivalence relation which is compatible with intersection. R_f is not in general compatible with residuation but the semilattice $(B \times L)/R_f$ is a Brouwer semilattice in which

$$(\alpha, x)/R_f : (\beta, y)/R_f = (\alpha \cup \beta', f_\beta(x:y))/R_f .$$

Moreover, $(B \times L)/R_f$ is a Glivenko–Brouwer semilattice with algebra of pseudo-residuals isomorphic to B and dense filter isomorphic to L. Furthermore, if S is any Glivenko–Brouwer semilattice with dense filter D then the *mapping $g : S^{**} \times D \to D$ defined by $g(\alpha, x) = x : \alpha$ is admissible and*

$$S \simeq (S^{**} \times D)/R_g.$$

Proof. It is clear that $B \times L$ is a Brouwer semilattice and that R_f is an equivalence relation. Since each f_α is in particular an $\cap$-homomorphism it follows readily that R_f is compatible with intersection. Thus $(B \times L)/R_f$ forms an $\cap$-semilattice in which

$$(\alpha, x)/R_f \curlywedge (\beta, y)/R_f = (\alpha \cap \beta,\ x \cap y)/R_f.$$

Now from this we have $(\alpha, x)/R_f \curlywedge (\beta, y)/R_f \leq (\gamma, z)/R_f$ if and only if $(\alpha \cap \beta \cap \gamma,\ x \cap y \cap z)/R_f = (\alpha \cap \beta,\ x \cap y)/R_f$ which in turn holds if and only if $a \cap \beta \cap \gamma = \alpha \cap \beta$ and $f_{\alpha\cap\beta}(x \cap y \cap z) = f_{\alpha\cap\beta}(x \cap y)$. Now the first of these holds if and only if $\alpha \cap \beta \leq \gamma$, i.e. if and only if $\beta \leq \gamma \cup \alpha'$. On the other hand, the second holds if and only if $f_{\alpha\cap\beta}(x \cap y) \leq f_{\alpha\cap\beta}(z)$ since each f_α is an $\cap$-homomorphism. Since each $f_\alpha \geq \mathrm{id}_L$, this is in turn equivalent to

$$y \leq f_{\alpha\cap\beta}(y) \leq f_{\alpha\cap\beta}(z) : f_{\alpha\cap\beta}(x) = f_{\alpha\cap\beta}(z : x) = f_\beta[f_\alpha(z : x)].$$

Since $f_\beta \circ f_\beta = f_{\beta\cap\beta} = f_\beta \geq \mathrm{id}_L$ this is equivalent to $f_\beta(y) \leq f_\beta[f_\alpha(z : x)]$. Having observed this, we now note that

$$(\beta, y)/R_f \leq (\gamma \cup \alpha', f_\alpha(z : x))/R_f$$

$$\Leftrightarrow (\beta, y)/R_f = (\beta \cap (\gamma \cup \alpha'), y \cap f_\alpha(z : x))/R_f$$

$$\Leftrightarrow \beta \leq \gamma \cup \alpha',\ f_\beta(y) = f_\beta(y) \cap f_\beta[f_\alpha(z : x)]$$

$$\Leftrightarrow \beta \leq \gamma \cup \alpha',\ f_\beta(y) \leq f_\beta[f_\alpha(z : x)].$$

It therefore follows that $(\gamma, z)/R_f \,\vdots\, (\alpha, x)/R_f$ exists and is given by $(\gamma \cup \alpha', f_\alpha(z : x))/R_f$.

To show that $(B \times L)/R_f$ is a Glivenko–Brouwer semilattice it suffices to show that it has a minimum element. It is readily seen that such an element is $(0_B, \pi_L)/R_f$. [Note that for each $x \in L$ we have $(0_B, \pi_L) \equiv (0_B, x)(R_f)$.] We also see that the greatest element of $(B \times L)/R_f$ is $(\pi_B, \pi_L)/R_f$.

Now in $(B\times L)/R_f$ we have

$$[(\beta, y)/R_f]^* = (0_B, \pi_L)/R_f : (\beta, y)/R_f = (\beta', f_\beta(\pi_L))/R_f = (\beta', \pi_L)/R_f$$

and so $[(\beta, y)/R_f]^{**} = (\beta, \pi_L)/R_f$. Thus $(\beta, y)/R_f$ is dense if and only if $\beta = \pi_B$; and $(\beta, y)/R_f$ is a pseudo-residual if and only if $(\beta, y)/R_f = (\beta, \pi_L)/R_f$. Since f_{π_B} is the identity map on L it is clear that the dense filter of $(B\times L)/R_f$ is isomorphic with L. It is also clear that $[(B\times L)/R_f]^{**}$ is isomorphic with B.

Let us now consider the situation where S is a Glivenko–Brouwer semilattice. Define $g : S^{**}\times D \to D$ by setting $g(\alpha, x) = x : \alpha$ (note that this is indeed an element of D since $x \in D$). Writing $g_\alpha(x) = g(\alpha, x) = x:\alpha$, it is readily seen that each $g_\alpha \geq \mathrm{id}_D$ with $g_\pi = \mathrm{id}_D$ and $g_0(x) = \pi_D$ for all x. Moreover, $g_\alpha \circ g_\beta = g_{\alpha\cap\beta}$ and each g_α is a loipomorphism since $(x\cap y):\alpha = (x:\alpha)\cap(y:\alpha)$ and $(x:y):\alpha = x:y\alpha = x:(y:\alpha)\,\alpha = (x:\alpha):(y:\alpha)$. This then shows that the mapping g is admissible.

It remains to show that $S \simeq (S^{**}\times D)/R_g$. For this purpose we wish to define a mapping $\zeta : (S^{**}\times D)/R_g \to S$. Now we note that

$$(\alpha, x) \equiv (\beta, y)\,(R_g) \Rightarrow \alpha \cap x = \beta \cap y.$$

In fact if $(\alpha, x) \equiv (\beta, y)\,(R_g)$, then $\alpha = \beta$ and $g_\alpha(x) = g_\alpha(y)$; i.e. $x:\alpha = y:\alpha$ which is the same as $x \equiv y(B_\alpha)$. But $B_\alpha = F_\alpha$ and so $x \equiv y(F_\alpha)$ whence $\alpha\cap x = \alpha \cap y = \beta \cap y$. We can therefore define our mapping by setting

$$\zeta\,((\alpha, x)/R_g) = \alpha \cap x.$$

That ζ is surjective follows from the fact that each $y\in S$ can be written in the form $y = y^{**}\cap y = y^{**}\cap(y:y^{**})$, where $y^{**}\in S^{**}$ and $y:y^{**} \in D$. It is clear that ζ is an $\cap$-homomorphism. Let us now show that it is a loipomorphism. On the one hand we have

$$\begin{aligned}\zeta\,((\alpha, x)/R_g : (\beta, y)/R_g) &= \zeta\,((\alpha \curlyvee \beta^*, (x:y):\beta)/R_g)\\ &= (\alpha \curlyvee \beta^*) \cap [(x:y):\beta];\end{aligned}$$

and, on the other,

$$\begin{aligned}\zeta((\alpha, x)/R_g):\zeta((\beta, y)/R_g) &= (\alpha \cap x):(\beta \cap y)\\ &= [\alpha:(\beta \cap y)] \cap [x:(\beta \cap y)]\\ &= [\alpha \curlyvee (\beta \cap y)^*] \cap [(x:y):\beta].\end{aligned}$$

Now since $y \in D$ we have $(\beta \cap y)^{**} = (\beta \cap y^{**})^{**} = \beta^{**}$ and so $(\beta \cap y)^* = \beta^*$. It follows that

$$\zeta((\alpha, x)/R_g : (\beta, y)/R_g) = \zeta((\alpha, x)/R_g):\zeta((\beta, y)/R_g)$$

and so ζ is a loipomorphism. Now $(\alpha, x)/R_g \in \operatorname{Ker} \zeta$ if and only if $\alpha \cap x = \pi_S$ which holds if and only if $\alpha = \pi_S = x$. Thus $\operatorname{Ker} \zeta = \{(\pi_S, \pi_S)/R_g\}$ from which it follows immediately that $S \simeq (S^{**} \times D)/R_g$.

EXERCISES

32.1. Let S be a Brouwer semigroup. Call a non-empty subset L of S a Brouwer subsemilattice of S if it forms an $\cap$-semilattice under the ordering on S and is residuated with respect to $\cap$ with residuals relative to $\cap$ the same as the corresponding residuals with respect to multiplication.

Given any element t of a Brouwer semigroup S show that the set $R(t)$ of residuals of t forms a Brouwer subsemilattice of S. Show also that for each $t \in S$ the set $(S:t) = \{x:t;\ x \in S\}$ is a Brouwer subsemilattice of S.

32.2. Prove that in a Brouwer semigroup $F_x = F_{x^2}$ and that $F_x = F_y$ if and only if $x^2 = y^2$.

32.3. If S is a Glivenko–Brouwer semigroup with dense filter D, prove that S is a semilattice if and only if

$$(\forall y \in S)\,(\exists x \in S^{**})\,(\exists d \in D) \quad y = x^{**}d.$$

32.4. Prove that the following algebraic structures are identical:

(a) a Glivenko–Brouwer semigroup;
(b) a residuated inverse semigroup with 0.

32.5. Prove that the following algebraic structures are identical:

(a) a Brouwer semilattice;
(b) a residuated naturally ordered idempotent semigroup;
(c) a residuated negatively ordered idempotent semigroup.

32.6. Define a *Brouwer algebra* to be a Brouwer $\cap$-semilattice which is also a $\cup$-semilattice. Prove that every Brouwer algebra is distributive. [*Hint:* use Exercise 22.6.]

32.7. Let L be a Glivenko–Brouwer algebra. Prove that the following statements are equivalent:

(1) L is a Boolean algebra;
(2) $(\forall a, b \in L) \quad a \cup (b:a) = \pi$;
(3) $(\forall a, b \in L) \quad b:(b:a) = a \cup b$;
(4) $(\forall a, b \in L) \quad a:(b:a) = a$.

32.8. Let F be a bounded totally ordered set. Show that for any ordered set E the set of isotone mappings from E to F forms a Glivenko–Brouwer algebra. Show that the dense filter of this algebra consists of those mappings f for which $\{x \in E; f(x) = 0_F\} = \emptyset$ and that the Boolean algebra of pseudo-residuals consists of those maps h for which $h(x)$ is either 0_F or π_F.

32.9. Show that a Brouwer semilattice L is *weakly distributive* in the sense that if $y \cup z$ exists then, for each $x \in L$, $(x \cap y) \cup (x \cap z)$ exists and equals $x \cap (y \cup z)$. Call an element $x \in L$ *complemented* if, for some $y \in L$, $x \cap y = 0$ and $x \cup y$ exists and equals π. Show that if $x \in L$ is complemented then it admits a unique complement, namely $x^* = 0:x$. Deduce that the set of complemented elements forms a subalgebra of L^{**}.

32.10. Let L be a Brouwer semilattice. Show that the set $F(L)$ of filters of L forms a Glivenko–Brouwer algebra in which residuals are given by

$$K:J = \{x \in L; [x, \rightarrow] \cap J \subseteq K\}.$$

Deduce that $J \in F(L)$ is complemented if and only if $J = [x, \rightarrow]$ where x is a complemented element of L.

32.11. Let L be a complete lattice. Show that L is a Glivenko–Brouwer algebra if and only if it satisfies the infinite distributive law (ID). Deduce that the open sets of any topological space T form a Glivenko–Brouwer algebra A. Show that the residuals in this algebra are given by $F:E = \text{Int}(F \cup E')$ where Int denotes interior and $'$ denotes complements in $\mathbf{P}(T)$. Deduce that the Boolean algebra A^{**} of pseudo-residuals consists of those open sets which are *regular* (where an open set is said to be regular if and only if it coincides with the interior of its closure) and that the dense filter D consists of those open sets which are dense in the topological sense.

BIBLIOGRAPHY

PART 1: REFERENCES MADE IN THE PREFACE AND IN THE TEXT

[1] I. AMEMIYA and H. ARAKI: A remark on Piron's paper, *Pub. Res. Inst. Math.*, Ser. A, **2**, 1966–67, 423–427.

[2] R. BAER: *Linear algebra and projective geometry*, Academic Press, New York, 1952.

[3] M. BENADO: Nouveaux théorèmes de décomposition et d'intercalation à la normalité, *C. R. Acad. Sc., Paris*, **228**, 1949, 529–531.

[4] A. BIGARD: Sur les images homomorphes d'un demi-groupe ordonné, *C. R. Acad. Sc., Paris*, **260**, 1965, 5987–5988.

[5] T. S. BLYTH: The general form of residuated algebraic structures, *Bull. Soc. Math. France*, **93**, 1965, 109–127.

[6] S. K. BERBERIAN: *Introduction to Hilbert space*, Oxford University Press, New York, 1961.

[7] C. C. CHEN and G. GRÄTZER: On the construction of complemented lattices, *J. Algebra*, **11**, 1969, 56–63.

[8] R. CROISOT: Applications résiduées, *Ann. Sci. Ecole Norm. Sup., Paris*, (3), **73**, 1956, 453–474.

[9] J. C. DERDERIAN: Residuated mappings, *Pacific J. Math.*, **20**, 1967, 35–43.

[10] R. P. DILWORTH: Lattices with unique complements, *Trans. Amer. Math. Soc.*, **57**, 1945, 123–154.

[11] P. DUBREIL and R. CROISOT: Propriétés générales de la résiduation en liaison avec les correspondances de Galois, *Collect. Math.*, **7**, 1954, 193–203.

[12] M. L. DUBREIL-JACOTIN, L. LESIEUR and R. CROISOT: *Leçons sur la théorie des treillis, des structures algébriques ordonnées et des treillis géométriques*, Gauthier-Villars, Paris, 1953.

[13] D. J. FOULIS: Baer *-semigroups, *Proc. Amer. Math. Soc.*, **11**, 1960, 648–654.

[14] P. R. HALMOS: *Introduction to Hilbert space and the theory of spectral multiplicity*, Chelsea Pub. Co., New York, 1951.

[15] S. S. HOLLAND, Jr: The current interest in orthomodular lattices, article in *Trends in lattice theory* (J. C. Abbott, Editor), van Nostrand-Reinhold, New York, 1970.

[16] M. F. JANOWITZ: Baer semigroups, *Duke Math. J.*, **32**, 1963, 85–96.

[17] M. F. JANOWITZ: A semigroup approach to lattices, *Canad. J. Math.*, **18**, 1966, 1212–1223.

[18] I. KAPLANSKY: *Rings of operators*, Benjamin, New York, 1968.

[19] L. H. LOOMIS: The lattice-theoretic background of the dimension theory of operator algebras, *Mem. Amer. Math. Soc.*, No. 18, Providence, 1955.

[20] I. MOLINARO: Demi-groupes résidutifs, *J. Math. pures et appl., série* 9, **39**, 1960, 319–356 and **40**, 1961, 43–110.

[21] J. von NEUMANN: *Continuous geometry*, Princeton, 1960.
[22] G. NÖBELING: Topologie der Vereine und Verbände, *Arch. Math.*, **1**, 1948, 154–159.
[23] G. NÖBELING: *Grundlagen der analytischen Topologie*, Springer-Verlag, Berlin, 1954.
[24] J. QUERRÉ: Equivalences de fermeture dans un demi-groupe résidutif, Séminaire Dubreil, Institut Poincaré, Paris, 1961–62, Exposé No. 3.
[25] C.H. RANDALL and D.J. FOULIS: An approach to empirical logic, *Amer. Math. Monthly*, **77**, 1970, 363–374.
[26] J. SCHMIDT: Beiträge zur Filtertheorie, *Math. Nachr.*, **10**, 1953, 197–232.
[27] M. SUZUKI: *Structure of a group and the structure of its lattice of subgroups*, Ergebnisse der Mathematik, Springer-Verlag, 1956.
[28] A. TAYLOR: *Introduction to functional analysis*, Wiley, New York, 1958.

PART 2: BOOKS ON LATTICE THEORY (OTHER THAN THOSE MENTIONED IN PART 1)

ABBOTT, J.C.: *Sets, lattices and Boolean algebras*, Allyn and Bacon, Boston, 1969.
BIRKHOFF, G.: *Lattice theory*, Amer. Math. Soc. Coll. Pub., Providence 1967 (3rd Ed.).
BLUMENTHAL, L.M. and MENGER, K.: *Studies in geometry*, Freeman, San Francisco, 1970.
DONNELLAN, T.: *Lattice theory*, Pergamon Press, Oxford, 1968.
DUBISCH, R.: *Lattices to logic*, Blaisdell, New York, 1963.
GERICKE, H.: *Theorie der Verbände*, Bibliographisches Institut Mannheim, 1963.
GOODSTEIN, R.L.: *Boolean algebra*, Pergamon Press, Oxford, 1963.
HERMES, H.: *Einführung in die Verbandstheorie*, Springer-Verlag, Berlin, 1955.
LIEBER, L.R.: *Lattice theory*, Galois Institute of Mathematics and Art, Brooklyn, 1959.
MAEDA, F.: *Kontinuierliche Geometrien*, Springer-Verlag, Berlin, 1958.
MAEDA, F. and MAEDA, S.: *Theory of symmetric lattices*, Springer-Verlag, Berlin, 1971.
RUTHERFORD, D.E.: *Introduction to lattice theory*, Oliver & Boyd, Edinburgh, 1965.
SIKORSKI, R.: *Boolean algebras*, Springer-Verlag, Berlin, 1960.
SKORNYAKOV, L.A.: *Complemented modular lattices and regular rings*, Oliver & Boyd, Edinburgh, 1964.
SZASZ, G.: *Introduction to lattice theory*, Academic Press, New York, 1963.

PART 3: RESEARCH PAPERS (OTHER THAN THOSE MENTIONED IN PART 1)

ADAMS, D.H.: The completion by cuts of an orthocomplemented modular lattice, *Bull. Austral. Math. Soc.*, **1**, 1969, 279–280.
ADAMS, D.H.: A note on a paper by P.D. Finch, *J. Austral. Math. Soc.*, **9**, 1970, 63–64.
ADAMS, D.H.: Semigroup completions of lattices, *Proc. London Math. Soc.*, (3), **20**, 1970, 659–668.
AUMANN, G.: Bemerkung über Galois-Verbindungen, *S. B. Acad. Wiss. Math. Nat. Kl.*, 1955, 281–284.

BALBES, R. and HORN, A.: Projective distributive lattices, *Pacific J. Math.*, **33**, 1970, 273–279.

BALBES, R. and HORN, A.: Stone lattices, *Duke Math. J.*, **38**, 1970, 537–545.

BENADO, M.: La notion de normalité et les théorèmes de décomposition de l'algèbre, *Acad. Repub. Pop. Romane Stud. Circ. Mat.*, **1**, 1950, 282–317.

BENNETT, M.K.: States and orthomodular lattices, *J. Nat. Sci. and Math.*, **8**, 1968, 47–52.

BENNETT, M.K.: A finite orthomodular lattice which does not admit a full set of states, *Siam Review*, **12**, 1970, 267–271.

BERGMANN, G.: Multiplicative closures, *Portugal Math.*, **11**, 1952, 169–172.

BEVIS, J.: Matrices over orthomodular lattices, *Proc. Glasgow Math. Assoc.*, **10**, 1969, 55–59.

BEVIS, J.: A note on a distributivity relation, *J. London Math. Soc.*, (2), **2**, 1970, 521–524.

BEVIS, J. and CHESLEY, D.S.: Determinants for matrices over lattices, *Proc. Roy. Soc. Edinburgh*, A, **68**, 1969, 138–142.

BEVIS, J. and MARTIN, C.K.: Residuation theory on orthomodular lattices, *Proc. Glasgow Math. Assoc.*, **10**, 1969, 60–65.

BLYTH, T.S.: Groupoïdes résidués et demi-groupes nomaux, Séminaire Dubreil, Institut Poincaré, Paris, 1962–63, exposé No. 24.

BLYTH, T.S.: Matrices over ordered algebraic structures, *J. London Math. Soc.*, **39**, 1964, 427–432.

BLYTH, T.S.: Residuation theory and Boolean matrices, *Proc. Glasgow Math. Assoc.*, **6**, 1964, 185–190.

BLYTH, T.S.: $\wedge$-distributive Boolean matrices, *Proc. Glasgow Math. Assoc.*, **7**, 1965, 93–100.

BLYTH, T.S.: Pseudo-residuals in semigroups, *J. London Math. Soc.*, **40**, 1965, 441–454.

BLYTH, T.S.: On eigenvectors of Boolean matrices, *Proc. Roy. Soc. Edinburgh*, **67**, A, 1966, 196–204.

BLYTH, T.S.: Sur les demi-groupes de Brouwer et Glivenko, *Bull. Soc. Math. France*, **96**, 1968, 15–40.

BLYTH, T.S.: Une question ouverte sur la similitude des matrices de Boole, *C. R. Acad. Sc., Paris*, **266**, 1968, 963–965.

BLYTH, T.S.: On the greatest isotone homomorphic group image of an inverse semigroup, *J. London Math. Soc.*, (2), **1**, 1969, 260–264.

BLYTH, T.S.: Residuated inverse semigroups, *J. London Math. Soc.*, (2), **1**, 1969, 243–248.

BLYTH, T.S.: On isotone homomorphic Boolean images of ordered semigroups, *Proc. Roy. Soc. Edinburgh*, A, **68**, 1969, 211–228.

BLYTH, T.S.: Homomorphic images of $\cup$-semigroups, *Bull. Soc. Roy. Sc. Liège*, **38**, 1969, 414–423.

BLYTH, T.S.: Sur certaines images homomorphes des demi-groupes ordonnés, *Bull. Sc. Math.*, (2), **94**, 1970, 101–111.

BLYTH, T.S.: Loipomorphisms, *J. London Math. Soc.*, (2), **2**, 1970, 635–642.

BLYTH, T.S.: Modules et matrices sur un gerbier, *Bull. Soc. Roy. Sc. Liège*, **39**, 1970, 451–469.

BLYTH, T.S.: Images homomorphes, ordonnées en treillis, des demi-groupes ordonnés,

Séminaire Dubreil, Institut Poincaré, Paris, 1970–71, Fascicule 2, Exposé No. 8 [International Congress, Nice, 1970.]

BLYTH, T.S. and JANOWITZ, M.F.: On decreasing Baer semigroups, *Bull. Soc. Roy. Sc. Liège*, **38**, 1969, 414–423.

BOGART, K.P.: Distributive local Noether lattices, *Mich. Math. J.*, **16**, 1969, 215–223.

BOGART, K.P.: Idempotent Noether lattices, *Proc. Amer. Math. Soc.*, **22**, 1969, 127–128.

BOGART, K.P.: Non-imbeddable Noether lattices, *Proc. Amer. Math. Soc.*, **22**, 1969, 129–133.

BOGART, K.P.: Small regular local Noether lattices, *Proc. Amer. Math. Soc.*, **25**, 1970, 423–428.

BRUNS, G.: Darstellungen und Erweiterungen geordneter Mengen, I, *J. reine angew. Math.*, **209**, 1962, 167–200.

BRUNS, G.: Darstellungen und Erweiterungen geordneter Mengen, II, *J. reine angew. Math.*, **210**, 1962, 1–23.

CATLIN, D.E.: Irreducibility conditions in orthomodular lattices, *J. Nat. Sci. and Math.*, **8**, 1968, 83–87.

CATLIN, D.E.: Spectral theory in quantum logic, *Inter. J. Theoret. Phys.*, **1**, 1968, 285–297.

CATLIN, D.E.: Implicative pairs in orthomodular lattices, *Carib. J. Sci. and Math.*, **1**, 1969, 69–79.

CHEN, C.C. and GRÄTZER, G.: Stone lattices I: Construction theorems, *Canad. J. Math.*, **21**, 1969, 884–894.

CHEN, C.C. and GRÄTZER, G.: Stone lattices II: Structure theorems, *Canad. J. Math.*, **21**, 1969, 895–903.

CLARK, W.E.: Baer rings which arise from certain transitive graphs, *Duke Math. J.*, **33**, 1966, 647–656.

CLARK, W.E.: Twisted matrix unit semigroup algebras, *Duke Math. J.*, **34**, 1967, 417–424.

CRAPO, H.: Möbius inversion in lattices, *Arch. der Math.*, **19**, 1968, 595–607.

CROWN, G.D.: Projectives and injectives in the category of complete lattices with residuated mappings, *Math. Ann.*, **187**, 1970, 295–299.

DERDERIAN, J.C.: Caractérisation des treillis de Brouwer et de Boole, *C. R. Acad. Sc., Paris*, **266**, 1968, 441–442.

DERDERIAN, J.C.: Généralisation d'un lemme de Fitting, *C. R. Acad. Sc., Paris*, **266**, 1968, 1089–1090.

DERDERIAN, J.C.: Galois connections and pair algebras, *Canad. J. Math.*, **21**, 1969, 498–501.

DILWORTH, R.P.: Non-commutative residuated lattices, *Trans. Amer. Math. Soc.*, **45**, 1939, 426–444.

DILWORTH, R.P.: Abstract commutative ideal theory, *Pacific J. Math.*, **12**, 1962, 481–498.

DILWORTH, R.P. and WARD, M.: Residuated lattices, *Trans. Amer. Math. Soc.*, **45**, 1939, 335–354.

DUBREIL-JACOTIN, M.L.: Sur les images homomorphes d'un demi-groupe ordonné, *Bull. Soc. Math. France*, **92**, 1964, 101–115.

DUBREIL-JACOTIN, M.L. and CROISOT, R.: Equivalences régulières dans un ensemble ordonné, *Bull. Soc. Math. France*, **80**, 1952, 11–35.

EVERETT, C.J.: Closure operators and Galois theory in lattices, *Trans. Amer. Math. Soc.*, **55**, 1944, 514–525.

FILLMORE, P.A.: An archimedean property of cardinal algebras, *Mich. Math. J.*, **11**, 1964, 315–317.

FILLMORE, P.A.: The dimension theory of certain cardinal algebras, *Trans. Amer. Math. Soc.*, **117**, 1965, 21–36.

FILLMORE, P.A.: Perspectivity in projection lattices, *Proc. Amer. Math. Soc.*, **16**, 1965, 383–387.

FILLMORE, P.A. and BRICKMAN, L.: The invariant subspace lattice of a linear transformation, *Canad. J. Math.*, **19**, 1967, 810–822.

FINCH, P.D.: Congruence relations on orthomodular lattices, *J. Austral. Math. Soc.*, **6**, 1966, 46–54.

FINCH, P.D.: On the structure of quantum logic, *J. Symbolic Logic*, **34**, 1969, 275–282.

FINCH, P.D.: Sasaki projections on orthocomplemented posets, *Bull. Austral. Math. Soc.*, **1**, 1969, 319–324.

FINCH, P.D.: On the lattice structure of quantum logic, *Bull. Austral. Math. Soc.*, **1**, 1969, 333–340.

FINCH, P.D.: On orthomodular posets, *J. Austral. Math. Soc.*, **9**, 1970, 57–62.

FINCH, P.D.: Orthogonality relations and orthomodularity, *Bull. Austral. Math. Soc.*, **2**, 1970, 125–128.

FINCH, P.D.: Quantum logic as an implication algebra, *Bull. Austral. Math. Soc.*, **2**, 1970, 101–106.

FINCH, P.D.: On the structure of Stone lattices, *Bull. Austral. Math. Soc.*, **2**, 1970, 401–413.

FOULIS, D.J.: Conditions for the modularity of an orthomodular lattice, *Pacific J. Math.*, **11**, 1961, 889–894.

FOULIS, D.J.: A note on orthomodular lattices, *Portugal Math.*, **21**, 1962, 65–72.

FOULIS, D.J.: Relative inverses in Baer *-semigroups, *Mich. Math. J.*, **10**, 1963, 65–84.

FOULIS, D.J.: Orthomodular lattices, mimeographed lecture notes, University of Florida, 1964, 159 pp.

FOULIS, D.J.: Semigroups coordinatizing orthomodular geometries, *Canad. J. Math.*, **17**, 1965, 40–51.

FOULIS, D.J.: Multiplicative elements in Baer *-semigroups, *Math. Ann.*, **175**, 1968, 297–302.

FRINK, O.: Pseudo-complements in semilattices, *Duke Math. J.*, **29**, 1962, 505–514.

FUCHS, L.: On group homomorphic images of partially ordered semigroups, *Acta Sc. Math. Szeged.*, **25**, 1964, 139–142.

FUNAYAMA, N.: Imbedding infinitely distributive lattices completely isomorphically into Boolean algebras, *Nagoya Math. J.*, **15**, 1959, 71–81.

FUNAYAMA, N. and NAKAYAMA, T.: On the distributivity of a lattice of lattice congruences, *Proc. Imp. Acad. Tokyo*, **18**, 1942, 553–554.

GARREN, K.R.: Unitary equivalence of spectral measures on a Baer *-semigroup, Virginia Poly. Inst., doctoral dissertation, 1968.

GRÄTZER, G. and SCHMIDT, E.T.: Ideals and congruence relations in lattices, *Acta Math. Acad. Sc. Hung.*, **9**, 1958, 137–175.

GRÄTZER, G. and SCHMIDT, E.T.: On a problem of M.H.Stone, *Acta Math. Acad. Sc. Hung.*, **8**, 1957, 455–460.

GRÄTZER, G. and SCHMIDT, E.T.: Standard ideals in lattices, *Acta Math. Acad. Sc. Hung.*, **12**, 1961, 17–86.

GREECHIE, R.J.: On the structure of orthomodular lattices satisfying the chain condition, *J. Comb. Theory*, **5**, 1968, 210–218.

GREECHIE, R.J.: Hyper-irreducibility in an orthomodular lattice, *J. Nat. Sc. and Math.*, **8**, 1968, 108–111.

GREECHIE, R.J.: An orthomodular lattice with a full set of states not embeddable in Hilbert space, *Carib. J. Sc. Math.*, **2**, 1969, 15–26.

GREECHIE, R.J.: A particular non-atomistic orthomodular poset, *Comm. Math. Phys.*, **14**, 1969, 326–328.

GUDDER, S.P.: Spectral methods for a generalised probability theory, *Trans. Amer. Math. Soc.*, **119**, 1965, 428–442.

GUDDER, S.P.: Representations of groups as automorphisms on orthomodular lattices and posets, University of Denver Technical Report, 1970.

GUDDER, S.P.: Axiomatic quantum mechanics and generalised probability theory. Appears in *Probabilistic methods in applied mathematics*, vol. II, Academic Press, New York, 1970 (A.Bharucha-Reid, Editor).

GUDDER, S.P.: Partial algebraic structures, University of Denver Technical Report, 1970.

GUDDER, S.P. and SCHELP, R.: Coordinatisation of orthocomplemented and orthomodular posets, *Proc. Amer. Math. Soc.*, **25**, 1970, 229–237.

HALMOS, P.R.: Algebraic logic I. Monadic Boolean algebras. *Comp. Math.*, **12**, 1955, 217–249.

HERMAN, L.M.: Semi-orthogonality in Rickart rings, University of Massachusetts doctoral dissertation, 1970.

HOLLAND, S.S., Jr: A Radon-Nikodym theorem in dimension lattices, *Trans. Amer. Math. Soc.*, **108**, 1963, 66–87.

HOLLAND, S.S., Jr: Distributivity and perspectivity in orthomodular lattices, *Trans. Amer. Math. Soc.*, **112**, 1964, 330–343.

HOLLAND, S.S., Jr: Partial solution to Mackey's problem about modular pairs and completeness, *Canad. J. Math.*, **21**, 1969, 1518–1525.

HOLLAND, S.S., Jr: An *m*-orthocomplete orthomodular lattice is *m*-complete, *Proc. Amer. Math. Soc.*, **24**, 1970, 716–718.

HUKUHARA, M.: ⊕-endomorphisme et ∩-endomorphisme d'un treillis en dualité et la théorie de Riesz sur l'endomorphisme complètement continue I, *Funk. Ekvac.*, **1**, 1958, 85–102.

HUKUHARA, M.: ⊕-endomorphisme et ∩-endomorphisme d'un treillis en dualité et la théorie de Riesz sur l'endomorphisme complètement continue II. Extension de la théorie de Riesz aux applications de treillis. *Funk. Ekvac.*, **1**, 1958, 103–120.

HUKUHARA, M.: ⊕-endomorphisme et ∩-endomorphisme d'un treillis en dualité et la théorie de Riesz sur l'endomorphisme complètement continue III. Applications aux endomorphismes d'un espace vectoriel. *Funk. Ekvac.*, **2**, 1959, 19–32.

JANOWITZ, M.F.: Quantifiers and orthomodular lattices, *Pacific J. Math.*, **13**, 1963, 1241–1249.

JANOWITZ, M.F.: On the antitone mappings of a poset, *Proc. Amer. Math. Soc.*, **15**, 1964, 529–533.

JANOWITZ, M.F.: IC-Lattices, *Portugal Math.*, **24**, 1965, 115–122.

JANOWITZ, M.F.: Quantifier theory on quasi-orthomodular lattices, *Illinois J. Math.*, **9**, 1965, 660–676.

JANOWITZ, M.F.: A characterisation of standard ideals, *Acta Math. Acad. Sc. Hung.*, **16**, 1965, 289–301.

JANOWITZ, M.F.: A note on normal ideals, *J. Sc. Hiroshima Univ.*, A-I, **30**, 1966, 1–9.

JANOWITZ, M.F.: The center of a complete relatively complemented lattice is a complete sublattice, *Proc. Amer. Math. Soc.*, **18**, 1967, 189–190.

JANOWITZ, M.F.: Residuated closure operators, *Portugal. Math.*, **26**, 1967, 221–252.

JANOWITZ, M.F.: A note on generalised orthomodular lattices, *J. Nat. Sc. and Math.*, **8**, 1968, 89–94.

JANOWITZ, M.F.: On conditionally upper continuous lattices, *J. Sc. Hiroshima Univ.*, A-I, **32**, 1968, 1–4.

JANOWITZ, M.F.: Perspective properties of relatively complemented lattices, *J. Nat. Sc. and Math.*, **8**, 1968, 193–210.

JANOWITZ, M.F.: Section semicomplemented lattices, *Math. Z.*, **108**, 1968, 63–76.

JANOWITZ, M.F.: Decreasing Baer semigroups, *Glasgow Math. J.*, **10**, 1969, 46–51.

JANOWITZ, M.F.: On the modular relation in atomistic lattices, *Fund. Math.*, **66**, 1970, 337–346.

JANOWITZ, M.F.: Principal multiplicative lattices, *Pacific J. Math.*, **33**, 1970, 653–656.

JANOWITZ, M.F.: Separation conditions in relatively complemented lattices, *Colloq. Math.*, **22**, 1970, 25–34.

JANOWITZ, M.F.: Indexed orthomodular lattices, *Math. Z.*, **119**, 1971, 28–32.

JANOWITZ, M.F. and JOHNSON, C.S., Jr: A note on Brouwerian and Glivenko semigroups, *J. London Math. Soc.*, (2), **1**, 1969, 733–736.

JOHNSON, C.S., Jr: A lattice whose residuated maps do not form a lattice, *J. Nat. Sc. and Math.*, **9**, 1969, 283–284.

JOHNSON, C.S., Jr: RAP congruences on Baer semigroups, University of Massachusetts doctoral dissertation 1970.

JOHNSON, E.W.: A-transforms and Hilbert functions on local lattices, *Trans. Amer. Math. Soc.*, **137**, 1969, 125–139.

JOHNSON, E.W. and LEDIAEV, J.P.: Representable distributive Noether lattices, *Pacific J. Math.*, **28**, 1969, 561–564.

JOHNSON, E.W. and LEDIAEV, J.P.: Normal decompositions in systems without the ascending chain condition, *Mich. Math. J.*, **17**, 1970, 143–148.

JOHNSON, E.W. and LEDIAEV, J.P.: Joint-principal elements and the principal ideal theorem, *Mich. Math. J.*, **17**, 1970, 255–256.

JOHNSON, E.W., JOHNSON, J.A. and LEDIAEV, J.P.: A structural approach to Noether lattices, *Canad. J. Math.*, **23**, 1970, 657–665.

JOHNSON, E.W. and JOHNSON, J.A.: M-primary elements of a local Noether lattice, *Canad. J. Math.*, **22**, 1970, 327–331.

KAPLANSKY, I.: Any orthocomplemented complete modular lattice is a continuous geometry, *Ann. of Math.*, **61**, 1955, 524–541.

KATRINAK, T.: Remark on Stone lattices, I, *Mat.-fyz. Casopis Sloven. Akad. Vied.*, **16**, 1966, 128–142.

KATRINAK, T.: A note on Stone lattices, II, *Mat.-fyz. Casopis Sloven. Akad. Vied.*, **17**, 1967, 20–37.

KATRINAK, T.: Pseudokomplementare Halbverbände, *Mat.-fyz. Casopis Sloven. Akad. Vied.*, **18**, 1968, 121–143.

KATRINAK, T.: Remarks on W.C. Nemitz's paper "Semi-Boolean Algebras", *Notre Dame J. Form. Logic*, **11**, 1970, 425–430.

KIST, J.: Minimal prime ideals in commutative semigroups, *Proc. London Math. Soc.*, (3), **13**, 1963, 31–50.

KIST, J.: Compact spaces of minimal prime ideals, *Math. Z.*, **111**, 1969, 151–158.

MacLAREN, M.D.: Atomic orthocomplemented lattices, *Pacific J. Math.*, **14**, 1964, 597–612.

MacLAREN, M.D.: Nearly modular orthocomplemented lattices, *Trans. Amer. Math. Soc.*, **114**, 1965, 401–416.

MacLAREN, M.D.: Notes on axioms for quantum mechanics, Argonne National Laboratory Report AN L-7065, 1965.

MacNEILLE, H.M.: Partially ordered sets, *Trans. Amer. Math. Soc.*, **42**, 1937, 416–460.

MAEDA, S.: On relatively semiorthocomplemented lattices, *J. Sc. Hiroshima Univ.*, A, **24**, 1960, 155–161.

MAEDA, S.: On the lattice of projections of a Baer *-ring, *J. Sc. Hiroshima Univ.*, A, **22**, 1958, 77–88.

MAEDA, S.: On a ring whose principal right ideals generated by idempotents form a lattice, *J. Sc. Hiroshima Univ.*, A, **24**, 1960, 509–525.

MAEDA, S.: Dimension theory on relatively semiorthocomplemented lattices, *J. Sc. Hiroshima Univ.*, A, **25**, 1961, 369–404.

MAEDA, S.: On conditions for the orthomodularity, *Proc. Japan Acad.*, **42**, 1966, 247–251.

MAEDA, S.: On atomistic lattices with the covering property, *J. Sc. Hiroshima Univ.*, A-I, **31**, 1967, 105–121.

MAEDA, S.: Modular pairs in atomistic lattices with the covering property, *Proc. Japan Acad.*, **45**, 1969, 149–153.

MAEDA, S.: Infinite distributivity in complete lattices, *Mem. Ehime Univ.*, II, A, **5**, 1969, 11–13.

MARTIN, C.K.: Distinguished rings with transitive graphs, *Duke Math. J.*, **36**, 1969, 369–378.

MANDELKER, M.: Relative annihilators in lattices, *Duke Math. J.*, **37**, 1970, 377–386.

MARSDEN, E.L., Jr: The commutator and solvability in a generalised orthomodular lattice, *Pacific J. Math.*, **33**, 1970, 357–361.

MARSDEN, E.L., Jr: Irreducibility conditions on orthomodular lattices, *Carib. J. Sc. Math.*, **1**, 1969, 27–39.

MAURY, G.: La condition "intégralement clos" dans quelques structures algébriques, *Ann. Sc. Ec. Norm. Sup.*, **78**, 1961, 31–100.

MAURY, G. and OUDIN, E.: Gerbier résidué intégralement clos, *C. R. Acad. Sc. Paris*, **264**, 1967, 170–172.

McALISTER, D.B. and O'CARROLL, L.: On B-nomal semigroups, *J. London Math. Soc.*, (2), **2**, 1970, 679–688.

McCARTHY, P.J.: Primary decomposition in multiplicative lattices, *Math. Z.*, **90**, 1965, 185–189.

McCarthy, P.J.: Homomorphisms of certain commutative lattice-ordered semigroups, *Acta Sc. Math. Szeged.*, **27**, 1966, 63–65.

McCarthy, P.J.: Note on abstract commutative ideal theory, *Amer. Math. Monthly*, **74**, 1967, 706–707.

McFadden, R.: Congruence relations on residuated semigroups, *J. London Math. Soc.*, **37**, 1962, 242–248.

McFadden, R.: Congruence relations on residuated semigroups II, *J. London Math. Soc.*, **39**, 1964, 150–158.

McFadden, R.: On homomorphisms of partially ordered semigroups, *Acta Sc. Math. Szeged.*, **28**, 1967, 241–249.

McFadden, R.: Homomorphisms of partially ordered semigroups onto groups, *Acta Sc. Math. Szeged.*, **28**, 1967, 251–254.

Morgado, J.: Some results on closure operators of partially ordered sets, *Portugal Math.*, **19**, 1960, 101–139.

Mowatt, D.G.: A Galois problem for mappings, *Bull. Amer. Math. Soc.*, **6**, 1968, 1095–1098.

Nachbin, L.: Une propriété caractéristique des algèbres booléiennes, *Portugal Math.*, **6**, 1947, 115–118.

Nakamura, M.: Center of closure operators and a decomposition of a lattice, *Math. Japon.*, **4**, 1954, 49–52.

Nakamura, M.: The permutability in a certain orthocomplemented lattice, *Kodai Math. Sem.*, **9**, 1957, 158–160.

Nemitz, W.C.: Implicative semilattices, *Trans. Amer. Math. Soc.*, **117**, 1965, 128–142.

Nemitz, W.C.: On the lattice of filters of an implicative semilattice, *J. Math. Mech.*, **18**, 1969, 683–688.

Nemitz, W.C.: Semi-Boolean algebras, *Notre Dame J. Form. Logic*, **10**, 1969, 235–238.

O'Carroll, L.: A basis for the theory of residuated groupoids, *J. London Math. Soc.*, (2), **3**, 1971, 7–20.

Ore, O.: Theory of equivalence relations, *Duke Math. J.*, **9**, 1942, 573–627.

Ore, O.: Galois connexions, *Trans. Amer. Math. Soc.*, **55**, 1944, 493–513.

Oudin, E.: Demi-groupes commutatifs réticulés résidués intégralement clos, *Pub. Dep. Math.*, Lyon, 1968, 5, 1.

Pickert, G.: Bemerkungen über Galois-Verbindungen, *Archiv. Math.*, **3**, 1952, 285–289.

Piron, C.: Axiomatique quantique, *Helv. Phys. Acta*, **37**, 1964, 439–468.

Piziak, R.: An algebraic generalisation of Hilbert space geometry, University of Massachusetts doctoral dissertation, 1970.

Pollingher, A. and Zaks, A.: On Baer and quasi-Baer rings, *Duke Math. J.*, **37**, 1970, 127–138.

Pool, J.C.T.: Baer *-semigroups and the logic of quantum mechanics, *Commun. Math. Phys.*, **9**, 1968, 118–141.

Pool, J.C.T.: Semimodularity and the logic of quantum mechanics, *Commun. Math. Phys.*, **9**, 1968, 212–228.

Querré, J.: Contribution à la théorie des structures ordonnées et des systèmes d'idéaux, *Ann. di Mat.*, **66**, 1964, 265–389.

Querré, J.: Plus grand groupe image homomorphe et isotone d'un monoïde ordonné, *Acta Math. Hung.*, **19**, 1968, 129–146.

RAMSAY, A.: Dimension theory in complete orthocomplemented weakly modular lattices, *Trans. Amer. Math. Soc.*, **116**, 1965, 9–31.

RAMSAY, A.: A theorem on two commuting observables, *J. Math. Mech.*, **15**, 1966, 227–234.

RANEY, G.N.: Completely distributive complete lattices, *Proc. Amer. Math. Soc.*, **3**, 1953, 677–680.

RANEY, G.N.: A subdirect union representation for completely distributive complete lattices, *Proc. Amer. Math. Soc.*, **4**, 1953, 518–522.

RANEY, G.N.: Tight Galois connections and complete distributivity, *Trans. Amer. Math. Soc.*, **97**, 1960, 418–426.

RIGUET, J.: Relations binaires, fermetures, correspondances de Galois, *Bull. Soc. Math. France*, **76**, 1948, 114–155.

SASAKI, U.: Orthocomplemented lattices satisfying the exchange axiom, *J. Sc. Hiroshima Univ.*, A, **17**, 1954, 293–302.

SCHELP, R.H.: Partial Baer *-semigroups and partial Baer semigroups, Kansas State University doctoral dissertation, 1970.

SCHREINER, E.A.: Modular pairs in orthomodular lattices, *Pacific J. Math.*, **19**, 1966, 519–528.

SCHREINER, E.A.: A note on O-symmetric lattices, *Carib. J. Sc. Math.*, **1**, 1969, 40–50.

SPEED, T.P.: A note on commutative semigroups, *J. Austral. Math. Soc.*, **8**, 1968, 731–736.

SPEED, T.P.: Some remarks on a class of distributive lattices, *J. Austral. Math. Soc.*, **9**, 1969, 289–296.

SPEED, T.P.: On Stone lattices, *J. Austral. Math. Soc.*, **9**, 1969, 297–307.

STONE, M.H.: The theory of representations for Boolean algebras, *Trans. Amer. Math. Soc.*, **40**, 1936, 37–111.

THORNE, B.J.: AP-congruences on Baer semigroups, *Pacific J. Math.*, **28**, 1969, 681–698.

TOPPING, D.M.: Asymptocity and semimodularity in projection lattices, *Pacific J. Math.*, **20**, 1967, 317–325.

TOPPING, D.M.: Jordan algebras of self-adjoint operators, *Mem. Amer. Math. Soc.*, **53**, 1965.

VARLET, J.C.: Contributions à l'étude des treillis pseudo-complémentés et des treillis de Stone, *Mem. Soc. Roy. Sc., Liège*, **5**, 8, 1963, 1–71.

VARLET, J.C.: On the characterization of Stone lattices, *Acta Sc. Math. Szeged.*, **27**, 1966, 81–84.

VARLET, J.C.: Congruences dans les treillis pseudo-complémentés, *Bull. Soc. Roy. Sc., Liège*, **9**, 1963, 623–635.

VARLET, J.C.: Idéaux dans les lattis pseudo-complémentés, *Bull. Soc. Roy. Sc., Liège*, **3–4**, 1964, 143–150.

VARLET, J.C.: A generalization of the notion of pseudo-complementedness, *Bull. Soc. Roy. Sc., Liège*, **3–4**, 1968, 149–158.

VARLET, J.C.: Fermetures multiplicatives, *Bull. Soc. Roy. Sc., Liège*, **11–12**, 1967, 628–642.

VARLET, J.C. and GRILLET, P.A.: Complementedness conditions in lattices, *Bull. Soc. Roy. Sc., Liège*, **38**, 1969, 101–115.

WARD, M.: Residuation in structures over which a multiplication has been defined, *Duke Math. J.*, **3**, 1937, 627–636.

WARD, M.: Residuated distributive lattices, *Duke Math. J.*, **6**, 1940, 641–651.

WEAVER, R.: Orthogonality spaces and the free orthogonality monoid, University of Massachusetts doctoral dissertation, 1969.

WILLE, R.: Halbkomplementare Verbände, *Math. Z.*, **94**, 1966, 1–31.

WOLFSON, K.G.: Baer subrings of the ring of linear transformations, *Math. Z.*, **75**, 1961, 328–332.

WOLFSON, K.G.: Baer rings of endomorphisms, *Math. Ann.*, **143**, 1961, 19–28.

WRIGHT, F.B.: Some remarks on Boolean duality, *Portugal Math.*, **16**, 1957, 109–117.

WRIGHT, F.B.: The ideals in a factor, *Ann. of Math.*, **68**, 1958, 475–583.

WRIGHT, F.B.: Polarity and duality, *Pacific J. Math.*, **10**, 1960, 723–730.

YOHE, C.R.: Commutative rings whose matrix rings are Baer rings, *Proc. Amer. Math. Soc.*, **22**, 1969, 189–191.

PART 4: FORTHCOMING PAPERS

BEVIS, J.: Characterization of a distributivity property in an orthomodular lattice.

BEVIS, J.: Quantifiers and dimension equivalence relations, *Carib. J. Math. and Sc.*

BEVIS, J. and MARTIN, C.K.: Ideals and congruence relations on matrices over lattices.

BLYTH, T.S. and HARDY, W.C.: Quasi-residuated mappings and Baer assemblies, *Proc. Roy. Soc. Edinburgh.*

BLYTH, T.S. and HARDY, W.C.: A coordinatisation of lattices by one-sided Baer assemblies, *Proc. Roy. Soc. Edinburgh.*

BOGART, K.P.: Noether lattices with trivial multiplication, *Proc. Amer. Math. Soc.*

CATLIN, D.E.: Cyclic atoms in orthomodular lattices, *Proc. Amer. Math. Soc.*

CROWN, G.D.: Some connections between orthogonality spaces and orthomodular lattices, *Carib. J. Sc. and Math.*

CROWN, G.D.: On the coordinatization theorem of Janowitz, *Glasgow Math. J.*

FOULIS, D.J.: Free Baer *-semigroups, *Carib. J. Sc. and Math.*

FOULIS, D.J. and RANDALL, C.H.: Conditioning maps on orthomodular lattices, *Glasgow Math. J.*

FOULIS, D.J. and RANDALL, C.H.: Lexicographic orthogonality, *J. Comb. Theory.*

GREECHIE, R.J.: Orthomodular lattices admitting no states, *J. Comb. Theory.*

GREECHIE, R.J. and GUDDER, S.P.: Is quantum logic a logic?

JANOWITZ, M.F.: On the lattice of left annihilators of certain rings, *Fund. Math.*

JANOWITZ, M.F.: Equivalence relations induced by Baer *-semigroups, *J. Nat. Sc. and Math.*

JANOWITZ, M.F.: The near center of an orthomodular lattice, *J. Austral. Math. Soc.*

JANOWITZ, M.F.: Constructible lattices, *J. Austral. Math. Soc.*

JOHNSON, C.S., Jr: UIG Baer semigroups, *J. Nat. Sc. and Math.*

JOHNSON, C.S., Jr: Quasi-multiplicative maps on Baer semigroups, *Glasgow Math. J.*

JOHNSON, C.S., Jr: Semigroups coordinatizing posets and semilattices, *J. London Math. Soc.*

JOHNSON, C.S., Jr: On certain poset and semilattice homomorphisms, *Pacific J. Math.*

MORASH, R.: The orthomodular identity and metric completeness of the coordinatizing division ring, *Proc. Amer. Math. Soc.*

PIZIAK, R.: Involution rings and projections, *J. Nat. Sc. and Math.*

INDEX

OTHER TITLES IN THE SERIES IN PURE AND APPLIED MATHEMATICS

Vol. 1. WALLACE—*An introduction to Algebraic Topology*
Vol. 2. PEDOE—*Circles*
Vol. 3. SPAIN—*Analytical Conics*
Vol. 4. MIKHLIN—*Integral Equations*
Vol. 5. EGGLESTON—*Problems in Euclidean Space: Application of Convexity*
Vol. 6. WALLACE—*Homology Theory on Algebraic Varieties*
Vol. 7. NOBLE—*Methods Based on the Wiener–Hopf Technique for the Solution of Partial Differential Equations*
Vol. 8. MIKUSINSKI—*Operational Calculus*
Vol. 9. HEINE—*Group Theory in Quantum Mechanics*
Vol. 10. BLAND—*The Theory of Linear Viscoelasticity*
Vol. 11. KURTH—*Axiomatics of Classical Statistical Mechanics*
Vol. 12. FUCHS—*Abelian Groups*
Vol. 13. KURATOWSKI—*Introduction to Set Theory and Topology*
Vol. 14. SPAIN—*Analytical Quadrics*
Vol. 15. HARTMAN and MIKUSINSKI—*Theory of Lebesgue Measure and Integration*
Vol. 16. KULCZYCKI—*Non-Euclidean Geometry*
Vol. 17. KURATOWSKI—*Introduction to Calculus*
Vol. 18. GERONIMUS—*Polynomials Orthogonal on a Circle and Interval*
Vol. 19. ELSGOLC—*Calculus of Variations*
Vol. 20. ALEXITS—*Convergence Problems of Orthogonal Series*
Vol. 21. FUCHS and LEVIN—*Functions of a Complex Variable, Volume II*
Vol. 22. GOODSTEIN—*Fundamental Concepts of Mathematics*
Vol. 23. KEENE—*Abstracts Sets and Finite Ordinals*
Vol. 24. DITKIN and PRUDNIKOV—*Operational Calculus in Two Variables and its Applications*
Vol. 25. VEKUA—*Generalized Analytic Functions*
Vol. 26. FASS and AMIR-MOÉZ—*Elements of Linear Spaces*
Vol. 27. GRADSHTEIN—*Direct and Converse Theorems*
Vol. 28. FUCHS—*Partially Ordered Algebraic Systems*
Vol. 29. POSTNIKOV—*Foundations of Galois Theory*
Vol. 30. BERMANT—*A Course of Mathematical Analysis, Part II*
Vol. 31. LUKASIEWICZ—*Elements of Mathematical Logic*
Vol. 32. VULIKH—*Introduction to Functional Analysis for Scientists and Technologists*
Vol. 33. PEDOE—*An Introduction to Projective Geometry*
Vol. 34. TIMAN—*Theory of Approximation of Functions of a Real Variable*
Vol. 35. CSÁSZÁR—*Foundations of General Topology*